NELSON

MATHEMATICS 10

Authors

David Zimmer
Chris Kirkpatrick
Ralph Montesanto
Christine Suurtamm
Susanne Trew
Dan Charbonneau

NELSON

™

THOMSON LEARNING

Australia • Canada • Mexico • Singapore • Spain • United Kingdom • United States

NELSON
THOMSON LEARNING

Mathematics 10

by David Zimmer. Chris Kirkpatrick,
Ralph Montesanto, Christine Suurtamm,
Susanne Trew, and Dan Charbonneau

Director of Publishing:
David Steele

Publisher, Mathematics:
Cheryl Turner

Project Manager:
Robert Templeton,
First Folio Resource Group, Inc.

Content Editor:
Don Rowsell

Copy Editor:
Michael Waters,
General Ideas

Production Coordinator:
Sharon Latta Paterson

Creative Director:
Angela Cluer

Cover Design:
Linda O'Neill

Senior Designer:
Suzanne Peden

Composition:
Nelson Gonzalez

Photographs and Permissions:
Vicki Gould

Creative Art/Technical Art:
Irma Ikonen, David McKay,
Deborah Crowle

Printer:
Transcontinental Printing Inc.

The authors wish to thank
Matthew Grey, David Hamilton,
Alwynn Hickey, Kristy McGowan,
Adam Peleshok, Andrew Peredun,
Mary Reeve, David Rowbottom,
Susan Woollam, and David Wright
for their assistance in the
development of this textbook.

**Canadian Cataloguing in
Publication Data**

Main entry under title:

Mathematics 10

Includes index.

ISBN 0-17-615704-2

1. Mathematics. I. Zimmer, David.
II. Mathematics ten.

QA39.2.M343 2000   510
C00-930353-7

Assessment Consultant

Damian Cooper

Advisory Panel

Paul Costa
Mathematics Department Head
Marshall McLuhan Catholic Secondary School
Toronto Catholic District School Board
Toronto, Ontario

Paul R. Cox
Vice-Principal
Resurrection Catholic Secondary School
Waterloo Catholic District School Board
Kitchener, Ontario

Stewart Craven
District-Wide Coordinator, Mathematics
Toronto District School Board
Toronto, Ontario

Beverly Farahani
Head of Mathematics
Kingston Collegiate and Vocational Institute
Limestone District School Board
Kingston, Ontario

Mary Lou Kestell
Education Officer
Education Quality and Accountability Office
Toronto, Ontario

Mike Lauzon
Head of Mathematics
Iona Catholic Secondary School
Dufferin – Peel Separate School Board
Mississauga, Ontario

Tom Steinke
Consultant
Educational Programs Department
Ottawa-Carleton Catholic District School Board
Ottawa, Ontario

Kathy Wilkinson
Mathematics Department Head
Collingwood Collegiate Institute
Simcoe County District School Board
Collingwood, Ontario

Reviewers

Kaye Appleby
Retired Department Head of Mathematics
London, Ontario

Alex Belloni
Department Head of Mathematics
Mother Theresa Catholic High School
Ottawa-Carleton Catholic School Board
Nepean, Ontario

Pamela J. Bradshaw
Department Head of Mathematics
Lambton Central Collegiate & Vocational Institute
Lambton Kent District School Board
Petrolia, Ontario

Karen Bryan
Department Head of Mathematics
North Dundas District High School
Upper Canada District School Board
Chesterville, Ontario

Mike Cafferata
Head of Mathematics
Agincourt Collegiate Institute
Toronto District School Board East
Agincourt, Ontario

Tom Chapman
Curriculum Coordinator
Education Centre
Hastings and Prince Edward District School Board
Belleville, Ontario

Richard Clausi
Head of Mathematics
Elmira District Secondary School
Waterloo Region District School Board
Elmira, Ontario

Angela M. Con
Educational Services Resource Teacher
Kawartha Pine Ridge District School Board
Peterborough, Ontario

Frank Dalla Corte
Department Head of Mathematics
Cardinal Carter High School
York Catholic District School Board
Aurora, Ontario

Mary Ellen Diamond
Math Consultant
Niagara Catholic District School Board
Welland, Ontario

Frank DiPietro
Consultant
Windsor-Essex Catholic District School Board
Windsor, Ontario

Judy Dussiame
Curriculum Coordinator
Rainbow District School Board
Sudbury, Ontario

Reviewers (continued)

Niki Garland
Department Head of Mathematics
Rosedale Heights Secondary School
Toronto District School Board
Toronto, Ontario

Andrew Hallikas
Head of Science and Mathematics
Fort Frances High School
Rainy River District School Board
Fort Frances, Ontario

Sue Hessey
Learning Coordinator
Program Department
Thames Valley District School Board
London, Ontario

Mary Howe
Coordinator; Math, Science and Technology
London Catholic District School Board
London, Ontario

Patricia Kehoe
Teacher
Mother Theresa Catholic High School
Ottawa-Carleton Catholic District School Board
Nepean, Ontario

Jean-Pierre LeRoy
Education Consultant
Ministry of Education
Nanaimo, British Columbia

Clara Madonia
Head of Mathematics
Don Bosco Catholic Secondary School
Toronto Catholic District School Board
Toronto, Ontario

Frank Maggio
Mathematics Consultant
Halton Catholic District School Board
Burlington, Ontario

Irene McEvoy
Math Coordinator
Peel District School Board
Mississauga, Ontario

Keith McLean
Head of Mathematics
Northern Secondary School
Toronto District School Board
Toronto, Ontario

Marisa Palma
Department Head of Mathematics
St. Elizabeth Central High School
York Catholic District School Board
Thornhill, Ontario

Elizabeth Pattison
Department Head of Mathematics
Westlane Secondary School
Niagara District School Board
Niagara Falls, Ontario

Sue Pyke
Head of Mathematics
Richview Collegiate Institute
Toronto District School Board
Etobicoke, Ontario

Ann Rubin
Head of Mathematics
Milliken Mills High School
York Region District School Board
Unionville, Ontario

Rinaldo Schiabel
Mathematics Department Head
Chaminade College School
Toronto Catholic District School Board
Toronto, Ontario

Silvana Simone
Department Head of Mathematics
Emercy Collegiate Institute
Toronto District School Board
Toronto, Ontario

Peter Wei
Mathematics Department Head
North Toronto Collegiate Institute
Toronto District School Board
Toronto, Ontario

Jack Weiner
Associate Professor
Department of Mathematics and Physics
University of Guelph
Guelph, Ontario

Betsy Wimbs
Assistant Head of Mathematics
R.H. King Academy
Toronto District School Board
Scarborough, Ontario

Arlene Wood
Teacher
Dr. F. J. Donevan Collegiate Institute
Durham District School Board
Oshawa, Ontario

Bill Woodcock
Program Consultant
Lambton Kent District School Board
Sarnia, Ontario

Contents

ANALYTIC GEOMETRY

5

TRIGONOMETRY

7

Introduction to Nelson Mathematics 10

Nelson Mathematics 10 is designed to help you develop your skill at solving real problems using mathematical skills and logical reasoning. There are questions that give you a chance to practise familiar mathematical skills like solving equations and graphing data. You will also have opportunities to tackle problems that require you to develop your own strategy for solving them. Throughout the book, you will be encouraged to use a variety of methods to communicate what you have learned to others.

Inquiry

When you are faced with a new situation or problem, you have to examine the problem and figure out how to solve it. This might involve analyzing the information you have, deciding if you need more information, and figuring out how you can get that information. You also need to develop a plan for working through the problem.

Problem-Solving

In your life, you deal with many situations in which you have to figure out the best solution to a problem. The following steps may help you organize your thoughts and work.

1. **Understand the problem.**
   List all the information you have and what you need to find out.

2. **Create a mathematical model of the problem.**
   This model might be an algebraic model like a table of values, a graph, or an equation or a geometric model like a labelled diagram.

3. **Plan a solution using your model.**

4. **Execute the plan.**

5. **Interpret and evaluate the solution.**
   Determine the significance and reasonableness of your answer.

6. **Generalize your results.**
   Check to see if the method you used will work in similar or more complex situations.

Reasoning

As you work at solving a problem, you have to keep questioning whether you are on the right track. You may have collected information that is not useful or tried the wrong strategy. It is important to reflect on what you are doing and change your approach if it is not working.

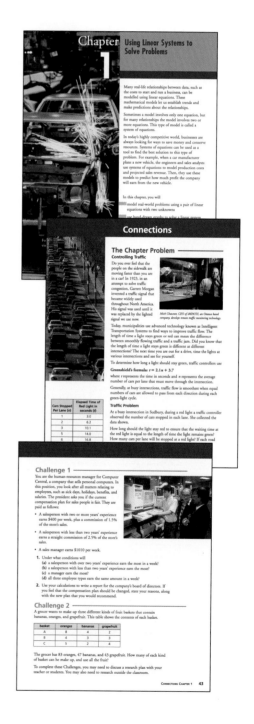

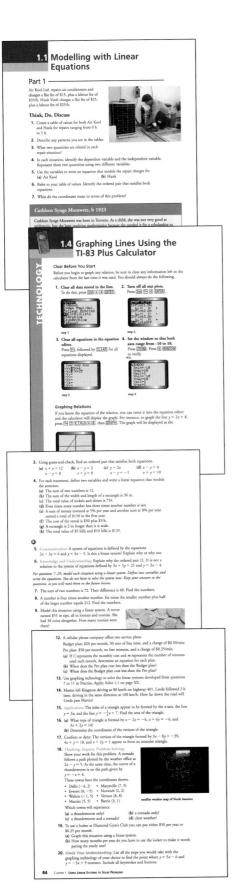

Mathematical Modelling

An important skill for you to develop is your ability to create a mathematical model for a real situation. The model can sometimes take the form of a physical model or a computer model. In this course, models such as graphs, table of values, or equations can be used to describe linear and quadratic relationships. Geometric models such as sketches and scale diagrams, as well as coordinate diagrams can be used to represent situations that involve triangles and other two dimensional figures. Models help you to analyze a situation or relationship, predict patterns or trends, and communicate ideas.

Technology

Advances in computer technology have made it possible for people to solve complex problems more easily and quickly than in the past. Graphing calculators, graphing software, spreadsheets, and geometry software can all be used to explore ideas and analyze data. You can also use computers to do research on the internet. On the opening page of each chapter you will find the web-site address: **www.math.nelson.com**, which has links to the topics and problems in each chapter.

Communication

Throughout the chapters in *Nelson Mathematics 10*, you will be encouraged to discuss, present, write about, and report on what you are learning. This gives you the opportunity to reflect on your understanding of topics and share your ideas with other students. It also gives you a chance to develop your skill at communicating your ideas clearly to others and listening or thinking carefully about the ideas you hear or read.

Connections

Mathematics is not just something you do in math class. You use it in other classes and in your daily life. Mathematics is also something that many people (not just mathematicians and teachers) need in their careers. The chapter problem and other problems throughout the text show how people use mathematics in their jobs.

Features That Help You Prepare

Review of Essential Skills and Knowledge (Part I/ Part II/ Part III)

These pages give a brief overview of important concepts from previous grades that will help you prepare for this course. Try using these pages in the following way:

1. Cover up the solution to each example.

2. Read the example and try to answer it on your own. Show all of your work in your notebook.

3. Check your solution by comparing it with the one in the book.

4. If you do not understand how to do the example, ask another student or your teacher for help.

5. When you understand how to do the examples, work through the practise questions. Be sure to check your work by comparing your answers to the answers in the back of the book.

Getting Ready

These pages review important ideas from previous grades and chapters. These ideas will often be the starting points for new learning within each chapter. You can use this page to determine if you are ready for the new work of the chapter. If you find questions that you cannot do, ask the teacher or another student for help with them.

Technology Lessons

These lessons provide guidance on using the TI-83 Plus Graphing calculator and *The Geometer's Sketchpad*.

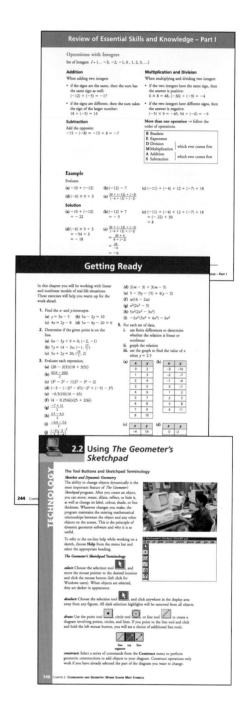

Features That Help You Review

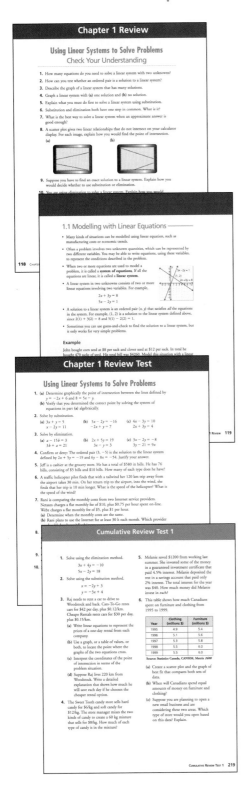

Check Your Understanding

At the beginning of the Review section for each chapter, there is a Check Your Understanding page. The questions on this page will help you decide if you understand the important ideas of a chapter. Think about each question and write the answer in your notebook. As you do, you will be creating your own summary of the chapter. You can use your answers to these questions, along with the Chapter Review, to help you prepare for quizzes, tests, and exams.

Chapter Review

The concepts and skills you have developed through the work of the chapter are summarized and supported by examples and practice questions.

You can use this section to review and study.

Chapter Review Test

You can use this test to review and find out if you are ready for a class test or exam.

Cumulative Review Test

There is a cumulative review test at the end of chapters 2, 4, and 6. Each test incorporates concepts and ideas from both of the previous two chapters. You can use these tests as another source of review and extra practice when preparing for tests and exams.

Features of a Section

Exploration Lessons

In these lessons, you will explore ideas and relationships, often through hands-on experience. These lessons introduce a new idea and will help you understand a new concept in a more meaningful way. They often demonstrate math in action in the world outside the math classroom.

Concept Lessons

Some lessons help you to develop your understanding of mathematics through examples and questions. Others give you a chance to explore and investigate a problem. Problems are presented in a real-life context.

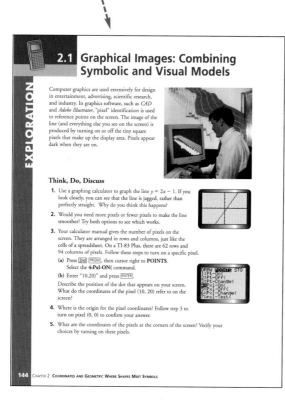

Icons

These two icons identify an opportunity to use technology.

 You will be using a graphing calculator or you will be using a data probe to collect data.

 You will be using a computer to develop a spreadsheet or graph, or using *The Geometer's Sketchpad*.

Think, Do, Discuss

These questions help you to develop an understanding of the main ideas in a lesson and make connections between them.

Examples

Sample problems with solutions and notes provide examples of how to do the *Practise, Apply, Solve* questions. The examples tie together the key ideas of the lesson.

Key Ideas

The Key Ideas present the important ideas and skills introduced in the lesson. They provide definitions of mathematical terms and ideas to remember.

Practise, Apply, Solve

At the end of each section is a set of Practise, Apply, Solve questions, which range from practice questions to more complex problems.

Each set has are four questions, labelled **Knowledge and Understanding**; **Communication**; **Application**; and **Thinking, Inquiry, Problem Solving**, that you can use them to help determine your strengths and weaknesses, and, with the help of your teacher, develop a plan for improving your achievement.

Also, in each set is a **Check Your Understanding** question. This question will help you determine if you understand the main ideas of the section.

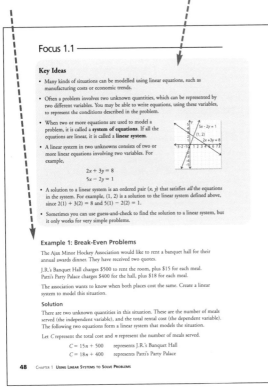

Focus 1.1

Key Ideas

- Many kinds of situations can be modelled using linear equations, such as manufacturing costs or economic trends.
- Often a problem involves two unknown quantities, which can be represented by two different variables. You may be able to write equations, using these variables, to represent the conditions described in the problem.
- When two or more equations are used to model a problem, it is called a **system of equations**. If all the equations are linear, it is called a **linear system**.
- A linear system in two unknowns consists of two or more linear equations involving two variables. For example,

$$2x + 3y = 8$$
$$5x - 2y = 1$$

- A solution to a linear system is an ordered pair (x, y) that satisfies *all* the equations in the system. For example, $(1, 2)$ is a solution to the linear system defined above, since $2(1) + 3(2) = 8$ and $5(1) - 2(2) = 1$.
- Sometimes you can use guess-and-check to find the solution to a linear system, but it only works for very simple problems.

Example 1: Break-Even Problems

The Ajax Minor Hockey Association would like to rent a banquet hall for their annual awards dinner. They have received two quotes.

J.R.'s Banquet Hall charges $500 to rent the room, plus $15 for each meal. Patti's Party Palace charges $400 for the hall, plus $18 for each meal.

The association wants to know when both places cost the same. Create a linear system to model this situation.

Solution

There are two unknown quantities in this situation. These are the number of meals served (the independent variable), and the total rental cost (the dependent variable). The following two equations form a linear system that models the situation.

Let C represent the total cost and n represent the number of meals served.

$$C = 15n + 500 \quad \text{represents J.R.'s Banquet Hall}$$
$$C = 18n + 400 \quad \text{represents Patti's Party Palace}$$

48 Chapter 1 Using Linear Systems to Solve Problems

Practise, Apply, Solve 2.3

A

1. Refer to the map on p. 149.
   (a) State the coordinates of the points representing Barrie, Sudbury, and Peterborough.
   (b) How far is each of these cities from the accident site?

2. Plot each point and connect it to the origin with a straight line. Calculate the distance from the point to the origin.
   (a) $(5, 12)$ (b) $(-3, 9)$ (c) $(1, -1)$ (d) $(-7, -25)$

3. Knowledge and Understanding: Which of these points is closest to the origin: $X(4, 6)$, $Y(-5, 5)$, or $Z(3, -7)$? Explain your answer.

4. Why is it useful to have a coordinate grid on a map? Explain, with examples, how people would use the coordinates.

B

5. Communication: If you know the coordinates of a point, how do you determine how far it is from the origin? How far is $P(10, -8)$ from the origin?

6. An airport control tower at $(0, 0)$ locates two airplanes on its radar screen. Plane

---

20. The small triangles $\triangle DEF$ and $\triangle GHI$ in this diagram were drawn by joining the midpoints of the sides of the next larger triangles. If AC is 160 cm, AB is 180 cm, and BC is 200 cm, what is the perimeter of the smallest triangle?

Chapter Problem

As you work through the sections of the chapter, there are questions to help you solve the chapter problem on the Connections page.

Careers

Read these to find out how mathematics is used in the world of work.

People of Mathematics

These brief biographies tell you about women and men who have made a contribution to the world and work of mathematics. You may want to do further research (not shown).

Chapter Problem—Modelling the Solar System

In this section you solved problems involving similar triangles. Apply what you learned to answer these questions about the chapter problem.

A total eclipse of the sun occurs when the ratio of the diameter of the moon to its distance from Earth is about the same as the ratio of the sun's diameter to its distance from Earth.

1. Draw a diagram of triangles to model the situation.
2. Label the vertices of the triangles.
3. Determine which triangles are similar.
4. Write out the proportions represented in your diagram.
5. The sun's diameter is about 1.392×10^6 km. It is about 1.5×10^8 km from the Earth to the sun, and about 3.84×10^5 km from the Earth to moon. What is the moon's diameter?

Career: City Planner

City or town planners check for proposed new development to ensure that buildings meet community standards. In addition to safety and health requirements, plans are checked for shadow impact. For example, a city plan may stipulate that in some neighbourhoods the sidewalk and buildings of the north side of the street are entitled to five hours of sunlight during peak hours of use. The same standard might apply to a park or school playground.

When a plan is submitted for approval, planners use a CAD (Computer-Aided Design) program to generate two-dimensional diagrams modelling the shadows cast. Seasonal sun angles, times of the day, and geographic location are programmed in relation to the height and mass of the building. If the planned building would shadow a street or park, changes to the design of the building will be requested such as lowering the height or changing the design of the roof to minimize the shadow.

544 Chapter 6 Investigating Non-Right Triangles as Models for Problems

Performance Tasks

These tasks range from short problem-solving questions to longer experiments and investigations. Your teacher may assign these activities so you can both see how well you understand the concepts of the chapters. These may be done in class or as take-home tasks. You can also do these activities on your own, for extra practice and review. For some of these activities you will work on your own, while for others you will likely work in a group. Along with quizzes, test, and exams, these activities provide an opportunity for you to demonstrate your understanding of the most important ideas in the grade 10 mathematics course.

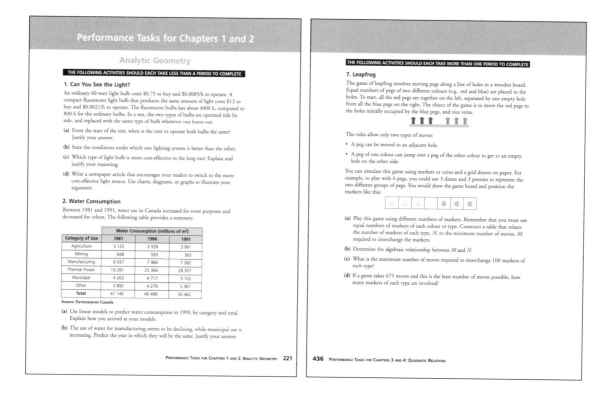

Performance Tasks for Chapters 1 and 2

Analytic Geometry

THE FOLLOWING ACTIVITIES SHOULD EACH TAKE LESS THAN A PERIOD TO COMPLETE

1. Can You See the Light?

An ordinary 60-watt light bulb costs $0.75 to buy and $0.0085/h to operate. A compact fluorescent light bulb that produces the same amount of light costs $12 to buy and $0.0021/h to operate. The fluorescent bulbs last about 4000 h, compared to 800 h for the ordinary bulbs. In a test, the two types of bulbs are operated side by side, and replaced with the same type of bulb whenever one burns out.

(a) From the start of the test, when is the cost to operate both bulbs the same? Justify your answer.

(b) State the conditions under which one lighting system is better than the other.

(c) Which type of light bulb is more cost-effective in the long run? Explain and justify your reasoning.

(d) Write a newspaper article that encourages your readers to switch to the more cost-effective light source. Use charts, diagrams, or graphs to illustrate your argument.

2. Water Consumption

Between 1981 and 1991, water use in Canada increased for some purposes and decreased for others. The following table provides a summary.

Category of Use	Water Consumption (millions of m³)		
	1981	1986	1991
Agriculture	3 125	3 559	3 991
Mining	648	593	363
Manufacturing	9 937	7 984	7 282
Thermal Power	19 281	25 364	28 357
Municipal	4 263	4 717	5 102
Other	3 892	4 279	5 367
Total	41 146	46 496	50 462

Source: Environment Canada

(a) Use linear models to predict water consumption in 1999, by category and total. Explain how you arrived at your models.

(b) The use of water for manufacturing seems to be declining, while municipal use is increasing. Predict the year in which they will be the same. Justify your answer.

THE FOLLOWING ACTIVITIES SHOULD EACH TAKE MORE THAN ONE PERIOD TO COMPLETE

7. Leapfrog

The game of leapfrog involves moving pegs along a line of holes in a wooden board. Equal numbers of pegs of two different colours (e.g., red and blue) are placed in the holes. To start, all the red pegs are together on the left, separated by one empty hole from all the blue pegs on the right. The object of the game is to move the red pegs to the holes initially occupied by the blue pegs, and vice versa.

The rules allow only two types of moves:

• A peg can be moved to an adjacent hole.

• A peg of one colour can jump over a peg of the other colour to get to an empty hole on the other side.

You can simulate this game using markers or coins and a grid drawn on paper. For example, to play with 6 pegs, you could use 3 dimes and 3 pennies to represent the two different groups of pegs. You would draw the game board and position the markers like this:

(a) Play this game using different numbers of markers. Remember that you must use equal numbers of markers of each colour or type. Construct a table that relates the number of markers of each type, N, to the minimum number of moves, M, required to interchange the markers.

(b) Determine the algebraic relationship between M and N.

(c) What is the minimum number of moves required to interchange 100 markers of each type?

(d) If a game takes 675 moves and this is the least number of moves possible, how many markers of each type are involved?

Getting Ready for Analytic Geometry

Operations with Integers

Set of Integers $I = \{\ldots -3, -2, -1, 0, 1, 2, 3, \ldots\}$

Addition

When adding two integers

- if the signs are the same, then the sum has the same sign as well:
  $(-12) + (-5) = -17$

- if the signs are different, then the sum takes the sign of the larger number:
  $18 + (-5) = 13$

Subtraction

Add the opposite:
$-15 - (-8) = -15 + 8 = -7$

Multiplication and Division

When multiplying and dividing two integers

- if the two integers have the same sign, then the answer is positive:
  $6 \times 8 = 48, (-36) \div (-9) = 4$

- if the two integers have different signs, then the answer is negative:
  $(-5) \times 9 = -45, 54 \div (-6) = -9$

More than one operation $\rightarrow$ follow the order of operations.

B Brackets	
E Exponents	
D Division	$\Big\}$ whichever comes first
M Multiplication	
A Addition	$\Big\}$ whichever comes first
S Subtraction	

Example

Evaluate.

(a) $-10 + (-12)$ **(b)** $(-12) + 7$ **(c)** $(-11) + (-4) + 12 + (-7) + 18$

(d) $(-6) \times 9 \div 3$ **(e)** $\dfrac{20 + (-12) \div (-3)}{(-4 + 12) \div (-2)}$

Solution

(a) $-10 + (-12)$
$= -22$

(b) $(-12) + 7$
$= -5$

(c) $(-11) + (-4) + 12 + (-7) + 18$
$= (-22) + 30$
$= 8$

(d) $(-6) \times 9 \div 3$
$= -54 \div 3$
$= -18$

(e) $\dfrac{20 + (-12) \div (-3)}{(-4 + 12) \div (-2)}$
$= \dfrac{20 + 4}{8 \div (-2)}$
$= \dfrac{24}{-4}$
$= -6$

Practise

1. Evaluate.
  (a) $6 + (-3)$
  (b) $(-12) + (-11)$
  (c) $15 + (-18)$
  (d) $12 - (-13)$
  (e) $-17 - 7$
  (f) $(-23) + 9 - (-4)$
  (g) $(-3) + (-16) - 10$
  (h) $24 - 36 - (-6)$
  (i) $32 + (-10) + (-12) - 18 - (-14)$

2. Which choice would make each statement true: >, <, or =?
  (a) $-5 - 4 - 3 + 3 \blacksquare -4 - 3 - 1 - (-2)$
  (b) $4 - 6 + 6 - 8 \blacksquare -3 - 5 - (-7) - 4$
  (c) $8 - 6 - (-4) - 5 \blacksquare 5 - 13 - 7 - (-8)$
  (d) $5 - 13 + 7 - 2 \blacksquare 4 - 5 - (-3) - 5$
  (e) $7 - 2 - (-15) - 11 \blacksquare -7 - 3 - (-11) - 6$

3. In each row, which expression has the greatest value? the least value?
  (a) $-4 - 3 + 4, 3 - 3 - (-4), 6 - (-3) - 10$
  (b) $4 - 2 - 1, -5 - (-2) + 4, -14 + 5 + 6$
  (c) $9 - (-2) - 6, 5 - (-7) + (-9), -5 - 3 + 7$
  (d) $-5 + 4 + 3 - 2, 4 - (-3) - 7, 5 - (-2) - 7$
  (e) $-5 - 2 + 3, 3 - 10 + 2, -7 - (-2) + 1$

4. Evaluate.
  (a) $(-11) \times (-5)$ **(b)** $(-6) \times 7$
  (c) $(-3)(5)(-4)$ **(d)** $(-6)(7)(8)(-2)$
  (e) $35 \div (-5)$ **(f)** $(-72) \div (-9)$
  (g) $132 \div 12$ **(h)** $(8)(-4) \div (-2)$
  (i) $(5)(-9) \div (-3)(7)$ **(j)** $56 \div (8)(7) \div 49$

5. Evaluate.
  (a) $-12 \div (-3) + (-3)$
  (b) $(-3)^2 - (-2)^2$
  (c) $(-5)^2 - (-7) + (-12)$
  (d) $-4 + 20 \div (-4)$
  (e) $-3(-4) + 8^2$
  (f) $(-16) - ((-8) \div 2)$
  (g) $8 \div (-4) + 4 \div (-2)^2$
  (h) $(-8 + 2) \div (-3 + 2)$

6. Evaluate.
  (a) $\dfrac{-12 - 3}{-3 - 2}$
  (b) $\dfrac{-18 + 6}{(-3)(-4)}$
  (c) $\dfrac{(-16 + 4) \div 2}{8 \div (-8) + 4}$
  (d) $\dfrac{-5 + (-3)(-6)}{(-2)^2 + (-3)^2}$
  (e) $-9 - 3[2(2 - 3)]$
  (f) $-4[(-3)(-2) + 4]$
  (g) $160 \div (-4) + 2[3(8 - 4)]$
  (h) $(-12) \div (-6) + (-3)(-2)$

7. (a) Subtract the sum of $-2 + 3$ and $-4 - 3^2$ from the sum of $-3(-2)$ and $(-4)(-3)^2$.
  (b) How much less is $-3(-3)^2$ than $-4(-2)^3$?
  (c) Find the sum of -3^2, $-4^2 + 2$, $(-3)(-2) + 3$, and $-3(-2 + 5)$.

Operations with Rational Numbers

Set of rational numbers $Q = \{\frac{a}{b} \mid a, b, \in I, b \neq 0\}$

Addition and Subtraction

To add or subtract rationals, you need to find a common denominator.

Division

To divide by a rational number, multiply by the reciprocal.

$$\frac{a}{b} \div \frac{c}{d} = \frac{a}{b} \times \frac{d}{c}$$
$$= \frac{ad}{bc}$$

Multiplication

$\frac{a}{b} \times \frac{c}{d} = \frac{ac}{bd}$, but first reduce to lowest terms where possible.

More Than One Operation

Follow the order of operations.

Example 1

Simplify $\frac{-2}{5} + \frac{3}{-2} - \frac{3}{10}$.

Solution

$$\frac{-2}{5} + \frac{3}{-2} - \frac{3}{10} = \frac{-4}{10} + \frac{-15}{10} - \frac{3}{10}$$
$$= \frac{-4 - 15 - 3}{10}$$
$$= \frac{-22}{10}$$
$$= \frac{-11}{5} \text{ or } -2\frac{1}{5}$$

Example 2

Simplify $\frac{3}{4} \times \frac{-4}{5} \div \frac{-3}{7}$.

Solution

$$\frac{3}{4} \times \frac{-4}{5} \div \frac{-3}{7} = \frac{3}{4} \times \frac{-4}{5} \times \frac{-7}{3}$$
$$= \frac{\overset{1}{\cancel{3}}}{\underset{1}{\cancel{4}}} \times \frac{\overset{-1}{\cancel{-4}}}{5} \times \frac{-7}{\underset{1}{\cancel{3}}}$$
$$= \frac{7}{5} \text{ or } 1\frac{2}{5}$$

Practise

1. Evaluate.

(a) $\frac{1}{4} + \frac{-3}{4}$ (b) $\frac{1}{2} - \frac{-2}{3}$

(c) $\frac{-3}{4} - \frac{1}{-4}$ (d) $\frac{-3}{5} + \frac{3}{-4}$

(e) $\frac{-1}{4} - 1\frac{1}{3}$ (f) $-8\frac{1}{4} - \frac{-1}{-3}$

(g) $\frac{2}{-3} - 1\frac{5}{6}$ (h) $\frac{5}{-6} - 2\frac{1}{3}$

(i) $\frac{-3}{5} + \frac{-3}{4} - \frac{7}{10}$ (j) $\frac{2}{3} - \frac{-1}{2} - \frac{1}{-6}$

2. Evaluate.

(a) $\frac{4}{5} \times \frac{-20}{25}$ (b) $\frac{3}{-2} \times \frac{6}{5}$

(c) $\left(\frac{-1}{3}\right)\left(\frac{2}{-5}\right)$ (d) $\left(\frac{9}{4}\right)\left(\frac{-2}{-3}\right)$

(e) $\left(\frac{1}{-2}\right)\left(\frac{-2}{5}\right)$ (f) $\frac{-4}{5} \times \frac{10}{-4}$

(g) $\left(\frac{-5}{12}\right)(-24)$ (h) $\left(-2\frac{1}{4}\right)\left(\frac{2}{-9}\right)$

(i) $\left(-1\frac{1}{10}\right)\left(3\frac{1}{11}\right)$ (j) $-4\frac{1}{6} \times -7\frac{3}{4}$

3. Evaluate.

(a) $\frac{-4}{3} \div \frac{2}{-3}$

(b) $-7\frac{1}{8} \div \frac{3}{2}$

(c) $\frac{-2}{3} \div \frac{-3}{8}$

(d) $\frac{-3}{-2} \div \left(\frac{-1}{3}\right)$

(e) $-6 \div \left(\frac{-4}{5}\right)$

(f) $\left(-2\frac{1}{3}\right) \div \left(-3\frac{1}{2}\right)$

(g) $\left(-2\frac{1}{2}\right) \div \left(\frac{-1}{2}\right)$

(h) $\left(-\frac{-2}{3}\right) \div \left(-1\frac{1}{5}\right)$

(i) $\left(-3\frac{1}{4}\right) \div \left(-2\frac{3}{4}\right)$

(j) $\left(-1\frac{5}{8}\right) \div 13$

4. Simplify.

(a) $\frac{-2}{5} - \left(\frac{-1}{10} + \frac{1}{-2}\right)$

(b) $\frac{-1}{4} - \left(\frac{3}{4} - \frac{4}{-5}\right)$

(c) $\frac{-3}{5}\left(\frac{-3}{4} - \frac{-1}{4}\right)$

(d) $\left(\frac{3}{5}\right)\left(\frac{1}{-6}\right)\left(\frac{-2}{3}\right)$

(e) $\left(2\frac{3}{4}\right)\left(-1\frac{1}{4}\right)\left(\frac{-3}{8}\right)$

(f) $\frac{-5}{7} \times \frac{28}{5} \div \frac{-8}{6}$

(g) $\left(\frac{-2}{3}\right)^2\left(\frac{1}{-2}\right)^3$

(h) $\frac{-1}{3} \div -1\frac{1}{9} \times \frac{5}{6}$

5. Calculate. Follow the order of operations.

(a) $\left(\frac{3}{4}\right) \div \left(\frac{-1}{2}\right) \div \left(\frac{2}{3}\right)$

(b) $\left(\frac{-2}{5} + \frac{1}{-2}\right) \div \left(\frac{5}{-8} - \frac{-1}{2}\right)$

(c) $\left(\frac{2}{3} - \frac{-1}{3}\right) \div \left(\frac{-3}{4} - \frac{-2}{3}\right)$

(d) $\left(\frac{-1}{8} + \frac{1}{-4}\right)\left(\frac{-1}{-2} + \frac{-1}{6}\right)$

(e) $\left(\frac{2}{-3} - \frac{-1}{2}\right) \div \left(\frac{-3}{2} - \frac{3}{2}\right)$

(f) $\left(\frac{4}{5} - \frac{3}{-4}\right)\left(\frac{-1}{3} - \frac{1}{4}\right)$

6. Evaluate the expression.

(a) $\dfrac{\frac{-4}{5} - \frac{-3}{5}}{\frac{1}{3} - \frac{-1}{5}}$

(b) $\dfrac{\frac{3}{5} - \frac{-1}{10}}{\frac{-1}{4} - 1\frac{2}{3}}$

(c) $\dfrac{\frac{1}{-4} - \frac{-1}{3}}{\frac{5}{-12} - 1\frac{3}{4}}$

7. Calculate. Verify your answer using a calculator.

(a) $\frac{-2}{3} + \frac{3}{-4} - 1\frac{2}{3}$

(b) $\frac{-3}{16} \times 3\frac{1}{5} \div \left(-1\frac{2}{3}\right)$

(c) $\left(6\frac{1}{4} - \frac{-3}{8}\right) \times \frac{3}{7}$

(d) $\frac{3}{5} \div \frac{2}{-1} + \left(-1\frac{3}{4}\right)$

Evaluating Algebraic Expressions and Formulas

Algebraic expressions and formulas are evaluated by substituting the given numbers in place of the variables. Then follow the order of operations to calculate the answer.

Example 1

Find the value of $2x^2 - y$ if $x = -2$ and $y = 3$.

Solution

$$2x^2 - y = 2(-2)^2 - 3$$
$$= 2(4) - 3$$
$$= 8 - 3$$
$$= 5$$

Example 2

If $a = \frac{-1}{2}$ and $b = 1\frac{2}{3}$, evaluate $3a - 2b$.

Solution

$$3a - 2b = 3\left(\frac{-1}{2}\right) - 2\left(1\frac{2}{3}\right)$$
$$= \frac{-3}{2} - 2\left(\frac{5}{3}\right)$$
$$= \frac{-3}{2} - \frac{10}{3}$$
$$= \frac{-9 - 20}{6}$$
$$= \frac{-29}{6} \text{ or } -4\frac{5}{6}$$

Example 3

The formula for finding the volume of a cylinder is $V = \pi r^2 h$. Find the volume for a cylinder with a radius of 2.5 cm and a height of 7.5 cm.

Solution

$$V = \pi r^2 h$$
$$= (3.14)(2.5)^2(7.5)$$
$$= (3.14)(6.25)(7.5)$$
$$= 147.1875 \text{ cm}^3$$

Practise

1. Find the value of each expression for $x = -5$ and $y = -4$.

(a) $-x + 2y$ (b) $-4x - 2y$
(c) $3x^2 - 5y$ (d) $-3x - 2y^2$
(e) $y^2 - 3x^2$ (f) $2xy - y^3$
(g) $5xy - 3x + 4y$ (h) $(3x - 4y)^2$
(i) $(3x)^3 + (2y)^2$ (j) $\left(\frac{x}{y}\right) - \left(\frac{y}{x}\right)$

2. If $a = -\frac{1}{2}$ and $b = \frac{2}{3}$, find the value of each expression.

(a) $x + y$ (b) $x - y$
(c) $x + 2y$ (d) $3x - 2y$
(e) $\frac{1}{2}x - \frac{1}{2}y$

3. Simplify each expression using $a = \frac{1}{3}$, $b = \frac{1}{2}$, and $c = -\frac{1}{8}$.

   (a) $ab + c$ **(b)** $2a - 4b + c$

   (c) $c(a + b)$ **(d)** $\frac{a}{b + c}$

4. Simplify each expression if $x = -\frac{2}{3}$ and $y = \frac{3}{4}$.

   (a) $\frac{-2x + 4y}{x + y}$ **(b)** $\frac{x^2 + 2xy + y^2}{x + y}$

   (c) $\frac{x^2 - y^2}{x - y}$ **(d)** $\frac{5x}{4y} + \frac{3x}{2y}$

5. Find the value of each expression if $c = 1.5$ and $d = -2.4$.

   (a) $5c - 3d$ **(b)** $-4cd + 2c - 8d$

   (c) $(cd)^2$ **(d)** $\frac{5c}{2d}$

   (f) $3c - 6d + 4c^2 d^3$

6. (a) The formula for the area of a triangle is $A = \frac{1}{2}bh$. Find the area of a triangle when $b = 13.5$ cm and $h = 12.2$ cm.

   (b) The area of a circle is found using the formula $A = \pi r^2$. Find the area of a circle with a radius of 4.3 m.

   (c) The volume of a box can be determined using the formula $V = lwh$. Find the volume of a box that is 28 mm wide, 56 mm long, and 15 mm high.

(d) The hypotenuse of a right triangle, c, is found using the formula $c = \sqrt{a^2 + b^2}$. Find the length of the hypotenuse when $a = 6$ m and $b = 8$ m.

(e) A sphere's volume is calculated using the formula $V = \frac{4}{3}\pi r^3$. Determine the volume of a sphere with a radius of 10.5 cm.

(f) If you stand on the moon and jump up at a speed of 4 m/s, your approximate height, h, above the surface, in metres, is given by $h = 4t - 0.8t^2$, where t is the time in seconds after you jump. Determine your height above the surface of the moon 2 s after you jump.

(g) A satellite will stay in orbit above the Earth if its speed is $s = \sqrt{\frac{5.15 \times 10^{12}}{d}}$, where s is the speed in kilometres per hour and d is the distance between the satellite and the centre of the Earth. Determine the speed at which a satellite that is 32 000 km from the Earth's centre must travel to stay in orbit.

Simplifying Algebraic Expressions

Algebraic expressions contain both numbers and letters. The letters are often called **variables**.

Algebraic expressions can only be simplified if they contain **like terms**. Like terms must have the same variables and the same exponents.

Example: $3x^2$ and $-5x^2$ are like terms. $2xy$ and $7yz$ are unlike terms.

Terms are the product of a **coefficient** and a variable. In an algebraic expression, terms are separated by plus or minus signs.

Example: The expression $5x^2 + 3x - 7$ has three terms: $5x^2$, $3x$, and -7. In these terms: 5, 3, and -7 are coefficients, while x is the variable.

Algebraic expressions with one or more terms are called **polynomials.** Simple polynomials are given special names.

Monomial $\rightarrow$ one term $\rightarrow 8x$

Binomial $\rightarrow$ two terms $\rightarrow 5x - 9$

Trinomial $\rightarrow$ three terms $\rightarrow 6x^2 - 8x + 12$

Algebraic expressions can be multiplied by a constant. This is done by expanding using the **distributive property**.

$$a(b + c) = ab + ac$$

Example 1

Simplify $2c + 3c + 4$.

Solution

$2c + 3c + 4 = 5c + 4$ Collect like terms.

Example 2

Simplify $(2x^2 + 3) + (-4x^2 + 8)$.

Solution

$(2x^2 + 3) + (-4x^2 + 8)$

$= 2x^2 + 3 - 4x^2 + 8$ Rearrange.

$= 2x^2 - 4x^2 + 3 + 8$ Collect like terms.

$= -2x^2 + 11$

Example 3

Simplify $2(2a + b) - 3(3a - 2b)$.

Solution

$2(2a + b) - 3(3a - 2b)$ Expand.

$= 4a + 2b - 9a + 6b$ Rearrange.

$= 4a - 9a + 2b + 6b$ Collect like terms.

$= -5a + 8b$

Practise

1. Identify the variable and the coefficient in each expression.

    (a) $5x^3$ (b) $-13a$ (c) $7c^4$

    (d) $-1.35m$ (e) $\frac{4}{7}y$ (f) $\frac{5x}{8}$

2. Which terms are like terms?

    (a) a, $5x$, $-3a$, $12a$, $-9x$

    (b) c^2, $6c$, $-c$, $13c^2$, $1.25c$

    (c) $3xy$, $5x^2y$, $-3xy$, $9x^2y$, $12x^2y$

    (d) x^2, y^2, $2xy$, $-y^2$, $-x^2$, $-4xy$

3. Identify each polynomial as a monomial, binomial, or trinomial

    (a) $6x^3 - 5x$ (b) $5x^3y$

    (c) $7 + 3x - 4x^2$ (d) $-yxz^3$

    (e) $5x - 2y$ (f) $3a + 5c - 4b$

4. Simplify.

    (a) $4x + 5x - 6x$ (b) $3a - 7a + 12a$

    (c) $4c + 7c - 15c$ (d) $6x^2 - 8x^2 + 3x^2$

    (e) $5xy + 7xy + 9xy$

    (f) $2a + 6b - 5a - 3b$

    (g) $3c + 8m - 10m + 5c$

    (h) $6x^2 - 3x - 8x^2 + 2x$

    (i) $4x^2 - 5x^3 + 7x^2$

    (j) $6x + 5 + 7x - 9$

    (k) $5 - 7x + 6y - 8x + 2 - 8y$

    (l) $7xy - 8x^2 + 6xy - 2x^2 - 12xy + 10x^2$

    (m) $5x - x^3 + 4x^2 - 7x^2 + 6x^3 - x$

    (n) $7x^2y - 8xy^2 + 4x^2y - 5x^2y^2$

    (o) $8x - 9y + 2z - 8z + 5x - 12y + 7$

    (p) $x^{-2} + 5x^2 - 8x^2 + 6x^{-2} + 3x^3$

5. Expand.

    (a) $2(3x - 5y + 2)$

    (b) $-3(4x + 5 - 2x^2)$

    (c) $8(3a - 5c + 6b)$

    (d) $-4(-3g + 2h - 7)$

    (e) $5(4t - v + 2r^2)$

    (f) $-5(-x - y + z)$

    (g) $-7(x^2 - 2y^2 + x^3)$

    (h) $12(3a + 2b - 6c + 2)$

6. Simplify.

    (a) $(4x - 5y) + (6x + 3) - (7x - 2y)$

    (b) $(4x + 9y) - (5x - 7y) + (2x + 5y)$

    (c) $(2a - 8ab) - (7b + 9a) + (ab - 2a + 6b)$

    (d) $(9x^2 + 2x + 2y) + (-5y - 6x^2 - 7x)$
        $\quad - (5x^2 - 2x + 4y)$

    (e) $(7x^2 - 3x + y) - (8y - 2x^2 + 5x)$
        $\quad - (2x^2 - 10x + 14y)$

7. Simplify.

    (a) $(2x - 5) + (8x + 13)$

    (b) $(3x + 8y) - (5x - 7y)$

    (c) $(5a - 7ab) + (6b + 4a)$
        $\quad - (9ab - 3a + 3b)$

    (d) $3(3x - 8) - 4(8x + 1)$

    (e) $-2(4x + 5y) - 4(8x - 7y)$

    (f) $5(7xy - 4x + 8y) - (6x - 9yx + 2y)$

    (g) $2(7x^2 + 3x + 5y) + 3(-2y - 9x^2 + 4x)$

    (h) $(3d^3 - 6 + 5d^2) + 4(9 - 2d^3 - 4d^2)$

    (i) $2(9a - 7ab) - 3(6b + 8a)$
        $\quad - 4(5ab - 2a + 9b)$

    (j) $-7(x^2 + 6x + 9y) + 5(-9y - 2x^2 + x)$

    (k) $6(2d^3 - 1 + 5d^2) - 5(10 - 3d^3 - 8d^2)$

    (l) $-4(9xy - 2x + 5y) - 2(6x - 12yx + 12y)$

Solving Equations

Any mathematical sentence that states that two quantities are equal is called an **equation**.

Example: $5x + 6 = 2(x + 5) + 5$ is an equation. The expression $5x + 6$ is on the left side and $2(x + 5) + 5$ is on the right side.

A **solution**, or **root**, to an equation is a number which makes the left side equal to the right side.

Example: $x = 3$ is the solution to the equation $5x + 6 = 2(x + 5) + 5$. When x is replaced with 3, both sides of the equation result in 21.

A linear equation in one variable is solved by isolating the variable. Before this can be done:

- all brackets must be eliminated using the distributive property
$a(b + c) = ab + ac$

- all fractions must be eliminated by multiplying each term of the equation by the lowest common denominator

Example 1

Solve $13x + 9 = 11x + 5$.

Solution

$$13x + 9 = 11x + 5$$
$$13x - 11x = 5 - 9$$
$$\frac{2x}{2} = \frac{-4}{2}$$
$$x = -2$$

Example 2

Solve $y + 6(y - 3) = 2(3y - 2)$.

Solution

$$y + 6(y - 3) = 2(3y - 2)$$
$$y + 6y - 18 = 6y - 4$$
$$y + 6y - 6y = -4 + 18$$
$$y = 14$$

Example 3

Solve $\frac{3}{4}t - 2 = \frac{1}{2}(t + 2)$.

Solution

$$\frac{3}{4}t - 2 = \frac{1}{2}(t + 2)$$
$$^1\cancel{4}(\tfrac{3}{\cancel{4}}t) - 4(2) = {}^2\cancel{4}(\tfrac{1}{\cancel{2}}(t + 2))$$
$$3t - 8 = 2(t + 2)$$
$$3t - 8 = 2t + 4$$
$$3t - 2t = 4 + 8$$
$$t = 12$$

Practise

1. Solve.

(a) $3y + 5 = 11$

(b) $4x - 3 = -11$

(c) $17 = 4c - 3$

(d) $6x + 8 = 4x - 10$

(e) $9p - 10 = 6 + p$

(f) $2m + 6.1 = 16.5$

(g) $4a - 2.8 = 6.8$

(h) $15.8 - 6m = 3.8$

(i) $8y - 6.9 = 3y + 3.6$

(j) $12.8 - 3m = 8m - 33.4$

2. Find the root of each equation.

(a) $3(n + 4) = 5n$

(b) $3x - 10 = 2(x - 3)$

(c) $2(x - 2) = 2(3 - x)$

(d) $4(c - 2) = 3(c + 1)$

(e) $8(m - 1) = 4(m + 4)$

(f) $4(3 - r) = 5(2r + 1)$

(g) $12(2m - 3) = 2(m + 4)$

(h) $0.5(x + 2) = 0.1x + 0.6(x - 3)$

(i) $6.5(x - 3) = 2.4(3 - x)$

3. Solve.

(a) $\frac{x}{2} = 4$　　(b) $\frac{3x}{5} = -9$

(c) $6 = \frac{m}{4}$　　(d) $2\frac{x}{-7} = 6$

(e) $3 = \frac{3}{2}x - 3$　　(f) $\frac{1}{4}x - 3 = 4$

(g) $\frac{4}{5}x - 3 = 5$　　(h) $7 = 1 + \frac{2}{3}x$

(i) $7 + \frac{1}{2}y = 10$　　(j) $\frac{1}{3}b - 2 = 2$

(k) $16 = 10 + \frac{3}{5}x$

(l) $-5 + \frac{1}{4}x = -7$

4. Solve.

(a) $2y + \frac{1}{2} = \frac{2}{3}$

(b) $\frac{7}{6}x - 2 = \frac{1}{3}$

(c) $\frac{n}{4} - 1 = \frac{n}{5}$

(d) $3 - \frac{m}{2} = 5 - \frac{m}{3}$

(e) $\frac{2}{3}y - 3 = \frac{4}{5}y - 5$

(f) $\frac{3}{5}x - 2 = \frac{2}{3}x + 3$

(g) $\frac{x}{8} - \frac{3}{2} = -\frac{1}{40}$

(h) $\frac{1}{2}x + \frac{1}{3}x = 10$

(i) $\frac{3}{4}x - \frac{1}{8}x = 5$

5. Solve.

(a) $\frac{1}{3}(2x - 1) = 1$

(b) $\frac{1}{6}(6 + 2y) = 2$

(c) $\frac{1}{2}(x - 5) = \frac{x}{4}$

(d) $\frac{1}{2}(y + 2) = \frac{y}{3}$

(e) $\frac{3}{5}(2x + 15) = 3$

(f) $\frac{1}{2}(x - 1) = \frac{1}{4}(x + 1)$

(g) $\frac{4x - 1}{5} = \frac{2x + 3}{2}$

(h) $\frac{y - 7}{3} = \frac{y - 2}{4}$

(i) $\frac{y + 4}{3} = \frac{y + 1}{2}$

6. Determine the value of the unknown variable using the given formula and information.

(a) $A = lw$; $A = 464$, $w = 4$, $l = $ ■

(b) $A = \frac{1}{2}bh$; $A = 288$, $h = 24$, $b = $ ■

(c) $A = \frac{1}{2}(a + b)\,h$; $A = 96$, $a = 4$, $b = 8$, $h = $ ■

(d) $P = 2l + 2w$; $P = 80$, $l = 8$, $w = $ ■

(e) $A = s^2$; $A = 625$, $s = $ ■

(f) $I = 4.5A + 2.5S$; $A = 120$, $I = 700$, $S = $ ■

7. At the December concert, 209 tickets were sold. There were 23 more student tickets sold than twice the number of adult tickets. How many of each were sold?

8. A rectangle with a perimeter of 54 cm is 3 cm longer than it is wide. What are its length and width?

Graphing Linear Relationships

The graph of a linear relationship ($ax + by + c = 0$) is a straight line. The graph can be drawn if at least two ordered pairs of the relationship are known. This information can be determined several different ways.

Example 1: Table of Values

Sketch the graph of $2y = 4x - 2$.

Solution

A table of values can be created.

Express the equation in the form $y = mx + b$.

$$\frac{2y}{2} = \frac{4x - 2}{2}$$
$$y = 2x - 1$$

x	y
–1	2(–1) – 1 = –3
0	2(0) – 1 = –1
1	2(1) – 1 = 1
2	2(2) – 1 = 3

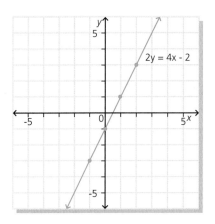

Example 2: Using Intercepts

Sketch the graph of $2x + 4y = 8$.

Solution

The intercepts of the line can be found.

For the x-intercept, let $y = 0$.

$$2x = 8$$
$$x = 4$$

For the y-intercept, let $x = 0$.

$$4y = 8$$
$$y = 2$$

x	y
4	0
0	2

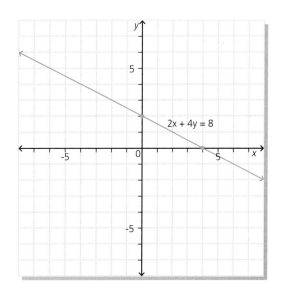

Example 3: Using the Slope and y-intercept

Sketch the graph of $y = 3x + 4$.

Solution

When the equation is in the form $y = mx + b$, the slope and y-intercept can be determined.

For $y = 3x + 4$, the line has a slope of 3 and a y-intercept of 4.

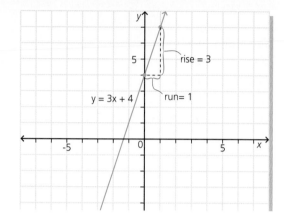

Practise

1. Express each equation in the form $y = mx + b$.

   (a) $3y = 6x + 9$

   (b) $2x - 4y = 8$

   (c) $3x + 6y - 12 = 0$

   (d) $5x = y - 9$

   (e) $2x - 5y = 20$

   (f) $4x - y - 6 = 0$

   (g) $2x + 2y = 2$

   (h) $5x - 10 = -3y$

   (e) $36 = 9y - 4x$

   (f) $50 - 10x - y = 0$

   (g) $\frac{x}{2} + \frac{y}{4} = 1$

   (h) $\frac{x}{5} - \frac{y}{10} = 2$

2. Graph each equation using a table of values where $x \in \{-2, -1, 0, 1, 2\}$.

   (a) $y = 3x - 1$ (b) $y = 5x + 2$

   (c) $y = \frac{1}{2}x + 4$ (d) $y = \frac{2x + 4}{2}$

   (e) $2y = 4x + 8$ (f) $2x + 3y = 6$

   (g) $y = 4$ (h) $x = -5$

3. Determine the x- and y-intercepts of each equation.

   (a) $x + y = 10$

   (b) $2x + 4y = 16$

   (c) $5x - 7y = 35$

   (d) $9x = 54 - 6y$

4. Graph each equation by determining the intercepts.

   (a) $x + y = 4$ (b) $x - y = 3$

   (c) $2x + y = 6$ (d) $-x + 4y = 8$

   (e) $2x + 5y = 10$ (f) $3x - 4y = 12$

   (g) $2x - 4y = -8$ (h) $-7x - 3y = 21$

5. Graph each equation using the slope and y-intercept.

   (a) $y = 2x + 3$ (b) $y = -x - 5$

   (c) $y = \frac{2}{3}x + 1$ (d) $y = -\frac{3}{4}x - 2$

   (e) $2y = x + 6$ (f) $2x + 3y = -6$

   (g) $8 - x = 4y$ (h) $x + y + 1 = 0$

6. Graph each equation. Use the most suitable method.

   (a) $y = 5x + 2$ (b) $3x - y = 6$

   (c) $y = -\frac{2}{3}x + 4$ (d) $4x = 20 - 5y$

Slope and the Equation of a Line

The **slope** of a line, m, is a measure of how steep a line is. The greater the magnitude of m, the steeper the line. A line with a positive slope rises to the right, while a line with a negative slope falls to the right. A horizontal line has a slope of zero. A vertical line has a slope that is undefined. Parallel lines have the same slope. Perpendicular lines have slopes that are negative reciprocals.

$$m = \text{slope}$$
$$= \frac{\text{rise}}{\text{run}}$$
$$= \frac{\Delta y}{\Delta x}$$
$$= \frac{y_2 - y_1}{x_2 - x_1}$$

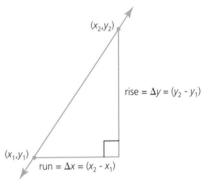

rise $= \Delta y = (y_2 - y_1)$

(x_1, y_1)

run $= \Delta x = (x_2 - x_1)$

(x_2, y_2)

To find the equation of a line when two points on the line are known

1. Calculate the slope of the line.

2. Find the y-intercept by substituting the coordinates from a point on the line and the slope into $y = mx + b$ and solve for b.

3. Write the equation, using the values for m and b.

4. If necessary, express the equation in standard form: $Ax + By + C = 0$, where A, B, and C are integers and A is positive.

Example 1

Determine the slope of AB where $A(4, -13)$ and $B(-5, 5)$.

Solution

$$m = \frac{(y_2 - y_1)}{(x_2 - x_1)}$$
$$m = \frac{5 - (-13)}{-5 - 4}$$
$$m = \frac{18}{-9}$$
$$m = -2$$

Example 2

Determine the equation of the line that has a slope of 2 and passes through $(-2, 5)$.

Solution

$$y = mx + b$$
$$y = 2x + b$$
$$5 = 2(-2) + b$$
$$5 = -4 + b$$
$$5 + 4 = b$$
$$9 = b$$

The equation is $y = 2x + 9$.

Example 3

Determine the equation of the line that passes through $(2, 6)$ and $(-1, 7)$.

Solution

① $m = \frac{(y_2 - y_1)}{(x_2 - x_1)}$

$$m = \frac{7 - 6}{-1 - 2}$$
$$m = -\frac{1}{3}$$

② $y = mx + b$

$$y = -\frac{1}{3}x + b$$

③ $6 = -\frac{1}{3}(2) + b$ $6 + \frac{2}{3} = b$

$$6 = -\frac{2}{3} + b$$ $6\frac{2}{3} = b$

The equation is $y = -\frac{1}{3}x + \frac{20}{3}$.

Practise

1. Determine the slope of the line that passes through each pair of points.
   - (a) $(5, 2)$ and $(-1, 8)$
   - (b) $(-8, 1)$ and $(-9, 2)$
   - (c) $(3, 7)$ and $(-5, -9)$
   - (d) $(-4, 0)$ and $(4, 6)$

2. Write, in the form $y = mx + b$, the equation of the line that has
   - (a) a slope of 2 and a y-intercept of 8
   - (b) a slope of $\frac{3}{4}$ and a y-intercept of -6
   - (c) a slope of 6 and passes through $(1, 5)$
   - (d) a slope of $\frac{5}{6}$ and passes through $(-12, 3)$

3. Express each equation in standard form.
   - (a) $3x + y = 10$
   - (b) $-2x - 2y - 8 = 0$
   - (c) $6x + 3y = 12$
   - (d) $2x - 3y = 5$
   - (e) $\frac{5}{2}x - \frac{3}{4}y = \frac{1}{3}$

4. For each line in question 1
   - i. draw a diagram and determine the y-intercept
   - ii. determine the equation of the line in the form $y = mx + b$
   - iii. express the equation in standard form

5. Are the lines with the given slopes parallel, perpendicular, or neither?
   - (a) $m_1 = 5$, $m_2 = \frac{1}{5}$
   - (b) $m_1 = -3$, $m_2 = \frac{1}{3}$
   - (c) $m_1 = \frac{3}{4}$, $m_2 = 0.75$
   - (d) $m_1 = -0.6$, $m_2 = \frac{3}{5}$
   - (e) $m_1 = \frac{4}{7}$, $m_2 = -1\frac{3}{4}$

6. Write an equation for the line that is
   - (a) parallel to $x = 3$ and passes through $(-4, 3)$
   - (b) parallel to $y = 2$ and passes through $(2, 5)$
   - (c) perpendicular to $x = -1$ and passes through $(-2, -3)$
   - (d) perpendicular to $y = 4$ and passes through $(1, 1)$
   - (e) parallel to $y = -2x + 3$ and passes through $(-2, 1)$
   - (f) perpendicular to $y = \frac{3}{2}x + 2$ and has a y-intercept of -2
   - (g) perpendicular to $y = 3x + 4$ and has the same y-intercept as the line $y = 2x - 6$

Creating Scatter Plots and the Line of Best Fit

A **scatter plot** is a graph that shows the relationship between two sets of numeric data. The points in a scatter plot often show a general pattern or **trend**. A line that approximates a trend for the data in a scatter plot is called a **line of best fit**.

A line of best fit passes through as many points as possible, with the remaining points grouped equally above and below the line.

Data that has a **positive correlation** has a pattern that slopes up and to the right. Data that has a **negative correlation** has a pattern that slopes down and to the right. If the points nearly form a line, then the correlation is strong. If the points are dispersed, but still form some linear pattern, then the correlation is weak.

Example 1

(a) Make a scatter plot of the data and describe the kind of correlation the scatter plot shows.

(b) Draw the line of best fit.

Long-Term Trends in Average Cigarettes Per Day by Smokers Aged 15–19

Year	1981	1983	1985	1986	1989	1990	1991	1994	1995	1996
Number Per Day	16.0	16.6	15.1	15.4	12.9	13.5	14.8	12.6	11.4	12.2

Solution

(a)

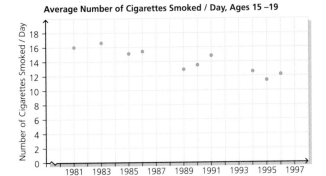

The scatter plot shows negative correlation.

(b)

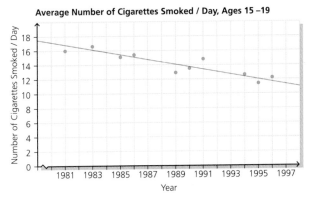

Practise

1. For each set of data
   i. create a scatter plot and draw the line of best fit
   ii. describe the type of correlation the trend in the data displays

(a) Property Crimes Reported in Toronto 1992−1998

Year	1992	1993	1994	1995	1996	1997	1998
Number of Crimes	5188	4839	4495	4494	4314	3932	3354

Source: Uniform Crime Reporting Survey, Canadian Centre for Justice Statistics

(b) Percentage of Canadian Households Owning Televisions

Year	1965	1970	1975	1980	1985	1990	1997
Percentage of Households	92.6	96.0	96.8	97.7	98.3	99.0	99.1

Source: Statistics Canada

(c) Population of the Region Hamilton-Wentworth, Ontario

Year	1966	1976	1986	1996	1998
Population	449 116	529 371	557 029	624 360	618 658

Source: Census of Canada, Statistics Canada

(d) Percentage of Canadians with Less than Grade 9 Education

Year	1976	1981	1986	1991	1996
Percentage of the Population	25.4	20.7	17.7	14.3	12.4

Source: Census of Canada, Statistics Canada

The Pythagorean Theorem

The three sides of a right triangle are related to each other in a unique way. Every right triangle has a longest side, called the **hypotenuse**, which is always opposite the right angle. One of the important relationships in mathematics is known as the **Pythagorean theorem**. It states that the area of the square of the hypotenuse is equal to the sum of the areas of the squares of the other two sides.

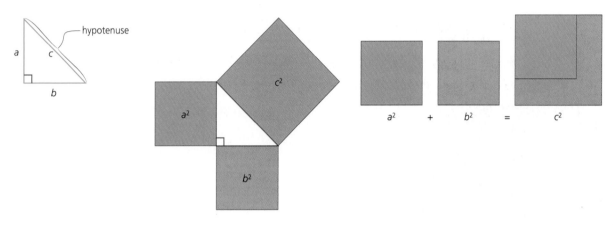

Practise

1. For each right triangle, write the equation for the Pythagorean theorem.

(a)

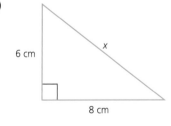
6 cm
x
8 cm

(b)

13 cm
c
6 cm

(c)

9 m
y
5 m

(d)

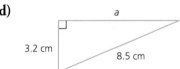
a
3.2 cm
8.5 cm

2. Calculate the length of the unknown side of each triangle in question 1. Round all answers to one decimal place.

3. Find the value of each unknown measure to the nearest hundredth.

   (a) $a^2 = 5^2 + 12^2$

   (b) $f^2 = 9^2 + 15^2$

   (c) $10^2 = 8^2 + m^2$

   (d) $26^2 = b^2 + 12^2$

   (e) $2.3^2 + 4.7^2 = c^2$

   (f) $2.6^2 = 1.8^2 + d^2$

4. Determine the length of the diagonals of each rectangle to the nearest tenth.

   (a)

   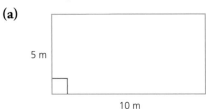

   5 m

   10 m

   (b)

   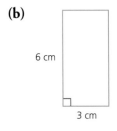

   6 cm

   3 cm

(c)

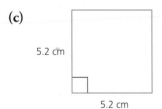

5.2 cm

5.2 cm

(d)   1.2 m

4.8 m

5. An isosceles triangle has a hypotenuse 15 cm long. Determine the length of the two equal sides.

6. An apartment building casts a shadow. From the tip of the shadow to the top of the building is 100 m. The tip of the shadow is 72 m from the base of the building. How tall is the building?

7. A communications tower is supported by four guy wires. The tower is 155 m tall, and each guy wire is staked into the ground at a distance of 30 m from the base of the tower. What is the total length of wire used to support the tower?

Properties of Triangles

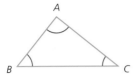

The sum of the **interior angles** is 180°.
$\angle A + \angle B + \angle C = 180°$

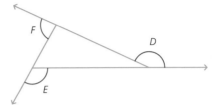

The sum of the **exterior angles** of a triangle is 360°. $\angle D + \angle E + \angle F = 360°$

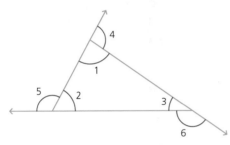

Each exterior angle is equal to the sum of the interior angles at the opposite vertices. These are called **remote interior angles**.

$\angle 4 = \angle 2 + \angle 3$, $\angle 5 = \angle 1 + \angle 3$,
$\angle 6 = \angle 1 + \angle 2$

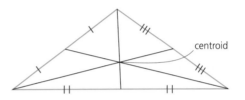

The **medians** of a triangle intersect at a common point called the **centroid**. The centroid divides each median in the ratio 1 : 2.

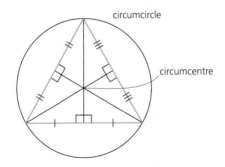

The **perpendicular bisectors** of the sides of a triangle intersect at a common point called the **circumcentre.** This point is the centre of the circle that passes through all the vertices of the triangle. This circle is called the **circumcircle** or **circumscribed** circle.

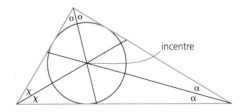

The **bisectors** of the interior angles of a triangle intersect at a common point called the **incentre**. This point is the centre of the circle that meets each side of the triangle at exactly one point. This circle is called the **inscribed circle** or **incircle.**

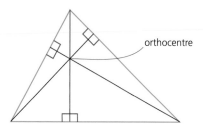

The altitudes of a triangle intersect at a common point called the **orthocentre**.

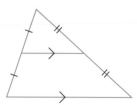

The **midsegment** of a triangle is parallel to the opposite side. This midsegment is half the length of the parallel side.

Practise

1. Find the value of x in each diagram.

(a)

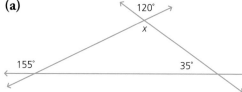

120°
x
155°
35°

(b)

x
$(x - 15)°$
150°

(c)

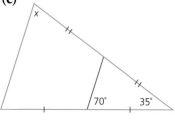

x
70°
35°

(d)

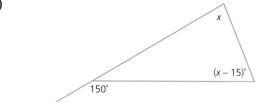

89°
60°
x

(e)

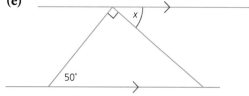

x
50°

(f)

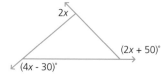

$2x$
$(2x + 50)°$
$(4x - 30)°$

(g)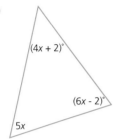

(h)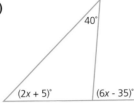

(i)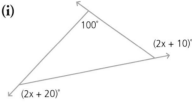

2. Match each centre with the segments needed to find it.

(a) incentre   **i.**   angle bisectors

(b) centroid   **ii.**   medians

(c) orthocentre   **iii.**   altitudes

(d) circumcentre   **iv.**   perpendicular bisectors

3. Given that DE is a midsegment of $\triangle ABC$, $CD = 4.2$ cm, and $BE = 3.6$ cm, find

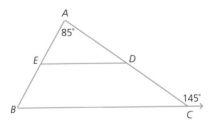

(a) the length of AD

(b) the length of AB

(c) the measure of $\angle ADE$

(d) the measure of $\angle AED$

4. Point E is the centroid of $\triangle ABC$. Suppose $BD = 12$ cm. Find the length of BE and DE.

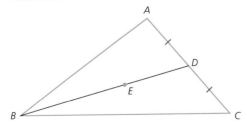

5. Construct a large scalene triangle.

(a) Locate and label the incentre I.

(b) Locate and label the centroid C.

(c) Locate and label the circumcentre D.

(d) Locate and label the orthocentre O.

(e) Three of these points should be **collinear**; that is, in a straight line. Draw the line that contains the three points.

6. Construct a large equilateral triangle.

(a) Locate and label the incentre I.

(b) Locate and label the centroid C.

(c) Locate and label the circumcentre D.

(d) Locate and label the orthocentre O.

(e) What special triangle centre property does an equilateral triangle have?

7. Construct a large right triangle.

(a) Locate and label the incentre I.

(b) Locate and label the centroid C.

(c) Locate and label the circumcentre D.

(d) Locate and label the orthocentre O.

(e) Do any of the triangle centres occur in the same location in a right triangle?

8. Construct a large isosceles triangle.

(a) Locate and label the incentre I.

(b) Locate and label the centroid C.

(c) Locate and label the circumcentre D.

(d) Locate and label the orthocentre O.

(e) What special triangle centre property does an isosceles triangle have?

Properties of Quadrilaterals

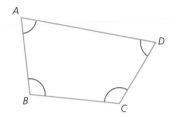

In a **quadrilateral**, the sum of the interior angles is 360°.

$$\angle A + \angle B + \angle C + \angle D = 360°$$

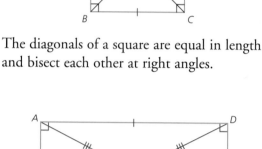

The diagonals of a square are equal in length and bisect each other at right angles.

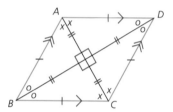

The diagonals of a rhombus bisect each other at right angles and bisect the angles at the vertices.

The diagonals of a rectangle are equal and bisect each other.

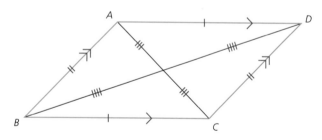

The diagonals of a parallelogram bisect each other.

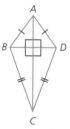

The diagonals of a kite are perpendicular to each other.

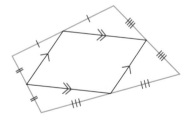

The midsegments of a quadrilateral form a parallelogram.

Practise

1. Match each name to its definition. Use each name only once.
  (a) a quadrilateral with only one pair of parallel sides
  (b) a parallelogram with diagonals that bisect each other and are equal
  (c) a parallelogram that is a rhombus and a square
  (d) a quadrilateral with two pairs of adjacent sides that are equal
  (e) a parallelogram with four sides congruent and diagonals that intersect
  i. square **ii.** trapezoid **iii.** kite
  iv. rhombus **v.** rectangle

2. Construct a figure to match each description. Label diagrams and indicate all equal angles, right angles, line segments, and parallel sides.
  (a) a parallelogram with diagonals that intersect at right angles
  (b) a rhombus with a 90° angle
  (c) a trapezoid with one pair of opposite sides equal
  (d) a parallelogram with diagonals that are equal and intersect at right angles

3. True or False?
  (a) The diagonals of a parallelogram are always equal in length.
  (b) A square is also a rhombus.
  (c) A rhombus is also a parallelogram.
  (d) The diagonals of a kite bisect each other.
  (e) The diagonals of a rectangle bisect each other at right angles.

4. Find the measures of angles x, y, and z.
  (a)
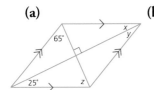
  (b)
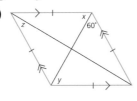

(c)
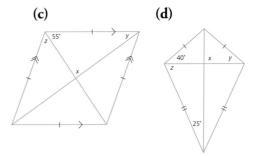

(d)

5. Name all the types of quadrilaterals whose diagonals
  (a) bisect each other
  (b) intersect at right angles
  (c) are equal in length
  (d) bisect the angles at the vertices

6. Draw the figure formed by joining, in order, all the midpoints on the sides of any quadrilateral.

7. Find the value of x.
  (a)
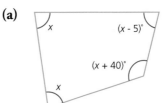

  (b)
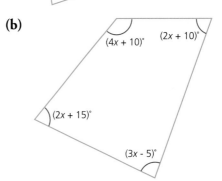

  (c)
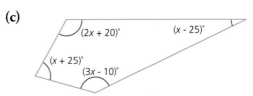

Area and Perimeter

Perimeter measures the distance around the outside of a closed figure.

Area measures the number of square units needed to cover a surface.

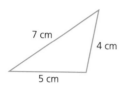

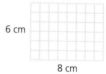

The perimeter of this triangle is

$$P = 7 + 4 + 5$$
$$= 16 \text{ cm}$$

The area of this surface is

$$A = 6 \times 8$$
$$= 48 \text{ cm}^2$$

Shape	Perimeter	Area
triangle	$P = a + b + c$	$A = \frac{1}{2}(b \times h)$
square 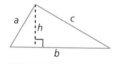	$P = 4s$	$A = s^2$
rectangle 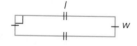	$P = 2(l + w)$	$A = lw$
parallelogram 	$P = a + b + c + d$	$A = bh$
trapezoid 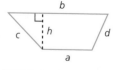	$P = a + b + c + d$	$A = \frac{1}{2}(a + b)\,h$

circle	In a circle, the distance around the outside is called the **circumference**.	$A = \pi r^2$

$$C = 2\pi r \text{ or } C = \pi d$$

regular polygon	$P = nl$ where n is the number of sides and l is the length of each side	$A = \dfrac{Pa}{2}$ where P is the perimeter of the polygon and a is the apothem

Practise

1. Find the area of each figure.

(a) rectangle: $l = 5$ cm and $w = 2.6$ cm

(b) triangle: $b = 9$ cm and $h = 8$ cm

(c) square: $s = 2.5$ m

(d) circle: $r = 5.8$ mm

(e) parallelogram: $b = 3.6$ cm and $h = 2.4$ cm

(f) trapezoid: $h = 32$ mm, $a = 25$ mm, and $b = 42$ mm

(g) circle: $d = 98$ cm

(h) rhombus: $b = 5.5$ cm and $h = 4.2$ cm

2. Determine the perimeter of each figure.

(a) rectangle: $l = 32$ cm and $w = 20$ cm

(b) square: $s = 2.45$ m

(c) parallelogram: longest side $= 10$ cm, shortest side $= 7$ cm

(d) rhombus: each side measures 3.25 cm

3. Determine the circumference/perimeter of each figure.

(a) circle: $r = 4.8$ mm (b) circle: $d = 30$ m

(c) semicircle: $d = 10$ cm

(d) quarter-circle: $r = 4$ m

4. Determine the perimeter and area of each regular polygon, where l is the length of each side and a is the apothem.

(a) pentagon: $l = 6.4$ cm, $a = 4.4$ cm

(b) decagon: $l = 3.25$ m, $a = 5.00$ m

(c) octagon: $l = 8.3$ cm, $a = 10.0$ cm

(d) hexagon: $l = 17.8$ m, $a = 15.4$ m

(e) heptagon: $l = 7.5$ mm, $a = 7.8$ mm

(f) nonagon: $l = 18.2$ cm, $a = 25.0$ cm

5. Determine the unknown dimension.

(a) rectangle: $A = 228$ cm^2, $l = 19$ cm, $w = \blacksquare$

(b) circle: circumference $= 37.68$ m, $r = \blacksquare$

(c) square: perimeter $= 22.4$ cm, $s = \blacksquare$

(d) triangle: area $= 21.84$ m^2, $b = 7.8$ m, $h = \blacksquare$

(e) circle: area $= 283.385$ cm^2, $r = \blacksquare$

(f) parallelogram: area $= 4928$ mm^2, $b = 88$ mm, $h = \blacksquare$

(g) circle: area $= 40.6944$ m^2, $d = \blacksquare$

(h) rhombus: perimeter $= 49.6$ cm, $s = \blacksquare$

6. Calculate the shaded area of each figure.

(a)
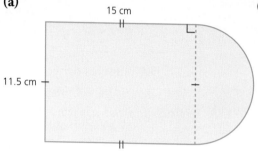
15 cm

11.5 cm

(b)
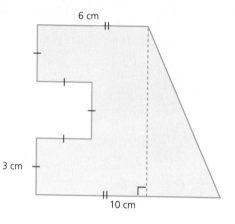
6 cm

3 cm

10 cm

(c)
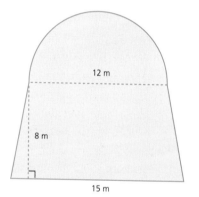
12 m

8 m

15 m

(d)
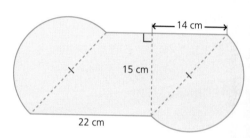
14 cm

15 cm

22 cm

(e)
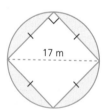
17 m

(f)
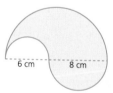
6 cm   8 cm

(g)
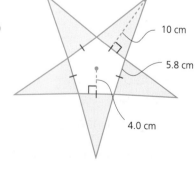
10 cm

5.8 cm

4.0 cm

(h)
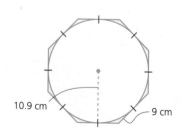
10.9 cm   9 cm

Chapter 1

Using Linear Systems to Solve Problems

Many real-life relationships between data, such as the costs to start and run a business, can be modelled using linear equations. These mathematical models let us establish trends and make predictions about the relationships.

Sometimes a model involves only one equation, but for many relationships the model involves two or more equations. This type of model is called a system of equations.

In today's highly competitive world, businesses are always looking for ways to save money and conserve resources. Systems of equations can be used as a tool to find the best solution to this type of problem. For example, when a car manufacturer plans a new vehicle, the engineers and sales analysts use systems of equations to model production costs and projected sales revenue. Then, they use these models to predict how much profit the company will earn from the new vehicle.

In this chapter, you will

- model real-world problems using a pair of linear equations with two unknowns

- use hand-drawn graphs to solve a linear system

- use graphing technology to produce graphs to solve a linear system

- use linear regression to produce the line of best fit for a collection of data that can be represented by a linear model

- use substitution to solve a linear system

- add or subtract two linear equations to solve a linear system

For connections to this chapter, visit **www.math.nelson.com**.

Connections

The Chapter Problem

Controlling Traffic

Do you ever feel that the people on the sidewalk are moving faster than you are in a car? In 1923, in an attempt to solve traffic congestion, Garrett Morgan invented a traffic signal that became widely used throughout North America. His signal was used until it was replaced by the lighted signal we use now.

Mick Chawner, CEO of iMPATH, an Ottawa-based company, develops remote traffic monitoring technology.

Today, municipalities use advanced technology known as Intelligent Transportation Systems to find ways to improve traffic flow. The length of time a light stays green or red can mean the difference between smoothly flowing traffic and a traffic jam. Did you know that the length of time a light stays green is different at different intersections? The next time you are out for a drive, time the lights at various intersections and see for yourself.

To determine how long a light should stay green, traffic controllers use

Greenshield's formula: $t = 2.1n + 3.7$

where t represents the time in seconds and n represents the average number of cars per lane that must move through the intersection.

Generally, at busy intersections, traffic flow is smoothest when equal numbers of cars are allowed to pass from each direction during each green-light cycle.

Traffic Problem

At a busy intersection in Sudbury, during a red light a traffic controller observed the number of cars stopped in each lane. She collected the data shown.

How long should the light stay red to ensure that the waiting time at the red light is equal to the length of time the light remains green? How many cars per lane will be stopped at a red light? If each road at the intersection consists of four lanes, how many cars can pass through on a green light?

For help with this problem, see p. 53, 63, 85, 95, 104, and 117.

Cars Stopped per Lane (n)	Elapsed Time of Red Light in Seconds (t)
1	3.0
2	6.2
3	10.1
5	14.0
6	16.8
7	18.2
9	22.1

Challenge 1

You are the human-resources manager for Computer Central, a company that sells personal computers. In this position, you look after all matters relating to employees, such as sick days, holidays, benefits, and salaries. The president asks you if the current compensation plan for sales people is fair. They are paid as follows:

- A salesperson with two or more years' experience earns $400 per week, plus a commission of 1.5% of the store's sales.

- A salesperson with less than two years' experience earns a straight commission of 2.5% of the store's sales.

- A sales manager earns $1010 per week.

1. Under what conditions will
   (a) a salesperson with over two years' experience earn the most in a week?
   (b) a salesperson with less than two years' experience earn the most?
   (c) a manager earn the most?
   (d) all three employee types earn the same amount in a week?

2. Use your calculations to write a report for the company's board of directors. If you feel that the compensation plan should be changed, state your reasons, along with the new plan that you would recommend.

Challenge 2

A grocer wants to make up three different kinds of fruit baskets that contain bananas, oranges, and grapefruit. This table shows the contents of each basket.

basket	oranges	bananas	grapefruit
A	8	4	2
B	4	3	3
C	5	2	4

The grocer has 83 oranges, 47 bananas, and 43 grapefruit. How many of each kind of basket can he make up, and use all the fruit?

To complete these Challenges, you may need to discuss a research plan with your teacher or fellow students. You may also need to research outside the classroom.

In this chapter, you will be working with linear equations, linear graphs, and algebraic expressions.

These exercises will help you warm up for the work ahead.

1. Evaluate for $x = -2$.
   (a) $6x - 3$ (b) $\frac{1}{2}x + 5$
   (c) $-12x - 10$ (d) $3.75x + 1.5x$

2. Evaluate for $p = -\frac{1}{8}$, $q = \frac{3}{-4}$, and $r = \frac{3}{8}$.
   (a) $p + q + r$ (b) $pq + r$
   (c) $pr - pq$ (d) pqr

3. Find the value of y when $x = -4$.
   (a) $y = 3x - 12$ (b) $2x - 4y = 8$
   (c) $2x - 5y - 2 = 0$ (d) $6x - 6y = 16$

4. Solve.
   (a) $20 = 7k + 6$
   (b) $3m - 12 = -18$
   (c) $7x + 3 - 2x = 23$
   (d) $8x - 12 = 5x + 9$
   (e) $5(y + 2) = 17$
   (f) $-3 = 3(x + 2)$
   (g) $2y - 5 - (y - 3) = 7$
   (h) $6.5(x - 3) = 2.4(3 - x)$
   (i) $\frac{x}{4} - 1 = \frac{x}{5}$
   (j) $\frac{x}{8} - \frac{3}{2} = -\frac{1}{4}$
   (k) $\frac{2}{3}(p - 2) = p + 5$
   (l) $\frac{1}{3}(6y - 9) = \frac{1}{2}(8y - 4)$

5. Express in the form $y = mx + b$.
   (a) $6x + y = 12$
   (b) $2x - 3y - 12 = 0$
   (c) $14 - 7x = 2y$
   (d) $-5y + 6x - 11 = 0$

6. Use a table of values to graph.
   (a) $y = 3x - 4$ (b) $y = \frac{3}{4}x + 2$
   (c) $2y = 10x - 6$ (d) $2x - 3y = 6$

7. Use the x- and y-intercepts to graph.
   (a) $x + y = 5$ (b) $2x - 4y = -8$
   (c) $3x = 12 - 9y$ (d) $6x - 3y + 9 = 0$

8. Use the slope and y-intercept to graph.
   (a) $y = 3x + 1$ (b) $y = -\frac{2}{3}x - 2$
   (c) $3y = 4x + 6$ (d) $2x + 5y = 10$

9. Simplify.
   (a) $(2x + 5y - 6) + (3x - 4y + 12)$
   (b) $(-3x - 5 + 2y) - (5x - 3 - 4y)$
   (c) $(x + 5) + (2y - 6) - (3x - 2y)$
   (d) $(10x - 4y - 12) - (6y - 5 - 2x)$
       $- (3x + 5y)$

10. Add or subtract, as directed.
    (a) Add.   (b) Add.
        $2x + 3y$ $9x - 3y$
        $3x + 5y$ $-5x - 2y$
    (c) Subtract.   (d) Subtract.
        $6x + 5y$ $5x - 3y$
        $3x - 2y$ $4x - 5y$

11. Write each sentence as an equation with two unknowns.
    (a) The sum of two numbers is 12.
    (b) Premium gasoline costs 15% more than regular gasoline.
    (c) It cost $135 to rent the car, based on $25 per day, plus $0.15/km.
    (d) The total number of adults and children at the circus was 1254.
    (e) Benoit invested some money at 8% and some at 10%. He earned a total of $235 in interest.

(f) Oak Furniture's startup cost was $12 500. It will cost the company $12.35 to make one stool and $12.65 to make one chair.

(g) Sarah has $5.75 in dimes and quarters.

12. Graph each line. Then determine its equation, in the form $y = mx + b$.

(a) the line that has a slope of 5 and passes through point $(2, 10)$

(b) the line that has a slope of $-\frac{2}{3}$ and passes through point $(-2, 6)$

(c) the line that passes through points $(3, 4)$ and $(5, 10)$

(d) the line that passes through points $(-1, 5)$ and $(3, -2)$

13. Determine the slope of the line segment connecting each pair of points.

(a) $A(2, 3)$ and $B(8, 11)$

(b) $C(-1, -3)$ and $D(4, 2)$

(c) $E(-4, -6)$ and $F(-6, -12)$

(d) $G(4.5, 3.1)$ and $H(-1.2, -2.7)$

14. For each set of data

i. draw a scatter plot and line of best fit

ii. use the slope and y-intercept to determine the equation for the line of best fit

iii. determine whether the data shows a positive correlation, a negative correlation, or no correlation. If there is a correlation, tell if it is strong or weak.

(a) Students' marks on a test and time spent studying.

Student	A	B	C	D	E	F	G	H	I
Hours of Study	4	1	1	1	0	2	3	0	2
Mark (%)	88	71	87	80	68	76	70	58	84

(b) Average height of baby boys at different ages.

Age (months)	0	5	12	6	8	24	26	15	30	19
Height (cm)	56	62	78	65	73	96	94	82	104	91

(c) Life expectancy for people born in different years.

Year of Birth	1900	1910	1920	1930	1940
Life Expectancy (years)	47.3	50.0	54.1	59.7	62.9

Year of Birth	1950	1960	1970	1980	1990
Life Expectancy (years)	68.2	69.7	70.8	73.7	75.4

(d) Distance driven and volume of gasoline consumed.

Volume of Gas (L)	11.4	20.0	30.4	40.6	48.5	60.0
Distance (km)	84	165	288	357	412	500

15. Does each pair of lines intersect at the given point?

(a) $y = x + 1$ and $y = 2x - 4$; $(2, 3)$

(b) $y = 3x + 2$ and $y = -2x + 7$; $(1, 5)$

(c) $y = x - 3$ and $2x + 3y = 6$; $(3, 0)$

(d) $y = 2x + 1$ and $5x + 2y = 0$; $(-2, 5)$

16. Find the point where each pair of lines intersects by drawing a graph.

(a) $y = 4x - 1$
$y = 3x + 4$

(b) $y = -x + 8$
$y = 2x - 7$

(c) $y = 4x + 6$
$y = -x + 1$

(d) $y = 5$
$x = -3$

1.1 Modelling with Linear Equations

Part 1

Air Kool Ltd. repairs air conditioners and charges a flat fee of $15, plus a labour fee of $35/h. Hank Verdi charges a flat fee of $25, plus a labour fee of $25/h.

Think, Do, Discuss

1. Create a table of values for both Air Kool and Hank for repairs ranging from 0 h to 5 h.

2. Describe any patterns you see in the tables.

3. What two quantities are related in each repair situation?

4. In each situation, identify the dependent variable and the independent variable. Represent these two quantities using two different variables.

5. Use the variables to write an equation that models the repair charges for
   (a) Air Kool   (b) Hank

6. Refer to your table of values. Identify the ordered pair that satisfies both equations.

7. What do the coordinates mean in terms of this problem?

Cathleen Synge Morawetz, b. 1923

Cathleen Synge Morawetz was born in Toronto. As a child, she was not very good at arithmetic, but she kept studying mathematics because she needed it for a scholarship to the University of Toronto. After university, the American mathematician Richard Courant offered her a job soldering computer connections at New York University (NYU). But when she arrived at NYU, she found that the job had been given to another student. To make up for this, Courant offered Morawetz another job editing a physics book he had just written. The editing of this book, *Supersonic Flow and Shock Waves*, marked the beginning of a long career at NYU studying wave patterns. This work has led to such advances as engineers being able to design improved wings for aircraft that fly at the speed of sound. Cathleen Morawetz has received many awards, including the 1997 Krieger-Nelson Award of the Canadian Mathematics Society. In 1993 the Association for Women in Science named her the year's Outstanding Woman Scientist.

Part 2

Alicia works on an assembly line making motherboards for computers. Some of the boards are for large desktop computers and the rest are for smaller laptop computers. Alicia is paid by the number of motherboards she completes: $1 for each laptop board and $1.50 for each desktop board. Last week, she earned $1015 for assembling a total of 795 motherboards.

Think, Do, Discuss

1. How many motherboards did Alicia make last week?

2. How much did she earn last week?

3. How much does she earn for each laptop motherboard? for each desktop motherboard?

4. What two pieces of information are you missing?

5. In this case, can you identify the independent and dependent variables? Choose two different variables to represent these unknown quantities.

6. The information in the problem relates these two unknowns in two different ways. What are they?

7. Write an equation that represents the total number of motherboards Alicia made.

8. Write an expression for the amount of money she earned for the desktop motherboards.

9. Write an expression for the amount she earned for the laptop motherboards.

10. Use the variables to write an equation that represents the total amount of money Alicia earned last week. What type of relationship do Alicia's equations represent?

11. In part 1, you found an ordered pair that satisfied both equations in the table of values. Use the equations you found to create a table of values for each of Alicia's equations. Can you find in your table an ordered pair that satisfies both equations?

12. You modelled Alicia's situation using two different equations. Each equation has many ordered pair solutions. What must be true about an ordered pair that meets the conditions of this problem?

13. Use a guess-and-test strategy to try to determine the ordered pair that meets the conditions described by both equations. How effective is this method? Explain.

14. Are both equations satisfied when Alicia has made 355 laptop and 440 desktop motherboards? Explain how you made your decision.

Focus 1.1

Key Ideas

- Many kinds of situations can be modelled using linear equations, such as manufacturing costs or economic trends.

- Often a problem involves two unknown quantities, which can be represented by two different variables. You may be able to write equations, using these variables, to represent the conditions described in the problem.

- When two or more equations are used to model a problem, it is called a **system of equations**. If all the equations are linear, it is called a **linear system**.

- A linear system in two unknowns consists of two or more linear equations involving two variables. For example,

$$2x + 3y = 8$$
$$5x - 2y = 1$$

- A solution to a linear system is an ordered pair (x, y) that satisfies *all* the equations in the system. For example, $(1, 2)$ is a solution to the linear system defined above, since $2(1) + 3(2) = 8$ and $5(1) - 2(2) = 1$.

- Sometimes you can use guess-and-check to find the solution to a linear system, but it only works for very simple problems.

Example 1: Break-Even Problems

The Ajax Minor Hockey Association would like to rent a banquet hall for their annual awards dinner. They have received two quotes.

J.R.'s Banquet Hall charges $500 to rent the room, plus $15 for each meal. Patti's Party Palace charges $400 for the hall, plus $18 for each meal.

The association wants to know when both places cost the same. Create a linear system to model this situation.

Solution

There are two unknown quantities in this situation. These are the number of meals served (the independent variable), and the total rental cost (the dependent variable). The following two equations form a linear system that models the situation.

Let C represent the total cost and n represent the number of meals served.

$$C = 15n + 500 \quad \text{represents J.R.'s Banquet Hall}$$
$$C = 18n + 400 \quad \text{represents Patti's Party Palace}$$

Example 2: Relative Value Reasoning Problems

The difference between two numbers is 45. Three times the larger number less five times the smaller number equals 75. Model this problem with a linear system.

Solution

The two numbers are unknown. Let x represent the larger number. Let y represent the smaller number.

$$x - y = 45 \quad \text{represents the difference between the two numbers}$$
$$3x - 5y = 75 \quad \text{represents the combination of the numbers}$$

Example 3: Mixture Problems

Yasmin has $8000 to invest and would like to earn $500 from the money. How much should she invest in a stock that has been getting a 10% annual return and how much should she invest in savings bonds that pay 4% annual interest? Model this situation with a linear system.

Solution

Yasmin needs to know how much money to put into each type of investment. In this case, neither variable is clearly independent or dependent. Let s represent the amount she invests in the stock. Let b represent the amount she invests in saving bonds.

$$s + b = 8000 \quad \text{represents the amount of the total investment}$$
$$0.10s + 0.04b = 500 \quad \text{represents the earnings from the investment}$$

Did You Know?

With credit card purchases, bank transfers, and email messages all becoming more frequent on the Internet, security on the Internet is an important issue. Today, private information is usually encoded in one of two ways, factoring integers or using an elliptic curve algorithm. Currently, the factoring approach is more popular, but that may change in the future.

In 1998, a Canadian company, Certicom, developed a code using the elliptic curve approach. Certicom offered $5000 to anyone who could break the code. Eventually, in September 1999, a group of mathematicians did break the code, but it took them five weeks, 740 computers from around the world, and 130 000 billion calculations to do it.

Do some research on Internet security. How many bits do normal Internet codes have?

Example 4: Rate Problems

José travelled the 95 km from Oakville to Oshawa by car and GO train. The car averaged 60 km/h, and the train averaged 90 km/h. The whole trip took 1.5 h. How long was he in the car? Model this situation with a linear system.

Solution

Let x represent the time in the car in hours.
Let y represent the time on the train in hours.

This problem uses the relationship between distance, speed, and time:

$$\text{distance} = \text{speed} \times \text{time}$$

$$\text{time} = \frac{\text{distance}}{\text{speed}} \qquad \text{speed} = \frac{\text{distance}}{\text{time}}$$

Use a table to organize what you know about the problem.

	Speed (km/h)	Time (h)	Distance (km)
Car	60	x	$60x$
Train	90	y	$90y$
Total		1.5	95

The columns for time and speed can be filled in first. The column for distance can be completed using the relationship distance = speed × time.

$$x + y = 1.5 \qquad \text{represents the total time}$$
$$60x + 90y = 95 \qquad \text{represents the total distance}$$

Practise, Apply, Solve 1.1 ⎯⎯⎯⎯⎯⎯⎯⎯⎯

Ⓐ

1. Determine which ordered pairs are solutions to each equation.

(a) $x + y = 10$ $(1, 9), (2, -8), (20, -10), (5\frac{1}{4}, 4\frac{3}{4}), (-15, 5)$

(b) $2x - y = 4$ $(3, 4), (4, 4), (-2, -8), (0.5, 5), (12, 20)$

(c) $x - 6y = 12$ $(0, 2), (12, 0), (18, 1), (0, -2), (6, 3)$

(d) $y - x = -2$ $(5, 7), (3, 1), (12, 10), (9, 5), (1, -1)$

2. Determine which ordered pair satisfies both equations.

(a) $x + y = 8$
$2x - y = 10$
$(4, 4), (10, 10), (6, 2), (3, 5)$

(b) $x - y = 1$
$x + y = 5$
$(4, 1), (2, 3), (3, 2), (6, 5)$

(c) $y = 3x$
$x + y = -8$
$(1, 3), (-2, -6), (-4, -4), (3, 9)$

(d) $y = x$
$y = -x$
$(1, 1), (-5, 5), (0, 0), (6, -6)$

3. Using guess-and-check, find an ordered pair that satisfies both equations.

(a) $x + y = 12$
$x - y = 8$

(b) $x - y = 2$
$x + y = 8$

(c) $y = 2x$
$x - y = -1$

(d) $x - y = 4$
$x + y = 10$

4. For each statement, define two variables and write a linear equation that models the sentence.

(a) The sum of two numbers is 12.

(b) The sum of the width and length of a rectangle is 36 m.

(c) The total value of nickels and dimes is 75¢.

(d) Fives times some number less three times another number is ten.

(e) A sum of money invested at 5% per year and another sum at 8% per year earned a total of $150 in the first year.

(f) The cost of the rental is $50 plus $5/h.

(g) A rectangle is 2 m longer than it is wide.

(h) The total value of $5 bills and $10 bills is $135.

B

5. **Communication:** A system of equations is defined by the equations $2x - 3y = 6$ and $y = 4x - 5$. Is this a linear system? Explain why or why not.

6. **Knowledge and Understanding:** Explain why the ordered pair (2, 3) is not a solution to the system of equations defined by $3x + 5y = 21$ and $y = 3x - 4$.

For questions 7–26, model each situation using a linear system. Define two variables and write the equations. You do not have to solve the system now. Keep your answers to the questions, as you will need them in future lessons.

7. The sum of two numbers is 72. Their difference is 48. Find the numbers.

8. A number is four times another number. Six times the smaller number plus half of the larger number equals 212. Find the numbers.

9. Model this situation using a linear system. A server earned $55 in tips, all in loonies and toonies. She had 38 coins altogether. How many toonies were there?

10. Sook-Lee wants to rent a car for a day so she can visit her sister at university. She has called two car-rental agencies. Rent-a-Heap charges $50 per day, plus $0.12/km. Kurt's Rent-a-Car charges $40 per day, plus $0.20/km. At what distance will the cost of renting a car be the same from both companies?

11. Jacques has a total of $155 in $2 and $5 pizza coupons. If he has 40 coupons in all, how many of each kind does he have?

12. The sum of John's age and Margie's age is 36 years. John is four years younger than Margie. How old are John and Margie?

13. Erica's job is to collect money from the pop machines. From one machine she collects a total of 76 dimes and quarters. If the total value is $13, how many dimes and quarters are there?

14. Provincial Express charges $4, plus $1.50/kg, to deliver a package overnight. The Package People charge $5, plus $1/kg. When is Provincial Express less expensive to use?

15. An investment club invested part of $8000 at 10% annual interest and the rest at 12%. If the annual income from these investments is $900, how much was invested at each rate?

16. Rajah earns an hourly wage plus tips. One week he worked 12 h and made a total of $117. The next week he worked 10 h and earned the same amount in tips as the week before, for a total of $110. What is Rajah's hourly wage?

17. A candy store is preparing a mixture of chocolate raisins and chocolate peanuts. The raisins sell for $2.25/kg and the peanuts for $1.75/kg. How much of each type must be mixed to make 20 kg of a mixture that will sell for $41?

18. Raoul drove at a speed of 50 km/h from Ancaster to Oakville. From Oakville to Sudbury, he drove 80 km/h. If the whole trip was 550 km and took 8 h, what is the distance from Oakville to Sudbury?

19. It took the high school hockey team 5 h to travel to a tournament in Thunder Bay. They travelled by bus and plane a total distance of 1320 km. If the bus averaged 40 km/h and the plane averaged 600 km/h, determine the time they spent travelling by plane.

20. A basketball coach bought 20 basketballs for a total of $700. If the practice balls cost $30 and the official balls used for games cost $50, how many of each did the coach buy?

21. Petra won $2000 in a chess competition. She invested part of it at 9% and the remainder at 10%. If the total interest was $191 for the first year, how much was invested at each rate?

22. Twice Sari's age plus half her mother's age is 48. Three times Sari's age less half her mother's age is 27. How old are Sari and her mother?

23. Two different kinds of coffee beans were blended. Individually, they cost $2.30/kg and $3.20/kg. How much of each kind was used if 200 kg of the resulting mixture cost $3/kg?

24. Garry drove to Sarnia. Part of his trip was along major highways and the rest was along country roads. The speed limit is 100 km/h on the highways and 80 km/h on the other roads. He spent a total of 12 h driving 1050 km. How much time did he spend on each type of road?

25. **Thinking, Inquiry, Problem Solving:** Lee is starting a cake-decorating and baking business. She had to invest $455 in her business to get started. If she pays $4 per cake for ingredients, and she sells each cake for $25, what is her break-even point?

26. Sabrina has two part-time jobs delivering flyers. She earns $9/h at her weekday job and $12/h at her weekend job. Last week she worked 23 h and earned a total of $231. How many hours did she work at each job?

27. Determine the ordered pair that satisfies $5x + 3y = 36$ and $2x - y = 10$. Justify your answer.

28. A survey crew took a canoe up the river and back, paddling for 10 h. They went at 4 km/h going upstream and at 12 km/h going downstream. How far upstream did they go?

29. **Check Your Understanding:** Write down, in order, the three most important steps you should follow when you model a situation using a linear system.

C

30. **Application:** Create a problem that could be modelled by each linear system.

    (a) $x + y = 1200$
    $0.09x + 0.04y = 88$

    (b) $3s + 2p = 200$
    $s = p + 20$

    (c) $C = 45 + 0.18k$
    $C = 55 + 0.10k$

31. True or false? The ordered pair $(\frac{1}{2}, 1)$ is a solution to the system of equations $\frac{3}{x} + \frac{4}{y} = 10$ and $\frac{2}{x} - \frac{1}{y} = 3$, where $x, y \neq 0$. Explain.

32. The greater of two numbers equals 3 times the smaller number. The smaller number increased by 5 equals the greater number decreased by 45. What are the numbers?

33. One thousand people attended the Boat Show. Some paid $8.50 for their tickets; the others paid $6. The total gate receipts were $7950. How many paid $6?

The Chapter Problem—Controlling Traffic

In this section, you used a linear system to model a situation. Apply what you learned to answer these questions about the chapter problem on page 42.

1. What does Greenshield's formula model?
2. Explain how an algebraic expression could be determined for the data for the red light.
3. Explain how the traffic controller can use a linear system to determine how long to set the traffic lights on green or red.

1.2 Tables of Values and Linear Systems

Very simple linear systems can often be solved using the guess-and-check method. However, if the equations are complicated, guess-and-check is impractical and you have to use a more organized approach. A spreadsheet or a graphing calculator like the TI-83 Plus are powerful tools that can be used to solve a linear system.

Solve this linear system.

$$y = 2x - 10$$
$$y = -6x + 46$$

Think, Do, Discuss

1. Create a spreadsheet with three columns, labelled X, Y1, and Y2 in cells A1, B1, and C1 respectively.

2. In cells A2 through A12, enter the integers from −5 to 5.

   In cell B2, enter the expression that calculates the value of *y* in the equation $y = 2x - 10$. Select the rest of the column and use the **Fill Down** command to complete the column (select **Fill** from the **Edit** menu and then go to **Down**).

   In cell C2, enter the expression that calculates the value of *y* in the equation $y = -6x + 46$. Select the rest of the column and use the **Fill Down** command to complete the column. In the spreadsheet expressions, how do you specify the value of the variable *x*?

	A	B	C	D
1	x	y1	y2	
2	-5			
3	-4			
4	-3			
5	-2			
6	-1			
7	0			
8	1			
9	2			
10	3			
11	4			
12	5			

Spreadsheet at the start of step 2

3. If you are trying to solve the system of equations, which two columns of the spreadsheet should you examine? What should you look for? Why?

4. Does the solution to this linear system appear in the table you have created?

5. Will the solution occur when the value of x is less than -5? How can you tell?

6. Will the solution occur when the value of x is greater than 5? How can you tell?

7. As you move down the table, what happens to the difference between Y2 and Y1? What does this mean?

8. Create a fourth column, labelled Y2 $-$ Y1, in cell D1. In D2, enter the expression that calculates this difference for the values in cells B2 and C2. Use the **Fill Down** command to complete the rest of this column. What does it mean when an entry in this column has a value of 0?

9. In the first column, enter the numbers 6 to 10 in cells A13 to A17. In the second column, select cells B12 to B17 and use the **Fill Down** command to complete the column. Repeat for cells C12 to C17 and D12 to D17.

10. Does the solution appear in your table of values now? If so, what is the value of x in the row that contains the solution? How do you know that this is the solution?

11. It can be hard to see the solution in a table of values like this. From what you have just learned, describe a more visual method for finding the solution.

Garrett Augustus Morgan (1877–1963)

Garrett Morgan, who invented the traffic signal, started several companies, including a newspaper, and became a prosperous, well-respected businessman. In addition to his traffic signal, Morgan developed many inventions, most of them designed to make life easier and safer for people. For instance, in 1916, Morgan became famous when he used a gas mask he had invented to save the lives of some men who were trapped in a tunnel under Lake Erie. A later version of this gas mask won a gold award from the International Association of Fire Chiefs.

Use the Internet or the library to investigate Garrett Morgan and find out more about his other inventions. What prompted him to invent a traffic signal? How do his other inventions show that he wanted to make life easier and safer for other people?

1.3 Solving Linear Systems: Graphing by Hand

Suregrip Footwear is going to launch a new, all-purpose court shoe by spending a total of $22 million on television and magazine advertising. The marketing department believes that television is the most effective medium, so they plan to spend three times as much on television advertisements as on magazine ads. How much should they budget for each type of advertising?

Think, Do, Discuss

1. What two unknown quantities does the marketing department need to determine? Choose two different variables to represent these unknowns.

2. Write an equation that represents the total amount of money the company will spend on advertising.

3. Write an equation that relates the amount of money to be spent on television ads to the amount to be spent on magazine ads.

4. The marketing department needs to determine how much money to spend on each type of advertising. Explain why they must consider both equations when making their decision.

5. What type of relationship do both equations represent? Use the equations you have found to graph both relationships on the same set of axes. On your graph, let one unit represent one million dollars.

6. Can you accurately identify the coordinates of the point of intersection? What are the coordinates? What does the point of intersection mean in this situation?

7. Do the coordinates of the point of intersection provide a solution that works in both equations? How can you tell?

Career: Marketer

Marketing involves promoting the sales of a product. For instance, a marketer might supervise an ad campaign, or decide which products to put in a catalogue, or develop commercials. A marketer needs to research what customers want and to understand the company's products. Do some investigation to find out how marketers use mathematics in their jobs.

Focus 1.3

Key Ideas

- A **linear system** can be solved by graphing. The equations can be graphed on the same axes. The point, or points, of intersection of the lines represent the solution to the linear system.

- With a hand-drawn graph, you may not be able to find the exact solution to a linear system. This is especially difficult when the point of intersection does not fall on one of the grid lines of the graph paper.

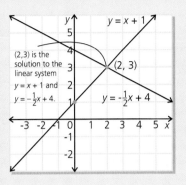

Example 1

Solve this linear system graphically.

$$y = 2x - 8$$
$$y + x = 7$$

Solution

Find the solution by drawing the lines for both equations on the same graph.
The equation $y = 2x - 8$ can be graphed using the slope and y-intercept of the line and the equation $y + x = 7$ can be graphed easily using the intercepts.

For $y = 2x - 8$,

the slope of the line is 2.

$$2 = \frac{2}{1} = \frac{\text{rise}}{\text{run}}$$

To find the y-intercept, let $x = 0$.

$$y = 2(0) - 8$$
$$y = -8$$

The y-intercept is -8.

Graph this line by plotting the y-intercept and using the rise and run to locate a second point on the line.

For $y + x = 7$,

to find the x-intercept, let $y = 0$.

$$0 + x = 7$$
$$x = 7$$

To find the y-intercept, let $x = 0$.

$$y + 0 = 7$$
$$y = 7$$

Graph this line by plotting the intercepts $(0, 7)$ and $(7, 0)$ and joining them with a straight line.

The lines intersect at (5, 2). This point represents the solution to the linear system.

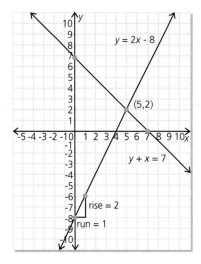

Example 2

Victor owns a candy store. He sells hard candy for $2/kg and soft candy for $4/kg. How can he mix the two kinds of candy to create 60 kg of a mixture that he can sell for $3/kg?

Solution

A linear system with two equations and two variables can be used to represent this problem.

Let x represent the amount of hard candy in the mixture, and y the amount of soft candy (in kilograms).

$$x + y = 60 \qquad \text{represents the total weight of the mixture}$$
$$2x + 4y = 60(3) \qquad \text{represents the value of the mixture}$$
or $\qquad 2x + 4y = 180$

This is the linear system to solve. Both equations can be graphed by determining their intercepts.

For $x + y = 60$, at the x-intercept, $y = 0$ and $x = 60$. At the y-intercept, $x = 0$ and $y = 60$.

For $2x + 4y = 180$,

at the x-intercept, $y = 0$.

$$2x + 0 = 180$$
$$2x = 180$$
$$x = 90$$

at the y-intercept, $x = 0$.

$$0 + 4y = 180$$
$$4y = 180$$
$$y = 45$$

The point of intersection is (30, 30). This means that the new mixture should have 30 kg of soft candy and 30 kg of hard candy.

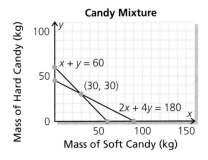

Candy Mixture

Example 3

Stuart wants to rent a small truck for one day to move into his university residence. Rent a Truck charges $80 per day, plus $0.22/km. Tony's Truck Town charges $100 per day, plus $0.12/km. Which company should Stuart choose?

Solution

Use a linear system with two equations and two variables to represent this problem. Let x represent the distance driven, in kilometres. Let y represent the total cost of the rental.

$y = 0.22x + 80$ represents the cost to rent from Rent a Truck

$y = 0.12x + 100$ represents the cost to rent from Tony's Truck Town

Both linear equations can be graphed using a table of values.

$y = 0.22x + 80$

x	y
0	0.22(0) + 80 = 80
50	91
100	102

$y = 0.12x + 100$

x	y
0	0.12(0) + 100 = 100
50	106
100	112

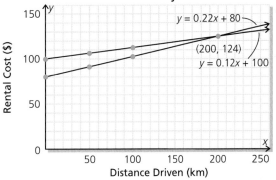

Rent a Truck vs. Tony's Truck Town

The point of intersection is (200, 124). If Stuart drives 200 km, both rental agencies charge $124. From the graph, you can see that if he drives less than 200 km, Rent a Truck is cheaper. For distances over 200 km, Tony's Truck Town is cheaper. Stuart must first estimate how far he will drive; then he can decide which company to use.

Practise, Apply, Solve 1.3

A

1. Express each equation in the form $y = mx + b$.

(a) $2y = 4x - 8$ (b) $5x - y = 10$ (c) $3x + 4y = 8$

(d) $5y - 15 = 3x$ (e) $8x - 12 = -3y$ (f) $4x - 7y - 10 = 0$

2. Determine the x- and y-intercepts of each line.

(a) $3x - y = 9$ (b) $x + y = 6$ (c) $y = 3x - 6$

(d) $2x + 3y = 6$ (e) $4x - 3y = 12$ (f) $y = x + 6$

3. Determine the slope and y-intercept of each line.

(a) $y = 5x - 6$ (b) $x - y = 3$ (c) $2x + 4y = 12$

(d) $3x - 5y - 8 = 0$ (e) $\frac{1}{4}x + \frac{3}{4}y = \frac{1}{2}$ (f) $0.6x - 0.3y = 1.5$

4. For each graph,

   i. identify the point of intersection

   ii. verify your answer by substituting into the equations

(a)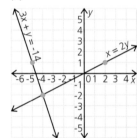

(b)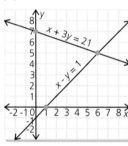

(c)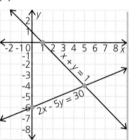

5. For each system of equations, decide whether the ordered pair is a solution.

(a) $3x + 2y = 4$ and $-x + 3y = -5$; $(2, -1)$

(b) $x + y = 5$ and $2x + 2y = 8$; $(1, 4)$

(c) $4x - 5y = 0$ and $6x - 5y = 10$; $(5, 4)$

(d) $3x - 2y = -4$ and $-4x + 3y = 5$; $(0, 2)$

(e) $y = 3x - 5$ and $y = 2x - 4$; $(1, -2)$

(f) $x - y = -10$ and $0.1x - 0.5y = -9$; $(10, 20)$

B

6. Solve each linear system by graphing each line from a table of values.

(a) $y = x + 1$ (b) $y = 2x - 1$ (c) $x + y = 4$

   $y = -2x + 4$ $y = 3x - 3$ $x - 2y = 10$

7. For each linear system
   i. find the x- and y-intercepts
   ii. use the intercepts to graph the system and solve it

   (a) $x + y = 4$
   $2x - y = 2$

   (b) $3x + 4y = 12$
   $2x + 3y = 9$

   (c) $8x - 4y = 32$
   $2x - 2y = 12$

8. For each linear system
   i. find the slope and y-intercept
   ii. use the slope and y-intercept to graph the system and solve it

   (a) $y = -2x - 5$
   $y = 3x + 5$

   (b) $y = -x - 4$
   $y = 2x - 4$

   (c) $x - y = -4$
   $x + 2y = 2$

9. Solve each linear system by graphing. Use the most suitable method for each system.

   (a) $y = -2x + 6$
   $y = 2 + 2x$

   (b) $x + y = -1$
   $2x + 8 = y$

   (c) $x - 8y = -40$
   $-5x + 8y = 8$

   (d) $x + 2y = 1$
   $2x - y = -3$

   (e) $x + 3y = 9$
   $x = y - 3$

   (f) $x - 3y + 1 = 0$
   $2x + y = 4$

10. **Communication:** You are trying to solve a linear system graphically and you find that the point of intersection does not appear on the graph you have drawn. Explain what you would do to find the point of intersection.

11. Tools-R-Us rents snow blowers for a base fee of $20, plus $8/h. XYZ Rentals rents them for a base fee of $12, plus $10/h.

   (a) Find an equation that represents the cost of renting a snow blower from Tools-R-Us.
   (b) Find the corresponding equation for XYZ Rentals.
   (c) Solve the system of equations by graphing.
   (d) What does the point of intersection mean in this situation?
   (e) Suppose that you want to rent a snow blower for a weekend. Which company would you choose? Why?
   (f) Janelle needs a snow blower for longer than a weekend. Based on the fees described, what would you advise Janelle to do?

12. Beatrice bought 3 m of denim fabric and 5 m of cotton fabric. The total bill, excluding tax, was $22. Candice bought 2 m of cotton and 6 m of denim at the same store for $28.
   (a) Write a linear system whose solution will give you the price of cotton and denim fabric.
   (b) Solve the system by graphing.
   (c) How much will it cost if Anne buys 8 m of denim and 5 m of cotton?

13. Application: Max is starting a landscaping business, specializing in cutting lawns. His startup cost to purchase two lawn mowers is $450. He figures that he will use about $1 in gas for each lawn. If he charges $10 per lawn, what is his break-even point?

14. Alamin needs to rent a car to drive to Sault Ste. Marie and back. Ottoz rents cars for $55 per day, plus $0.08/km. Karz Rentals charges $45 per day, plus $0.16/km.
  (a) Write a linear system to represent the prices of a one-day rental for both companies.
  (b) Solve the system by graphing.
  (c) What does the solution mean in terms of the problem?
  (d) Which company should Alamin rent from if he lives 135 km from Sault Ste. Marie?

15. The school athletic council sold 835 tickets to the championship football game for a total of $5792. Students pay $4 and non-students pay $8. Now the council wants to know how many non-students attended the game.
  (a) Write a linear system that you can solve to find how many tickets were sold to students and how many to non-students.
  (b) Solve the system by graphing.

16. The Totally Stoked Surfboard Co. makes custom surfboards at a cost of $125 per board. The company's startup costs were $15 000. The president decides to sell the surfboards for $500 each.
  (a) Write a linear system of equations, with one equation representing the company's costs and the other representing the company's revenue.
  (b) How many surfboards does the company need to sell to break even?
  (c) What must the company do to make a profit?

17. Knowledge and Understanding: Without graphing, show that the ordered pair $(-2, -5)$ is a solution to the system of equations defined by $3x - 4y = 14$ and $5x + 3y = -25$.

18. The graphs of $2x + 4y = 10$, $4x - y = 11$, and $3x + ay = 14$ all intersect at the same point. Find the value of a. Justify your answer.

19. The equations $y = 2$, $y = 4x - 2$, and $y = -2x + 10$ form the sides of a triangle.
  (a) Graph the triangle and find the coordinates of the vertices.
  (b) Find the area of the triangle.

20. The vertices of square $ABCD$ are $A(3, -2)$, $B(7, -2)$, $C(7, 2)$, and $D(3, 2)$.
  (a) Draw a graph to find the coordinates of the point where the diagonals intersect.
  (b) Find the equations of the diagonals.
  (c) Verify that the point you found in (a) satisfies the equations of the diagonals.

21. The vertices of $\triangle ABC$ are $A(0, 4)$, $B(-4, -4)$, and $C(4, -4)$.
   (a) Plot the points and sketch the triangle.
   (b) What type of triangle does $\triangle ABC$ appear to be?
   (c) What are the coordinates of the centroid of $\triangle ABC$?

22. Check Your Understanding: Arrange in order the following steps for solving a system of two linear equations in two unknowns graphically.
   i. Graph both equations on the same set of axes.
   ii. Determine the coordinates of the point of intersection from the graph.
   iii. Choose the best method to graph each equation.
   iv. Label the graph.
   v. Verify that you have the correct solution by substituting it in both equations.

C

23. Thinking, Inquiry, Problem Solving: François is stocking a new fish pond on his farm. The pond is filling slowly and the volume of water in it can support a certain number of fish, F. $F = 42m + 250$, where m is the number of months the pond has been filling.
The pond was stocked initially with 110 fish, a population that will grow at a rate of 8% per month. $P = 110(1.08)^m$ is the equation that models the population of fish after m months.

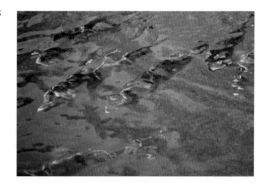

   (a) When will P equal F?
   (b) What will happen after this point has been reached? Explain your answer.

24. Solve this system of equations.
$$y = -2x + 7$$
$$3x + y = 6$$
$$5x - 4y + 41 = 0$$

25. Solve for x and y.
   (a) $\dfrac{2}{x} + \dfrac{8}{y} = 0$ **(b)** $y = \dfrac{1}{2}x$ **(c)** $y = x^2$
   $\dfrac{3}{x} + \dfrac{4}{y} = \dfrac{-2}{xy}$ $y = \sqrt{x}$ $y = 2x + 3$

The Chapter Problem—Controlling Traffic

In this section, you drew graphs to solve a linear system. Apply what you learned to answer these questions about the chapter problem on page 42.

1. Create by hand a scatter plot using the data for the red light.
2. Draw the line of best fit through the data.
3. On the same set of axes, graph the line represented by Greenshield's formula.
4. What does the point of intersection mean in this situation? Explain how to interpret the coordinate values.

1.4 Graphing Lines Using the TI-83 Plus Calculator

TECHNOLOGY

Clear Before You Start

Before you begin to graph any relation, be sure to clear any information left in the calculator from the last time it was used. You should always do the following.

1. Clear all data stored in the lists.
To do this, press 2nd + 4 ENTER.

step 1

2. Turn off all stat plots.
Press 2nd Y= 4 ENTER.

step 2

3. Clear all equations in the equation editor.
Press Y=, followed by CLEAR for all equations displayed.

step 3

4. Set the window so that both axes range from –10 to 10.
Press ZOOM. Press 6 WINDOW to verify.

step 4

Graphing Relations

If you know the equation of the relation, you can enter it into the equation editor and the calculator will display the graph. For instance, to graph the line $y = 2x + 8$, press Y= 2 X,T,Θ,n + 8, then GRAPH. The graph will be displayed as shown.

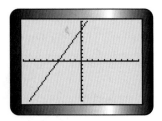

With the TI-83 Plus, all linear equations must be entered in the form $y = mx + b$. Before you can graph a line, its equation must be put into this form. If the equation has fractional values for m or b, enter the fractions between brackets. For example, $2x + 3y = 7$ becomes $y = -\frac{2}{3}x + \frac{7}{3}$ and is entered as follows:

[Y=] [(] [(-)] [2] [÷] [3] [)] [X,T,Θ,n] [+] [(] [7] [÷] [3] [)]. Press [GRAPH] to view the graph.

 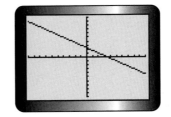

Tracing on the Graph

Once you have created a graph like $y = 2x + 8$, you can find the coordinates of any points on the graph using the [TRACE] button. The location of the cursor point and its coordinates will be displayed. Use the left and right arrow keys to move the cursor along the graph.

Pressing [ZOOM] [8] [ENTER], followed by [TRACE], allows you to trace at integer intervals along the graph of $y = 2x + 8$.

Zoom

You can zoom in and zoom out on a graph. To zoom in, move the cursor to the point you want to examine.
Press [ZOOM] [2] [ENTER]. You will see a closer view of this area of the graph.
Press [ZOOM] [3] [ENTER] to see a broader view.

Sometimes when you have entered an equation and pressed the [GRAPH] button, the line does not appear in the viewing window or it appears incorrectly as a vertical or horizontal line. This happens when the viewing window is too small or too big. The easiest way to see the graph properly is to use the ZoomFit feature.
Press [ZOOM] [0]. You may still have to zoom in or out.

Practise 1.4

Graph the linear equation and use [TRACE] to determine the x- and y-intercepts.

(a) $y = 5x + 6$

(b) $2x + y = 10$

(c) $3x + 5y = 15$

(d) $22x - 34y = 50$

(e) $y = 250x + 600$

(f) $1000x + 452 = 2y$

1.5 Investigating the Ways That Two Lines Can Intersect

Here are three different linear systems. Do the graphs of all linear systems look the same? How can they differ? Does a linear system always have a solution? Can a system have more than one solution?

A	B	C
$y = 2x + 1$	$-3y = 5 - 2x$	$4x - 2y = 6$
$y = -x + 7$	$4x - 1 = 6y$	$6x = 9 + 3y$

You can investigate the answers to these questions using either graphing technology or graph paper.

Think, Do, Discuss

1. How many different ways can a pair of lines intersect? Have you thought of all possible cases?

2. Construct a graph for each of the linear systems above.

3. For each case, how many solutions does the linear system have?

4. Explain whether you can decide how the lines will intersect before you actually try to find the solution.

5. Express each equation in the form $y = mx + b$. Use these equations and your graphs to complete the following table.

	A	B	C
Linear System	$y = 2x + 1$ $y = -x + 7$	$-3y = 5 - 2x$ $4x - 1 = 6y$	$4x - 2y = 6$ $6x = 9 + 3y$
Slope of the Lines			
y-Intercepts			
Number of Solutions			

6. Use the table to determine how to predict the number of solutions to a given linear system.

Focus 1.5

Key Ideas

- A linear equation must be in the form $y = mx + b$ to be graphed on a graphing calculator.

- A linear system can have no solution, one solution, or an infinite number of solutions.

- The equations in a linear system provide information that helps determine the number of solutions that are possible.

  ♦ In a linear system with **no solution**, the two linear equations have the *same slope* and *different y-intercepts*.

  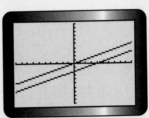

  ♦ In a linear system with **one solution**, the two linear equations have *different slopes*. The *y*-intercepts have no influence.

  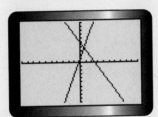

  ♦ In a linear system with **an infinite number of solutions**, the two linear equations have the *same slope* and the *same y-intercept*.

  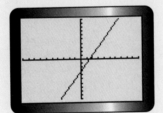

Example 1

Determine the number of solutions to this linear system.

$$y = 3x - 5$$
$$2x + 3y = 6$$

Solution

The equations can be graphed using the TI-83 Plus calculator. The equation $2x + 3y = 6$ must first be rewritten in the form $y = mx + b$.

$$2x + 3y = 6$$
$$3y = -2x + 6$$
$$\frac{3y}{3} = \frac{-2x + 6}{3}$$
$$y = \frac{-2}{3}x + 2$$

Enter the two equations as follows:

- For Y1, $\boxed{3}$ $\boxed{\text{X,T,$\Theta$,$n$}}$ $\boxed{-}$ $\boxed{5}$ $\boxed{\text{ENTER}}$

- For Y2, $\boxed{(}$ $\boxed{(-)}$ $\boxed{2}$ $\boxed{\div}$ $\boxed{3}$ $\boxed{)}$ $\boxed{\text{X,T,$\Theta$,$n$}}$ $\boxed{+}$ $\boxed{2}$ $\boxed{\text{ENTER}}$.

Press $\boxed{\text{GRAPH}}$.

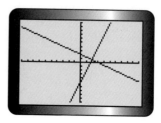

The lines meet at one point, so this linear system has one solution.

Example 2

Without graphing, determine the number of solutions to this linear system.

$$3x + 4y = 12$$
$$36 - 12y = 9x$$

Solution

Compare the slopes and y-intercepts of the equations to determine how the lines intersect. Express both equations in the form $y = mx + b$.

$$3x + 4y = 12$$
$$4y = -3x + 12$$
$$\frac{4y}{4} = \frac{-3x + 12}{4}$$
$$y = -\frac{3}{4}x + 3$$

$$36 - 12y = 9x$$
$$-12y = 9x - 36$$
$$\frac{-12y}{-12} = \frac{9x - 36}{-12}$$
$$y = -\frac{3}{4}x + 3$$

Both lines have the same slope, $-\frac{3}{4}$, and the same y-intercept, 3. Therefore, both equations represent the same line. Every point on the line is a point of intersection. This linear system has an infinite number of solutions.

Example 3

Nadia plans to make a quilt. She can spend $100 for material. The design requires a combination of two different fabrics, totalling 25 m.

(a) Two fabrics that Nadia likes, silk and satin, both cost $10/m. What combination of silk and satin should she buy?

(b) Nadia also likes two other materials, blue cotton and gingham, that both cost $4/m. What combination of blue cotton and gingham should she buy?

Solution

(a) In this case, both fabrics cost the same amount, $10/m. Nadia needs 25 m, but $25 \times \$10 = \$250$ and she has only $100 to spend. This means she cannot afford any combination of these fabrics. Let's look at how this is reflected when a linear system is used to analyze this problem.

Let k and n represent the number of metres of silk and satin. Then,

$$k + n = 25$$
or $n = -k + 25$ represents the total length

$$10k + 10n = 100$$
or $n = -k + 10$ represents the cost

The two lines have the same slope and different y-intercepts. They are parallel and do not intersect. The linear system has no solution.

No combination of silk and satin will work.

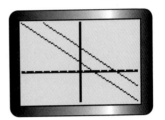

(b) Again, both fabrics she has selected cost the same amount, $4/m. She needs 25 m and $25 \times \$4 = \$100$. This amount is within her budget, but how much of each type can she buy? Let's analyze this situation using a linear system.

Let c and g represent the number of metres of blue cotton and gingham respectively. Then,

$$c + g = 25$$
or $g = -c + 25$ represents the total length

$$4c + 4g = 100$$
or $g = -c + 25$ represents the cost

These two lines have the same slope and the same y-intercept. They are the same line. Any point on the line solves the system, and there is an infinite number of solutions.

Nadia can buy any combination of blue cotton and gingham, as long as the total length is 25 m.

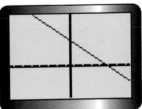

Practise, Apply, Solve 1.5

A

1. Copy this table into your notebook and complete it. Lines l_1 and l_2 correspond to the two equations in a linear system. Predict the number of solutions to the system.

	Line l_1		Line l_2		Number of Solutions
	Slope	**y-intercept**	**Slope**	**y-intercept**	
	3	2	**(a)** -2	4	1
(b)	$\frac{1}{2}$	3	2	−5	1
(c)	−5	−1	−5	7	0
(d)	$\frac{3}{4}$	$\frac{1}{2}$	0.75	0.5	infinitely many

2. Draw a graph that shows a system of equations with
   (a) one solution
   (b) many solutions
   (c) no solution

3. A line is defined by the equation $2x + 4y = -8$. Determine the equation of another line that will create a linear system with
   (a) no solution
   (b) many solutions
   (c) one solution

4. Create a pair of equations that represents a system of equations with
   (a) one solution
   (b) many solutions
   (c) no solution

B

5. Determine the number of solutions to each linear system.

   (a) $y = 3x - 5$
   $y = 4x + 6$

   (b) $y = 4x - 3$
   $y = 4x - 7$

   (c) $y = 5x - \frac{3}{2}$
   $y = 5x - 1.5$

   (d) $x + 2y = 10$
   $y = 8 - 0.5x$

   (e) $2x + 3y = 10$
   $10x + 15y = 50$

   (f) $3x - 5y - 2 = 0$
   $4x + 5y + 2 = 0$

   (g) $y = 1.25x - 0.375$
   $5y = 4x$

   (h) $2x - 5 = 4y$
   $0.01x - 0.02y = 0.25$

   (i) $x + y = 0$
   $x - y = 0$

6. Communication: How can you tell—just by looking at the equations—whether or not a system of equations has a solution?

7. For each graph, determine the equations of the linear system.

   (a)

   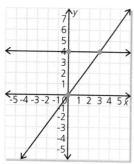

   (b)

   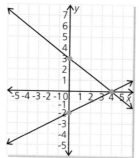

   (c)

   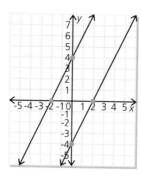

   (d)

   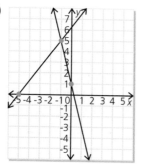

   (e)

   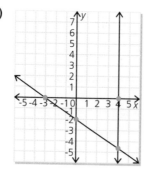

   (f)

   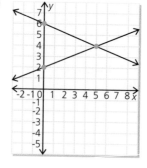

8. **Application:** An air traffic controller is plotting the course of two jets scheduled to land in about 15 minutes. One aircraft is following a path defined by the equation $3x - 5y = 20$ and the other by the equation $18x = 30y + 72$. Should the controller alter the paths of either aircraft?

9. Refer back to example 3 on page 68. The fabric store holds a one-day sale where all fabric in the store is sold for 50% off. Determine how much Nadia can buy for her quilt if she makes it with silk and gingham.

10. The sales department at Light Speed Computers collected this data about the growth of their company and their competitor, Byte Inc.

Number of Units Sold (in hundreds of thousands)

	1996	1997	1998	1999
Light Speed	3.2	3.7	4.2	4.7
Byte Inc.	2.8	3.1	3.4	3.7

If both companies maintain their current rates of growth, when will Byte Inc. overtake Light Speed Computers in sales?

11. Sarah and Shannon mow lawns during the summer to earn money. They both calculated their startup expenses, operating expenses, and income per hour of mowing. They wrote these equations for their income, I, after h hours of mowing.

$$I = 10.25h - 125 \quad \text{represents Sarah's income}$$
$$I = 10.25h - 100 \quad \text{represents Shannon's income}$$

   (a) What are Shannon's startup costs?
   (b) What does Sarah charge per hour?
   (c) After working for 40 h, who has the higher income?
   (d) If they both work the same number of hours, when will Sarah have the same income as Shannon? Explain your answer.

12. **Knowledge and Understanding:** A line has a slope of -3 and a y-intercept of 7. How many other lines have a single point of intersection with the given line?

13. You and your friends are planning a canoe trip to Algonquin Park. You have to decide which rental company will be the least expensive. True North Outfitters charge $15/day, while Portage Suppliers charge an $8 usage fee, plus $13/day. You wrote these equations for the two companies: $c = 15d$ and $c = 13d + 8$.
   (a) Which equation represents True North Outfitters?
   (b) After how many days are the rental costs the same for both companies?
   (c) If you plan to go on a three-day trip, which rental company will cost less?

14. Statistics Canada uses data collected from the most recent census to make predictions about Canada's population.

Using the data collected in the 1996 census, they made these projections about the number of males and females residing in Canada in the 21st century.

Year	Males (millions)	Females (millions)
2001	15.4	15.7
2006	15.9	16.3
2011	16.5	16.9
2016	17.0	17.4
2021	17.5	17.9
2026	17.9	18.3

Source: Statistics Canada

(a) Construct a scatter plot for the male population and draw a line of best fit.

(b) On the same graph, construct a scatter plot for the female population and draw a line of best fit.

(c) Determine the equations of the lines that model the male and female population.

(d) Will the male population ever equal the female population? What does this indicate about the lines (that is, are they parallel or not)?

15. This table compares the amount of tissue paper and newsprint produced in the United States between 1985 and 1988.

U.S. Paper Production (millions of tonnes)

Year	Tissue Paper	Newsprint
1985	4.9	5.4
1986	5.1	5.6
1987	5.3	5.8
1988	5.5	6.0

Source: American Paper Institute

(a) Construct a scatter plot of the data.

(b) What appears to be the trend in both cases?

(c) Confirm your observation by finding the equations of the lines of best fit.

16. (a) Show that the system of equations defined by $2x + y = 3$ and $10x = 15 - 5y$ has infinitely many solutions.

(b) Find three ordered pairs that are solutions to this system of equations.

17. Thinking, Inquiry, Problem Solving: A linear system contains two equations. The graph of the first equation is a line that passes through points $A(2, 3)$ and $B(-2, 7)$. Determine the equation of the second line if it is perpendicular to the first and the lines intersect at $(0, 5)$. Explain your reasoning as you work through the problem.

18. A rule of thumb for converting from Celsius to Fahrenheit is to double the Celsius reading and add 30. The exact formula is $F = 1.8C + 32$.

(a) Write an equation that models the rule of thumb.

(b) Will the lines that represent the two equations intersect?

(c) Graph both equations on the same set of axes. Determine the coordinates of the point of intersection.

(d) The rule of thumb provides a good estimate if it is within 5° F of the actual reading. Use the graph to find the values of C for which this is true.

19. Is it possible for a linear system to have exactly two solutions? Explain.

20. **Check Your Understanding:** A linear system defined by two equations may or may not have a solution. Copy this table and complete it in your notes.

Number of Solutions	How the Slopes Are Related	How the y-Intercepts Are Related
no solutions		
one solution		
many solutions		

C

21. The system $6x + 5y = 10$ and $ax + 2y = b$ has an infinite number of solutions. Find a and b.

22. The system $y = 4x - 7$ and $2y = ax + b$ has no solution. Find the value of a. Find a value that b cannot have. Explain why it cannot have this value.

23. The system $ax - by = -16$ and $ax + 2y = 20$ has one solution at the point $(3, 4)$. Find a and b.

24. How many solutions does this system of equations have?

$$\frac{x - 2}{3} - \frac{y + 5}{2} = -3$$
$$x + y = 8$$

1.6 Determining the Point of Intersection Using the TI-83 Plus Calculator

More than one graph can be drawn at the same time on the TI-83 Plus graphing calculator. This feature allows you to represent simple linear systems, involving two equations. The point of intersection can be found in two ways, one way being more accurate than the other.

Investigate both methods using the equations $y = 5x + 4$ and $y = -2x + 18$.

Approximating the Point of Intersection

1. Enter both linear equations into the equation editor.

2. Then press GRAPH. The point of intersection is out of view in a window from -10 to 10.

step 1   step 2

3. Use 0:ZoomFit to display the point of intersection. Press ZOOM 0.

4. Use the TRACE button and the left or right arrow keys to move the cursor to the point of intersection to get an approximation of the coordinates.

5. For a better approximation, use 2:Zoom In by pressing ZOOM 2 ENTER. Relocate the cursor on the point of intersection and repeat as many times as needed.

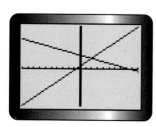

step 3   step 4   step 5

TECHNOLOGY

Finding the More Accurate Point of Intersection

You can also use the TI-83 Plus to find a more accurate point of intersection. To begin, enter the equations and graph the lines, just as in steps **1** and **2** on the previous page. Then follow the steps below.

3. To find the coordinates of the point of intersection, use the **intersect** command on the **CALC** menu. Press 2nd TRACE 5.

step 3

4. You will be asked to verify the two curves and enter a guess (optional) for the point of intersection. Press ENTER after each screen appears.

step 4   step 4 repeated

 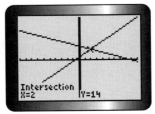

step 4 repeated again   step 4 repeated: a more accurate point of intersection

The point of intersection is (2, 14).

Practise 1.6

Locate the point of intersection for each linear system. First find an approximate location and then a more accurate location.

(a) $y = 2x + 1$
  $y = -x + 10$

(b) $y - 3x = 5$
  $y + 2x = -5$

(c) $x + 2y = -4$
  $-x + 2y = 2$

(d) $x + y = 39$
  $5x + 10y = 300$

(e) $40x + 500y = 830$
  $y = 3.5 - x$

(f) $4x + 5y = 90$
  $10x + 8y = 80$

1.7 Solving a Linear System Using Graphing Technology

Sung Lee got job offers from two software companies before she graduated from a computer college. NewTech offered a job starting at $40 000 per year, plus a guaranteed raise of $2000 per year. ProSof offered a job starting at $25 000, plus a guaranteed raise of $4000 per year. After how many years would she have the same annual salary in either job? Which job should she take?

Think, Do, Discuss

1. What two variables should Sung Lee use to model this problem?

2. Identify the independent variable and the dependent variable in this problem.

3. Determine the equations that represent Sung Lee's yearly salary for each job offer.

4. Draw a graph by hand to represent this linear system.

5. Determine the point of intersection from the graph you created. What does it mean in this situation?

6. State the disadvantages of using the graph you drew to find the point of intersection.

7. Use graphing technology to find the point of intersection of this linear system.

8. List the disadvantages of using graphing technology to find the point of intersection. Explain.

9. List the advantages of using graphing technology to find the point of intersection.

10. Which graph do you think shows a better approximation to the exact point of intersection?

11. Which job should Sung Lee take? Explain your reasoning.

Focus 1.7

Example 1

At the Rockton Town Fair, 600 admission tickets were sold in one night. Adult tickets cost \$10 and children's tickets cost \$5. If \$4375 was collected, how many children's tickets were sold?

Solution

This problem has been solved using the TI-83 Plus graphing calculator.

Let c represent the number of children's tickets sold. Let a represent the number of adult tickets sold.

$$c + a = 600 \qquad \text{represents the total number of tickets sold}$$
$$5c + 10a = 4375 \qquad \text{represents the total amount collected}$$

1. Convert both equations to the form $y = mx + b$.

$$c + a = 600$$
$$a = -c + 600$$

$$5c + 10a = 4375$$
$$\frac{10}{10}a = \frac{-5c + 4375}{10}$$
$$a = \frac{-5c}{10} + \frac{4375}{10}$$

2. Enter the equations.

step 2

3. Use (0:ZoomFit), followed by (3:Zoom Out), from the **ZOOM** menu, several times, until the point of intersection is displayed. Press [2nd] [TRACE] [5] followed by [ENTER] three times to get the coordinates of the point of intersection.

step 3

The solution to the linear system occurs at (325, 275). This means that 325 children's tickets and 275 adult tickets were sold.

Example 2

Solve the linear system defined by

$$4x - 3y = 6$$
$$3x + 2y = 30$$

Solution

This problem has been solved using a spreadsheet.

1. Express both equations in the form $y = mx + b$.

$$
\begin{array}{l|l}
4x - 3y = 6 & 3x + 2y = 30 \\
-3y = -4x + 6 & 2y = -3x + 30 \\
\dfrac{-3y}{-3} = \dfrac{-4x + 6}{-3} & \dfrac{2y}{2} = \dfrac{-3x + 30}{2} \\
y = \dfrac{4}{3}x - 2 & y = \dfrac{-3}{2}x + 15
\end{array}
$$

	A	B	C	D
1	x	y1	y2	
2	-5			
3	-4			
4	-3			
5	-2			
6	-1			
7	0			
8	1			
9	2			
10	3			
11	4			
12	5			
13	6			
14	7			
15	8			
16	9			
17	10			

2. Open the spreadsheet and create a table of values. Enter the headings x, y1, and y2 in cells A1, B1, and C1 respectively. Enter the values −5 to 10, in steps of 1, in column A, beginning with cell A2.

3. In cell B2, enter the expression "= 4*A2/3 − 2", for the first equation. Press ENTER for the corresponding value for y1 to be calculated. Highlight cells B2 to B17 and use the **Fill Down** command to complete the column for y1.

	A	B	C	D
1	x	y1	y2	
2	-5	-8.66667	22.5	
3	-4	-7.33333	21	
4	-3	-6	19.5	
5	-2	-4.66667	18	
6	-1	-3.33333	16.5	
7	0	-2	15	
8	1	-0.66667	13.5	
9	2	0.666667	12	
10	3	2	10.5	
11	4	3.333333	9	
12	5	4.666667	7.5	
13	6	6	6	
14	7	7.333333	4.5	
15	8	8.666667	3	
16	9	10	1.5	
17	10	11.33333	0	

4. In cell C2, enter the expression "= −3*A2/2 + 15", for the second equation. Press ENTER for the corresponding value for y2 to be calculated. Highlight cells B2 to B17 and use the **Fill Down** command to complete the column for y2.

5. The solution that appears in the table can be determined from the row where y1 = y2. In this case, the solution occurs when $x = 6$ and $y = 6$. If it is not apparent, then additional values for x must be entered into column A repeating steps **3** and **4**.

6. A graph can be drawn that also assists in determining the solution. Highlight the table of values in the spreadsheet and create a **Chart**. Choose **XY - Scatter** to draw the graph.

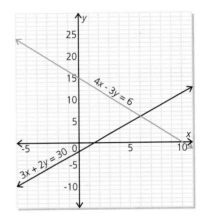

7. The point of intersection can be read from the graph on some spreadsheets. Moving the mouse pointer onto the point of intersection will display the coordinates of the point. In this case (6, 6) is the solution.

Example 3

Henri manages a manufacturing plant that makes softballs and hardballs. Each hardball requires 1 min on the stitching machine and 3 min on the covering machine. Each softball requires 2 min on each machine.

If the stitching machine is available for only 100 min each day and the ball-covering machine is available for 3 h each day, how many balls of each type can be made?

Solution

This problem has been solved using *The Geometer's Sketchpad.*

Let x represent the number of hardballs. Let y represent the number of softballs.

$$x + 2y = 100 \qquad \text{represents the time on the stitching machine}$$
$$3x + 2y = 180 \qquad \text{represents the time on the covering machine}$$

Use *The Geometer's Sketchpad* to find the intercepts and create a graph.

$x + 2y = 100$		$3x + 2y = 180$	
Let $x = 0$.	Let $y = 0$.	Let $x = 0$.	Let $y = 0$.
Then	Then	Then	Then
$2y = 100$	$x = 100$	$2y = 180$	$3x = 180$
$y = 50$		$y = 90$	$x = 60$

1. To draw the graph using *The Geometer's Sketchpad,* choose **Create Axes** from the **Graph** menu.

2. Drag the unit point (point *B*) toward the origin to adjust the scale. Drag the origin (point *A*) so that only the first quadrant is displayed.

3. Choose **Plot Points** from the **Graph** menu and enter the coordinates of the intercepts for the first equation. Make sure that both of these points are selected and choose **Segment** from the **Construct** menu.

4. Repeat step **3** for the intercepts of the second equation.

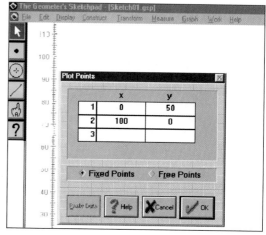

step 4

5. To find the point of intersection, select both lines and choose **Point at Intersection** from the **Construct** menu.

With the point of intersection selected, choose **Coordinates** from the **Measure** menu.

On the graph, the solution occurs at point (40, 30). This means that Henri can make 40 hardballs and 30 softballs.

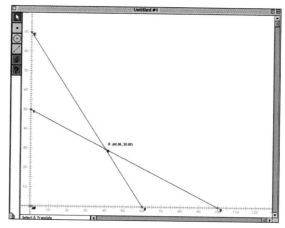

step 5

Example 4

Angel invested $1400 in two mutual funds. One fund earned interest at 7% per year and the other earned interest at 8% per year. If she received $104 in interest after one year, how much did she invest in each fund?

Solution

This problem has been solved using *Zap-a-Graph*.

Let x represent the amount invested at 7%.
Let y represent the amount invested at 8%.

$$x + y = 1400 \qquad ① \qquad \text{represents the total amount invested}$$
$$0.07x + 0.08y = 104 \quad ② \qquad \text{represents the interest earned}$$

Both equations can be graphed and the point of intersection determined using *Zap-a-Graph*. Lines can be graphed in three forms, slope-y-intercept form, standard form, and slope-point form.

1. Express equation ① in slope-y-intercept form: $y = -x + 1400$.

2. Express equation ② in standard form: $0.07x + 0.08y - 104 = 0$.

3. To graph equation ①, choose **Line** from the **Define** menu and select **y = mx + b**. Enter the values for m and b. A warning will appear that the graph is off the screen. The scales need to be adjusted.

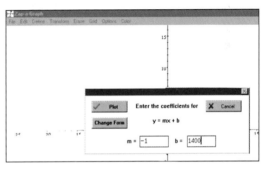

step 3

4. Select **Move Origin** from the **Grid** menu. Move the cursor to the bottom left corner and click the mouse. Select **Scale** from the **Grid** menu and change the interval to 200. Replot the line.

5. Graph equation ② by choosing **Line** from the **Define** menu and selecting **Ax + By + C = 0**. Enter the coefficients for A, B, and C. Left click the mouse and position the cursor at the point of intersection. The coordinates of this point are displayed in a box below the horizontal axis.

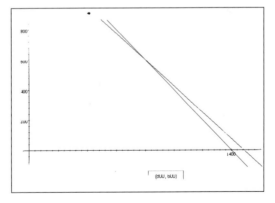

step 5

The point of intersection is (800, 600). This means that Angel invested $800 at 7% and $600 at 8%.

Practise, Apply, Solve 1.7

A

1. Solve each linear system. Use graphing technology.

   (a) $y = 4x - 1$
   $y = 3x + 4$

   (b) $y = -x + 8$
   $y = 2x - 7$

   (c) $y = 3x + 9$
   $y = 3x - 1$

   (d) $y = 3x + 6$
   $y = 5x - 4$

   (e) $y = x$
   $y = -x$

   (f) $y = 4x + 6$
   $y = -x + 1$

   (g) $y = 2x - 7$
   $y = 6x - 19$

   (h) $y = 2x + 6$
   $y = 5x - 2$

2. Determine the point of intersection for each pair of equations.

   (a) $a - 15b = 3$
   $3b + a = 21$

   (b) $41 + 9y = 8x$
   $4x = 3 - 3y$

   (c) $2x + 5y = 19$
   $3x = y + 3$

   (d) $3x + y = 5$
   $x - 2y = 11$

   (e) $3x - 2y = -8$
   $y - 7 = 3x$

   (f) $a - 3b = -2$
   $2b + a = 8$

3. Solve.

   (a) $2x + 3y = -1$
   $2x + 3y = 4$

   (b) $x + 4y = -5$
   $2y + 3x = 5$

   (c) $\frac{1}{2}x + \frac{3}{4}y = -1$
   $2x + 3y = -4$

   (d) $\frac{1}{4}x + \frac{1}{2}y = 8$
   $2x - y = 14$

   (e) $1.9x - 3.3 = 2.8y$
   $4.1y + 5.2x - 8.3 = 0$

   (f) $2.4x = 2.2y - 3.2$
   $1.6x + 1.2y = 3.2$

B

4. **Communication:** Write a paragraph explaining the advantages of solving a linear system using graphing technology instead of drawing a graph by hand.

5. **Knowledge and Understanding:** Movies To Go rents videos for $5 each and has no membership fee. Videorenters rents videos for $4.50 each and has a $10 membership fee.

   (a) Write an equation for each store's rental charges.

   (b) Graph both equations on the same axis and find the point of intersection.

   (c) Interpret the meaning of the point of intersection.

   (d) What advice would you give someone trying to decide which video store to use?

6. To send a letter from any city in Ontario to any other city in Ontario, Trillium Express charges $5, plus $1/kg. For the same service, Day by Day Delivery charges $3.50, plus $1.25/kg.
  (a) Write equations to model this situation.
  (b) Graph both equations on the same set of axes.
  (c) What does the point of intersection mean in this situation?
  (d) When does Trillium Express cost less than Day by Day Delivery? cost more?

7. The total cost to print a book includes a printer setup fee and a charge for each book printed.
The cost to print 1000 books is $29 175.
The cost to print 2000 books is $57 675.
How much is the setup fee?

8. Sanjay wants to earn extra money for college. Because he likes baking, he decides to sell chocolate chip cookies on campus. The cost to start his business is $120 and each cookie costs 10¢ to make. He will sell the cookies for 50¢ each.
  (a) Determine the equation that represents his costs.
  (b) Determine the equation that represents his revenue.
  (c) Graph both equations on the same set of axes.
  (d) What does the point of intersection mean in this case?
  (e) Determine if Sanjay makes a profit or loses money if he sells
    i. 200 cookies   **ii.** 300 cookies   **iii.** 500 cookies

9. Refer to question 8. The cost of chocolate increases, so the cost of making cookies increases to 15¢ per cookie.
  (a) Can Sanjay still make a profit if he does not increase his selling price? Explain.
  (b) How will this appear on your graph?
  (c) What should he charge to maintain the same break-even point?

10. A truck rental agency offers two daily rental plans.
Plan 1: $65 per day, with unlimited mileage
Plan 2: $30 per day, plus 20¢/km
  (a) Under what conditions is plan 1 better for someone renting a truck?
  (b) Under what conditions is plan 2 better?

11. Explain how you can use the TI-83 Plus calculator to accurately determine the point of intersection of two graphed lines. Is this technique better than repeated zooming?

12. A cellular phone company offers two service plans.

Budget plan: $20 per month, 30 min of free time, and a charge of $0.50/min

Pro plan: $50 per month, no free minutes, and a charge of $0.25/min

    (a) If C represents the monthly cost and m represents the number of minutes used each month, determine an equation for each plan.

    (b) When does the Pro plan cost less than the Budget plan?

    (c) When does the Budget plan cost less than the Pro plan?

13. Use graphing technology to solve the linear systems developed from questions 7 to 11 in Practise, Apply, Solve 1.1 on page 50.

14. Martin left Kingston driving at 80 km/h on Highway 401. Linda followed 2 h later, driving in the same direction at 100 km/h. How far down the road will Linda pass Martin?

15. Application: The sides of a triangle appear to be formed by the x-axis, the line $y = 3x$, and the line $y = -\frac{1}{2}x + 7$. Find the area of the triangle.

16. **(a)** What type of triangle is formed by $x - 2y = -6$, $x + 6y = -6$, and $3x + 2y = 14$?

    (b) Determine the coordinates of the vertices of the triangle.

17. Confirm or deny: The vertices of the triangle formed by $3x - 8y = -39$, $4x + y = 18$, and $x + 2y = 1$ appear to form an isosceles triangle.

18. Thinking, Inquiry, Problem Solving:
Show your work for this problem. A tornado follows a path plotted by the weather office as $2x - y = 5$. At the same time, the centre of a thunderstorm is on the path given by $y = -x + 4$.

These towns have the coordinates shown.

- Delhi $(-4, 2)$ • Marysville $(7, 9)$
- Everett $(0, -5)$ • Norwich $(2, 2)$
- Walton $(-1, 5)$ • Vernon $(8, 8)$
- Mactier $(5, 5)$ • Barrie $(3, 1)$

satellite weather map of North America

Which towns will experience

    (a) a thunderstorm only?   **(b)** a tornado only?

    (c) a thunderstorm and a tornado?   **(d)** clear weather?

19. To use a locker at Diamond Gym's Club you can pay either $50 per year or $6.25 per month.

    (a) Graph this situation using a linear system.

    (b) How many months per year do you have to use the locker to make it worth paying the yearly rate?

20. Check Your Understanding: List all the steps you would take with the graphing technology of your choice to find the point where $y = 5x - 6$ and $y = -3x + 9$ intersect. Include all keystrokes and buttons.

C

21. Find the coordinates of the point where each set of linear systems intersects.

(a) $\dfrac{(x+1)}{2} + \dfrac{(3y-3)}{8} = 0$

$\dfrac{(2x+3)}{3} + 6y = -1$

(b) $\dfrac{2}{x} - \dfrac{1}{y} = 13$

$\dfrac{3}{x} + \dfrac{2}{y} = 2$

22. Solve each system of equations.

(a) $y = 2x^2 + 1$

$y = -3x + 1$

(b) $y = \dfrac{1}{x}$

$y = 4x$

(c) $y = x^3$

$y = x^2$

(d) $y = x^2 - 3$

$y = -x^2 + 3$

The Chapter Problem—Controlling Traffic

In this section, you used technology to solve a linear system. Apply what you learned to answer these questions about the chapter problem on page 42.

1. Use the scatter plot you created to determine the equation of your line of best fit for the data for the red light. Remember you will need to approximate the y-intercept and calculate the slope of the line.

2. Use graphing technology to graph the line of best fit you created and the line represented by Greenshield's formula on the same set of axes.

3. Determine the point of intersection between the two lines you have graphed. How do the coordinates of this point compare with the coordinates you found using the hand-drawn graph?

Etta Falconer, b.1933

Dr. Etta Falconer was born in Tupelo, Mississippi. She has taught for over 40 years, in schools and universities, including Spelman College, a historically black college for women. She is currently the Calloway Professor of Mathematics at Spelman College and serves as Associate Provost for Science Programs and Policy.

Professor Falconer has also been involved in the NASA Women in Science Program, directing promising undergraduate students toward doctoral programs. She also was a founder of the National Association of Mathematicians, an organization that promotes concerns of black students and mathematicians.

In 1995, Dr. Falconer was awarded the Louise Hay Award for outstanding achievements in mathematics education. Despite the great demands on her time, Dr. Falconer continues to teach mathematics courses because of her desire to stay in touch with students.

1.8 Solving a Linear System Using Algebra: Substitution

Last night, the students at Trillium High School staged a drama festival at the local theatre. Student tickets were $4 and adult tickets were $12. All 300 seats were sold, and the box office collected $3024.

Manny is the cashier. The manager wants to know how many tickets were sold at each price, but the cash register jammed and Manny had to sell tickets manually. He was so busy, he was unable to keep track of sales.

Think, Do, Discuss

1. Use different letters to identify the variables in this situation.

2. A linear system can be used to model this problem. What relationship does each equation represent?

3. Use the variables you chose to write the two equations that represent this problem.

4. Isolate, on the left side, one of the variables in one of the equations.

5. Substitute the expression from the right side of the equation in step 4 for that variable in the other equation.

6. Solve the resulting equation in step 5. What does the solution to this equation mean in terms of Manny's problem?

7. How can Manny come up with the other information his manager wants?

8. How can Manny be sure that he has the right information for his manager?

9. Suppose Manny solved this problem graphically by hand or with technology, instead of algebraically. How confident would you be that he had the exact information his manager wants?

10. In step 4, you isolated one of the variables in one of the equations. Would you get the same solution if you isolated the other variable first, and then substituted? Try it. Solve the system using this approach. What do you notice?

Focus 1.8

Key Ideas

- Algebraic methods for solving a linear system give exact solutions. Graphing techniques can be used when an exact answer is not necessary.

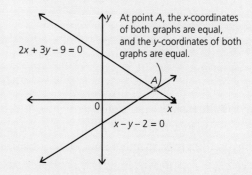

$2x + 3y - 9 = 0$

At point *A*, the *x*-coordinates of both graphs are equal, and the *y*-coordinates of both graphs are equal.

A

$x - y - 2 = 0$

- At the point where two graphs intersect, the *x*-coordinates for both graphs are equal, and the *y*-coordinates are equal. The method of substitution uses this relationship to replace one variable with an expression in terms of the other. This results in one equation, with one unknown, that can be solved.

- To solve a linear system using substitution, follow these steps:

  1. Choose one of the equations and isolate one of its variables by expressing that variable in terms of the other.

  2. Substitute the expression that you have determined in place of the corresponding variable in the other equation.

  3. Solve the new equation.

For instance, to solve the equations in the graph above,

Step 1: Examine the equations for a variable that is easy to isolate.

$2x + 3y - 9 = 0$ ①
$x - y - 2 = 0$ ②

It looks easier to isolate *x* in equation ②.

$x - y - 2 = 0$ ②
$x = y + 2$

Step 2: Substitute this expression for *x* in equation ①.

$2x + 3y - 9 = 0$ ①
$2(y + 2) + 3y - 9 = 0$

Step 3: Solve for *y*.

$$2(y + 2) + 3y - 9 = 0$$
$$2y + 4 + 3y - 9 = 0$$
$$2y + 3y = 9 - 4$$
$$5y = 5$$
$$y = 1$$

4. To find the value of the other variable, substitute the number you found into one of the original equations and solve.

5. Verify that the ordered pair you determined works in both equations by replacing the variables with the numbers you found in **both** equations.

- When using substitution, always look for a variable that is easy to solve for in one of the equations. This will ensure that the solution process will be as simple as possible.

Step 4: Substitute this value into equation ② and solve for x.

$$x - y - 2 = 0 \qquad ②$$
$$x - 1 - 2 = 0$$
$$x = 3$$

Step 5: Verify the solution (3, 1) satisfies both equations.

Equation ①		Equation ②	
L.S.	R.S.	L.S.	R.S.
$2x + 3y - 9$	0	$x - y - 2$	0
$= 2(3) + 3(1) - 9$		$= 3 - 1 - 2$	
$= 6 + 3 - 9$		$= 0$	
$= 0$		L.S. = R.S.	
L.S. = R.S.			

The solution (3, 1) does satisfy both equations.

Example 1

Use substitution to solve this linear system.

$$y = 5x - 2 \qquad ①$$
$$6x + 3y = 36 \qquad ②$$

Solution

$$y = 5x - 2 \qquad \text{Equation ① already has one of its variables isolated.}$$
$$6x + 3(5x - 2) = 36 \qquad \text{Substitute } 5x - 2 \text{ for } y \text{ in equation ②.}$$
$$6x + 15x - 6 = 36 \qquad \text{Solve for } x.$$
$$6x + 15x = 36 + 6$$
$$21x = 42$$
$$\frac{21x}{21} = \frac{42}{21}$$
$$x = 2$$

To find y, substitute 2 for x in equation ①. (You could also use equation ②.)

$$y = 5(2) - 2$$
$$y = 10 - 2$$
$$y = 8$$

Express the solution as an ordered pair. The solution is (2, 8).

Example 2

Guarantee Pool Repair charges $50 for a service call, plus $40/h for labour. Oasis Pools and Spas charges $30 for a service call, plus $45/h for labour. Find the length of a service call for which both companies charge the same amount.

Solution

Let t represent the time to complete a job.
Let c represent the total cost of the job.

$$c = 40t + 50 \quad \text{①} \qquad \text{represents the total cost of Guarantee}$$
$$c = 45t + 30 \quad \text{②} \qquad \text{represents the total cost of Oasis}$$

$$45t + 30 = 40t + 50 \qquad \text{Substitute } 45t + 30 \text{ for } c \text{ in equation ①.}$$
$$45t - 40t = 50 - 30 \qquad \text{Solve for } t.$$
$$5t = 20$$
$$\frac{5t}{5} = \frac{20}{5}$$
$$t = 4$$

To find c, substitute 4 for t in either of the original equations.

$$c = 40(4) + 50 \qquad \text{Substitute into equation ①.}$$
$$c = 160 + 50$$
$$c = 210$$

At 4 h, both companies charge the same, $210, to make a repair.

Did You Know?

When a person communicates about mathematics using phrases, he or she can only be understood by someone who speaks the same language. When mathematical word phrases are translated into symbols, however, they are understood throughout the great part of the world. That is because most cultures have adopted the Hindu-Arabic system of numeration. This system was probably developed in India and distributed to the west by the Arabs.

At one point, different systems of written numerals were in use by different cultures. In fact, some cultures had more than one set of symbols for numbers. The Chinese, for instance, had five different types of written numerals—two for counting boards, one for basic numerals, and three for commercial purposes.

Example 3

Use the diagram and your knowledge of parallelograms to find the value of x and y.

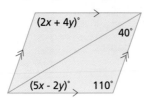

Solution

$(5x - 2y) + 110 + 40 = 180$ ① The sum of the angles in a triangle equals $180°$.

$2x + 4y = 110$ ② Opposite angles of a parallelogram are equal.

$5x = 2y - 110 - 40 + 180$ Solve for x in equation ①.

$5x = 2y + 30$

$x = \dfrac{2y + 30}{5}$

Substitute $\dfrac{2y + 30}{5}$ for x in equation ②.

$2\left(\dfrac{2y + 30}{5}\right) + 4y = 110$

$\dfrac{4y + 60}{5} + 4y = 110$

$5\left(\dfrac{4y + 60}{5}\right) + 5(4y) = 5(110)$ Multiply by 5 to eliminate all fractions.

$4y + 60 + 20y = 550$ Solve for y.

$4y + 20y = 550 - 60$

$24y = 490$

$y = \dfrac{490}{24}$

$y = 20\dfrac{5}{12}$

To find x, substitute $20\dfrac{5}{12}$ or $\dfrac{245}{12}$ for y in one of the original equations.

$2x + 4y = 110$

$2x + \overset{1}{4}\left(\dfrac{245}{\underset{3}{12}}\right) = 110$

$2x + \dfrac{245}{3} = 110$

$3(2x) + 3\left(\dfrac{245}{3}\right) = 3(110)$ Multiply by 3 to eliminate all fractions.

$6x + 245 = 330$ Solve for x.

$6x = 330 - 245$

$6x = 85$

$x = \dfrac{85}{6}$

$x = 14\dfrac{1}{6}$

Then, $x = 14\dfrac{1}{6}°$ and $y = 20\dfrac{5}{12}°$.

Example 4

A rectangle has vertices at $A(2, 2)$, $B(2, 6)$, $C(4, 6)$, and $D(4, 2)$. Develop an algebraic solution to determine the coordinates of the point of intersection of the diagonals.

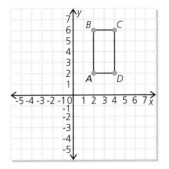

Solution

Draw a diagram.

Find the equation, in the form $y = mx + b$, of each diagonal.

For diagonal AC,

$$\text{slope} = \frac{6 - 2}{4 - 2}$$

$$= \frac{4}{2}$$

$$= 2$$

Find b using $A(2, 2)$.

$$y = 2x + b$$

$$2 = 2(2) + b$$

$$2 = 4 + b$$

$$2 - 4 = b$$

$$-2 = b$$

The equation of AC is $y = 2x - 2$.

For diagonal BD,

$$\text{slope} = \frac{6 - 2}{2 - 4}$$

$$= \frac{4}{-2}$$

$$= -2$$

Find b using $B(2, 6)$.

$$y = -2x + b$$

$$6 = -2(2) + b$$

$$6 = -4 + b$$

$$6 + 4 = b$$

$$10 = b$$

The equation of BD is $y = -2x + 10$.

Find the point where the diagonals intersect by solving the system.

$$y = 2x - 2 \qquad ①$$

$$y = -2x + 10 \qquad ②$$

Substitute ① into ②.

$$2x - 2 = -2x + 10$$

$$2x + 2x = 10 + 2$$

$$4x = 12$$

$$x = 3$$

Substitute 3 in for x and solve for y.

$$y = 2(3) - 2$$

$$y = 6 - 2$$

$$y = 4$$

The diagonals intersect at $(3, 4)$.

Practise, Apply, Solve 1.8

(A)

1. Solve for y in terms of x.

(a) $3x + y = 12$ (b) $y - 4x = 15$ (c) $12x - y = 3$

(d) $8x = y + 6$ (e) $2y - 2x = 18$ (f) $13x - 12y = 14$

2. Solve for x in terms of y.

(a) $x + 3y = 5$ (b) $x - 2y = 18$ (c) $8y - x = 5$

(d) $3y = 8 - x$ (e) $5x - y + 1 = 0$ (f) $7y - x + 6 = 0$

3. Solve for the variable indicated.

(a) $8a = 4 - b$, b (b) $8m - 2n = 6$, n (c) $6r + 3s = 9$, r

(d) $4d - 5e - 12 = 0$, e (e) $6p = 12 - 3q$, p (f) $3u + 7v = 21$, v

4. For each system, use the given value to find the value of the other variable.

(a) $x = 2$ (b) $y = 2$ (c) $3 = y - x$
$\quad 2x + y = 3$ $\quad 4x - 2y = 8$ $\quad x = -3$

(d) $r = 3$ (e) $2m - 3n = 5$ (f) $3a - b + 1 = 4$
$\quad 2s - 3r = 6$ $\quad n = -6$ $\quad a = 2$

5. A system of equations is defined by

$$x + 4y = -10 \quad \text{①}$$
$$2x + y = 1 \quad\quad \text{②}$$

(a) Obtain from equation ① an expression for x and solve the system.
(b) Obtain from equation ② an expression for y and solve the system.
(c) What can you conclude from your results in (a) and (b)?

(B)

6. **Communication:** Write a paragraph comparing the substitution method to the graphing method for solving a linear system. What are the advantages and disadvantages of each method?

7. Solve using substitution.

(a) $y = x - 1$ (b) $x = -2y + 3$ (c) $y = x - 1$
$\quad y = 2x - 3$ $\quad x = 3y - 7$ $\quad y = 3 - 3x$

(d) $a = 1 - b$ (e) $m = -3 - 2n$ (f) $p = 2q - 2$
$\quad a = 1 - 2b$ $\quad m = 2n + 1$ $\quad p = -3 + 3q$

8. Solve using substitution.

(a) $y = 3x - 8$ (b) $a = 2b + 2$ (c) $x = 4 - y$
$\quad 5x + y = 6$ $\quad 5a - 9b = 12$ $\quad 2y + 2x = 8$

(d) $3m - 2n = -5$ (e) $2a - 3b = -4$ (f) $2x - 3y = 1$
$\quad m = n - 2$ $\quad a = 5 - 2b$ $\quad x = y + 1$

(g) $2r - s = -11$ (h) $3p + 2q - 1 = 0$ (i) $2x + y = 5$
$\quad s = r - 1$ $\quad p = q + 2$ $\quad x - 3y = 13$

9. A system of equations is defined by

$$2y = 5x - 3$$
$$y = 2.5x - 3$$

(a) Solve by substitution.

(b) What happens when you try to solve this system? What does this mean?

(c) Draw a diagram to represent this situation. How does it support your answer to part (b)?

10. A system of equations is defined by

$$3y + 5x = 30$$
$$y = -\frac{5}{3}x + 10$$

(a) Solve by substitution.

(b) What happens when you try to solve this system? What does this mean?

(c) Draw a diagram to represent this situation.

11. Application: A sales clerk in Hedy's Clothing Store can choose between two salary plans: Straight 10% commission or $250 per month plus 5% commission.

(a) How much would the clerk have to sell under each plan to earn the same monthly paycheque?

(b) Why might someone choose the second plan?

12. Find the coordinates of the point of intersection for each system.

(a) $x - y = -2$
$2x - 7y = 11$

(b) $2q - p = 3$
$q + 2p = 24$

(c) $3x - 12z = -15$
$z - 2x = 7$

(d) $2m + 5n = -18$
$m + 2n = -6$

(e) $2y = w + 5$
$w - 3y = 0$

(f) $3s + 2t = -24$
$2s + 5t = -38$

(g) $5x + 2y = 18$
$2x + 3y = 16$

(h) $6a + 2b = 0$
$2a + 5b = -13$

(i) $9 = 6x - 3y$
$4x - 3y = 5$

13. Two meshing gears in a printer have a total of 89 teeth. One of the gears has 4 teeth less than twice the number of teeth of the other gear. How many teeth does each gear have?

14. A small plane flying in the same direction as the wind, travelled 600 km in 2 h. The return trip, flying against the wind, took 3 h. Find the speed of the plane and the wind.

15. **Knowledge and Understanding:** Explain why the algebraic method described in this section is called substitution. Use the linear system $x + 2y = 13$ and $4x - 5y = -13$ as an example in your explanation.

16. A rectangle with a perimeter of 40 m is 2 m longer than it is wide. Determine the dimensions of the rectangle.

17. A publishing company in Ontario mails 1040 brochures promoting a new university textbook. Each brochure costs $0.46 to mail within North America and $0.48 to mail elsewhere. If the total mailing cost was $483, how many brochures were mailed to universities in North America?

18. You are starting a business that sells air filters for homes. Your startup costs for the business are $1250 and each air filter kit costs $40. If you sell the filters for $60, how many must you sell to break even?

19. Use substitution to solve the linear systems developed from questions 12 to 16 in the Practise, Apply, Solve 1.1 on page 51.

20. **Thinking, Inquiry, Problem Solving:** If you buy 7 hamburgers and 3 slices of pizza from Sizzler, you get $1 change from a $20 bill. If you buy 8 hamburgers and 2 slices of pizza, you get $0.50 back from a $20 bill. How much change would you get from a $20 bill if you bought 3 slices of pizza and 5 hamburgers?

21. Solve for x and y in each diagram.

(a)

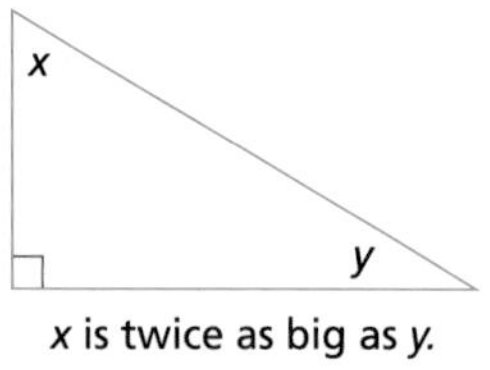

x is twice as big as y.

(b)

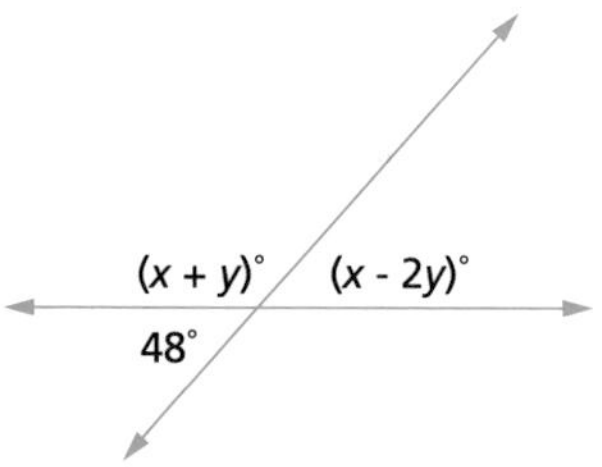

(c)

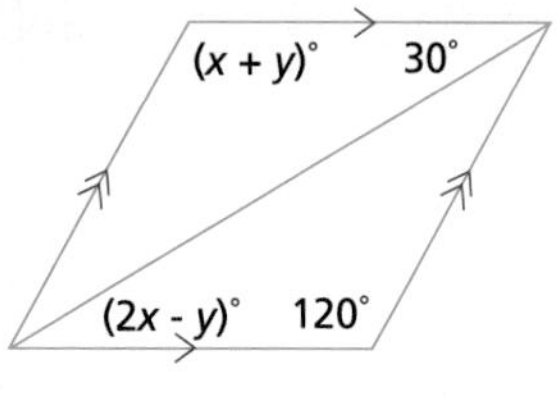

(d)

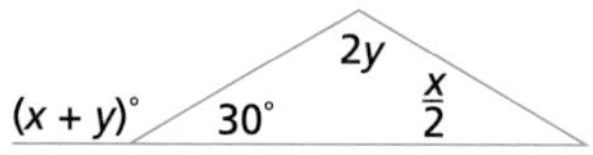

(e)

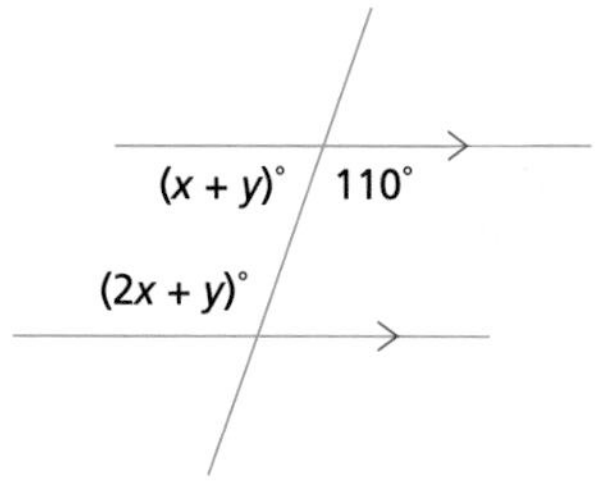

(f)

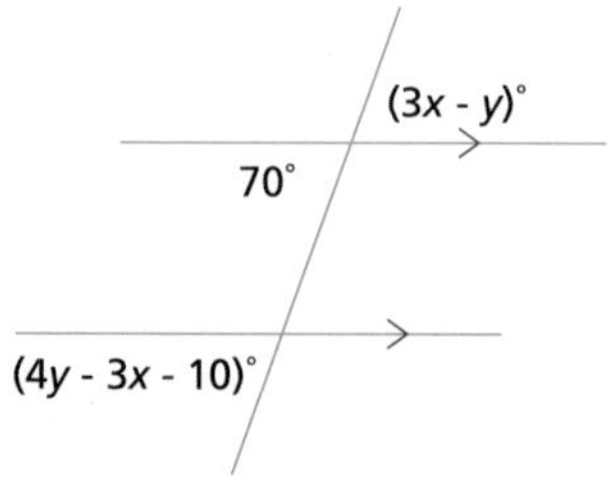

22. Darius saved $500 and wants to open a chequing account. Ontario Trust charges $8 per month, plus $0.50 per cheque. Maple Leafs Savings charges $6 per month, plus $0.75 per cheque. Which bank offers the lower monthly charge?

23. Check Your Understanding: Monique is solving the system of equations defined by $2x - y = 4$ and $y = 4x - 10$ by substitution. She obtained $-2x - 10 = 4$. What did she do wrong? Write out the correct way to solve this linear system. Explain your steps.

C

24. Solve for x and y.
$$xy + y - 3x - 3 = xy - 2y + 3x - 6$$
$$xy - y + 5x - 5 = xy + 2y + 4x + 8$$

25. Total sales on Wednesday at Daynite Submarines were $4200. The restaurant makes a profit of 4% on meat submarines and a profit of 5% on veggie submarines. The profit from meat submarines was $51 more than the profit from veggie submarines. How much of the sales was accounted for by each type of submarine?

26. Solve by substitution. (Hint: Let m represent $\frac{1}{x}$ and let n represent $\frac{1}{y}$.)

(a) $\dfrac{1}{x} + \dfrac{1}{y} = \dfrac{3}{4}$

$\dfrac{3}{x} - \dfrac{1}{y} = \dfrac{1}{4}$

(b) $\dfrac{2}{x} - \dfrac{2}{y} = \dfrac{1}{2}$

$\dfrac{1}{x} + \dfrac{5}{y} = \dfrac{3}{4}$

27. Solve for x and y in terms of a and b.

(a) $x + y = 8a$
$2x + 5y = 10a$

(b) $x + y = a + 2b$
$3x - 2y = 3a - 4b$

The Chapter Problem—Controlling Traffic

In this section, you solved linear systems using substitution. Apply what you learned to answer these questions about the chapter problem on page 42.

1. Using the equation of your line of best fit for the data for the red light and the equation from Greenshield's formula, determine the coordinates of the point of intersection using substitution.
2. Compare the coordinates you found with those determined from the scatter plot. Which do you think is more accurate? Why?
3. How many cars will be stopped in each lane if these settings are used for the red light?
4. How long should the light remain green?

1.9 Solving a Linear System Using Algebra: Elimination

Part 1: The Simplest Case

A linear system is defined by these equations.

$$x + y = 8$$
$$x - y = 2$$

Think, Do, Discuss

1. Solve this system of equations by inspection or using guess-and-check. What is the solution?

2. Create a new equation by vertically adding the like terms of the two equations. What happens to the y-term?

3. Solve the new equation for x.

4. Now, create a new equation by vertically subtracting the like terms of the two equations. What happens to the x-term?

5. Solve the new equation for y.

6. Summarize your findings.

Part 2: A More Complex System

Mark is training for the upcoming basketball season. He wants to design a daily 45 min workout using a combination of the stationary bike and the treadmill. To be in top shape, he should burn 400 cal during his workout. On the bike he burns 8 cal/min and on the treadmill he burns 10 cal/min.

Think, Do, Discuss

1. What are the two variables in this situation? Use the letters k and d to represent these quantities.

2. What two relationships can be represented by equations using these variables?

3. Write the equations that describe this situation. Express both in the form $ax + by = c$.

4. Can you eliminate either the k-term or the d-term by adding or subtracting the equations? Explain.

5. Suppose you would like to eliminate the *k*-term from this system of equations. What could you do first to make addition or subtraction work?

6. What if you decided to eliminate the *d*-term first?

7. Eliminate either the *k*- or *d*-term and solve the resulting equation.

8. Once you determined the value of one variable, what is the easier method to find the other value?

9. What do the values of *k* and *d* mean in this situation?

10. Explain how Mark can be sure that his training program meets the conditions he set.

Focus 1.9

Key Ideas

- If the coefficients of the same variable in both equations have the same value or the opposite value, you can eliminate that variable in a two-variable linear system by adding or subtracting the equations. The result is a new equation with one variable that can be solved directly.

  When you add or subtract equations to eliminate a variable, the coefficients of the selected variable must be the same in both equations (although they may have opposite signs). To achieve this, you can multiply all the terms of an equation by the same number.

- When the coefficients of a variable are exactly the same, subtract the two equations to eliminate the variable.

- When the coefficients have the same value but opposite signs, add the two equations to eliminate the variable.

- To solve a linear system using elimination, follow these steps.

1. Express both equations in the form $ax + by = c$.	For example, to solve the linear system $3x + 2y - 13 = 0$ ① $-2x + 4y - 2 = 0$ ②
2. Choose a variable to eliminate. Multiply each equation by a number that gives the same or opposite coefficients for that variable in both equations.	**Step 1:** Express both equations in $ax + by = c$ form. $3x + 2y = 13$ ③ $-2x + 4y = 2$ ④ **Step 2:** Multiply equation ③ by 2 so that the coefficient of y is the same in both equations. $6x + 4y = 26$ ③ × 2 $-2x + 4y = 2$ ④

3. Add or subtract like terms in the equation to eliminate the chosen variable.

Step 3: Subtract equation ④ to eliminate the y variable.

$$\begin{array}{rll} 6x + 4y &= 26 & \text{③} \times 2 \\ -2x + 4y &= 2 & \text{④} \\ \hline 8x &= 24 & \end{array}$$

4. Solve the resulting equation for the remaining variable.

Step 4: Solve for x.

$$8x = 24$$
$$x = \frac{24}{8}$$
$$x = 3$$

5. Determine the value of the other variable by substituting the solved value of the now known variable into one of the other equations.

Step 5: Substitute this value into equation ③ and solve for y.

$$3x + 2y = 13 \qquad \text{③}$$
$$3(3) + 2y = 13$$
$$2y = 13 - 9$$
$$2y = 4$$
$$y = 2$$

6. Verify your solution in the original equations.

Step 6: Verify the solution (3, 2) satisfies both equations.

Equation ①		Equation ②	
L.S.	R.S.	L.S.	R.S.
$3x + 2y - 13$	0	$-2x + 4y - 2$	0
$= 3(3) + 2(2) - 13$		$= -2(3) + 4(2) - 2$	
$= 9 + 4 - 13$		$= -6 + 8 - 2$	
$= 0$		$= 0$	
L.S. = R.S.		L.S. = R.S.	

The solution (3, 2) does satisfy both original equations.

Did You Know?

The ENIAC (Electronic Numerical Integrator and Computer) was the first fully electronic, digital computer. It was controlled by 18 000 vacuum tubes, each one the size of a small light bulb. It was built in 1946 at the University of Pennsylvania.

The ENIAC could perform about 5000 arithmetic operations in one second—which was a giant leap forward for the time. Find out more about the speed of your calculator. How many times faster is it than the ENIAC?

Example 1

Solve using elimination.

$$3x - 2y = 2$$
$$-10x + 3y = 8$$

Solution

Eliminate the *x*-term. Make the *x*-coefficients 30 in the first equation and -30 in the second.

$$10(3x) - 10(2y) = 10(2) \qquad \text{Multiply all terms in the first equation by 10.}$$
$$3(-10x) + 3(3y) = 3(8) \qquad \text{Multiply all terms in the second equation by 3.}$$

$$
\begin{aligned}
30x - 20y &= 20 \\
-30x + 9y &= 24 \qquad \text{Add to eliminate the } x\text{-terms.} \\
\hline
-11y &= 44 \qquad \text{Solve for } y. \\
\frac{-11y}{-11} &= \frac{44}{-11} \\
y &= -4
\end{aligned}
$$

Find the value of *x* by substituting $y = -4$ into one of the original equations.

$$
\begin{aligned}
3x - 2(-4) &= 2 \\
3x + 8 &= 2 \\
3x &= 2 - 8 \\
3x &= -6 \\
x &= -2
\end{aligned}
$$

The solution is $(-2, -4)$.

Verify.

L.S.	R.S.
$3x - 2y$	2
$= 3(-2) - 2(-4)$	
$= -6 + 8$	
$= 2$	
L.S. $=$ R.S.	

L.S.	R.S.
$-10x + 3y$	8
$= -10(-2) + 3(-4)$	
$= 20 - 12$	
$= 8$	
L.S. $=$ R.S.	

The solution $(-2, -4)$ does satisfy both original equations.

Example 2

Mario operates a bakery. Every day, he bakes fresh loaves of bread and fresh rolls. Both types of dough require milk, water, and flour plus other ingredients. One batch of bread uses 5 cups of flour and 2 cups of milk. One batch of rolls uses 3.5 cups of flour and 0.5 cups of milk. How many batches of bread and rolls can he make if he has 17 cups of flour and 5 cups of milk plus all the other ingredients?

Solution

Let b represent the number of batches of bread. Let r represent the number of batches of rolls.

$$5b + 3.5r = 17 \qquad \text{represents the amount of flour}$$
$$2b + 0.5r = 5 \qquad \text{represents the amount of milk}$$

Eliminate the r-term.

$$7(2b) + 7(0.5r) = 7(5) \qquad \text{Multiply the second equation by 7 to get a}$$
coefficient of 3.5 for the r-term in both equations.

$$5b + 3.5r = 17$$
$$\underline{14b + 3.5r = 35} \qquad \text{Subtract to eliminate the } r\text{-term.}$$
$$-9b = -18 \qquad \text{Solve for } b.$$
$$b = 2$$

To find r, substitute $b = 2$ into one of the original equations.

$$2(2) + 0.5r = 5$$
$$4 + 0.5r = 5$$
$$0.5r = 5 - 4$$
$$0.5r = 1$$
$$\frac{0.5r}{0.5} = \frac{1}{0.5}$$
$$r = 2$$

Mario can make 2 batches of bread and 2 batches of rolls.

Example 3

Flying into the wind, an airliner takes 4 h to go 960 km. The same plane flying with the wind takes only 3 h to make the same trip. Find the speed of the plane and the speed of the wind.

Solution

Let p represent the speed of the plane in kilometres per hour. Let w represent the speed of the wind in kilometres per hour.

Direction	Distance (km)	Speed (km/h)	Time (h)
with the wind	960	$p + w$	3
against the wind	960	$p - w$	4

Use the formula distance = speed × time.

$960 = (p + w)(3)$ represents the distance travelled with the wind $\left.\begin{matrix} \\ \\ \end{matrix}\right\}$ Expand both equations.
$960 = (p - w)(4)$ represents the distance travelled against the wind

$960 = 3p + 3w$
$960 = 4p - 4w$

$(960)(4) = (3p + 3w)(4)$ Eliminate w by arranging a coefficient of 12 or -12 in
$(960)(3) = (4p - 4w)(3)$ each w-term. Multiply the first expanded equation by 4 and the second expanded equation by 3.

$3840 = 12p + 12w$
$\underline{2880 = 12p - 12w}$ Add the equations.
$6720 = 24p$ Solve for p.
$p = 280$

To find w, substitute $p = 280$ into one of the equations.

$$960 = 3p + 3w$$
$$960 = 3(280) + 3w$$
$$960 = 840 + 3w$$
$$120 = 3w$$
$$w = 40$$

The plane is flying at an airspeed of 280 km/h. The wind speed is 40 km/h. Verify each answer. Use the relation $\frac{\text{distance}}{\text{speed}}$ = time. Then, $\frac{960}{280 + 40} = 3$ and $\frac{960}{280 - 40} = 4$.

Practise, Apply, Solve 1.9 ———————————

A

1. A linear system is defined by $x + y = 15$ and $x - y = 1$.
   (a) Solve the system by first eliminating y.
   (b) Solve the system again, this time by first eliminating x.
   (c) Are both solutions the same? Should they be?

2. For each linear system, state which variable can be eliminated more easily. Would you use addition or subtraction to eliminate it?

   (a) $x + y = 4$ (b) $x + 2y = 0$ (c) $2x + y = 1$
        $x - 2y = 1$ $x - y = 3$ $x + y = 2$

   (d) $3x - y = 3$ (e) $3x - 2y = 4$ (f) $4x + y = 13$
        $y - 2x = -2$ $x - 2y = 4$ $4x - y = 11$

3. Solve the systems of equations in question 2.

4. The equations $3x + y = 9$ and $x - 2y = -7$ form a linear system.
   (a) Explain how you would eliminate x from the equations.
   (b) Explain how you would eliminate y from the equations.
   (c) Solve the system.

B

5. A small plane flying into the wind takes 3 h 20 min to complete a flight of 960 km. Flying with the wind, the same plane takes 2 h 30 min to make the trip. What is the speed of the plane? What is the speed of the wind?

6. Solve each system of equations. Use substitution or elimination as appropriate.

   (a) $2x + y = 3$
   $3x + 2y = 5$

   (b) $x - 3y = 0$
   $3x - 2y = -7$

   (c) $2a - 3b = 13$
   $5a - b = 13$

   (d) $3a = 2b - 10$
   $b + 15 = 3a$

   (e) $2x + 5y = 8$
   $5x - 2y = 20$

   (f) $3x + 21 = 5y$
   $4y + 6 = -9x$

   (g) $m - 3n = 11$
   $2m = -10n + 6$

   (h) $18 = 6x - 3y$
   $4x - 3y = 8$

   (i) $8x - 3y = 22$
   $6x + 12y = -12$

   (j) $6x = 12 - 3y$
   $y - 2x = -16$

   (k) $4x - 3y = -13$
   $x + y = 9$

   (l) $7 + y = 4x$
   $3x + 2y = -3$

7. **Communication:** Explain the advantages and disadvantages of both the substitution method and the elimination method for solving a system of equations. Use the systems below in your explanation.

   (a) $3x + 2y = 6$
   $x + 3y = 16$

   (b) $2x + 3y = 18$
   $5x - 4y = -1$

8. A system of equations consists of $3(x - 1) - 2(y + 2) = 7$ and $x - 5y = -4$.
   (a) What is the first step in solving this system?
   (b) Solve the system.

9. **Knowledge and Understanding:** Explain what to do to this linear system to eliminate x from both equations.

$$3x + 2y = 22$$
$$5x - 4y = 22$$

10. Find the coordinates of the point of intersection of the graphs defined by each linear system.

   (a) $3(x - 1) - 2(y - 2) = 0$
   $x + 3y = -4$

   (b) $2x - \frac{1}{3}y = \frac{1}{3}$
   $3(x + 1) - 2(y - 3) = 11$

   (c) $a = 6 + 3b$
   $3(a - 2) = 4 + 2(b - 3)$

   (d) $\frac{1}{2}x - y = -3$
   $x - \frac{2}{3}y = -2$

(e) $a - \frac{3}{4}b = -4$

$a + \frac{1}{4}b = 0$

(f) $x - \frac{1}{3}y = -1$

$\frac{2}{3}x - \frac{1}{4}y = -1$

11. **(a)** Create a linear system of two equations that has no solution.
   (b) What happens when you use elimination to solve this system? Show an
   example and explain.

12. Application:
   (a) Create a linear system of two equations that has many solutions.
   (b) What happens when you use elimination to solve this system? Show an
   example and explain.

13. Thinking, Inquiry, Problem Solving:
   (a) Make up a word problem that you can solve using a linear system with a
   solution of (5, 35).
   (b) Ask a classmate to solve the problem, then check his or her work. If the
   solution is incorrect, write suggestions explaining how to correct it.

14. As the owner of a banquet hall, you are in charge of catering a reception. There
   are two dinners: a chicken dish that costs $16 and a beef dish that costs $18.
   The 300 wedding guests have ordered their meals in advance, and the total cost
   to prepare the dinner is $5256. How many of each type of type of dinner are
   you preparing?

15. The student council made $750 from a dance. They put part of the $750 in a
   savings account that earns 4% interest and the rest in a chequing account that
   pays 2%. If the total interest for a year was $27, how much was put in each
   account?

16. At a silversmith's shop, they have alloys that contain 40% silver and others that
   are 50% silver. A custom order for a bracelet requires 150 g of 44% silver.
   How much of each alloy should be melted together to make the bracelet?

17. During a training exercise, a submarine
   travels 16 km/h on the surface, but it
   goes only 10 km/h underwater. If the
   submarine travelled a distance of 160
   km in 12.5 h, how long was it
   underwater?

18. Each spring, the conservation authority
   stocks the local lake with 10 000 bass
   and perch. If there were three times as
   many bass and twice as many perch, the total number of fish would be 22 000.
   How many of each type of fish make up the 10 000?

19. Use elimination to solve the linear systems you developed for questions 17 to 22
   in the Practise, Apply, Solve 1.1 on page 52.

20. Check Your Understanding: When you solve a system of equations by elimination, you have to decide whether to eliminate a variable by adding the two equations together or by subtracting them. Explain how you make this decision.

C

21. Solve for x and y. Both variables must satisfy the equations $3^{(3(x+2y)-2(x-2y)-y)} = 81$ and $9^{((2x+y)-(x+2y))} = 243$.

22. The solution to this system of equations is $(-2, 1)$. Find the values of p and q.
$$px + (9 - q)y = -10$$
$$(3p + 1) - (q - 6)y = -21$$

23. Amy ran part of a 42 km marathon at an average speed of 10 km/h and walked the rest at an average speed of 6 km/h. She spent 1 h more time running than walking. How long did it take her to finish the marathon?

24. The sum of the digits of a two-digit number is 9. If the number is doubled, then decreased by 36, the answer is the original number with the digits reversed. Find the number.

25. The general system of linear equations is
$$ax + by = e$$
$$cx + dy = f$$
The symbols a, b, c, d, e, and f represent constant values. Using elimination, develop a formula to solve the system for x and y in terms of the other variables. Are there any restrictions on the possible values of a, b, c, d, e, and f?

The Chapter Problem—Controlling Traffic

In this section, you used elimination to solve linear systems. Apply what you learned to answer these questions about the chapter problem on page 42.

1. Using the equation of your line of best fit for the data for the red light and the equation in Greenshield's formula, determine the coordinates of the point of intersection by elimination.

2. Which algebraic method allowed you to find the point of intersection more easily, elimination or substitution?

3. How long should the light stay green? red?

Linear Regression 1.10
Using the TI-83 Plus Calculator

One reason that data is collected is so that it can be used to make predictions about future events. Data that is collected by observation does not always fit an exact linear pattern. But even so, it is often possible to use a linear model to represent data that has a strong correlation. A line of best fit is often drawn on a scatter plot to represent the relationship. This line makes it easier to make predictions.

Graphing calculators can be used to create a scatter plot and draw a line of best fit. The graphing calculator determines the equation of the line of best fit using **linear regression**.

Creating a Scatter Plot

The coach of a soccer team wants to know the relationship between the number of shots his team takes during a game and the number of goals they score. He collected the following data from the last few games.

Soccer Scoring Statistics

Shots	11	20	24	28	27	33	17	38
Goals	1	2	0	3	2	3	1	4

1. **Enter the data into lists.**
   On the TI-83 Plus calculator, the data must be entered into a list. To start, press $\boxed{\text{STAT}}$ $\boxed{\text{ENTER}}$. Move the cursor to the first position in L1 and enter the values for shots. **Press $\boxed{\text{ENTER}}$ after each value.** Repeat this for goals in L2.

step 1

2. **Create the scatter plot by turning on the stat plots.**
   To create a scatter plot, press $\boxed{\text{2nd}}$ $\boxed{\text{Y=}}$ and $\boxed{1}$ $\boxed{\text{ENTER}}$. Turn on Plot1 by making sure the cursor is over **On**, the Type is set to the graph type you prefer, and L1 and L2 appear after Xlist and Ylist.

step 2

3. Display the graph.

Press ZOOM 9 to activate 9:Zoom Stat .

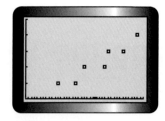

step 3

Drawing The Line of Best Fit

4. Draw the linear regression line.

Superimpose a line of best fit on the scatterplot by pressing STAT and moving the cursor over to CALC and pressing 4. This activates the linear regression function.

step 4

5. Identify the data to which the linear regression functions is applied.

Enter the lists separated by a comma.
Press 2nd 1 , 2nd 2 , VARS .
Scroll over to Y-VARS and press 1 then 1.
This stores the equation of the line of best fit into Y1 in the equation editor.

step 5

6. Display the results of the linear regression analysis.

Press ENTER to execute.
Note: If the correlation coefficient, r, is not displayed, turn on the diagnostics function. To do this, press 2nd 0. Press x^{-1} and scroll down to DiagnosticOn .
Press ENTER twice. Repeat steps 4 and 5.

step 6

7. Plot the line.

Press GRAPH to view the line.

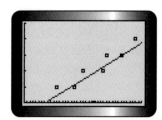

step 7

Analyzing the Equation

In this case, the equation of the line is
$y = 0.114\,769\,520\,2x - 0.840\,545\,625\,6$.

- a is the slope of the line

- b is the y-intercept

- r^2 indicates the percentage of data
  that is explained by the model

- r is the correlation coefficient, which indicates how well the model fits the data

Practise 1.10

For each set of data, determine the equation of the line of best fit using linear regression on a graphing calculator. Describe how well the model fits the data.

(a)

x	0	1	2	3	4	5	6	7	8	9	10
y	5	9	13	17	21	28	30	32	34	40	41

(b)

x	2	3	2	5	6	7	8	8	9	10	13
y	1	1	2	4	7	5	9	11	10	12	16

(c)

x	5	10	15	20	25	30	35	40	45	50	55
y	13	26	39	52	65	78	91	104	117	130	143

(d) Olympics Women's 100 m Freestyle Swimming

Year	1952	1956	1960	1964	1968	1972	1976	1980	1984	1988	1992
Time (s)	66.8	62.0	61.2	59.5	60.0	58.6	55.7	54.8	55.9	54.9	54.6

(e) Varsity Football Home Game Attendance

Game	1	2	3	4	5	6	7
Attendance	223	287	412	634	587	986	1178

(f) Live Bacteria Counts

Temperature (°C)	20	22	24	26	28	30	32	34	36
Bacteria (000s)	2.1	4.3	5.2	6.1	6.8	7.6	10.3	8.2	14.1

1.11 Modelling Using Linear Systems

Two Experts Say Women Who Run May Overtake Men

If women's running performance continues to improve at the rate at which it has soared since the 1920s, the top women will soon be running as swiftly as the best men, and may even outrun them someday, two physiologist say.

The researchers suggest that elite female runners have been getting so much faster at such a rapid pace that they should be running marathons as quickly as men by 1998, and other shorter track events before the middle of the next century.

These startling predictions are based on a new statistical analysis that compares trends in men's and women's world records over the past 70 years and projects those patterns into the future. The researchers, Dr. Brian J. Whipp and Dr. Susan A. Ward of the University of California at Los Angeles, published their conclusions in the current issue of the British journal Nature.

Other experts dismissed the predictions. "I wonder why they're even bothering to do this," said Dr. Peter Snell, an exercise physiologist at the University of Texas Health Sciences Center in Dallas. "I'd agree that there's a way to go yet in women's performance, but if they're suggesting that women will approach men, that's ludicrous."

The *New York Times*, **January 7, 1992**

Think, Do, Discuss

1. Read the article about men's and women's running performance. Who do you think is right, the researchers or the exercise physiologist? Explain your reasoning.

2. Test the data to see if the researchers' claim is valid. On a TI-83 Plus calculator, enter the men's data into a list. Enter the years in L1 and the times in L2.

3. Create a scatter plot. Find the linear regression equation for the line of best fit. How well does the model fit the data? Explain.

4. Graph the line of best fit.

5. Bring up the lists you have created and enter the women's times into L3.

Winning Times in the Men's and Women's 200 m Olympic Sprint

Year	Men's (s)	Women's (s)
1948	21.1	24.4
1952	20.7	23.7
1956	20.6	23.4
1960	20.5	24.0
1964	20.3	23.0
1968	19.83	22.5
1972	20.00	22.40
1976	20.23	22.37
1980	20.19	22.03
1984	19.80	21.81
1988	19.75	21.34
1992	19.73	21.72
1996	19.32	22.12

6. Create a scatter plot for the women's data. (You will need to turn on the second stat plot (Plot2) and make sure that L1 and L3 are plotted. Choose a different symbol to represent the points of this scatter plot.)

7. Find the linear regression equation for this line of best fit. Remember that you are using L1 and L3. How well does the model fit the women's data?

8. Graph the line of best fit for the women's data. Store the linear regression equation in Y2=.

9. Determine the point where the lines of best fit intersect. What do the coordinates of this point mean in terms of this situation?

10. How confident are you that your model will accurately predict the date when women's times in the 200 m sprint will equal the men's times? Explain.

Focus 1.11

Key Ideas

- You can use graphing technology to find and graph an equation for the line of best fit. This is called the **linear regression equation.**

- The linear regression line is calculated algebraically to be the *best* line of best fit.

- The linear regression equation is stated in the form $y = ax + b$, where a is the slope of the line of best fit and b is the y-intercept.

- The correlation coefficient, r, is a measure of the goodness of fit of the line to the data. The value of r is 1 if the regression line fits the data exactly and has a positive slope. The value of r is -1 if the line fits the data exactly and has a negative slope.

- You can use a linear regression equation to predict values for the relation represented by the data. The accuracy of the predictions depends on how well the line fits the data.

For example, the screen capture below shows a scatter plot of the data in the table.

x	y
12	8
15	21
4	19
35	37
41	28
48	45

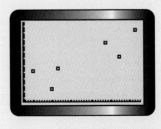

This screen capture shows the linear regression equation for the data. It was obtained using the calculator's LinReg function. The value of *r* is positive, so the line has a positive slope. Also, the value of r is close to 1, so the equation fits the data well. You can expect that a prediction based on this line will be reasonable.

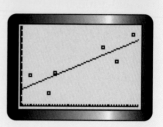

Here, the linear regression equation has been plotted on the same axes as the scatter plot.

- If two sets of data can be represented by linear models, the point of intersection between these data sets can be found using the linear regression equations. Once the equations are known, solve the system of equations using substitution or elimination. Or use the calculator to find the solution. Rounding off the values of *a* and *b* in the regression equations will affect the accuracy of all calculations.

Example

The table shows the average earnings of male and female workers in Canada since 1982.

(a) Use the data to predict when women's earnings will equal men's earnings.

(b) How confident are you that this prediction will come true?

	Average Annual Earnings (1976 $)	
Year	Men	Women
1982	30 969	17 051
1983	31 160	17 207
1984	30 581	17 596
1985	31 311	17 637
1986	31 746	18 248
1987	32 037	18 523
1988	32 842	18 884
1989	32 913	19 445
1990	32 517	19 459
1991	31 619	19 458
1992	31 516	20 133
1993	30 872	19 865
1994	32 255	20 086
1995	31 527	20 528
1996	32 248	20 902

Source: Statistics Canada

Solution

Use a graphing calculator to generate two linear models and find the point of intersection.

1. Enter the data into a list.
   Enter the years in L1, the men's earnings in L2, and the women's earnings in L3. Press STAT ENTER and enter the data.

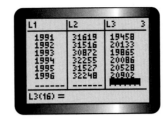

step 1

2. **(a)** Create a scatter plot for the men's data using L1 and L2 and STAT Plot1. To do this press 2nd Y= ENTER ENTER followed by ZOOM 9.
   (b) To find the linear regression equation and the correlation coefficient, press STAT ▶ 4 2nd 1 , 2nd 2 , VARS ▶ 1 1 ENTER. To see the line, press GRAPH.

step 2(a)

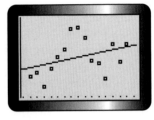

step 2(b)

3. **(a)** Create a scatter plot for the women's data using L1 and L3 and STAT Plot2. Determine the linear regression equation. Use the same keystrokes as above, substituting L3 for L2. Be sure to enter the resulting equation in Y2 =.
   (b) Press GRAPH.

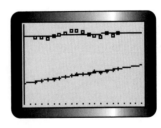

step 3(a)

step 3(b)

4. Zoom out to see the point of intersection, then use the calculator to identify its coordinates.

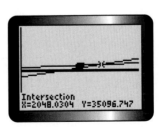

step 4

According to our model, the women's and men's average annual salaries will be equal in the year 2048. The salary will be $35 097.

Note that the data for women's earnings is modelled very closely by a linear relationship ($r = 0.986$), while the men's data is not ($r = 0.356$). Based on this observation, which prediction would you expect to be more accurate over a long period of time?

Practise, Apply, Solve 1.11

A

1. **(a)** Use the data for the average salaries of male and female workers in Canada (see page 110) to create a hand-drawn scatter plot. Graph both sets of data on the same axes. Use different markers for the men's and women's data.
   (b) Draw the line of best fit for the men's data. Repeat with a different colour for the women's data.
   (c) Using your graph, predict where the two lines will intersect.
   (d) Compare your answer to the linear regression result in the example. How close is your answer?
   (e) If you have to make a prediction about where two linear relationships will meet, what is the best method to use—a hand-drawn scatter plot or one created using linear regression?
   (f) Discuss the advantages and disadvantages of the two methods.

2. Each of **(a)**, **(b)**, **(c)**, and **(d)** show the correlation coefficients, r_1 and r_2, for two sets of data. For each situation, describe how confident you would be that the model can accurately predict where the two sets of data will intersect.

	r_1	r_2
(a)	0.856723	0.534721
(b)	0.453326	0.231666
(c)	0.953723	−0.934721
(d)	−0.756829	−0.126433

3. In **A** and **B**, a linear regression analysis has been done on two sets of data.
   (a) Use algebra to find the points of intersection of the lines of best fit. (Round all values to the nearest hundredth.)

A

Data Set 1	Data Set 2
LinReg	LinReg
y=ax+b	y=ax+b
a=−22.5	a=25.12
b=6.34	b=4.125
r^2=.72829156	r^2=.3119692775
r=.8534	r=.5585421

B

Data Set 1	Data Set 2
LinReg	LinReg
y=ax+b	y=ax+b
a=3.56	a=−4.2
b=3.4567	b=−5.234
r^2=.89562	r^2=.767801795
r=.9463720199	r=.876243

   (b) To verify your answers, use graphing technology to determine the points of intersection.
   (c) Discuss your confidence in the accuracy of the point of intersection in each case.

B

Use linear regression to find the line of best fit equations to answer these questions.

4. Use the data to predict when the number of females and males in this age group will be equal.

Population of Canada 15–24 Years Old (thousands)

Year	Male	Female
1901	543	530
1911	745	653
1921	757	761
1931	990	962
1941	1083	1069
1951	1070	1077
1961	1316	1301
1971	2016	1988
1981	2356	2303
1991	1944	1887
1998	2090	1994

Source: Statistics Canada

5. Application: Use the data to predict when or if the full-time enrollment in colleges will surpass the enrollment in universities. Why might this happen?

Full-time Enrollment in Canadian Post-Secondary Schools (thousands)

Year	Colleges	Universities
1971	173.8	323.0
1981	273.4	401.9
1991	349.1	554.0
1996	395.3	573.6
1997	396.7	573.0
1998	397.7	578.6

Source: Statistics Canada

6. This table compares the number of people living in urban and rural areas of Canada. *Urban* is defined as "a built-up area having a population of 1000 or more." *Rural* is everywhere outside an urban area. By what year did the majority of Canadians live in urban areas? Project the number of people in Canada living in urban and rural areas in 2011.

Urban vs. Rural Population of Canada (thousands)

Year	Urban	Rural
1871	722	2967
1881	1 110	3215
1891	1 537	3296
1901	2 014	3357
1911	3 273	3934
1921	4 352	4436
1931	5 469	4908
1941	6 271	5236
1951	8 817	5192
1961	12 700	5538
1971	16 410	5158
1981	18 436	5907
1991	20 907	6390

Source: Statistics Canada

Ottawa

7. Communication: Write a step-by-step description that explains how to predict where the point of intersection will occur for two given sets of data.

8. Today, many people watch movies at home on rented videos or pay-per-view TV. Using the data in the table, determine when equal numbers of Canadians had access to cable television and to a video cassette recorder (VCR).

Cable TV and VCRs in Canadian Households

Year	Cable TV	VCR
1980	54.8%	n/a
1985	62.5%	23.5%
1990	71.4%	66.3%
1996	74.0%	83.5%
1997	73.7%	84.7%

Source: Statistics Canada

9. It seems that there are more and more trucks on the highways every year.
  (a) Use this data to determine if this observation is correct.
  (b) What is the trend for commercial vehicles? For passenger vehicles?
  (c) Predict when the sales of new commercial vehicles will exceed the sales of passenger vehicles.

New Vehicle Sales in Canada

Year	Commercial Vehicles (000s)	Passenger Vehicles (000s)
1985	393	1135
1986	422	1102
1987	469	1061
1988	508	1056
1989	496	985
1990	433	885
1991	415	873
1992	429	798
1993	454	739
1994	511	749
1995	496	670
1996	544	661
1997	685	739
1998	688	741

Source: Statistics Canada

10. This table shows the winning times for the men's and women's 100 m Olympic sprint. Predict when the women's winning time will equal the men's.

Winning Times for 100 m Olympic Sprint (s)

Year	Men	Women
1928	10.8	12.2
1932	10.3	11.9
1936	10.3	11.5
1948	10.3	11.9
1952	10.4	11.5
1956	10.5	11.5
1960	10.2	11.0
1964	10.0	11.4
1968	9.95	11.0
1972	10.14	11.07
1976	10.06	11.08
1980	10.25	11.06
1984	9.99	10.97
1988	9.92	10.54
1992	9.96	10.82
1996	9.84	10.94

11. Do women spend more money on clothing than men?
   (a) Use this data to discuss the trend since 1993.
   (b) Will men ever spend more money on clothing than women? Explain your reasoning.

Spending on Clothing by Men and Women ($millions)

Year	Men	Women
1993	1730	3872
1994	1687	4127
1995	1623	4229
1996	1516	4203
1997	1570	4335
1998	1582	4406

Source: Statistics Canada

12. The average resale price of a house in Vancouver is higher than anywhere else in Canada. Use the table to predict when the average resale price of a house in Toronto will exceed the price in Vancouver.

Average Resale Price of a House in Toronto and Vancouver

Year	Toronto	Vancouver
1980	$75 621	$100 065
1985	109 094	112 852
1990	254 890	226 385
1995	203 028	307 747
1996	198 150	288 268
1997	211 307	287 094
1998	216 815	278 659

Source: Canadian Real Estate Association

13. Thinking, Inquiry, Problem Solving: Do some research on the Internet or in the newspaper to find two sets of data that can be represented by linear models. Compare the data to determine if a point of intersection will occur. What is the meaning of the point of intersection? Discuss how confident you are that your model can make an accurate prediction. Discuss any outside factors that may influence the trends in the data and cause your model to be inaccurate.

14. You are a criminologist studying rates of violent crime in different cities. As part of your research, you collect this data. What conclusions can you draw from this data? How reliable are your conclusions?

Violent Crimes per 100 000 Population

Year	Toronto	Calgary
1992	996	880
1993	1010	823
1994	962	832
1995	909	739
1996	873	769
1997	852	833
1998	836	849

Source: Uniform Crime Reporting Survey, Canadian Centre for Justice Statistics

15. In the article on page 108, researchers claim that women will be running marathons as quickly as men by 1998. Do some research on the Internet to determine the winning times in the Olympic marathon (men's and women's) to see if this claim is valid. Justify your answer with a statistical analysis of the data.

16. Knowledge and Understanding: Linear regression analysis can be used to make predictions about a set of data using the equation of the line of best fit. Will the predictions always be accurate or come true? Explain why or why not.

17. Check Your Understanding: Here is a sample screen from a calculator after a linear regression calculation. Explain the meaning of each letter on the display: x, y, a, b, r^2, and r.

```
LinReg
 y=ax+b
 a=56.85
 b=-81333.78333
 r²=.1269668696
 r=.3563241075
```

The Chapter Problem—Controlling Traffic

In this section you modelled linear systems and used linear regression. Apply what you learned to answer these questions on the chapter problem on page 42.

1. Use graphing technology to create a scatter plot of the data for the red light.

2. Determine the equation of the line of best fit using linear regression.

3. Graph the regression line and the line for Greenshield's formula on the same set of axes.

4. Determine the point of intersection using graphing technology.

5. In this chapter, you found the point of intersection in several different ways. As the traffic controller, which estimate would you use to set the times for the red light and the green light at the intersection? Explain.

6. How long will the light stay green? How many cars will be stopped for a red light?

Roberta Bondar, b. 1945

Astronauts conduct experiments in space, often involving relationships between time spent in space and the reaction of the human body. Roberta Bondar, the first Canadian woman to travel in space, conducted such experiments on the space shuttle *Discovery*. She was responsible for investigating how the nervous system adapts to weightlessness, whether humans expend more energy in space than on the ground, and for testing an anti-gravity suit. Do some research on the NASA Web site. What benefits do you think could result from her experience?

Using Linear Systems to Solve Problems
Check Your Understanding

1. How many equations do you need to solve a linear system with two unknowns?

2. How can you test whether an ordered pair is a solution to a linear system?

3. Describe the graph of a linear system that has many solutions.

4. Graph a linear system with **(a)** one solution and **(b)** no solution.

5. Explain what you must do first to solve a linear system using substitution.

6. Substitution and elimination both have one step in common. What is it?

7. What is the best way to solve a linear system when an approximate answer is good enough?

8. A scatter plot gives two linear relationships that do not intersect on your calculator display. For each image, explain how you would find the point of intersection.

(a)

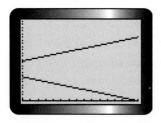

(b)

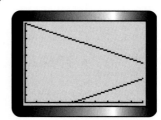

9. Suppose you have to find an exact solution to a linear system. Explain how you would decide whether to use substitution or elimination.

10. You are using elimination to solve a linear system. Explain how you would decide whether to add or subtract the two equations.

11. A flow chart is a set of steps that describes how to do something. Create a flow chart showing how to solve a linear system using elimination.

12. Can data always be represented by a linear model? Explain.

13. When you use linear regression, how can you decide whether a linear relationship is the best model to use?

14. Rank these methods of solving a linear system, from most effective to least effective. Give your reasons for ranking the first one first and the last one last.
    (a) graphing by hand   **(b)** elimination   **(c)** graphing with technology
    (d) substitution   **(e)** guess and test

1.1 Modelling with Linear Equations

- Many kinds of situations can be modelled using linear equation, such as manufacturing costs or economic trends.

- Often a problem involves two unknown quantities, which can be represented by two different variables. You may be able to write equations, using these variables, to represent the conditions described in the problem.

- When two or more equations are used to model a problem, it is called a **system of equations**. If all the equations are linear, it is called a **linear system**.

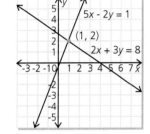

- A linear system in two unknowns consists of two or more linear equations involving two variables. For example,

$$2x + 3y = 8$$
$$5x - 2y = 1$$

- A solution to a linear system is an ordered pair (x, y) that satisfies *all* the equations in the system. For example, $(1, 2)$ is a solution to the linear system defined above, since $2(1) + 3(2) = 8$ and $5(1) - 2(2) = 1$.

- Sometimes you can use guess-and-check to find the solution to a linear system, but it only works for very simple problems.

Example

John bought corn seed at \$8 per sack and clover seed at \$12 per sack. In total he bought 470 sacks of seed. His total bill was \$4260. Model this situation with a linear system.

Solution

Let x represent the number of sacks of corn John bought. Let y represent the number of sacks of clover he bought.

$$x + y = 470 \qquad \text{represents the total number of sacks}$$
$$8x + 12y = 4260 \qquad \text{represents the total cost}$$

Extra Practice

1. Is $(2, 3)$ the solution to the linear system defined by

$$y = 3x - 3$$
$$2x + 4y = 16$$

2. Model each situation using a linear system. Do not solve the system of equations.
   (a) David works part-time for a bike repair shop. He earns $1 for each tire he installs and $4 for each gear mechanism he assembles. If he did a total of 50 installations and assemblies and earned $92, how many tires did he install?
   (b) A car rental agency rents cars under two plans:
   Plan 1: $55 per day and $0.10/km
   Plan 2: $40 per day and $0.25/km
   Determine when both plans will result in the same charge for a one-day rental.
   (c) From Vancouver International Airport a Piper Cub took off 2 h before a jet. The Piper Cub accidentally flew on the same course as the jet. The jet travelled 190 km/h faster than the other plane. If the jet caught up with the Piper Cub 3 h later, how far had the planes travelled?
   (d) The cost of running a car in the city is $0.42/km. The cost is $0.33/km on the highway. In one month, Cheryl drove 1200 km and the total cost was $457.02. How many kilometres did she drive in the city?

1.2–1.3 Solving Linear Systems: Graphing by Hand

- A **linear system** can be solved by graphing. The equations can be graphed on the same graph. The point, or points, of intersection of the lines represent the solution to the linear system.

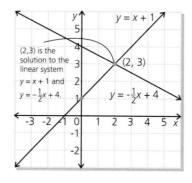

- With a hand-drawn graph, you may not be able to find the exact solution to a linear system. This is especially difficult when the point of intersection does not fall on one of the grid lines of the graph paper.

Example

Solve this linear system graphically.

$$y = -2x + 3$$
$$y = 4x - 3$$

Solution

Draw the lines for both equations on the same graph, using a separate table of values for each equation.

$y = -2x + 3$:

x	y
0	3
1	1
2	−1
3	−3

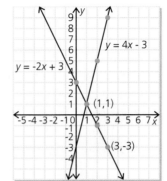

$y = 4x - 3$:

x	y
0	−3
1	1
2	5
3	9

The point of intersection represents the solution to the linear system. The ordered pair (1, 1) (and no other ordered pair) satisfies both equations. The solution to the linear system is (1, 1).

Extra Practice

3. Solve each system of equations graphically.

   (a) $x + y = 2$
       $x = 2y + 2$

   (b) $y - x = 1$
       $2x - y = 1$

   (c) $-3x + y = 10$
       $-x + y = -2$

4. Determine the point of intersection.

   (a) $y = 4x + 6$ and $y = -x + 1$

   (b) $2x + 5y = 10$ and $x = 10$

5. Emmitt has $300 in his savings account and plans to save $20 every two weeks from his paycheque. Denitra has only $175 in her account, but can save $35 every two weeks from her paycheque.

   (a) Model this situation using a linear system.

   (b) Solve the system by graphing.

   (c) What does the point of intersection mean in this situation?

1.4–1.5 Investigating the Ways That Two Lines Can Intersect

- A linear equation must be entered in the form $y = mx + b$ to be graphed on a graphing calculator.

- A linear system can have no solution, one solution, or an infinite number of solutions.

- The equations in a linear system provide information that helps determine the number of solutions that are possible.

  - In a linear system with **no solution**, the two linear equations have the *same slope* and *different y-intercepts*.

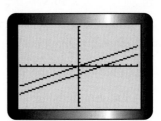

  - In a linear system with **one solution**, the two linear equations have *different slopes*. The *y*-intercepts have no influence.

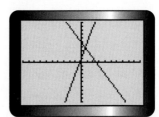

  - In a linear system with **an infinite number of solutions**, the two linear equations have the *same slope* and the *same y-intercept*.

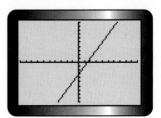

Example

Without graphing, determine the number of solutions to the linear system defined by

$$2x + 5y = 10$$
$$3x + y = 6$$

Solution

The number of solutions can be determined by comparing the slope and y-intercept of both lines. To do this, both equations must be expressed in the form $y = mx + b$.

$$2x + 5y = 10 \qquad\qquad\qquad 3x + y = 6$$
$$5y = -2x + 10 \qquad\qquad\qquad y = -3x + 6$$
$$\frac{5y}{5} = \frac{-2x + 10}{5}$$
$$y = -\frac{2}{5}x + 2$$

The two lines have the different slopes of $-\frac{2}{5}$ and -3. Both lines have different y-intercepts of 2 and 6. The two equations represent different lines. In this case, there is only one point of intersection.

Extra Practice

6. Without graphing. determine if the linear system has zero, one, or many solutions.

(a) $y = x + 5$ (b) $4x - y = -3$ (c) $y = -x + 4$
     $y = x - 1$ $2x - y = -1$ $3y = -3x + 12$

7. The Grain Co-op pays farmers \$5.50 per bushel of soybeans, less a \$35 processing fee. Soybean Storage Inc. charges a \$25 fee and pays \$5.50 per bushel.
(a) Model this situation using a linear system.
(b) How many bushels of soybeans must a farmer sell before the payment from the Grain Co-op exceeds the cost to use Soybean Storage Inc.? Explain.

8. One of the equations of a linear system that has an infinite number of solutions is $2x = y + 4$.
(a) Determine an equation for another line in the system.
(b) Determine three ordered pairs that would satisfy both equations.

9. A linear system has the ordered pair $(1, 5)$ as its solution. Determine a pair of equations that would represent this linear system.

10. Draw a graphical model that represents a linear system with
(a) no solution
(b) one solution
(c) exactly four solutions

1.6–1.7 Solving a Linear System Using Graphing Technology

- Graphing technology can be used to draw graphs of linear systems more quickly, with less effort, and with more accuracy than by hand.

- Graphing technology can give a better approximation of the point of intersection of a pair of linear equations than a hand-drawn graph.

- Graphing technology can be used to determine a very close approximation to the exact point of intersection of a pair of linear equations.

- When a linear system problem involves large numbers, the graphical solution found using technology will be more accurate than one found using a hand-drawn graph. For example, this screen shows that the equations $y = 3000x + 35\ 000$ and $y = 5000x + 10\ 000$ intersect at $(12.5, 72\ 500)$.

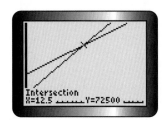

- Even though graphing technology provides a fast and accurate method for determining points of intersection, it is not always available. Other methods that do not rely on the use of technology must often be used.

Example

The city of Thunder Bay recycles cardboard. It rents a baler to package the cardboard, which it sells to paper companies. The bailing machine costs $330 per month to lease; wire for the machine costs $4.20/t of cardboard; and labour costs are $32.50/t. The city sells the baled cardboard for $42/t. What is the break-even point?

Solution

Let t represent the number of tonnes of cardboard that are recycled in one month. Let c represent the cost or revenue for the month.

The expenses are represented by the equation

$$c = 330 + 4.2t + 32.5t$$

or $\quad c = 36.7t + 330 \qquad$ represents the expenses

$\qquad c = 42t \qquad$ represents the revenue

The break-even point is the point where expenses equal revenue.

1. Both lines can be graphed on the
   TI-83 Plus calculator. Enter the equations as shown.

step 1

2. To find the point of intersection visually,
   zoom out and adjust the window, as shown.

step 2

3. Now use the intersect operation on the
   CALCULATE menu to find the point of
   intersection. Press [2nd] [TRACE] [5]. The result
   of completing the operation is shown.

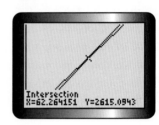

step 3

The point of intersection is approximately (62.26, 2615.09). This means that for the
city to break even, it must collect and sell 62.26 t of cardboard a month. If more
cardboard is sold, there will be a profit; if less is sold, there will be a loss.

Extra Practice

Solve each linear system. Use graphing technology.

11. (a) $2x + y = 2$ **(b)** $y - 2x = -3$ **(c)** $N = 1500 + 20t$
         $y = x - 1$ $y + 5 = 3x$ $N = -20 + 40t$

12. The Sports Shop sells Venus running shoes for $82 a pair and Extreme court
shoes for $95 a pair. One day, the Sports Shop sells 75 pairs of Venus and
Extreme shoes for $6241. How many pairs of each shoe were sold?

13. A rectangle with a perimeter of 180 cm is four times longer than it is wide.
What are its dimensions?

14. Fraser's Plumbing charges $50 for a service call, plus $40/h for labour. Gus's
Plumbing charges $30 for a service call, plus $45/h for labour.
(a) When do both companies charge the same?
(b) Which company would you hire for a repair lasting 5 h?

15. Solve the system.

$$2(x + 1) + 3(y - 3) - 4y + 4 = -5$$
$$4(2x + y) - 3(x + y) - x = 5$$

1.8 Solving a Linear System Using Algebra: Substitution

- Algebraic methods for solving a linear system give exact solutions. Graphing techniques can be used when an exact answer is not necessary.

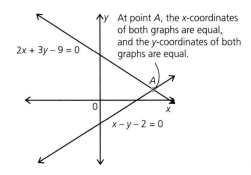

$2x + 3y - 9 = 0$

$x - y - 2 = 0$

At point A, the x-coordinates of both graphs are equal, and the y-coordinates of both graphs are equal.

- At the point where two graphs intersect, the x-coordinates for both graphs are equal, and the y-coordinates are equal. The method of substitution uses this relationship to replace one variable in terms of another. This results in one equation, with one unknown, that can be solved.

- To solve a linear system using substitution, follow these steps:

  1. Choose one of the equations and isolate one of its variables by expressing that variable in terms of the other.

For instance, to solve the equations in the graph above,

Step 1: Examine the equations for a variable that is easy to isolate.

$$2x + 3y - 9 = 0 \qquad ①$$
$$x - y - 2 = 0 \qquad ②$$

It looks easier to isolate x in equation ②.

$$x - y - 2 = 0 \qquad ②$$
$$x = y + 2$$

  2. Substitute the expression that you have determined in place of the corresponding variable in the other equation.

Step 2: Substitute this expression for x in equation ①.

$$2x + 3y - 9 = 0 \qquad ①$$
$$2(y + 2) + 3y - 9 = 0$$

3. Solve the new equation.

Step 3: Solve for y.

$$2(y + 2) + 3y - 9 = 0$$
$$2y + 4 + 3y - 9 = 0$$
$$2y + 3y = 9 - 4$$
$$5y = 5$$
$$y = 1$$

4. To find the value of the other variable, substitute the number you found into one of the original equations and solve.

Step 4: Substitute this value into equation ② and solve for x.

$$x - y - 2 = 0 \qquad ②$$
$$x - 1 - 2 = 0$$
$$x = 3$$

5. Verify that the ordered pair you determined works in both equations by replacing the variables with the numbers you found in **both** equations.

Step 5: Verify the solution $(3, 1)$ satisfies both equations.

Equation ①		Equation ②	
L.S.	R.S.	L.S.	R.S.
$2x + 3y - 9$	0	$x - y - 2$	0
$= 2(3) + 3(1) - 9$		$= 3 - 1 - 2$	
$= 6 + 3 - 9$		$= 0$	
$= 0$		L.S. = R.S.	
L.S. = R.S.			

- When using substitution, always look for a variable that is easy to solve for in one of the equations. This will ensure that the solution process will be as simple as possible.

The solution $(3, 1)$ does satisfy both equations.

Example

Two cruise ships are sailing toward each other from Caribbean islands that are 264 km apart. One ship travels 4 km faster than the other. If they both started at the same time, and meet after 6 h, how fast is each ship travelling?

Solution

Let x represent the speed of the slower ship. Let y represent the speed of the faster ship.

	Speed (m/h)	Time (h)	Distance (km)
Slower ship	x	6	x
Faster ship	y	6	$6y$

$$6x + 6y = 264 \qquad ① \qquad \text{represents the total distance}$$
$$y = x + 4 \qquad ② \qquad \text{represents speed relationship}$$

The variable y is already isolated in equation ②. Substitute the expression $x + 4$ into equation ①.

$$6x + 6y = 264$$
$$6x + 6(x + 4) = 264$$
$$6x + 6x + 24 = 264$$
$$12x = 264 - 24$$
$$12x = 240$$
$$x = \frac{240}{12}$$
$$x = 20$$

To find y, let $x = 20$.
$$y = x + 4$$
$$y = 20 + 4$$
$$y = 24$$

The slower ship travels at 20 km/h and the faster ship travels at 24 km/h.

Extra Practice

16. Solve each linear system by substitution.

(a) $x + 2y = 6$
  $4x + 3y = 4$

(b) $x + 5y = 11$
  $4x - y = 2$

(c) $x - 7 = y$
  $\frac{1}{4}x - 1 = y$

17. Solve each linear system by substitution.

(a) $2(2x - 1) - (y - 4) = 11$
  $3(1 - x) - 2(y - 3) = -7$

(b) $\frac{(x - 1)}{3} - \frac{2(y - 2)}{2} = 11$
  $2x - y = 16$

18. The sum of Louise's age and Todd's age is 34 years. Five years ago, the sum of twice Louise's age and three times Todd's age was 61 years. How old are they now?

19. Kelly invested her savings of $4800. She invested part in mutual funds, at 9% per year, and the rest in GICs, at 10% per year. At the end of the year, the interest from the mutual funds investment was $43 less than the interest from the GIC investment. How much was invested in each type of investment?

20. A hovercraft travels over flat land at 40 km/h and over rough water at 10 km/h. If it takes 5.75 h to travel 185 km, then how far did it travel over
(a) land?   (b) water?

1.9 Solving a Linear System Using Algebra: Elimination

- If the coefficients of the same variable in both equations have the same value or the opposite value, you can eliminate that variable in a two-variable linear system by adding or subtracting the equations. The result is a new equation with one variable that can be solved directly. When you add or subtract equations to eliminate a variable, the coefficients of the selected variable must be the same in both equations (although they may have opposite signs). To achieve this, you can multiply all the terms of an equation by the same number.

- When the coefficients of a variable are exactly the same, subtract the two equations to eliminate the variable.

- When the coefficients have the same value but opposite signs, add the two equations to eliminate the variable.

- To solve a linear system using elimination, follow these steps.

  1. Express both equations in the form $ax + by = c$.

  2. Choose a variable to eliminate. Multiply each equation by a number that gives the same or opposite coefficients for that variable in both equations.

  3. Add or subtract like terms in the equation to eliminate the chosen variable.

  4. Solve the resulting equation for the remaining variable.

For example, to solve the linear system

$$3x + 2y - 13 = 0 \quad ①$$
$$-2x + 4y - 2 = 0 \quad ②$$

Step 1: Express both equations in $ax + by = c$ form.

$$3x + 2y = 13 \quad ③$$
$$-2x + 4y = 2 \quad ④$$

Step 2: Multiply equation ③ by 2 so that the coefficient of y is the same in both equations.

$$6x + 4y = 26 \quad ③ \times 2$$
$$2x + 4y = 2 \quad ④$$

Step 3: Subtract equation ④ to eliminate the y variable.

$$
\begin{array}{ll}
6x + 4y = 26 & ③ \times 2 \\
-2x + 4y = 2 & ④ \\
\hline
8x = 24 &
\end{array}
$$

Step 4: Solve for x.

$$8x = 24$$
$$x = \frac{24}{8}$$
$$x = 3$$

5. Determine the value of the other variable by substituting the solved value of the now known variable into one of the other equations.

Step 5: Substitute this value into equation ③ and solve for y.

$$3x + 2y = 13 \qquad ③$$
$$3(3) + 2y = 13$$
$$2y = 13 - 9$$
$$2y = 4$$
$$y = 2$$

6. Verify your solution in the original equations.

Step 6: Verify the solution (3, 2) satisfies both equations.

Equation ①		Equation ②	
L.S.	R.S.	L.S.	R.S.
$3x + 2y - 13$	0	$-2x + 4y - 2$	0
$= 3(3) + 2(2) - 13$		$= -2(3) + 4(2) - 2$	
$= 9 + 4 - 13$		$= -6 + 8 - 2$	
$= 0$		$= 0$	
L.S. = R.S.		L.S. = R.S.	

The solution (3, 2) does satisfy both original equations.

Example

In a laboratory, only 40% and 50% alcohol solutions were available. For an experiment, Charmine must use alcohol with a concentration of 45%. If 200 L of the solution are needed, how many litres of each solution should be mixed?

Solution

Let x represent the number of litres of the 40% solution. Let y represent the number of litres of the 50% solution.

$$x + y = 200 \qquad \text{represents the total amount needed}$$
$$0.4x + 0.5y = 0.45(200)$$
or $\quad 0.4x + 0.5y = 90 \qquad \text{represents the concentration of alcohol}$

This system can be solved by elimination.

Multiply $(x + y = 200)$ by 4. $\rightarrow 4x + 4y = 800$

Multiply $(0.4x + 0.5y = 90)$ by 4. $\rightarrow \underline{4x + 5y = 900} \qquad$ Subtract to eliminate x.

$$-y = -100 \quad \text{Solve for } y.$$
$$y = 100$$

To find x, substitute $y = 100$.

$$x + y = 200$$
$$x + 100 = 200$$
$$x = 100$$

To make the required solution, 100 L of each type must be mixed together.

Extra Practice

21. Solve each linear system by elimination.

(a) $3x + y = 5$
$x - 2y = 11$

(b) $3x - 2y = -8$
$y - 7 = 3x$

(c) $3a + b = 12$
$2a + 5b = 21$

22. Solve each linear system by elimination.

(a) $\frac{1}{2}x + \frac{1}{3}y = \frac{5}{6}$
$\frac{1}{2}y + \frac{3}{4}x = \frac{5}{4}$

(b) $1.2x + 2.4y = -36$
$3.2x + 2.4y = 64$

(c) $2x + \frac{4y + 3}{2} = 2$
$\frac{3x + 1}{3} = y + \frac{5}{4}$

23. In a white water relay race, one kayak team averaged 26 km/h downstream but only 6 km/h upstream in the white water course. What was the rate of the kayak in still water? What was the rate of the current?

24. Joshua earns extra money by typing papers and reports. He estimates that his cost for supplies is about $1.50/h. He decides to invest in a new computer that sells for $750. If he charges $15/h for typing, how long will it take him to break even?

25. Marcia, a lab technician, needs three litres of an 8% saline solution. She has a 5% saline solution and a 9% solution in the lab stock room. How many litres of the 5% and 9% solution should she mix together?

1.10–1.11 Modelling Using Linear Systems——

- You can use graphing technology to find and graph an equation for the line of best fit. This is called the **linear regression equation**.

- The linear regression line is calculated algebraically to be the *best* line of best fit.

- The linear regression equation is stated in the form $y = ax + b$, where a is the slope of the line of best fit and b is the y-intercept.

- The correlation coefficient, r, is a measure of the goodness of fit of the line to the data. The value of r is 1 if the regression line fits the data exactly and has a positive slope. The value of r is -1 if the line fits the data exactly and has a negative slope.

- You can use a linear regression equation to predict values for the relation represented by the data. The accuracy of the predictions depends on how well the line fits the data.

For example, the following screen capture show a scatter plot of this data on a TI-83 Plus calculator:

x	y
12	8
15	21
4	19
35	37
41	28
48	45

This screen capture shows the linear regression equation for the data. It was obtained using the calculator's LinReg function. The value of r is positive, so the line has a positive slope. Also, the value of r is close to 1, so the equation fits the data well. You can expect that a prediction based on this line will be reasonable.

Here, the linear regression equation has ben plotted on the same axes as the scatter plot.

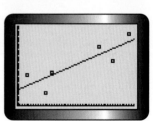

- If two sets of data can be represented by linear models, the point of intersection between these data sets can be found using the linear regression equations. Once the equations are known, solve the system of equations using substitution or elimination. Or use the calculator to find the solution. Rounding off the values of a and b in the regression equations will affect the accuracy of all calculations.

Example

Using this data, predict when the population of London, Ontario, was the same as the population of Kitchener, Ontario. Which city is growing at a faster rate?

Year	London (000s)	Kitchener (000s)
1966	207 396	192 275
1976	270 383	272 158
1986	342 302	311 195
1996	398 616	382 940
1998	418 180	409 520

Solution

Create a scatter plot and draw the lines of best fit using the linear regression feature on the TI-83 Plus calculator.

1. Enter the data into a list.

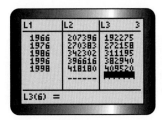

step 1

2. Create a scatter plot for L1 and L2.

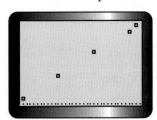

step 2

3. Use linear regression to draw the line of best fit.

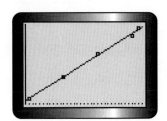

step 3

4. Repeat steps 2 and 3 for L1 and L3.

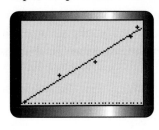

step 4

5. Zoom out and locate the point of intersection.

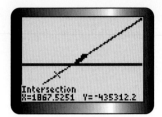

step 5

From the model for this data, we see that the point of intersection occurs at a point where the value of y is negative. This is not possible, since y represents the population at any given time. This model predicts that the population of London and Kitchener were never equal. The model also predicts that they will never be equal in the future, since London is growing at a faster rate. (The top line is London, the lower line is Kitchener.)

Extra Practice

26. This data projects the populations of Canada and Italy through 2000 to 2030.

Year	Canada (000s)	Italy (000s)
2000	30 679	57 194
2030	36 633	50 109

Source: **World Population Prospects: The 1996 Revision, Population Division of The United Nations**

(a) Assume the data is linear. Create a scatter plot of the data and determine the linear regression equation of the lines of best fit.
(b) At what rate is the population of Canada increasing?
(c) At what rate is the population of Italy decreasing?
(d) Using this model, predict the year when the two countries' populations will be equal.
(e) How sure can you be that the assumption in (a) is reasonable?

27. This table compares the revenue generated by local phone calls and long distance calls in Canada. Perform a linear regression analysis of the data to determine when the revenue generated from local calls exceeded the revenue generated from long distance.

Year	Local ($ millions)	Long Distance ($ millions)
1990	4906	7143
1991	5137	7006
1992	5430	6915
1993	5827	6495
1994	6216	6475
1995	6647	5983
1996	6391	5483
1997	7080	5391
1998	8118	4793

Source: Statistics Canada

Chapter 1 Summary

In this chapter, you saw that many situations can be modelled by a system of linear equations. The solution to a linear system is the ordered pair, or set of ordered pairs, that satisfies all the equations that are being considered. In most cases, the linear systems you examined dealt with two equations and two unknowns.

You also learned three basic methods for solving a system of linear equations.

- You can graph both equations and look for the point of intersection. This can be done by hand or using graphing technology.

- You can solve for a variable in one equation and substitute the resulting expression in the other equation.

- You can add or subtract a multiple of one equation to the other equation.

Algebraic techniques allow you to calculate the solution accurately, whereas graphing tends to be less accurate. You also saw that data sets can be represented and compared using a model called linear regression. This allows you to make predictions about how the data is related.

You should become skilled at all the methods of solving a linear system developed in this chapter. Choosing the most appropriate method to solve a particular problem is part of becoming a good problem solver.

Using Linear Systems to Solve Problems

1. **(a)** Determine graphically the point of intersection between the lines defined by
   $y = -2x + 6$ and $8 = 5x - y$.
   (b) Verify that you determined the correct point by solving the system of
   equations in part **(a)** algebraically.

2. Solve by substitution.
   (a) $3x + y = 5$
   $x - 2y = 11$
   (b) $5x - 2y = -16$
   $-2x + y = 7$
   (c) $4x - 3y = 10$
   $2x + 3y = 4$

3. Solve by elimination.
   (a) $a - 15b = 3$
   $3b + a = 21$
   (b) $2x + 5y = 19$
   $3x - y = 3$
   (c) $3x - 2y = -8$
   $3y - 21 = 9x$

4. Confirm or deny: The ordered pair $(3, -5)$ is the solution to the linear system
   defined by $2x + 5y = -19$ and $6y - 8x = -54$. Justify your answer.

5. Jeff is a cashier at the grocery store. He has a total of $580 in bills. He has 76
   bills, consisting of $5 bills and $10 bills. How many of each type does he have?

6. A traffic helicopter pilot finds that with a tailwind her 120 km trip away from
   the airport takes 30 min. On her return trip to the airport, into the wind, she
   finds that her trip is 10 min longer. What is the speed of the helicopter? What is
   the speed of the wind?

7. Rani is comparing the monthly costs from two Internet service providers.
   Netaxes charges a flat monthly fee of $10, plus $0.75 per hour spent on-line.
   Webz charges a flat monthly fee of $5, plus $1 per hour.
   (a) Determine when the monthly costs are the same.
   (b) Rani plans to use the Internet for at least 30 h each month. Which provider
   should she choose? Explain.

8. Premium gasoline sells for 78.9¢/L. Regular gas sells for 71.9¢/L. To boost sales,
   a middle octane gasoline is formed by mixing premium and regular. If 1000 L of
   this middle octane gas is produced, and is sold at 73.9¢/L, then how much of
   each type of gasoline can you assume was used in the mixture?

9. Graph a linear system with no solution. Determine two possible equations that
   could represent both lines in your graph.

10. Solve.
    (a) $12(x - 2) - (2y - 1) = 14$
    $5(x - 1) + 2(1 - 2y) = 14$
    (b) $\dfrac{x - 2}{3} - \dfrac{y + 5}{2} = -3$
    $3x - \dfrac{2y}{3} = 13$

11. This data shows the percentage of the male and female population, aged 25 to 64, who smoke.

Year	1981	1983	1985	1986	1989	1990	1991	1994	1995
Male (%)	47.0	42.7	41.5	37.9	36.5	34.1	34.7	33.0	31.5
Female (%)	36.8	37.0	34.0	33.1	33.5	31.3	33.2	30.8	27.3

Source: Health Canada

(a) Create a scatter plot comparing the percentage of the population, male vs. female, who smoke in this age group.
(b) What trend does the data indicate in both the male and female population?
(c) Predict when equal percentages of both the male and female population will be smoking in this age group.
(d) According to this data, who will be smoking more in the year 2010, men or women?

Chapter

2

Coordinates and Geometry: Where Shapes Meet Symbols

René Descartes, a 17th-century French mathematician and philosopher, used ordered pairs to refer to the position of a figure. In doing so, he created the branch of mathematics that we call **analytic geometry**. Analytic geometry is a bridge between the world of physical objects and pure mathematics.

Coordinates and analytic geometry are important tools in many occupations. They are used by surveyors when they lay out exact positions for construction projects; by graphic artists who develop special effects for movies; and by scientists and engineers who use computer-generated images to visualize things that cannot be seen directly. For example, this scientist is studying the effect an earthquake would have on a highway.

In this chapter you will

use coordinates to reference points on a map or technical drawing

develop formulas for the distance of a point from the origin, and the length of a line segment and its midpoint

investigate the relationship between the x- and y-coordinates of the points on a circle and use the equation of a circle to model real-world situations

solve problems involving length, slope, and midpoint of a line segment

use the methods developed in the chapter to determine and verify properties of triangles and quadrilaterals

For connections to this chapter, visit **www.math.nelson.com**.

139

The Chapter Problem

Placing the Surveyor's Stakes

Have you ever noticed small metal markers on the sidewalk, on posts, or on the sides of buildings? Surveyors place these marks to record the coordinates of these points on a grid they have set up for the site. They use these coordinates to stake out the positions of buildings, highways, or other structures before construction begins.

A community centre is to be built on a large rural lot. The construction plans show that the front of the building will be parallel to the front lot line, set back 45 m. The centre of the front of the building will be on the perpendicular bisector of the front lot line. Before the excavation for the foundation begins, the surveyor has to mark the corners with wooden stakes and lines 1.5 m outside the actual walls of the building. (The markers are placed outside the actual excavation so they can remain in place when the hole is dug.) Use the information in the plan to find the coordinates of the corner stakes *P*, *Q*, *R*, *S*.

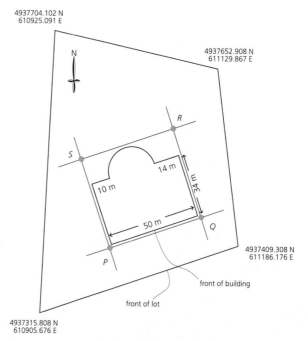

For help with this problem, see pages 140, 175, 184, 197, and 204.

Challenge 1

When a new road is cut into a hillside, creating a steep soil slope, it is usually necessary to stabilize the slope to make sure the soil does not slide down into the road. If the conditions are suitable, the engineer may choose to stabilize the slope by installing steel pins, called *soil nails*, into the ground. These nails must be installed at a certain angle and must extend beyond the critical "slip circle" by a certain amount. (Engineers assume that the side of the hill would slide along a circular arc, called the *slip circle*.) The engineer uses analytic geometry to calculate how long the nails must be.

Here is a diagram of a slope that needs soil nails.

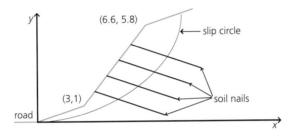

The slip circle is centred at (1.5, 7) and has a radius of 8 m.

The soil nails must slope downward with a slope of $-\frac{2}{3}$. They must extend 4 m past the slip circle and be spaced at 1.5 m intervals down the slope, starting at a point 0.6 m below the top of the slope.

Use all of this information to determine how long the nails should be.

Challenge 2

A fenced, circular field has a radius of 30 m. A goat is tethered by a rope to a fence post at the edge of the field. If the goat can graze over exactly half the area of the field, how long is the rope?

To complete these Challenges, you may need to discuss a research plan with your teacher or other students. You may also need to research outside the classroom.

In this chapter you will be working with

- squares and square roots

- slopes and equations of lines

- the properties of triangles and quadrilaterals

These exercises will help you warm up for the work ahead.

1. Simplify each expression.

(a) $\frac{1}{2}(-6) + \frac{3}{2}$ (b) $\frac{3}{8} - \frac{3}{7}$

(c) $\frac{2}{3}x + 11x$ (d) $\frac{3}{4}y - \frac{3}{8}y$

(e) $\left(\frac{2}{3}\right)\left(\frac{3}{5}\right) + \frac{3}{4}$

(f) $(-1.5)(0.625) + (4)(-0.125)$

2. Evaluate.

(a) $4^2 + 6^2$ (b) $\left(\frac{1}{2}\right)^2 + \left(\frac{2}{5}\right)^2$

(c) $\sqrt{0.0625}$ (d) $\sqrt{8^2 + 15^2}$

(e) $\sqrt{7^2 + 24^2}$

3. Solve for x.

(a) $3(7 - 4x) - \frac{4}{3}(2x + 1) = 49$

(b) $\frac{1}{4}(x + 3) + \frac{1}{3}(x - 2) = -\frac{1}{2}$

(c) $\frac{x + 4}{4} - \frac{x - 2}{3} = 1$

(d) $x^2 = 36$

(e) $x^2 + 16 = 25$

(f) $225 + x^2 = 289$

4. Find the point of intersection of the following lines.

(a) $y = 2x + 5$ (b) $4x + 2y = 7$
    $y = 3x + 4$ $6x - 4y = 0$

(c) $5x - 2y = 7$
    $10x + 2y = 11$

5. Find the unknown length.

(a)

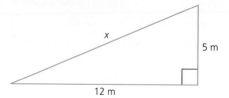

(b)

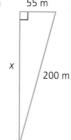

6. Find the mean of each set of numbers.

(a) $7, -11, 23, 5$ (b) $-\frac{1}{6}, \frac{2}{3}$

(c) $-1.4, 3.6, -0.1$

7. Find the slope of the line that

(a) has the equation $y = \frac{1}{2}x - 3$

(b) has points $(-1, 4)$ and $(1, 8)$ on it

(c) is parallel to $y = -3x + 5$

(d) is perpendicular to $y = \frac{2}{3}x - 1$

8. Find, in $y = mx + b$ form, the equation of the line that

(a) has points $(-5, 3)$ and $(7, 7)$ on it

(b) is parallel to $y = -\frac{3}{4}x - 6$ and passes through $(8, 1)$

(c) is parallel to $y = -3$ and passes through $(0, 1)$

(d) is perpendicular to $y = \frac{1}{4}x + 7$ and passes through $(-1, -2)$

9. Draw a diagram and write a sentence to explain each term.

  (a) median   **(b)** altitude

  (c) parallelogram   **(d)** isosceles triangle

  (e) midsegment   **(f)** square

  (g) scalene triangle

  (h) perpendicular bisector

  (i) rectangle

  (j) equilateral triangle

  (k) rhombus   **(l)** circumcentre

  (m) centroid   **(n)** incentre

  (o) orthocentre

10. Find the area.

  (a)

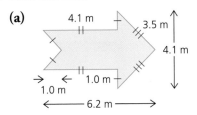

  (b)

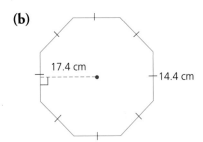

11. (a) Calculate the area of the shaded region.

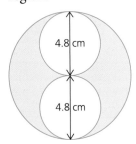

(b) Calculate the area and perimeter of the shaded region.

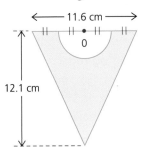

12. Find the value of the unknown quantities.

  (a)

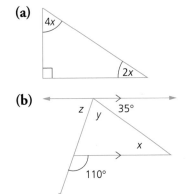

  (b)

  (c)   **(d)**

  (e)   **(f)**

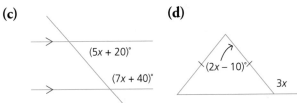

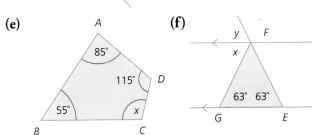

13. Find the measure of angles x, y, and z.

2.1 Graphical Images: Combining Symbolic and Visual Models

Computer graphics are used extensively for design in entertainment, advertising, scientific research, and industry. In graphics software, such as *CAD* and *Adobe Illustrator*, "pixel" identification is used to reference points on the screen. The image of the line (and everything else you see on the screen) is produced by turning on or off the tiny square pixels that make up the display area. Pixels appear dark when they are on.

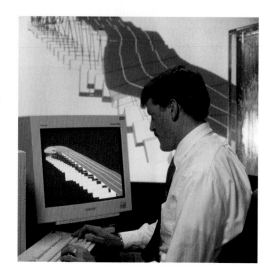

Think, Do, Discuss

1. Use a graphing calculator to graph the line $y = 2x - 1$. If you look closely, you can see that the line is jagged, rather than perfectly straight. Why do you think this happens?

2. Would you need more pixels or fewer pixels to make the line smoother? Try both options to see which works.

3. Your calculator manual gives the number of pixels on the screen. They are arranged in rows and columns, just like the cells of a spreadsheet. On a TI-83 Plus, there are 62 rows and 94 columns of pixels. Follow these steps to turn on a specific pixel.

    (a) Press [2nd] [PRGM], then cursor right to **POINTS**. Select the **4:Pxl-ON(** command.

    (b) Enter "10,20)" and press [ENTER].

    Describe the position of the dot that appears on your screen. What do the coordinates of the pixel (10, 20) refer to on the screen?

4. Where is the origin for the pixel coordinates? Follow step 3 to turn on pixel (0, 0) to confirm your answer.

5. What are the coordinates of the pixels at the corners of the screen? Verify your choices by turning on these pixels.

6. ⌐TRACE⌐ along the graph of $y = 2x - 1$. How does the x-value displayed at the bottom of the screen change each time you press the right arrow key?

7. Change the ⌐WINDOW⌐ settings to display x-values from -4.7 to 4.7 and y-values from -3.1 to 3.1. Press ⌐GRAPH⌐ to redraw. How has the appearance of the graph changed?

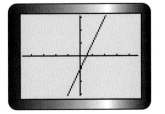

8. ⌐TRACE⌐ along the graph again. How does the x-value change each time you press the right arrow key?

9. What other ⌐WINDOW⌐ settings would work in a similar, user-friendly way?

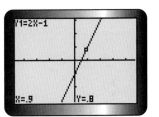

10. Turn off the pixels you drew by pressing ⌐2nd⌐ ⌐PRGM⌐ ⌐1⌐.

Practise 2.1

1. Graph each line with the given window. Then smooth out the line, if you can, by changing to different, more user-friendly ⌐WINDOW⌐ settings.

    (a) $y = 2x + 35$, with x- and y-values from -50 to 50

    (b) $y = -\frac{1}{2}x - 27$, with x-values from -60 to 30 and y-values from -40 to 20

2. Why are lines produced by a spreadsheet or graphing software on a computer screen smoother? Find out how many pixels are displayed on your school or home computer screen.

Did You Know?

In 1852, Francis Guthrie said that it was possible to colour all the regions of a flat map using no more than four colours so that no regions that touched each other would have the same colour. By a map, Guthrie meant any flat surface criss-crossed with lines. The lines could be straight or curved, and could form regions of many shapes. When mathematicians set out to prove this theorem, they were surprised at how hard it was to solve.

Finally, in 1976, Kenneth Appel and Wolfgang Haken at the University of Illinois proved the theorem—by using a computer program that took over 1200 hours to run.

Even today, there is still no quick way to determine whether a map requires two, three, or four colours. Finding an efficient way of answering this question remains one of the great unsolved problems in mathematics.

2.2 Using *The Geometer's Sketchpad*

The Tool Buttons and Sketchpad Terminology

Sketches and Dynamic Geometry

The ability to change objects dynamically is the most important feature of *The Geometer's Sketchpad* program. After you create an object, you can move, rotate, dilate, reflect, or hide it, as well as change its label, colour, shade, or line thickness. Whatever changes you make, the program maintains the existing mathematical relationships between the object and any other objects on the screen. This is the principle of dynamic geometry software and why it is so useful.

To refer to the on-line help while working on a sketch, choose **Help** from the menu bar and select the appropriate heading.

The Geometer's Sketchpad Terminology

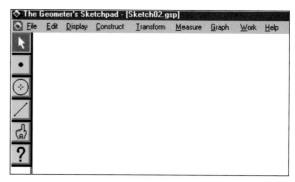

select: Choose the selection tool [image], and move the mouse pointer to the desired location and click the mouse button (left click for Windows users). When objects are selected, they are darker in appearance.

deselect: Choose the selection tool [image], and click anywhere in the display area away from any figures. All dark selection highlights will be removed from all objects.

draw: Use the point tool [image], circle tool [image], or line tool [image] to create a diagram involving points, circles, and lines. If you point to the line tool and click and hold the left mouse button, you will see a choice of additional line tools.

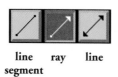

line segment   ray   line

construct: Select a series of commands from the **Construct** menu to perform geometric constructions to add objects to your diagram. Construct operations only work if you have already selected the part of the diagram you want to change.

drag: Move the mouse pointer to the point or line you want to move. Click on the point or line and, while holding down the mouse button, move it to a new location. Release the mouse button when the object is where you want it.

Points and Line Segments: Measuring Distance, Length, and Slope

1. **Start a new sketch.**
   Choose **New Sketch** from the **File** menu.

2. Set **Preferences** (from the **Display** menu) to show labels for points. Also set the **Distance Unit** to **cm**, the **Angle Unit** to **degrees**, and the **Precision** to **tenths** for distance units and **units** for angles.

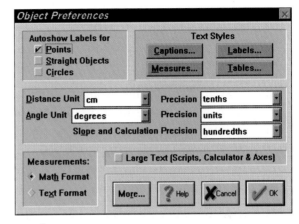

step 2

3. **Create a graph grid.**
   Choose **Show Grid** from the **Graph** menu.

4. **Measure the distance between points *A* and *B*.**
   Select both *A* and *B* with the selection tool: move the arrow to point *A* and click, then, while holding down the shift key, move the arrow to point *B* and click again. Choose **Distance** from the **Measure** menu. The distance between points *A* and *B* is displayed. This distance, 1 cm, is the base distance between grid points.

5. **Draw two new points, *C* and *D*, anywhere on the screen.**
   Using the point tool, click the mouse in the sketch area to plot a point at the cursor location. Repeat to plot the second point. Measure the distance between *C* and *D*.

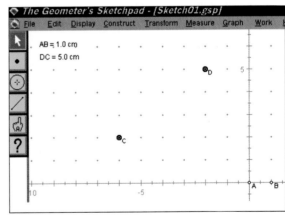

step 5

6. **Warning!** Point *B* is used to adjust the scale of your graph. Therefore, do not change the position of point *B* after you have measured a distance, because the old displayed measurement will no longer be valid for the new base unit. To demonstrate this fact, select *B* and drag it to a new location. The new distance between *A* and *B* is displayed, but the displayed distance between *C* and *D* does not change. Drag point *B* back so that *AB* = 1 cm again.

7. **Construct a line segment and measure its length.**

Select both *C* and *D* by using the selection tool while holding down the shift key. From the **Construct** menu, choose **Segment**. Make sure that the line segment is selected and choose **Length** from the **Measure** menu.

8. **Measure the slope of the line.**

Select the line and choose **Slope** from the **Measure** menu.

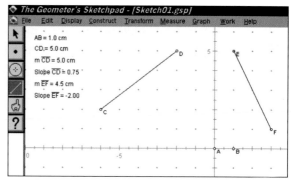

step 8

You can also draw line segments using the line segment tool. Select the line tool and position the cursor at the desired starting location. Click to create the starting point *E*, then hold the mouse button while you reposition the cursor to the location where you want the end point. Release the mouse button to draw the end point *F* and the segment *EF*. Measure the length and slope of this new segment.

Practise 2.2

1. **i.** Plot both points, then determine the distance between them.
   ii. Construct the line segment between the pair of points, then measure its length and slope.

   (a) $A(2, 3)$ and $B(5, 9)$

   (b) $A(-3, 7)$ and $B(6, -4)$

   (c) $A(-4, -2)$ and $B(3, 7)$

   (d) $A(-5, 5)$ and $B(2, 1)$

   (e) $A(0, 0)$ and $B(6, 8)$

   (f) $A(-5, -6)$ and $B(-4, 8)$

Le Corbusier (1887-1965)

The French architect known as Le Corbusier (Charles-Edouard Jeanneret) is probably the most important architect of the 20th century. The "International Style" he developed appears everywhere. He used reinforced concrete and attempted to use space in new ways, freeing buildings from structural limitations such as the typical frame of a wall. His buildings include such features as continuous horizontal windows, roof gardens, open metal spiral staircases, and columns to raise buildings above the ground.

Avoiding ornamentation, Le Corbusier used basic geometric shapes in simple but imaginative ways. Golden rectangles occur frequently in his works.

Distance on the Plane—Part I: Distance from the Origin

A car accident has occurred approximately 50 km north of Sturgeon Falls. One of the victims requires specialized surgery that is only performed at hospitals in Sault Ste. Marie, Toronto, and Ottawa. A helicopter will fly the injured person directly to the closest of the three hospitals. Where should the patient be flown?

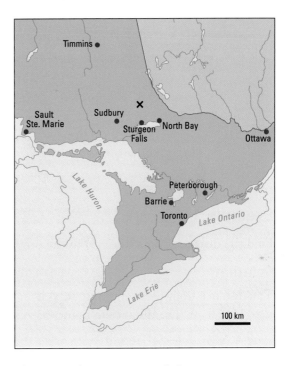

Think, Do, Discuss

1. Trace the map on graph paper and draw the x- and y-axes so that they cross at the accident site. What are the coordinates of the three hospitals?

2. Which hospital do you think is closest? Why do you think so?

3. On your map, draw a straight line from the origin to the point representing the hospital in Ottawa. Now make a right triangle with this line as its hypotenuse and the other sides parallel to the x- and y-axes respectively. How long is the vertical side of the triangle? How long is the horizontal side? How do these lengths relate to the coordinates of the point representing Ottawa?

4. If you know the lengths of two sides of a right triangle, how can you find the length of the third side?

5. Determine the scale of your map and calculate (do not measure) the distance from the accident site to Ottawa.

6. Repeat steps 3 and 5 to calculate the distances from the accident site to Sault Ste. Marie and Toronto.

7. Given the coordinates of any point on this map, describe a way to quickly find the distance of that point from the accident site without drawing a right triangle? Would your method work if the accident site was not at the origin? Explain.

8. Write a formula to calculate the distance of a point with coordinates (x, y) from the origin $(0, 0)$.

9. Which of the three hospitals is closest to the accident site? What other factors might affect the pilot's decision about which hospital to head for?

10. If a land-based ambulance had to be used instead of a helicopter, would the choice of hospital be the same? Explain.

Focus 2.3

Key Ideas

- The distance, d, from the origin $(0, 0)$ to any point (x, y) is $d = \sqrt{x^2 + y^2}$.

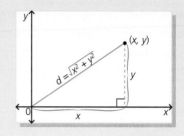

Example 1

Find the distance from $P(3, -5)$ to the origin.

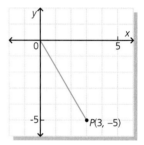

Solution

The distance from $(0, 0)$ to point (x, y) is
$d = \sqrt{x^2 + y^2}$. The distance to point $(3, -5)$ is

$$d = \sqrt{3^2 + (-5)^2} = \sqrt{9 + 25}$$
$$= \sqrt{34}$$
$$\doteq 5.8 \text{ units} \quad \text{(to one decimal place)}$$

Example 2

A boat's engine fails at sea. Coast Guard ships are at $(44, -22)$ and at $(16, -49)$, where the first coordinate is the distance (in nautical miles) due east from the boat, and the second coordinate is the distance due south from the boat. If the boat is at the origin, which Coast Guard ship is closer to it? (A *nautical mile* (nm) is a unit of distance used in navigation. One nautical mile equals 1852 m. It is longer than a standard mile because it takes the curvature of the Earth into account.)

Solution

The disabled boat is at the origin $(0, 0)$. The first Coast Guard ship is $\sqrt{44^2 + (-22)^2} \doteq 49$ nm away (to the nearest nautical mile). The second Coast Guard ship is $\sqrt{16^2 + (-49)^2} \doteq 52$ nm away.

The first ship, at $(44, -22)$, is closer to the disabled boat.

Practise, Apply, Solve 2.3 ———————————

A

1. Refer to the map on p. 149.

   (a) State the coordinates of the points representing Barrie, Sudbury, and Peterborough.

   (b) How far is each of these cities from the accident site?

2. Plot each point and connect it to the origin with a straight line. Calculate the distance from the point to the origin.

   (a) $(5, 12)$ **(b)** $(-3, 9)$ **(c)** $(1, -1)$ **(d)** $(-7, -25)$

3. Knowledge and Understanding: Which of these points is closest to the origin: $X(4, 6)$, $Y(-5, 5)$, or $Z(3, -7)$? Explain your answer.

4. Why is it useful to have a coordinate grid on a map? Explain, with examples, how people would use the coordinates.

B

5. Communication: If you know the coordinates of a point, how do you determine how far it is from the origin? How far is $P(10, -8)$ from the origin?

6. An airport control tower at $(0, 0)$ locates two airplanes on its radar screen. Plane A is at $(85, 95)$ and airplane B is at $(-64, 115)$. If both airplanes are approaching the airport at the same speed, which plane should be instructed to land first?

7. Application:

   (a) A forest fire is threatening two small towns. On a map, with the fire at $(0, 0)$, the first town is at $(26, 77)$ and the other town is at $(12, -88)$. Which town should be evacuated first?

   (b) What other variable must be considered, besides distance?

8. Thinking, Inquiry, Problem Solving: A triangle has vertices at $O(0, 0)$, $P(15, 8)$, and $Q(15, -9)$.

   (a) Draw the triangle on a grid.

   (b) Find the perimeter of the triangle.

   (c) What kind of triangle is $\triangle OPQ$?

9. In an animated cartoon, a journalist morphs into a superhero. The computer animator describes the shape change in terms of pixel coordinate transformations. As a result of the transformation, the tip of the journalist's chin moves from a point with coordinates $P(12, 33)$ to $R(9, 45)$. How much farther is his chin from the origin after the morphing?

10. In a video game, three animated characters are programmed to run out of a building and head in three different directions to escape a fire at the origin. After 2 s, Animal is at $A(22, 18)$, Beast is at $B(-3, 35)$, and Creature is at $C(7, -29)$. Who ran farthest?

11. A kite has vertices at $A(3, 3)$, $B(-2, 2)$, $C(-5, -5)$, and $D(2, -2)$.

   (a) Draw the kite on a grid.

   (b) Draw the kite's diagonals AC and BD.

   (c) Find the distance between points A and C.

   (d) Find the distance between points B and D.

12. The Ministry of Natural Resources tagged and equipped two moose with tracking collars. After their release the moose head in different directions. Two hours later, one moose's location is given by $(6, 8)$. The other moose's position is given by $(-3, 5)$. Assuming that they were captured at $(0, 0)$, determine the difference between the distance they travelled.

13. **Check Your Understanding:** A survey team is working in a remote part of northern Ontario when one of the team is injured in a fall and needs emergency treatment. An air ambulance is sent to take the injured surveyor to the nearest hospital. How would a coordinate grid help the team decide which major hospital is closest to the accident site? Describe the process in detail. Use examples in your description.

C

14. Two of the vertices of $\triangle MNO$ are $O(0, 0)$ and $M(3, -4)$. What are possible coordinates for N if $\triangle MNO$ is **(a)** isosceles? **(b)** equilateral? Explain how you found your answers.

15. Three of the vertices of a parallelogram are $O(0, 0)$, $J(3, 4)$, and $K(9, 4)$. By how much are the diagonals different in length?

16. Jeff and Monika each drew identical, numbered square grids on their own copies of the same map, with the axes parallel to the edges of the paper, but with the origins in different places. What is the relationship between the coordinates of a point on Jeff's map and the coordinates of the same point on Monika's map? Explain.

17. A goat is tethered by a 10 m long rope to a post in a large field. How can you use coordinates to describe the goat's available grazing area? What shape is the area that the goat can graze? Does the location of the post affect your answer? Does the shape of the field affect your answer? Investigate several different scenarios—different fields and different post locations—and write a report of your findings.

18. Determine the coordinates of the four vertices of a square whose diagonals measure 8.485 cm and intersect at the origin.

The Equation of a Circle 2.4

Communications satellites, which appear stationary from the ground, are in fact moving about the centre of Earth. What type of graphical model describes the path of these satellites?

Think, Do, Discuss

1. A certain type of graphical model is often used to describe things like the path of a geostationary satellite, the effect of an earthquake or explosion, or the cross-section of a tunnel. What common shape applies to these situations?

2. Draw a scale diagram on a coordinate grid to represent the satellite orbiting Earth, at a distance of 42 000 km from the centre of Earth. Plot a point to represent the centre of Earth at (0, 0) and draw a circle to represent the path of the satellite. What is the radius of the circle? Where does the circle cross the x-axis? the y-axis?

3. What do all points on this circle have in common?

4. Write an expression for the distance from any point $A(a, b)$ to the origin. If A is a point on the circle you have drawn, what must be true? Include an equation in your answer.

5. If point $P(x, y)$ is a point on the circle with its centre at (0, 0) and a radius of r units, how far is P from the origin? Write an equation like the one you wrote in question 4. Square both sides of your equation to put it in a form that does not contain a square root.

Focus 2.4

Key Ideas

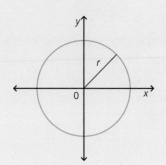

- A **circle** is the set of all points in a plane that are the same distance from a fixed point, the centre. The distance from any point on the circle to the centre is called the **radius**.

- If the centre of the circle is at the origin of the x-y plane and the radius is r units, then
$r = \sqrt{x^2 + y^2}$, which is equivalent to $x^2 + y^2 = r^2$.
This equation, $x^2 + y^2 = r^2$, is the equation of a circle with centre $(0, 0)$ and radius r.

Example 1

Write the equation of a circle with centre $(0, 0)$ and a radius of $\frac{1}{2}$ units.

Solution

The equation of a circle with its centre at $(0, 0)$ is $x^2 + y^2 = r^2$, where r is the radius.

The equation of a circle with radius $\frac{1}{2}$ is $x^2 + y^2 = \left(\frac{1}{2}\right)^2$ or $x^2 + y^2 = \frac{1}{4}$.

Example 2

A circle is defined by the equation $x^2 + y^2 = 9$. Sketch a graph of this circle.

Solution

The circle is centred at $(0, 0)$ and has a radius of 3. To graph this circle, plot the x-intercepts at $(3, 0)$ and $(-3, 0)$, and plot the y-intercepts at $(0, 3)$ and $(0, -3)$. Join these four points with a smooth circle.

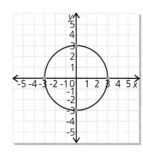

Example 3

A circle has centre (0, 0) and passes through point $(8, -6)$. Find the equation of the circle. What are the coordinates of the other end point of the diameter that passes through $(8, -6)$?

Solution

The equation has the form $x^2 + y^2 = r^2$.
Since $(8, -6)$ is on the circle,

$$8^2 + (-6)^2 = r^2$$
$$100 = r^2$$

The equation of the circle is $x^2 + y^2 = 100$.

By symmetry, the other end point of the diameter containing $(8, -6)$ is at $(-8, 6)$.

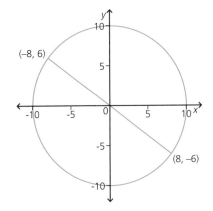

Example 4

A stone is dropped into a pond and sends out a circular ripple whose radius increases by 5 cm/s. Find the equation of the circle 12 s after the stone is dropped.

Solution

We can use a circle with centre at the origin as a graphical model of the ripple.
If the radius grows by 5 cm/s, then after 12 s the radius is $12 \times 5 = 60$ cm.
The equation of the circle at this time is $x^2 + y^2 = 60^2$ or $x^2 + y^2 = 3600$.

Practise, Apply, Solve 2.4 ——————

A

1. Write the equation of the circle with centre at (0, 0) and the given radius, r.

    (a) $r = 3$ **(b)** $r = 50$ **(c)** $r = 2\frac{1}{3}$ **(d)** $r = 400$ **(e)** $r = 0.25$

2. **i.** For each circle, state the location or value of the centre, the radius, and the x- and y-intercepts.
   ii. Graph each circle.

    (a) $x^2 + y^2 = 36$ **(b)** $x^2 + y^2 = 49$
    (c) $x^2 + y^2 = 0.04$ **(d)** $x^2 + y^2 = 169$

3. Write the equation of a graph that models the situation.

(a) the path of a satellite in orbit at a distance of 19 000 km from the centre of Earth

(b) the path of a point on the edge of a child's spinning top with a diameter of 70 cm

(c) the shock wave from an earthquake, 30 s after the quake. Assume that the wave travels at 6 km/s.

(d) the cross-section of a 7.5 m diameter railway tunnel

(e) the rim of a bicycle wheel with a 69 cm diameter

4. Find the radius of a circle with centre at (0, 0) that passes through

(a) $(-3, 4)$ (b) $(5, 0)$ (c) $(0, -3)$ (d) $(8, -15)$

5. For each circle in question 4

(a) write the equation

(b) give the coordinates of two other points on the circle

(c) sketch its graph

B

6. Communication: An earthquake is one physical phenomenon that can be modelled by a circle. Give examples of three other phenomena that can be modelled by circles. Include the equations.

7. Knowledge and Understanding: An underground explosion causes shock waves to radiate out from the explosion site. Draw a graphical model of the position of the shock waves at 5 s intervals. Describe the graphs in your own words. Write the equation for each graph.

8. Application: Two satellites are orbiting Earth. The path of one has the equation $x^2 + y^2 = 2\ 250\ 000$. The orbit of the other is 200 km farther from the centre of Earth. In one orbit, how much farther does the second satellite travel than the first one?

9. Determine if the point is on, inside, or outside the circle $x^2 + y^2 = 45$. Explain your reasoning.

(a) $(6, -3)$ (b) $(-1, 7)$ (c) $(-3, 5)$ (d) $(-7, -2)$

10. A rock dropped into a pond sends out a circular ripple whose radius increases steadily at 6 cm/s. A toy boat is floating on the pond 2 m east and 1 m north of the spot where the rock is dropped. How long does it take for the ripple to reach the boat?

11. Points $(a, 5)$ and $(9, b)$ are on the circle $x^2 + y^2 = 125$. What are the values of a and b?

12. A satellite orbits Earth on a path with equation $x^2 + y^2 = 45\ 000\ 000$. Another satellite, in the same plane, is currently located at $(12\ 504, 16\ 050)$. Is the second satellite inside or outside the orbit of the first satellite? Explain.

13. **Check Your Understanding:** Explain, with an example, how to find the equation of a circle with centre at the origin
  (a) if you know the radius of the circle
  (b) if you do not know the radius, but you know the coordinates of a point on the circle

C

14. Craig is adapting part of the pattern for a theatrical costume. He adds part of a square onto the outside of the circle. If the circle in the pattern has the equation $x^2 + y^2 = 0.062$, how much extra fabric is needed to make the pattern shown? (Measurements are in metres.)

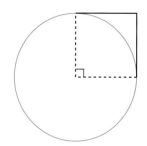

15. **Thinking, Inquiry, Problem Solving:** Chanelle is creating a design for vinyl flooring. She uses circles and squares to create the design shown. If the equation of the small circle is $x^2 + y^2 = 16$, what are the dimensions of the large square?

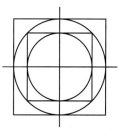

16. A truck with a wide load, proceeding slowly along a secondary road, is approaching a tunnel with a semicircular cross-section and a maximum height of 5.25 m. If the load is 8 m wide and 3.5 m high, will it fit through the tunnel? Explain your answer and include your calculations.

2.5 Distance on the Plane—Part II

Part 1: The Distance Between Any Two Points —

In section 2.3, you found the closest hospital to an accident site near Sturgeon Falls using coordinates and the Pythagorean theorem.

Immediately after delivering the accident victim to the closest hospital in Ottawa, the helicopter must carry some donated organs from Ottawa to a hospital in Peterborough. Help the pilot figure out how long it will take by calculating the distance from Ottawa to Peterborough.

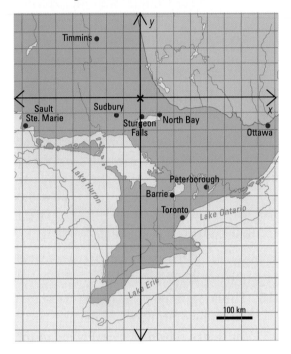

Think, Do, Discuss

1. Trace the map into your notebook and mark the coordinates of Ottawa and Peterborough. How far do you think it is between the two cities? How did you make your estimate?

2. Join the points representing Ottawa and Peterborough with a straight line. Create a right triangle that has this line as its hypotenuse, one side parallel to the *y*-axis, and one side parallel to the *x*-axis. What are the coordinates of the vertex with the right angle?

3. How long is the vertical side of the triangle? How could you calculate this length from the vertex coordinates?

4. How long is the horizontal side of the triangle? How could you calculate this length from the vertex coordinates?

5. Calculate the distance from Ottawa to Peterborough.

6. Another helicopter transports a newborn baby from Barrie to the neonatal unit at Sick Kids Hospital in Toronto. How far does this helicopter travel?

Part 2: Developing a Formula

Think, Do, Discuss

1. Sketch a coordinate grid and choose any two points on the grid. Call these points A and B. Label point A with coordinates (x_1, y_1) and B with (x_2, y_2).

   (a) How is the line segment joining A and B different from the line that passes through A and B?

   (b) What properties do the line segment AB and the line through A and B have in common?

2. Find the distance from A to B using the same method you used to find the distance between hospitals.

   (a) In your right triangle, what are the coordinates of the vertex with the right angle, in terms of the coordinates of A and B? Why?

   (b) Write an expression for the length of the vertical side in terms of the coordinates of the three vertices.

   (c) Write an expression for the length of the horizontal side.

   (d) Write an expression that represents the distance from A to B.

   (e) Explain how this formula can be used to find the distance between any two points whose coordinates are known.

3. **(a)** How would you calculate the slope of line segment AB?

   (b) Discuss whether any values used in the slope calculation are also used in the distance formula.

   (c) How would you know if another line segment CD is parallel to AB or perpendicular to AB?

Did You Know?

How important is nothing? When that nothing is zero, it can be very important. The notion of zero was known to various ancient cultures, but not all of them. For example, the Sumerians of Mesopotamia and the Maya of Central America used the concept of zero in their mathematics systems, but the Ancient Greeks and Romans did not. This point may not seem important to us today, but some people have speculated that if the Romans had had the notion of zero they might have developed calculators.

You might enjoy reading *The Nothing That Is*, by Robert Kaplan or *Zero, The Biography of a Dangerous Idea*, by Charles Seife, for more information about this strange number.

Focus 2.5

Key Ideas

- The distance between points $A(x_1, y_1)$ and $B(x_2, y_2)$ in the coordinate plane is

$$d = \sqrt{(\Delta x^2) + (\Delta y^2)}$$
$$= \sqrt{(x_2 - x_1)^2 + (y_2 - y_1)^2}$$

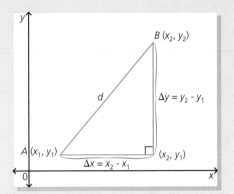

- A **line segment** is the part of a line between two specific points, including the points themselves.

- The slope of a line segment is the same as the slope of the line containing the line segment.

- Parallel line segments have the same slope.

- The slopes of two perpendicular line segments are negative reciprocals. (Their product is -1.) For example, $\frac{5}{4}$ and $-\frac{4}{5}$ are negative reciprocals.

Example 1

Find the length of the line segments with these end points.

(a) $A(-1, 0)$ and $B(5, 2)$ **(b)** $G(-7, 8)$ and $H(-7, -5)$ **(c)** $P(-4, 7)$ and $Q(3, 1)$

Solution

Use the distance formula, $d = \sqrt{(x_2 - x_1)^2 + (y_2 - y_1)^2}$

(a) $A(-1, 0)$ and $B(5, 2)$

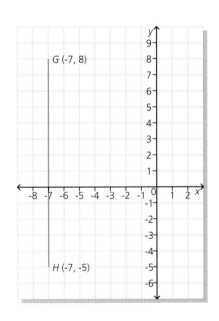

$$AB = \sqrt{(5 - (-1))^2 + (2 - 0)^2}$$
$$= \sqrt{6^2 + 2^2}$$
$$= \sqrt{40}$$
$$\doteq 6.3$$

AB is about 6.3 units long.

(b) Since $G(-7, 8)$ and $H(-7, -5)$ have equal x-coordinates, line segment GH is vertical.

The Pythagorean formula can be used to calculate the answer, but it is easier to calculate the difference between the y-coordinates of G and H.

$$GH = 8 - (-5)$$
$$= 13$$

GH is 13 units long.

(c) $P(-4, 7)$ and $Q(3, 1)$

$$PQ = \sqrt{(3 - (-4))^2 + (1 - 7)^2}$$
$$= \sqrt{7^2 + (-6)^2}$$
$$= \sqrt{49 + 36}$$
$$= \sqrt{85}$$
$$\doteq 9.2$$

PQ is about 9.2 units long.

Example 2

A triangle has vertices at $A(-1, -1)$, $B(2, 0)$, and $C(1, 3)$.
Find the lengths and slopes of the sides of the triangle. What kind of triangle is it?

Solution

A diagram is useful for solving or answering this type of question.

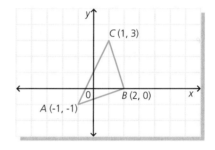

Use the distance formula to find the length of each side of the triangle.

$$AB = \sqrt{(2 - (-1))^2 + (0 - (-1))^2}$$
$$= \sqrt{3^2 + 1^2}$$
$$= \sqrt{10}$$
$$\doteq 3.2$$

$$BC = \sqrt{(1 - 2)^2 + (3 - 0)^2}$$
$$= \sqrt{(-1)^2 + 3^2)}$$
$$= \sqrt{10}$$
$$\doteq 3.2$$

$$AC = \sqrt{(1 - (-1))^2 + (3 - (-1))^2}$$
$$= \sqrt{2^2 + 4^2}$$
$$= \sqrt{20}$$
$$\doteq 4.5$$

The length of AB equals the length of BC, so $\triangle ABC$ is isosceles.

Use the slope formula, slope $= \frac{y_2 - y_1}{x_2 - x_1}$, to find the slope of each side of the triangle.

$$\text{Slope}_{AB} = \frac{0 - (-1)}{2 - (-1)} \qquad \text{Slope}_{BC} = \frac{3 - 0}{1 - 2} \qquad \text{Slope}_{AC} = \frac{3 - (-1)}{1 - (-1)}$$
$$= \frac{1}{3} \qquad\qquad\qquad = \frac{3}{-1} \qquad\qquad\qquad = \frac{4}{2}$$
$$\qquad\qquad\qquad\qquad = -3 \qquad\qquad\qquad = 2$$

Since the slopes of AB and BC are negative reciprocals, the line segments are perpendicular. Therefore, $\triangle ABC$ is an isosceles right triangle.

Example 3

An airplane at coordinates (150, 136), which is heading for Sudbury (0, 0), has to be diverted because of poor weather conditions to either North Bay (85, −10) or Timmins (−10, 155). If the airplane is carrying enough fuel to get to Sudbury, which alternate airport would it be safe to head for?

Solution

The distance of the airplane from Sudbury is $\sqrt{150^2 + 136^2} \doteq 202.5$ units. The airplane has only enough fuel to travel this distance.

Distance of the airplane from Timmins

$$= \sqrt{(-10 - 150)^2 + (155 - 136)^2}$$
$$= \sqrt{(-160)^2 + 19^2}$$
$$\doteq 161.1 \text{ units}$$

Distance of the airplane from North Bay

$$= \sqrt{(85 - 150)^2 + ((-10) - 136)^2}$$
$$= \sqrt{(-65)^2 + (-146)^2}$$
$$\doteq 159.8 \text{ units}$$

The plane has enough fuel to reach either Timmins or North Bay.

Practise, Apply, Solve 2.5 ——————————

A

1. Calculate the distance between each pair of points.

   (a) P and Q (b) P and R

   (c) Q and R (d) P and U

   (e) U and S (f) Q and T

   (g) R and U (h) S and T

   (i) P and S

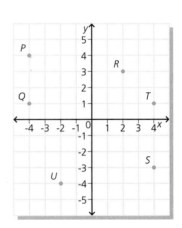

2. For each pair of points,
   i.   draw the line segment joining the points
   ii. calculate the length of the line segment
   iii. calculate the slope of the line segment

   (a) $A(2, 6)$ and $B(5, 2)$

   (b) $C(-3, 4)$ and $D(3, 2)$

   (c) $E(-6, 8)$ and $F(-6, -9)$

   (d) $G(0, -7)$ and H(1, 3)

   (e) $I(-3, -3)$ and $J(5, -4)$

   (f) $K(-10, -2)$ and $L(6, -2)$

   (g) $M(1, 10)$ and $N(20, 190)$

   (h) $P(-5, 5)$ and $Q(77, -70)$

3. Which of these points is closest to point $A(-3.2, 5.6)$: $B(1.8, -4.3)$, $C(0.7, 8.9)$, or $D(-7.6, 3.9)$?

4. Knowledge and Understanding

(a) Which of the line segments in question 2 are vertical? How can you tell from the coordinates of the end points that a line segment is vertical? How can you quickly calculate the length of a vertical line segment if you know the coordinates of its end points?

(b) Which of the line segments in question 2 are horizontal? How can you tell from the coordinates of the end points that a line segment is horizontal? How can you quickly calculate the length of a horizontal line segment if you know the coordinates of its end points?

5. Describe what is meant by the words *scalene*, *isosceles*, and *equilateral* triangles. The following points are the vertices of triangles. Draw each triangle on a coordinate grid. Predict if the triangle is scalene, isosceles, or equilateral. Calculate the length of each side to check your prediction.

(a) $A(3, 3)$, $B(-1, 2)$, $C(0, -2)$ (b) $D(2, -3)$, $E(-2, -4)$, $F(6, -6)$

(c) $G(-1, 3)$, $H(-2, -2)$, $I(2, 0)$ (d) $J(2, 5)$, $K(5, -2)$, $L(-1, -2)$

6. Communication

i. Do points $P(-2, -3)$, $Q(4, 1)$, and $R(2, 4)$ form a right triangle? Justify your answer. How can you find the answer by calculation alone?

ii. Without drawing any diagrams, explain which sets of points are the vertices of right triangles.

(a) $S(-2, 2)$, $T(-1, -2)$, $U(7, 0)$

(b) $X(3, 2)$, $Y(1, -2)$, $Z(-3, 6)$

(c) $A(5, 5)$, $B(3, 8)$, $C(8, 7)$

7. A quadrilateral has vertices $W(-3, 2)$, $X(2, 4)$, $Y(6, -1)$, and $Z(1, -3)$.

(a) Find the length and slope of each side of the quadrilateral.

(b) Based on your calculations in (a), what type of quadrilateral is *WXYZ*? Explain your answer.

(c) Find the difference in the lengths of the two diagonals of *WXYZ*.

8. Points $P(4, 12)$, $Q(9, 14)$, and $R(13, 4)$ are three vertices of a rectangle.

(a) Find the coordinates of the fourth vertex, *S*.

(b) Write a short description of how you found the coordinates of *S*.

(c) Find the lengths of the diagonals of rectangle *PQRS*. Comment on your results.

9. A coordinate grid is used on the plan of a new housing development. Fibre optic cable is being laid with a micro-tunnelling machine. The cable will link points with coordinates $A(-18, 12)$, $B(-8, 1)$, $C(3, 4)$, and $D(15, 7)$, in a run beginning at *A* and ending at *D*. If one unit on the grid represents 2.5 m, how much cable is required?

10. A coordinate grid is placed on a map showing the route of the Polar Bear Express, a train that carries tourists from Cochrane to Moosonee. One unit on the grid represents 60 km.

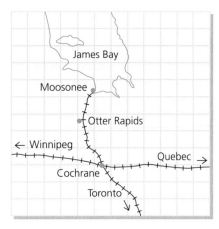

  (a) Calculate the distance from Moosonee to Otter Rapids.

  (b) Calculate the distance from Otter Rapids to Cochrane.

  (c) What is the direct distance by airplane from Cochrane to Moosonee?

11. A "leash-free area" for dogs is to be created in a field behind a recreation centre. What length of fencing will be required, if the plans show an irregular pentagonal area with vertices at (2, 0), (1, 6), (8, 9), (10, 7), and (6, 0)? (One unit represents 10 m.)

12. A builder needs to connect a partially built house to a temporary power supply. On the plan, the coordinates of the house are (50, 113) and the power supply is at (147, 82). What is the least amount of cable needed? Why is it likely that the builder will use more cable than this?

13. An architect uses a grid to help design a cottage. The diagram shows a side view plan.

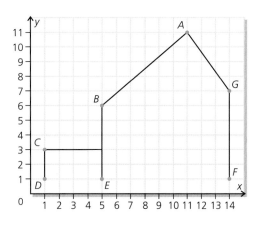

  (a) The architect knows that if the length of the roof is more than 18 units, the roof will need additional rafters for support. Calculate the distances AB and AG. Will these roofs need extra support?

  (b) A round window is to be at the midpoint of the line BG. Estimate the coordinates of the centre of the window. Explain how you obtained your estimate.

14. **Application:** A quadrilateral has vertices at $P(2, 0)$, $Q(4, 5)$, $R(-1, 3)$, and $S(-3, -2)$. Find the length and slope of each side and diagonal. Use this information to identify what type of quadrilateral $PQRS$ is. Write a paragraph describing your findings. Include the results of your calculations and a conclusion.

15. **Check Your Understanding**

  (a) Suppose you know the coordinates of three points. Explain how you would determine which of the first two points is closer to the third point. Describe any procedures, facts, or formulas that you would use. Give an example.

  (b) Describe two different ways you can determine if three given points are the vertices of a right triangle. Give an example.

16. Thinking, Inquiry, Problem Solving: In North America and in other parts of the world, the Universal Transverse Mercator (UTM) coordinate system is used for mapping and surveying and by the military. The UTM system divides the Earth into 60 zones. A square grid is superimposed on each zone, and UTM coordinates are expressed as a distance (in metres) to the east, called the "easting," and a distance to the north, called the "northing." The system has become better known as a result of increased use of global positioning system (GPS) devices.

(a) Do some research into the UTM coordinate system.
  i. Which UTM zone do you live in?
  ii. How wide is a zone? How long?
  iii. Where is the origin for the coordinates?

(b) Write a description and a brief history of the UTM system of coordinates.

(c) A straight road tunnel will be built between points A and B. How long will the tunnel be?

$$A: 611225.517 \text{ m E}, 4857116.341 \text{ m N}$$
$$B: 611248.114 \text{ m E}, 4856975.451 \text{ m N}$$

17. Triangle ABC, with vertices $A(1, 2)$, $B(4, 8)$, and $C(8, 4)$, is translated so that vertex A' is on the x-axis and vertex B' is on the y-axis.

(a) Find the coordinates of the translated vertices $A'B'C'$.

(b) Given the sets of vertices below, is $\triangle DEF$ or $\triangle GHI$ congruent to $\triangle ABC$? Justify your answer.

  i. $D(-1, 1)$, $E(-2, 6)$, $F(-8, 3)$ **ii.** $G(4, -1)$, $H(10, -4)$, $I(6, -8)$

18. How does the formula for the distance between two points in the plane differ from the formula for the distance of a point from the origin? You found the equation of a circle with centre at the origin by setting the distance from the origin equal to the radius of the circle. How could you use the formula for the distance between two points in the plane to find the equation of a circle whose centre is not at the origin?

19. Find the coordinates of three points that are 5 units from point $C(2, 3)$. Develop a rule for finding the coordinates of all points that are 5 units from C.

The Chapter Problem—Placing the Surveyor's Stakes

In this section, you found the distance between points. Apply what you learned to answer these questions about the chapter problem on page 140.

1. How wide is the front boundary of the parcel of land for the community centre?

2. Find the slope of the lot line that forms the front boundary of the lot.

3. Refer to the plan. What is the slope of each of the four marker lines?

2.6 *The Geometer's Sketchpad:* The Midpoint of a Line Segment

TECHNOLOGY

1. Open a new sketch, then choose **Show Grid** from the **Graph** menu. Draw a line segment.

2. You can label the end points of the line segment using the labelling tool 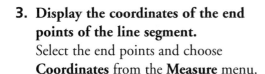.
   To do this, move the labelling tool to one of the end points. When the hand turns from white to black, click the mouse to turn the label on or off. Then do the same for the other end point. Alternatively, you can select all the objects you want to label and choose **Show Labels** from the **Display** menu.

3. **Display the coordinates of the end points of the line segment.**
   Select the end points and choose **Coordinates** from the **Measure** menu.

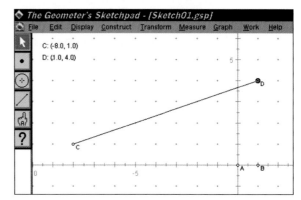

step 3

4. **Construct the midpoint of the line segment.**
   Select the line segment and choose **Point At Midpoint** from the **Construct** menu. Label the midpoint.

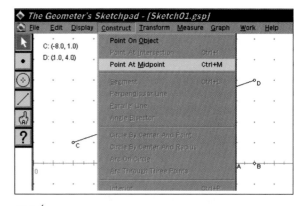

step 4

5. **Determine the coordinates of the midpoint.**
   Select the midpoint and choose **Coordinates** from the **Measure** menu.

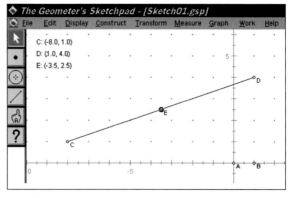

step 5

6. You can verify that the coordinates of the midpoint are correct by measuring the distance between the midpoint and each end point.

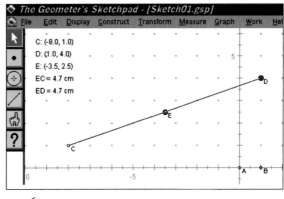

step 6

Practise 2.6

For each pair of end points,

i. draw the line segment
ii. construct the midpoint and display its coordinates
iii. verify that the location of the midpoint is correct

(a) $A(3, 4)$ and $B(7, -2)$

(b) $C(3, 2)$ and $D(7, 5)$

(c) $M(2, -9)$ and $N(-3, -1)$

(d) $Q(-10, 0)$ and $R(2, 0)$

(e) $F(-2, -2)$ and $G(4, 4)$

(f) $J(4, -2)$ and $K(-3, 4)$

René Descartes (1596-1650)

René Descartes was the cofounder of analytic or coordinate geometry, which connects algebra and geometry. Descartes was distracted one day by a buzzing fly that was crawling near the corner of the ceiling. He wondered how the fly's position could be described and reasoned that it could be expressed with reference to the distances from the two walls adjacent to the corner of the ceiling. Thus, if these distances became the x- and y-coordinates, the fly's path could be described algebraically.

René Descartes led a full life. He was a soldier, a mathematician, a philosopher, and an advisor to Queen Christine of Sweden. Investigate on the Internet or at the library to find out more about this fascinating man.

2.7 Finding the Midpoint of a Line Segment

A team of surveyors is marking out a large, rectangular city park. A monument will be erected in the centre of the park, so the surveyors need to find the coordinates of the centre point. They have already marked out the coordinates of the corners of the park.

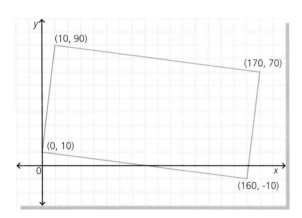

Part 1: Drawing the Plan

Think, Do, Discuss

1. Copy the plan on grid paper. Choose an appropriate scale for the given coordinate values.

2. Find and mark the centre of the rectangle.

3. What are the coordinates of the centre of the park?

4. Write a paragraph to explain how you found the centre. Did you construct any additional lines? Did you use the coordinates of the corners of the park?

Part 2: Finding the Coordinates of the Midpoint of a Line Segment

Think, Do, Discuss

1. Make a table like this in your notebook.

Coordinates of First End Point	Coordinates of Second End Point	Coordinates of Midpoint
(2, 6)	(8, 10)	

2. Plot the first two end points given in the table on a coordinate plane. Join the points to form a line segment.

3. Find and mark the midpoint of the line segment. Check the location by measuring. Enter the coordinates of the midpoint in the third column of your table.

4. Choose four additional points and add them to your table. Repeat steps 2 and 3 for these new points. (Do not use points that will lead to horizontal or vertical line segments.)

5. Examine the entries in your table and compare the coordinates of the midpoints to the coordinates of the end points. How could you obtain the coordinates of the midpoint of a line segment using the coordinates of its end points?

6. Use the method you just described in step 5 to find the midpoint of the line segment that joins $P(4, 5)$ and $Q(8, 1)$. To check your method, draw the line segment PQ and mark the midpoint by measuring with a ruler. If the results do not match, go back to step 5 and try to find a better method.

7. Draw a diagram showing a line segment with end points $A(x_1, y_1)$ and $B(x_2, y_2)$.
   (a) Draw the triangle that could be used to find the length of AB on your diagram.
   (b) Mark the position of the midpoint of AB on your diagram.
   (c) Mark the point on the base of the triangle directly below the midpoint. What expression represents its x-coordinate?
   (d) Mark the point on the altitude of the triangle that is level with the midpoint. What expression represents its y-coordinate?
   (e) Explain how the coordinates of these two points verifies the formula you developed in step 5 for the coordinates of the midpoint of a line segment.

Part 3: Finding The Equation of a Line that Passes Through the Midpoint of a Line Segment

In previous mathematics courses you investigated properties of geometric shapes. You also found equations of lines drawn in a coordinate plane. Analytic geometry expands the study of geometric shapes using equations of lines.

Think, Do, Discuss

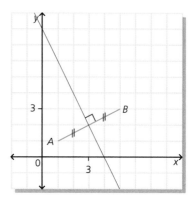

1. What information do you need to find the equation of a line?

2. Think about how to find the equation of the perpendicular bisector of the line segment with end points $A(1, 1)$ and $B(5, 3)$.

   (a) What is the bisector of a line segment? What is the line perpendicular to a line segment? What is the perpendicular bisector of a line segment?

   (b) What properties of the perpendicular bisector can you determine from the coordinates of A and B?

   (c) Describe how to find the coordinates of the point where the perpendicular bisector crosses the line segment AB.

   (d) Show how to use the slope of AB to find the slope of the perpendicular bisector.

   (e) Show how to use the slope and the coordinates of the point of intersection to determine the equation of the perpendicular bisector of AB.

3. Think about how to find the equation of the median from vertex R in a triangle with vertices at $P(5, 5)$, $Q(5, 10)$, and $R(10, 8)$.

   (a) What should you do to help visualize this problem? How does this help you solve the problem?

   (b) What is a median in a triangle?

   (c) What properties does the median have that you can determine from the description of $\triangle PQR$?

   (d) What points on $\triangle PQR$ does the median pass through?

   (e) Show how to use the coordinates of the vertices of $\triangle PQR$ to find the coordinates of two points on the median.

   (f) Show how to find the equation of the median using the coordinates of these points.

Focus 2.7

Key Ideas

- The coordinates of the midpoint of a line segment are the means of the coordinates of the end points.

- Given the line segment with end points $A(x_1, y_1)$ and $B(x_2, y_2)$, the midpoint is the point with coordinates $M\left(\frac{x_1 + x_2}{2}, \frac{y_1 + y_2}{2}\right)$.

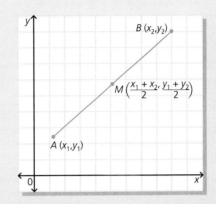

- A **median** (in geometry) is a line that joins a vertex of a triangle to the midpoint of the opposite side. For example, in $\triangle ABC$, CM is a median.

- The **perpendicular bisector** of a line segment is the line that is perpendicular to the line segment and passes through the midpoint of the line segment. For example, in $\triangle ABC$, CM is the perpendicular bisector of AB.

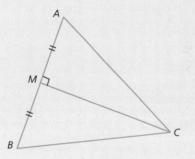

Example 1

Find the equation of the median line from vertex A in $\triangle ABC$, if the coordinates of the vertices are $A(-3, -1)$, $B(3, 5)$, and $C(7, -3)$.

Solution

The median connects vertex A to M, the midpoint of side BC.

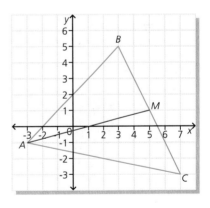

The coordinates of M are $\left(\frac{3 + 7}{2}, \frac{5 + (-3)}{2}\right) = (5, 1)$.

The slope of the line through A and M is

$$\frac{y_2 - y_1}{x_2 - x_1} = \frac{1 - (-1)}{5 - (-3)}$$

$$= \frac{2}{8}$$

$$= \frac{1}{4}$$

The equation of the line through A and M is $y = \frac{1}{4}x + b$.

To find b, substitute the coordinates of a known point, such as A, into the equation.

$$-1 = \tfrac{1}{4}(-3) + b$$

$$-1 + \tfrac{3}{4} = b$$

$$-\tfrac{1}{4} = b$$

The equation of the median from vertex A is $y = \tfrac{1}{4}x - \tfrac{1}{4}$.

Example 2

Find the equation of the perpendicular bisector of the line segment joining $P(-1, 4)$ to $Q(3, -2)$.

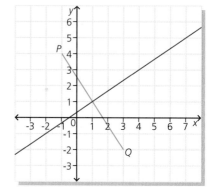

Solution

The slope of PQ is

$$\frac{y_2 - y_1}{x_2 - x_1} = \frac{-2 - 4}{3 - (-1)}$$

$$= \frac{-6}{4}$$

$$= -\frac{3}{2}$$

A line perpendicular to PQ has slope $\tfrac{2}{3}$, since $\tfrac{2}{3}$ is the negative reciprocal of $-\tfrac{3}{2}$.

A line that bisects PQ passes through its midpoint.

The midpoint of PQ has coordinates $\left(\frac{-1 + 3}{2}, \frac{4 + (-2)}{2}\right) = (1, 1)$.

The perpendicular bisector of PQ has the equation $y = \tfrac{2}{3}x + b$.

Since it passes through point $(1, 1)$,

$$1 = \tfrac{2}{3}(1) + b$$

$$1 - \tfrac{2}{3} = b$$

$$\tfrac{1}{3} = b$$

The equation of the perpendicular bisector of PQ is $y = \tfrac{2}{3}x + \tfrac{1}{3}$.

Did You Know?

Many sports involve intricately designed courts or playing fields. For instance, placing the lines on tennis courts or basketball courts involves constructing perpendicular bisectors. Can you spot the perpendicular bisectors in a tennis court or a basketball court? What other playing fields or courts involve bisectors?

Practise, Apply, Solve 2.7

A

1. Find the coordinates of the midpoint of each line segment on the grid.

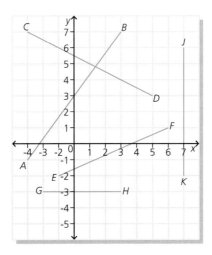

2. Find the coordinates of the midpoint of the line segment with these end points.

(a) $A(-1, 3)$ and $B(5, 7)$

(b) $X(6, -2)$ and $Y(-2, -2)$

(c) $J(-2, 3)$ and $K(3, 4)$

(d) $P(2, -4)$ and $Q(-3, 5)$

(e) $C(-6, -5)$ and $D(8, 3)$

(f) $M(5, -3)$ and $N(0, -1)$

(g) $S(4, -5)$ and $T(4, -12)$

(h) $U(\frac{1}{2}, -\frac{3}{2})$ and $V(-\frac{5}{2}, -\frac{1}{2})$

(i) $G(1.5, -2.5)$ and $H(-1, 4)$

3. On the plan of a garden design, a straight path runs from $(-25.6, 18.9)$ to $(40.5, 32.6)$. A lamp is to be placed at the midpoint. Find the coordinates of the lamp's position.

4. The end points of the diameter of a circle are $A(-1, 1)$ and $B(0.5, -3)$.
   (a) Find the coordinates of the centre of the circle.
   (b) Calculate the radius of the circle.

B

5. One end point of a line segment has coordinates $(-3, -1)$. The midpoint of the line segment is at $(1, 1)$. What is the location of the other end point?

6. A see-saw has its pivot at $P(2, 3)$ and one end at $A(-2, -3)$. Find the coordinates of the other end.

7. A radius of a circle has end points at $O(-1, 3)$ and $R(2, 2)$. Find two possible end points for the diameter that contains this radius. Describe any assumptions you make.

8. **Communication:** If you know the coordinates of the midpoint and one end point of a line segment, how can you find the coordinates of the other end point? Use an example to illustrate your explanation.

9. Find the midpoint of each diagonal of the quadrilateral with vertices $P(1, 3)$, $Q(6, 5)$, $R(8, 0)$, and $S(3, -2)$. Based on your results, what type of quadrilateral do you think $PQRS$ is?

10. The coordinates of one of the corners of a plan of a rectangular park have been erased. Explain how to use midpoints to find the missing coordinates.

11. A construction plan for a straight road tunnel to be built between points A and B, shows coordinates for A and B as "eastings" and "northings."

A: 611225.518 m E, 4857116.33 m N

B: 611248.114 m E, 4856975.45 m N

A junior engineer incorrectly marks out the midpoint of the tunnel, for access shaft, at the point with coordinates 611241.616 m E, 4857052.29 m N.
Find the correct coordinates for the shaft. How far must the markers be moved?

12. The points $P(5, -3)$, $Q(-2, 4)$, $R(-1, 7)$, and S are the vertices of a parallelogram $PQRS$. Find
(a) the coordinates of the midpoint of diagonal PR
(b) the coordinates of S

13. Find the lengths of the medians of the triangle with vertices at $A(2, -2)$, $B(-4, -4)$, and $C(0, 4)$.

14. Find the equations of the medians of the triangle with vertex coordinates $J(2, 5)$, $K(4, -1)$, and $L(-2, -5)$.

15. Find the equation of the perpendicular bisector of a chord of a circle, given that the end points of the chord are $C(-2, 0)$ and $D(4, -4)$.

16. **Knowledge and Understanding:** If you are given the equation of a line, how can you determine if it is
(a) a median of a given triangle?
(b) the perpendicular bisector of a side of a given triangle?

17. Application: A triangle has vertices $P(7, 7)$, $Q(-3, -5)$, and $R(5, -3)$.
   (a) Find the coordinates of the midpoints of the three sides of $\triangle PQR$.
   (b) Calculate the slopes of the midsegments of $\triangle PQR$. (Recall that a **midsegment** is a line segment that joins the midpoints of adjacent sides of a polygon.)
   (c) Calculate the slopes of the three sides of $\triangle PQR$.
   (d) Compare your answers in (b) and (c). What do you notice?

18. For $\triangle PQR$ in question 17,
   (a) calculate the lengths of the midsegments
   (b) calculate the lengths of the three sides of $\triangle PQR$
   (c) compare your answers in (a) and (b). What do you notice?

19. Check Your Understanding
   (a) Explain how to find the midpoint of a line segment.
   (b) Explain the steps you must take to find the equation of
      i. a median of a given triangle
      ii. the perpendicular bisector of a side of a given triangle
      Be sure to explain all mathematical terms that you use, and provide examples to illustrate your answer.

20. Thinking, Inquiry, Problem Solving: Prove that the properties that you discovered for the triangle formed by the midsegments of the triangle in questions 17 and 18 are true for all triangles.

21. Find the coordinates of the point that is one-third of the way from $A(1, 7)$ to $B(10, 4)$. Explain the method you used to find these coordinates.

22. A triangle has vertices at $S(6, 6)$, $T(-6, 12)$, and $U(0, -12)$. SM is the median from vertex S.
   (a) Find the coordinates of the point that is two-thirds of the way from S to M.
   (b) Repeat for medians TN and UO of the same triangle.
   (c) Prove that the medians intersect at a common point. What do you notice about this point?
   (d) Determine if this is true for all triangles.

The Chapter Problem—Placing the Surveyor's Stakes

In this section, you found the midpoints of line segments. Apply what you learned to answer these questions about the chapter problem on page 140.

1. Determine the radius of the semicircular part at the back of the building.
2. How long is the building from front to back?
3. How far apart are the diagonally opposite markers?
4. Find coordinates of the midpoint of the front lot line.

2.8 Classifying Shapes on a Coordinate Plane

When triangles and quadrilaterals are drawn on a coordinate plane, they are constructed from line segments. The lengths and slopes of the line segments can be used to classify or define specific types of triangles and quadrilaterals.

Part 1: Classifying Triangles

Think, Do, Discuss

1. On a coordinate plane, plot three points that are the vertices of a scalene triangle. Record the coordinates of each vertex.

   (a) Confirm that the triangle is scalene.

   (b) Describe how to use the coordinates of the vertices to verify that the triangle is scalene.

2. On a new grid, plot three points that are the vertices of an isosceles triangle. Record the coordinates of each vertex.

   (a) Confirm that the triangle is isosceles.

   (b) Describe how to use the coordinates of the vertices to verify that the triangle is isosceles.

3. Construct an equilateral triangle on a new grid and record the coordinates of each vertex.

   (a) How do you know that the triangle is equilateral?

   (b) How can you use the coordinates of the vertices to verify that the triangle is equilateral?

4. Construct a right triangle. Record the coordinates of each vertex. Explain how you can prove that the figure is a right triangle without actually drawing it, but referring only to the coordinates of the vertices.

5. Suppose that you are given the coordinates of the three vertices of a triangle. What calculations would you perform to determine if the triangle is isosceles? scalene? equilateral? a right triangle?

6. Suppose that you are given two identical triangles. One is drawn on a coordinate plane, with the coordinates of its vertices marked. The other is drawn accurately on a plain piece of paper. Which triangle will be easier to classify in terms of lengths and angles? Why?

Part 2: Classifying Quadrilaterals

Think, Do, Discuss

1. How can you prove, by calculation, that points $P(2, 3)$, $Q(5, 4)$, $R(6, 7)$, and $S(9, 8)$ are the vertices of a parallelogram? Do the calculations. Is *PQRS* a rectangle? Explain.

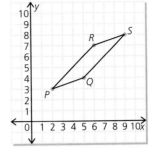

2. **(a)** Describe how to plot four points on a coordinate plane so that they form the vertices of a rhombus.

   (b) How can you use the coordinates to verify that the figure is a rhombus?

   (c) Use the procedure you described in (a) to construct a rhombus on the coordinate plane.

   (d) Verify that it actually is a rhombus.

3. Think about the rhombus you drew in step 2.

   (a) What would you have to do to make sure that the four points are the vertices of a square?

   (b) How can you use the coordinates to check?

4. A **kite** is a quadrilateral in which one of the diagonals is the perpendicular bisector of the other.

   (a) Plot four points that are the vertices of a kite.

   (b) Use the coordinates to determine the properties of the sides and diagonals.

   (c) How would you determine these properties if the kite had been drawn on a plain piece of paper instead of a coordinate plane? Discuss whether or not the task is simpler using a coordinate plane.

5. Draw any quadrilateral *ABCD*.

   (a) Find the coordinates of the midpoints of each side, and then join the midpoints to form a new quadrilateral.

   (b) Use the coordinates to show that the new quadrilateral is a parallelogram.

   (c) Suppose that the original quadrilateral had been drawn on a piece of paper with no coordinate system. You want to determine if the quadrilateral formed by the midsegments is a parallelogram. Is it more difficult or easier to do for the quadrilateral on plain paper or the quadrilateral defined by the coordinates of the vertices? Explain.

Focus 2.8

Key Ideas

- If you know the coordinates of the vertices of a triangle, then

  ♦ you can use the formula for the length of a line segment to determine the lengths of the sides of the triangle, and decide if the triangle is scalene (no sides equal), isosceles (two sides equal), or equilateral (all sides equal)

  ♦ you can use the slopes of the sides to determine if the triangle has a right angle

- If you know the coordinates of the vertices of a quadrilateral, you can determine the length and slopes of the sides and use the information to classify the quadrilateral as

  ♦ a parallelogram, if both pairs of opposite sides are parallel

  ♦ a rectangle, if the quadrilateral is a parallelogram and adjacent sides are perpendicular

  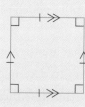

  ♦ a square, if the quadrilateral is a rectangle and all sides are the same length

  ♦ a rhombus, if both pairs of opposite sides are parallel and all sides are the same length

  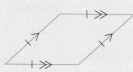

Example 1

A triangle has vertices at $L(-7, 0)$, $M(2, 1)$, and $N(-3, 5)$. Verify that this is an isosceles triangle with a right angle.

Solution

Start by sketching $\triangle LMN$.

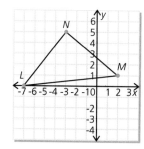

To classify the triangle, find the slope and length of each side.

$$\text{length} = \sqrt{(\Delta x)^2 + (\Delta y)^2}$$
$$= \sqrt{(x_2 - x_1)^2 + (y_2 - y_1)^2}$$

$$\text{slope} = \frac{\Delta y}{\Delta x}$$
$$= \frac{y_2 - y_1}{x_2 - x_1}$$

For LN,
$$\text{length} = \sqrt{(-3 - (-7))^2 + (5 - 0)^2}$$
$$= \sqrt{16 + 25}$$
$$= \sqrt{41} \text{ units}$$

$$\text{slope} = \frac{5 - 0}{-3 - (-7)}$$
$$= \frac{5}{4}$$

For NM,
$$\text{length} = \sqrt{(-3 - 2)^2 + (5 - 1)^2}$$
$$= \sqrt{25 + 16}$$
$$= \sqrt{41} \text{ units}$$

$$\text{slope} = \frac{5 - 1}{-3 - 2}$$
$$= \frac{4}{-5}$$
$$= -\frac{4}{5}$$

For LM,
$$\text{length} = \sqrt{(2 - (-7))^2 + (1 - 0)^2}$$
$$= \sqrt{81 + 1}$$
$$= \sqrt{82} \text{ units}$$

$$\text{slope} = \frac{1 - 0}{2 - (-7)}$$
$$= \frac{1}{9}$$

$LN = NM = \sqrt{41}$ units

Therefore, $\triangle LMN$ has two sides that are equal in length. This means that $\triangle LMN$ is isosceles.

$\text{slope}_{LN} = \frac{5}{4}$ and $\text{slope}_{NM} = -\frac{4}{5}$ $\left(\frac{5}{4} \times \left(-\frac{4}{5}\right) = -1\right)$

The slopes of these two line segments are negative reciprocals. This means that $LN \perp NM$ and $\angle LNM = 90°$. $\triangle LMN$ is a right triangle.

Example 2

An engineer needs to check the "setting out" of the base of a rectangular building before construction work on the foundations begins. Junior engineers have marked out the corners of the building at coordinates $P(6, 36)$, $Q(-30, 9)$, $R(-12, -15)$, and $S(24, 12)$, where each unit represents 1 m. The building is to be 45 m long and 30 m wide. Check that the given coordinates do mark out a rectangle with dimensions 45 m × 30 m.

Solution

Start by sketching *PQRS.*

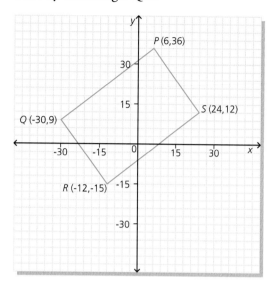

If *PQRS* is a rectangle, then opposite pairs of sides must be parallel and adjacent sides must be perpendicular. To confirm the shape and size of the quadrilateral, find the slope and length of each side, using the appropriate formulas:

$$\text{length} = \sqrt{(x_2 - x_1)^2 + (y_2 - y_1)^2} \qquad\qquad \text{slope} = \frac{y_2 - y_1}{x_2 - x_1}$$

For *PQ,*
$$\begin{aligned} \text{length} &= \sqrt{(-30 - 6)^2 + (9 - 36)^2} \\ &= \sqrt{1296 + 729} \\ &= \sqrt{2025} \\ &= 45 \text{ units} \end{aligned}$$
$$\begin{aligned} \text{slope} &= \frac{9 - 36}{-30 - 6} \\ &= \frac{-27}{-36} \\ &= \frac{3}{4} \end{aligned}$$

For *QR,*
$$\begin{aligned} \text{length} &= \sqrt{(-12 - (-30))^2 + (-15 - 9)^2} \\ &= \sqrt{324 + 576} \\ &= \sqrt{900} \\ &= 30 \text{ units} \end{aligned}$$
$$\begin{aligned} \text{slope} &= \frac{-15 - 9}{-12 - (-30)} \\ &= \frac{-24}{18} \\ &= -\frac{4}{3} \end{aligned}$$

For *RS,*
$$\begin{aligned} \text{length} &= \sqrt{(24 - (-12))^2 + (12 - (-15))^2} \\ &= \sqrt{1296 + 729} \\ &= \sqrt{2025} \\ &= 45 \text{ units} \end{aligned}$$
$$\begin{aligned} \text{slope} &= \frac{12 - (-15)}{24 - (-12)} \\ &= \frac{27}{36} \\ &= \frac{3}{4} \end{aligned}$$

For *SP,*
$$\begin{aligned} \text{length} &= \sqrt{(6 - 24)^2 + (36 - 12)^2} \\ &= \sqrt{324 + 576} \\ &= \sqrt{900} \\ &= 30 \text{ units} \end{aligned}$$
$$\begin{aligned} \text{slope} &= \frac{36 - 12}{6 - 24} \\ &= \frac{24}{-18} \\ &= -\frac{4}{3} \end{aligned}$$

Consider the slopes:

- *PQ* is parallel to *RS* and *QR* is parallel to *SP*. Both pairs of opposite sides are parallel.

- The slopes of all pairs of adjacent sides are negative reciprocals, so the vertex angles are all right angles.

The slope information verifies that *PQRS* is a rectangle.

Consider the side lengths:

- *PQ* and *RS* are both 45 m, and *QR* and *SP* are both 30 m.

The dimensions and shape of *PQRS* are correct.

Example 3

Points *J* and *K* lie on the same line, which has a slope of 2. *J* has coordinates (2, 3) and lies to the left of *K*. The length of segment *JK* is 15 units. What are the coordinates of *K*, correct to two decimal places?

Solution

Use the properties of slope and the Pythagorean theorem to answer this question.

Create a right triangle *JKL*, with *JK* as the hypotenuse.

Let the lengths of *JL* and *KL* be *x* and *y*, respectively.

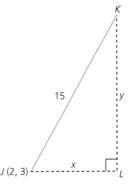

Then the coordinates of *K* are (2 + *x*, 3 + *y*).

Since the slope of *JK* is 2, $\frac{y}{x} = 2$. Therefore, *y* = 2*x*.

Use the Pythagorean theorem and substitute *y* = 2*x*:

$$x^2 + y^2 = 15^2$$
$$x^2 + (2x)^2 = 15^2$$
$$x^2 + 4x^2 = 225$$
$$5x^2 = 225$$
$$x^2 = 45$$
$$x = \sqrt{45}$$
$$x \doteq 6.71$$

Substitute the value of *x* into *y* = 2*x*.

$$y = 2x$$
$$y \doteq 2(6.71)$$
$$y \doteq 13.42$$

The coordinates of *K* are (2 + 6.71, 3 + 13.42) = (8.71, 16.42).

Practise, Apply, Solve 2.8

1. Consider this set of points: $A(-5, 1)$, $B(0, 3)$, $C(-1, 1)$, $D(-3, -3)$, $E(1, -3)$, $F(2, 1)$, $G(1, -1)$, $H(4, 3)$, $I(7, 3)$, $J(6, 6)$, $K(1, 3)$, and $L(1, 8)$.

   Determine if the two line segments are parallel, perpendicular, or neither:

   (a) AB and FI (b) CE and DG (c) HJ and CK

   (d) LH and KJ (e) CH and FI (f) GI and KJ

2. Show that
   (a) the line through $(1, 4)$ and $(5, 5)$ is parallel to the line through $(3, -4)$ and $(7, -3)$
   (b) the line through $(-1, 7)$ and $(3, 5)$ is perpendicular to the line through $(-4, 1)$ and $(-1, 7)$

3. For quadrilateral $ABCD$, the slopes of the sides are as follows:

Side	AB	BC	CD	DA
Slope	–5	$-\frac{1}{7}$	–5	$-\frac{1}{7}$

   What types of quadrilateral could $ABCD$ be? What other information is needed to exactly determine the type of quadrilateral?

4. The lengths of the sides in a quadrilateral are as follows:

   $PQ = 4.5$ units, $QR = 4.5$ units, $RS = 4.5$ units, $SP = 4.5$ units

   What types of quadrilateral could $PQRS$ be? What other information is needed to exactly determine the type of quadrilateral?

5. $P(-7, 1)$, $Q(-8, 4)$, and $R(-1, 3)$ are the vertices of a triangle. Show that $\triangle PQR$ is a right triangle.

6. Show that $\triangle KLM$, with vertices $K(-2, 1)$, $L(1, 5)$, and $M(5, 2)$, is isosceles.

7. Knowledge and Understanding: Show that the polygon defined by points $R(-5, 1)$, $S(5, 3)$, $T(2, -1)$, and $U(-8, -3)$ is a parallelogram.

8. Show that the quadrilateral with vertices $A(-2, 3)$, $B(-2, -2)$, $C(2, 1)$, and $D(2, 6)$ is a rhombus.

9. (a) Show that $EFGH$, where $E(-2, 3)$, $F(2, 1)$, $G(0, -3)$, and $H(-4, -1)$, is a a square.

   (b) Show that the diagonals of $EFGH$ are perpendicular to each other.

10. The vertices of quadrilateral $PQRS$ are $P(0, -5)$, $Q(-9, 2)$, $R(-5, 8)$, and $S(4, 2)$. Show that $PQRS$ is *not* a rectangle.

11. Determine the type of triangle described by each set of vertices in the table. Give reasons for your choices.

Triangle	(a)	(b)	(c)	(d)	(e)	(f)
Vertex 1	$A(2, 4)$	$P(-4, 8)$	$D(7, -8)$	$G(2, 9)$	$S(-1, -1)$	$K(-3, 4)$
Vertex 2	$B(5, -5)$	$Q(8, 2)$	$E(10, -4)$	$H(0, -2)$	$T(2, 3)$	$L(2, 6)$
Vertex 3	$C(-4, -2)$	$R(-4, 4)$	$F(-2, 5)$	$J(-8, 4)$	$U(5, -1)$	$M(4, 1)$
Scalene?						
Isosceles?						
Equilateral?						
Right?						
Reasons						

12. Communication: A square is a special type of rectangle. A square is also a special type of rhombus. How would you apply each of these descriptions when using the coordinates of the vertices of a quadrilateral to determine what type of quadrilateral it is? Include examples in your explanation.

13. Determine the type of quadrilateral described by each set of vertices. Give reasons for your answers.
(a) $J(-5, 2)$, $K(-1, 3)$, $L(-2, -1)$, $M(-6, -2)$ (b) $P(-5, 1)$, $Q(3, 3)$, $R(4, -1)$, $S(-4, -3)$
(c) $E(-5, -4)$, $F(-5, 1)$, $G(7, 4)$, $H(7, -1)$ (d) $A(3, -4)$, $B(9, 2)$, $C(14, -3)$, $D(8, -9)$
(e) $D(-1, 3)$, $E(6, 4)$, $F(4, -1)$, $G(-3, -2)$

14. A surveyor is marking the corners of a piece of land on which a building is to be constructed. If the corners have coordinates $(-5, 4)$, $(4, 9)$, $(9, 0)$, and $(0, -5)$, what shape is the building lot? Include your calculations in your answer.

15. Set up a computer spreadsheet to calculate the slope and the length of a line segment when the coordinates of the end points are entered. Use your spreadsheet to determine the type of each quadrilateral.
(a) $P(-2, -5)$, $Q(-6, 3)$, $R(2, 7)$, $S(6, -1)$
(b) $A(-2, 1)$, $B(-1, -3)$, $C(7, -1)$, $D(6, 3)$
(c) $J(-2, 5)$, $K(-3, -5)$, $L(2, -2)$, $M(3, 8)$

16. Suppose, when you are working with the vertex coordinates of a quadrilateral, you find that one pair of opposite sides is parallel, but the other pair is not. What type of quadrilateral is this? Investigate other types of quadrilaterals (for example, kites) and develop a method to identify these types from the vertex coordinates. Write a brief report of your findings.

17. (a) Points P and Q lie on the same straight line, which has a slope of 3. If P has coordinates $(2.5, 6)$ and Q is to the right of P by 5 units along the x-axis, determine the coordinates of Q, correct to two decimal places.
(b) Points S and T lie on the line $2x + y = 3$. If the length of ST is 13 units, and the coordinates of S are $(2, -1)$, determine all possible coordinate pairs for T, correct to two decimal places.

18. **Application:** An error has been made in setting out the square base of a building. The coordinates listed for the corners of the square are (60, 20), (90, 120), (−10, 140), and (−40, 50). Which coordinate pair is incorrect? Explain your choice. What should the coordinates be? Write a report explaining what the error is, how it was detected, and how it should be corrected.

19. **Check Your Understanding:** If you know the coordinates of the vertices of a quadrilateral, what calculations would help you determine if it is a special type of quadrilateral, such as a parallelogram, rectangle, rhombus, or square? How would you use the calculated values?

C

20. **Thinking, Inquiry, Problem Solving**
   (a) Show that the midpoints of the sides of any triangle are the vertices of a triangle exactly one-half the dimensions of the original and with sides parallel to the sides of the original.
   (b) Investigate whether a similar property exists for points that divide each of the sides in a ratio other than 1 : 1.

21. **(a)** Show that the midpoints of the sides of any quadrilateral are the vertices of a parallelogram.
   (b) Investigate whether this property is also true for points that divide the sides in a ratio other than 1 : 1.

The Chapter Problem—Placing the Surveyor's Stakes

In this section, you classified shapes on the coordinate plane. Apply what you learned to answer these questions about the chapter problem on page 140.

1. How far is the red marker line PQ, for the front of the building, from the front lot line?
2. What is the slope of the perpendicular bisector of the front lot line?
3. Determine the coordinates of the midpoint, N, of the front marker line PQ. (**Hint:** Use your answers to 1 and 2 and the method in example 3.)
4. How far is point N from point P? from point Q? Use the slope of PQ, lengths PN and NQ, and the method in example 3 to find the coordinates of points P and Q.
5. Use the slopes and lengths of PS and QR to find the coordinates of S and R.

The Geometer's Sketchpad: 2.9
Point of Intersection

The coordinates of the point where two line segments intersect can be found using *The Geometer's Sketchpad.*

1. Open a new sketch and create a graph with a grid.

2. Draw two line segments that cross and label all four end points.

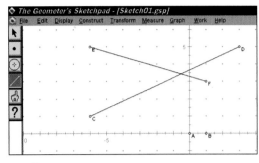

step 2

3. **Determine the point of intersection of the two line segments.**

   Select both line segments, then choose **Point At Intersection** from the **Construct** menu. (This option is not available unless both segments are selected.)

4. **Label the point and determine its coordinates.**

   Select the point, then choose **Coordinates** from the **Measure** menu.

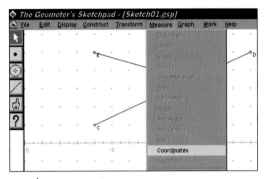

step 4a

As long as two line segments that intersect have been selected, steps 3 and 4 can always be used to determine the coordinates of the point of intersection.

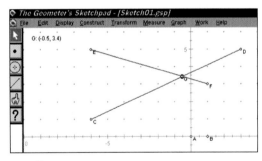

step 4b

Practise 2.9

Determine the coordinates of the point of intersection of line segments *AB* and *CD*.

	A	B	C	D
(a)	(4, 0)	(2, 2)	(1, 0)	(5, 2)
(b)	(–6, 3)	(4, –2)	(3, 0)	(–7, –2)
(c)	(–2, 3)	(2, –3)	(1, 4)	(–5, –4)
(d)	(–2, 2)	(7, 2)	(3, 4)	(3, –3)
(e)	(–5, 4)	(5, –2)	(–8, 1)	(3, 4)
(f)	(4, 4)	(4, –3)	(6, 2)	(–6, –4)

2.10 Using the Point of Intersection to Solve Problems

Analytic geometry is used in the design and manufacture of motor vehicles and airplanes. Designers use geometry because it allows them to create and test different designs cheaply and quickly.

An important consideration when designing a new vehicle is the position of its centre of mass.

Part 1: Modelling the Effect of Changes in the Centre of Mass

A paper airplane can be used to demonstrate the effect that a change in the position of the centre of mass has on a vehicle.

You will need some 8.5 × 11 in. paper (recycled is fine) and a small amount of clay or plasticene.

Think, Do, Discuss

1. Make a paper airplane and test it to see how it flies.

2. Add a small ball of plasticene to the nose of the airplane and fly the plane again. What effect does this weight have on the way the plane flies?

3. What effect do you think the plasticene weight has on the position of the centre of mass?

4. Move the weight back to the middle of the plane. Fly the plane again and note the effect of the weight in this position.

5. Now move the plasticene back to the tail of the plane. Fly the plane and note the effect of the weight in this position.

6. Write a report that summarizes what you discovered. Include a discussion of the implications for vehicle design.

Part 2: Points of Intersection and the Centre of Mass of a Triangle

One way to find the centre of mass of a complex object is to find the centres of mass of all the parts that make up the object. How could you find the centre of mass of the triangular-shaped parts of an object?

Think, Do, Discuss

1. On a coordinate grid, plot the three vertices of a triangle.
   (a) Draw the three **medians** of the triangle.
   (b) Find the coordinates of the point of intersection of the medians.
   (c) What is the name of the point where the three medians intersect? What is the geometric significance of this point?

2. On a new sketch, redraw the triangle you used in step 1.
   (a) Draw the **perpendicular bisectors** of all three sides.
   (b) Find the coordinates of the point of intersection of the perpendicular bisectors.
   (c) What is the name of the point where the three perpendicular bisectors meet? What is the significance of this point?

3. On another new sketch, redraw the same triangle.
   (a) Draw the **altitudes** from the three vertices.
   (b) Find the coordinates of the point of intersection of the altitudes.
   (c) What is the name of the point where the three altitudes meet? What is the significance of this point?

4. Describe some practical situations in which you would have to find the centre of one of these triangles. Try to think of at least one application for each of the three centres mentioned above.

5. What is the name of the point where the angle bisectors of a triangle intersect? Create a new triangle and construct this intersection.

6. In steps 1, 2, and 3, you found three different centres for a triangle. Which one of these centres represents the centre of mass of a triangular figure? Explain how to verify this assertion using the sketches you have created. Design and carry out an experiment to prove your theory.

Part 3: Using Analytic Geometry to Locate the Centroid

When design engineers are determining the centres of mass of all the parts of a new vehicle, they work with the coordinates of the different parts on a three-dimensional grid.

If a triangle is placed on a coordinate grid and the coordinates of the vertices are known, the coordinates of the **centroid** can be found using the properties of lines and line segments.

Consider the triangle with vertices at $A(0, 4)$, $B(-2, -2)$, and $C(6, 2)$.

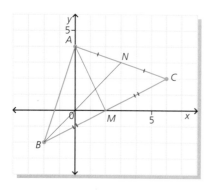

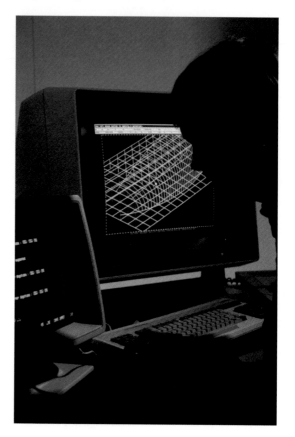

Think, Do, Discuss

1. If line segments AM and BN are medians, what are the coordinates of M and N?

2. Find the equation of the line containing line segment AM.

3. Find the equation of the line containing line segment BN.

4. What are the coordinates of the point where the two lines meet? What is the significance of this point?

5. Verify that the coordinates of this point can be found by calculating the mean of the x- and y-coordinates, respectively, of all three vertices.

Focus 2.10

Key Ideas

- For a triangle with known vertices on a coordinate plane, the centroid, the circumcentre, and the orthocentre can be located using properties of lines and line segments.

- The **centroid** of a triangle can be determined by finding the equations of two of the median lines, then finding the point of intersection of those two lines. It can also be found by calculating the mean of the x- and y-coordinates of all three vertices.

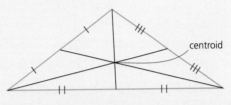

centroid

- The **circumcentre** can be determined by finding the equations of the perpendicular bisectors of two sides, then finding the point of intersection of those two lines.

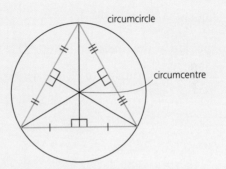

circumcircle

circumcentre

- The **orthocentre** can be determined by finding the equations of two of the altitude lines, and then finding the point of intersection of those two lines.

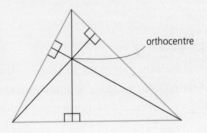

orthocentre

Example 1

A triangle has vertices at $A(-1, 4)$, $B(-1, -2)$, and $C(5, 1)$. Find the equation of the line that contains the altitude from vertex A.

Solution

Make a sketch.

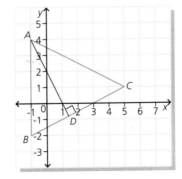

Let D be the foot of the altitude from A.

To find the equation of a line, you need to know the coordinates of two points on the line or the coordinates of one point and the slope of the line.

In this problem, you know that A is on the line.

You can find the slope of AD, since it is perpendicular to BC, whose slope can be determined from the coordinates of B and C.

$$\text{Slope of } BC = \frac{y_2 - y_1}{x_2 - x_1}$$
$$= \frac{1 - (-2)}{5 - (-1)}$$
$$= \frac{3}{6}$$
$$= \frac{1}{2}$$

The slope of AD is the negative reciprocal of $\frac{1}{2}$, which is -2.

The equation of the line containing AD is $y = -2x + b$.

Substitute the coordinates of $A(-1, 4)$ into the equation to find b.

$$4 = -2(-1) + b$$
$$4 - 2 = b$$
$$2 = b$$

The equation of the line that contains the altitude from A is $y = -2x + 2$.

Example 2

The plan shows the positions of three entrances to a parking lot. A tall mast light is to be erected to illuminate the three entrances, A, B, and C. Where should the light be located to illuminate each entrance equally?

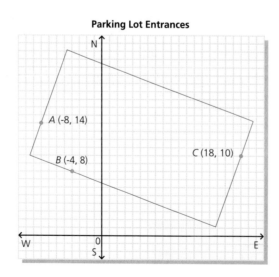

Parking Lot Entrances

Solution

The light should be located the same distance from each entrance. This point is the centre of the circle that contains the three entrance points—the circumcentre of the triangle formed by the three points. To find the circumcentre, you have to find the point where the perpendicular bisectors of two of the sides of the triangle intersect. To do this, you must find the equations of these perpendicular bisectors.

For line segment AB,

- the midpoint is $\left(\dfrac{-8 + (-4)}{2}, \dfrac{14 + 8}{2}\right)$ or $(-6, 11)$

- the slope is $\dfrac{8 - 14}{-4 - (-8)} = \dfrac{-6}{4} = -\dfrac{3}{2}$

For line segment BC,

- the midpoint is $\left(\dfrac{-4 + 18}{2}, \dfrac{8 + 10}{2}\right)$ or $(7, 9)$

- the slope is $\dfrac{10 - 8}{18 - (-4)} = \dfrac{2}{22} = \dfrac{1}{11}$

Since perpendicular lines have slopes that are negative reciprocals,

- the perpendicular bisector has slope $\dfrac{2}{3}$
- the equation is $y = \dfrac{2}{3}x + b$

Use the midpoint coordinates to find b.

$$11 = \tfrac{2}{3}(-6) + b$$
$$11 = -4 + b$$
$$15 = b$$

The equation is $y = \dfrac{2}{3}x + 15$.

- the perpendicular bisector has slope -11
- the equation is $y = -11x + b$

$$9 = -11(7) + b$$
$$9 = -77 + b$$
$$86 = b$$

The equation is $y = -11x + 86$.

One way to find the point of intersection is to enter these two equations into a graphing calculator and use the **intersect** function.

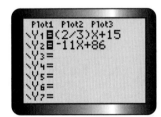 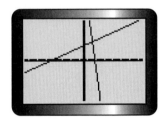 

Another way is to solve the system algebraically, using the substitution method, as follows.

At the point of intersection,

$$\frac{2}{3}x + 15 = -11x + 86$$

$$\frac{35}{3}x = 71$$

$$3\left(\frac{35x}{3}\right) = (71)3$$

$$35x = 213$$

$$x = \frac{213}{35}$$

$$x \doteq 6.09$$

Find the corresponding y-value by substituting this x-value into either equation.

$$y = \frac{2}{3}\left(\frac{213}{35}\right) + 15$$

$$y = \frac{142}{35} + 15$$

$$y \doteq 19.06$$

If the light is placed at (6, 19), it will be about the same distance from each entrance and illuminate each equally.

Example 3

The closest power line to the parking lot in example 2 runs along a straight line containing points (0, 4) and (12, 10). At what point should the lighting contractors connect to the power line, and how much cable will they need to reach the lamp? Each unit on the plan equals 1 m.

Solution

The light is at (6, 19). The shortest distance from the light to the power line is the perpendicular distance shown in the sketch.

You want to find the point of intersection of the power line and the perpendicular line from (6, 19).

Find the equations of the lines that contain these two line segments.

The slope of the power line is

$$\frac{10 - 4}{12 - 0} = \frac{6}{12}$$

$$= \frac{1}{2}$$

The y-intercept is at (0, 4).

The equation of the power line is $y = \frac{1}{2}x + 4$.

Since perpendicular lines have slopes that are negative reciprocals, the slope of the perpendicular from (6, 19) is the negative reciprocal of $\frac{1}{2}$, which is -2.

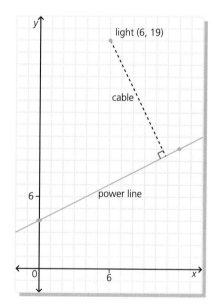

light (6, 19)

cable

power line

The equation of this line is $y = -2x + b$.

Find b by substituting the coordinates (6, 19) into the equation.

$$19 = -2(6) + b$$
$$19 = -12 + b$$
$$31 = b$$

The equation of the perpendicular from point (6, 19) is $y = -2x + 31$.

At the point where the perpendicular from (6, 19) meets the power line,

$$\tfrac{1}{2}x + 4 = -2x + 31$$
$$\tfrac{5}{2}x = 27$$
$$x = \tfrac{54}{5}$$
$$x = 10.8$$

Substituting this x-value to find the corresponding y-value,

$$y = \tfrac{1}{2}(10.8) + 4$$
$$y = 9.4$$

The contractors should connect into the power line at point (10.8, 9.4).

The length of cable required can be calculated using the distance formula:

$$\begin{aligned}
\text{length} &= \sqrt{(x_2 - x_1)^2 + (y_2 - y_1)^2} \\
&= \sqrt{(10.8 - 6)^2 + (9.4 - 19)^2} \\
&= \sqrt{23.04 + 92.16} \\
&= \sqrt{115.2} \\
&\doteq 10.7
\end{aligned}$$

The contractors will need about 10.7 m of cable to connect the light to the power line.

Practise, Apply, Solve 2.10

1. Given $A(2, 5)$, $B(-2, -1)$, and $C(6, 1)$,
   (a) classify line segment AM
   (b) find the coordinates of M

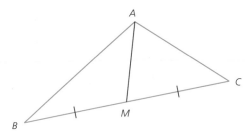

2. Given $P(1, 9)$, $Q(-3, 2)$, and $R(7, 0)$,
   (a) classify line segment PS
   (b) find the slope of line segment PS

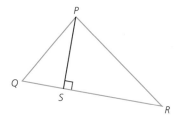

3. Given $D(0, 5)$, $E(-3, -2)$, and $F(3, 1)$,
   (a) classify line HJ
   (b) find the coordinates of G
   (c) find the slope of line segment HJ

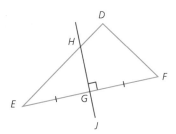

4. **Knowledge and Understanding:** Triangle ABC has vertices $A(3, 4)$, $B(4, -3)$, and $C(-4, -1)$.
   (a) Draw a sketch of the triangle.
   (b) Draw the altitude from vertex A.
   (c) Find the slope of side BC.
   (d) Find the slope of the altitude from A.
   (e) Find the equation of the line that contains this altitude.
   (f) Find the length of this altitude.
   (g) Find the area of the triangle.

5. Repeat question 4 for a triangle with vertices $A(-2, 2)$, $B(4, 0)$, and $C(-2, -3)$.

6. Triangle *DEF* has vertices *D*(2, 8), *E*(6, 2), and *F*(−3, 2).

    (a) Draw a sketch of the triangle.

    (b) Draw the altitudes from *D* and *E*.

    (c) Find the equation of the line that contains the altitude from *D*.

    (d) Find the equation of the line that contains the altitude from *E*.

    (e) Find the coordinates of the point of intersection of these two altitudes.

    (f) In geometrical terms, what is the point of intersection in (e) called?

7. Repeat question 6 (a) through (e) for a triangle with vertices *D*(−2, 5), *E*(5, 1), and *F*(−4, −5).

8. Triangle *PQR* has vertices *P*(−12, 6), *Q*(4, 0), and *R*(−8, −6).

    (a) Draw a sketch of the triangle.

    (b) Draw the medians from vertices *P* and *Q*.

    (c) Find the equation of the line that contains the median from *P*.

    (d) Find the equation of the line that contains the median from *Q*.

    (e) Find the coordinates of the point where the two medians intersect.

    (f) In geometrical terms, what is the point of intersection in (e) called? What is the significance of this point?

9. Repeat question 8 (a) through (e) for a triangle with vertices *P*(−6, 9), *Q*(6, 1), and *R*(−6, −7).

10. Triangle *JKL* has vertices *J*(−2, 0), *K*(2, 8), and *L*(7, 3).

    (a) Draw a sketch of the triangle.

    (b) Draw the perpendicular bisectors of *JK* and *LJ*.

    (c) Find the equations of these perpendicular bisectors.

    (d) Find the coordinates of the point where these two perpendicular bisectors intersect.

    (e) In geometrical terms, what is the point in (d) called? What is the significance of this point?

11. Repeat question 10 (a) through (d) for a triangle with vertices *J*(−2, 5), *K*(5, −2), and *L*(−8, −7).

12. Find the coordinates of the centroid of a triangular metal part with vertices at *A*(12, 18), *B*(18, 6), and *C*(3, 12).

13. Find the orthocentre of the triangle with vertices at *P*(−1, 5), *Q*(7, 2), and *R*(−1, −4).

14. Find the circumcentre of the triangle defined by *D*(5, 1), *E*(−2, 0), and *F*(4, 8).

15. An iceberg is situated off the coast of Newfoundland at map coordinates (40, 10). A cruise ship is at $(-20, 60)$ and is heading straight for $(50, -10)$. If the cruise ship maintains the same course, how close to the iceberg will the ship get?

16. Points $P(1, 8)$ and $Q(9, 2)$ are end points of a diameter of a circle, and $R(8, 9)$ is another point on the same circle.

   (a) Find the coordinates of the centre of the circle.

   (b) Determine the equations of the perpendicular bisectors of chords PQ and QR.

   (c) Show that these perpendicular bisectors intersect at the centre of the circle.

   (d) Show that $\triangle PQR$ is a right triangle.

17. Thinking, Inquiry, Problem Solving: A triangle has vertices at $A(-3, 2)$, $B(-5, -6)$, and $C(5, 0)$.

   (a) Find the equation of the line containing the median from vertex A.

   (b) Find the equation of the line containing the altitude from vertex A.

   (c) Find the equation of the perpendicular bisector of side BC.

   (d) What do you notice about the equations you found in (a), (b), and (c)? Give a possible explanation.

   (e) What type of triangle is $\triangle ABC$?

18. A design plan for a thin triangular computer component shows the coordinates of the vertices at (8, 12), (12, 4), and (2, 8). Find the coordinates of the centre of mass.

19. Communication: Write a paragraph to explain the importance of the centroid in design and manufacturing. Include a description of how the centroid of a triangular component of a design can be found using analytic geometry.

20. Application: Find the diameter of the largest circular pond that could fit in a triangular garden with vertices at (18, 54), $(-27, 36)$, and $(27, -18)$, where a unit represents 1 m.

21. Check Your Understanding: If you know the vertex coordinates of a triangle, how can you find the coordinates of

   (a) the centroid of the triangle?

   (b) the circumcentre of the triangle?

   (c) the orthocentre of the triangle?

C

22. Three homes in a rural area, marked *A*, *B*, and *C* in the diagram, are converting to natural gas heating. They will be connected to the gas line marked *GH* in the diagram. On a plan marked out in metres, the coordinates of the points are $A(-16, 32)$, $B(22, -24)$, $C(56, 8)$, $G(-16, -30)$, and $H(38, 42)$.

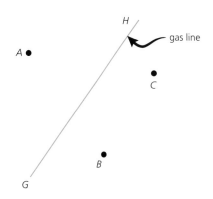

(a) Determine the length of pipe the gas company will need to connect the three houses to the gas line. Which homeowner will have the largest connection charge?

(b) Determine the best location for a light standard to illuminate the three homes equally.

23. Archeologists on a dig have found an outside fragment of an ancient circular platter. They want to construct a replica of the platter for a display. How could they use coordinates to find the diameter of the platter? Include a diagram in your explanation.

Note: When three or more lines intersect at the same point, the lines are said to be **concurrent**.

24. Triangle *DEF* has vertices $D(-2, 12)$, $E(-10, 4)$, and $F(2, 8)$. Show that the three medians are concurrent.

25. Triangle *JKL* has vertices $J(4, 3)$, $K(3, -4)$, and $L(-3, 0)$. Show that the three altitudes are concurrent.

26. Triangle *PQR* has vertices $P(6, 3)$, $Q(1, -2)$, and $R(4, -1)$. Show that the perpendicular bisectors of the three sides are concurrent.

27. Show that for any triangle, the triangle centres referred to in this section lie on the same line.

The Chapter Problem—Placing the Surveyor's Stakes

In this section, you found the point where lines intersect. Apply what you learned to answer these questions about the chapter problem on page 140.

1. Find the equation of the rear lot line.
2. Find the distance of marker stake *R* from the rear lot line.

2.11 Verifying Geometric Properties

In previous math courses, you explored the properties of midsegments and diagonals of polygons, using dynamic geometry software or investigating with paper and pencil. While it is interesting to observe these properties in sample diagrams, the properties are only really useful if they are stated precisely and if you know that they are always true—for all possible cases. By using coordinates and the properties of line segments, you can find this kind of assurance in the form of a **proof**.

Part 1: Recalling the Properties of the Diagonals of a Quadrilateral ———

Think, Do, Discuss

1. Plot and label four points, the vertices of a quadrilateral. Draw the diagonals of the quadrilateral and label the point of intersection.

   (a) Measure the angles at the point of intersection of the diagonals and the angles at the vertices. What properties or relationships seem to exist for these angles?

   (b) Measure the lengths of the line segments on the diagonals created by the point of intersection. What relationships seem to exist for these segments?

2. On a new sketch, repeat the construction in step 1, but this time draw a parallelogram. Repeat steps 1 (a) and (b) for this quadrilateral.

   (a) How are the properties of the diagonals of your parallelogram different from the properties of the diagonals of your quadrilateral in the first sketch?

   (b) Do you think these properties are true for any parallelogram?

3. If you know the coordinates of the vertices of a parallelogram, which diagonal property (or properties) could you verify for this parallelogram? How would you use the coordinates to verify the property?

4. Repeat the investigation for a rhombus, a rectangle, and a square.

5. Which diagonal properties can be verified if you know the vertex coordinates for a square, a rhombus, or a rectangle? Which properties cannot be verified?

Part 2: Verifying the Properties of the Diagonals of a Rectangle

Think, Do, Discuss

1. In your exploration you may have noticed that the diagonals of the rectangle you constructed bisect each other and are of equal length.

   (a) If every student in your class constructed a different rectangle and everyone noticed that the diagonals of their rectangle bisect each other and are of equal length, could you be certain that the diagonals of any given rectangle would have the same properties?

   (b) How many examples would you have to examine to be absolutely certain that the diagonals of every possible rectangle are equal in length and bisect each other?

   (c) Discuss whether studying a large number of examples would be sufficient to prove that the result holds for all rectangles.

   (d) If one person produced a rectangle that violated this property, what would that do to your confidence that the statement was always true?

2. Now you will prove that the diagonals of the rectangle with vertices at $A(-5, -1)$, $B(-5, 4)$, $C(7, 4)$, and $D(7, -1)$ are equal in length and bisect each other.

   (a) Sketch the rectangle. Mark all the information you have on the sketch.

   (b) Rewrite the property you have been asked to prove into a statement about the properties of angles or lengths of objects in your sketch.

   (c) What calculations do you need to make to prove that the diagonals of the rectangle are equal in length? Plan these calculations and then carry them out. Write a conclusion based on your results.

   (d) What must you show is true to prove that the diagonals bisect each other? Plan the steps needed to do this. Explain each step as you go and write a conclusion based on the results.

   (e) Describe how this proof for a specific rectangle could be adapted to prove that the result is true for all possible rectangles whose vertex coordinates are known.

Andrew Wiles, b. 1953

Andrew Wiles is the mathematician who proved Fermat's Last Theorem (page 577). You might try using the Internet to find out more about Dr. Wiles or to find the interview he did for the television show *Nova*. What does he have to say about the importance of proving something?

Focus 2.11

Example 1

Show that the midsegments of the quadrilateral with vertices at $P(-2, -2)$, $Q(0, 4)$, $R(6, 3)$, and $S(8, -1)$ form a parallelogram.

Solution

Start with a diagram.

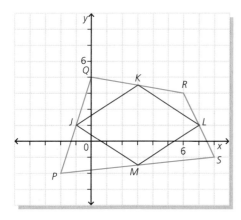

Then state what information is known and what needs to be shown.

Given: Quadrilateral $PQRS$ with vertices $P(-2, -2)$, $Q(0, 4)$, $R(6, 3)$, and $S(8, -1)$.

Show: The midsegments of $PQRS$ form a parallelogram (labelled $JKLM$ in the diagram).

What Needs to Be Done:

One way to show that *JKLM* is a parallelogram is to show that *JK* ∥ *LM* and *KL* ∥ *JM*. To show that, you have to know the slopes of the midsegments, and to find that you need to know the coordinates of *J, K, L,* and *M*.

Label the midpoints of *PQ, QR, RS,* and *SP* as *J, K, L,* and *M*.

Find the coordinates of the midpoints *J, K, L,* and *M*.

The coordinates of *J* are $\left(\dfrac{-2+0}{2}, \dfrac{-2+4}{2}\right) = (-1, 1)$.

The coordinates of *K* are $\left(\dfrac{0+6}{2}, \dfrac{4+3}{2}\right) = (3, 3.5)$.

The coordinates of *L* are $\left(\dfrac{6+8}{2}, \dfrac{3+(-1)}{2}\right) = (7, 1)$.

The coordinates of *M* are $\left(\dfrac{8+(-2)}{2}, \dfrac{-1+(-2)}{2}\right) = (3, -1.5)$.

Find the slopes of the midsegments.

The slope of *JK* is $\dfrac{3.5-1}{3-(-1)} = 0.625$.　　The slope of *KL* is $\dfrac{1-3.5}{7-3} = -0.625$.

The slope of *LM* is $\dfrac{-1.5-1}{3-7} = 0.625$.　　The slope of *MJ* is $\dfrac{1-(-1.5)}{-1-3} = -0.625$.

Compare the slopes to see if the opposite sides are parallel.

Side *JK* is parallel to side *LM*, since the slopes of these line segments are the same.

Side *KL* is parallel to side *MJ*, since the slopes of these line segments are the same.

Therefore, *JKLM* is a parallelogram, since both pairs of opposite sides are parallel.

Example 2

(a) Show that points *A*(−4, 3) and *B*(3, −4) lie on the circle with equation $x^2 + y^2 = 25$.

(b) Show that the perpendicular bisector of chord *AB* passes through the centre of the circle.

Solution

(a) Start with a sketch.

Given: The circle $x^2 + y^2 = 25$. Points *A*(−4, 3) and *B*(3, −4).

Show: *A* and *B* are points on the given circle.

If *A*(−4, 3) lies on the circle, then its coordinates satisfy the equation of the circle.

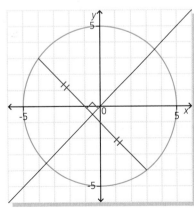

Substitute the coordinates of A into $x^2 + y^2 = 25$.

$$\text{Left side} = (-4)^2 + (3)^2 \qquad\qquad \text{Right side} = 25$$
$$= 16 + 9$$
$$= 25$$

Since the left side equals the right side, the coordinates of A satisfy the equation. Point A lies on the circle.

In the same way, for $B(3, -4)$,

$$x^2 + y^2 = 3^2 + (-4)^2$$
$$= 9 + 16$$
$$= 25$$

(b) Show: The perpendicular bisector of chord AB passes through the centre of the circle.

What Needs to Be Done:

Show that the perpendicular bisector of AB passes through the centre of the circle by showing that the coordinates of the centre satisfy the equation of the perpendicular bisector. To do that, first you must find that equation.

To find the equation of the perpendicular bisector you need to know a point on the bisector and its slope. Since the bisector is perpendicular to AB, its slope is the negative reciprocal of the slope of AB. The known point can be the midpoint of AB.

The midpoint of chord AB has coordinates $\left(\dfrac{-4 + 3}{2}, \dfrac{3 + (-4)}{2}\right) = \left(-\dfrac{1}{2}, -\dfrac{1}{2}\right)$.

The perpendicular bisector of AB passes through $\left(-\dfrac{1}{2}, -\dfrac{1}{2}\right)$.

The slope of AB is $\dfrac{-4 - 3}{3 - (-4)} = \dfrac{-7}{7}$ or -1.

The slope of the perpendicular bisector of AB is the negative reciprocal of -1, which is 1.

The equation of the perpendicular bisector is $y = x + b$.

To find b, substitute the coordinates $\left(-\dfrac{1}{2}, -\dfrac{1}{2}\right)$ into $y = x + b$.

$$-\frac{1}{2} = -\frac{1}{2} + b$$
$$0 = b$$

The equation of the perpendicular bisector of chord AB is $y = x$.

If the perpendicular bisector passes through the centre of the circle $x^2 + y^2 = 25$, the coordinates of the centre satisfy the equation $y = x$.

The centre of the circle $x^2 + y^2 = 25$ is at $(0, 0)$.

Substitute $(0, 0)$ into the equation $y = x$.

$$\text{Left side} = 0 \qquad\qquad \text{Right side} = 0$$

The coordinates satisfy the equation.

Therefore, the perpendicular bisector of chord AB passes through the centre of the circle $x^2 + y^2 = 25$.

Practise, Apply, Solve 2.11 ———————

A

1. A rectangle is defined by the vertices $A(-6, 5)$, $B(12, -1)$, $C(8, -13)$, and $D(-10, -7)$. Prove that the diagonals are equal in length.

2. Show that $\triangle PQR$, with $P(-2, 1)$, $Q(1, 5)$, and $R(5, 2)$, is isosceles.

B

3. **Knowledge and Understanding:** A rectangle is defined by the vertices $J(10, 0)$, $K(-8, 6)$, $L(-12, -6)$, and $M(6, -12)$. Show that the diagonals bisect each other.

4. A triangle has vertices $D(-5, 4)$, $E(1, 8)$, and $F(-1, -2)$. Show that the altitude from vertex D bisects side EF.

5. Triangle KLM has vertices at $K(4, 7)$, $L(8, 1)$, and $M(-2, 3)$. Show that the perpendicular bisector of LM passes through vertex K.

6. Show that the midsegments of the rhombus with vertices $R(-5, 2)$, $S(-1, 3)$, $T(-2, -1)$, and $U(-6, -2)$ form a rectangle.

7. Show that the midsegments of the square with vertices $A(2, -12)$, $B(-10, -8)$, $C(-6, 4)$, and $D(6, 0)$ form a square.

8. **Communication:** Explain why it is important to be able to prove the properties of geometric figures. How do the techniques of analytic geometry help with these proofs?

9. **Application:** A triangular lot has vertices at $A(8, 12)$, $B(-4, -4)$, and $C(8, -8)$. Show that the median from A coincides with the altitude from A and the perpendicular bisector of BC.

10. Show that points $(9, -3)$, $(8, 6)$, and $(-1, 5)$ lie on the same circle with its centre at $(4, 1)$.

11. A triangle has vertices at $P(-2, 2)$, $Q(-1, -3)$, and $R(4, 1)$. Show that the line segment joining the midpoints of PQ and PR is parallel to QR and half of its length.

12. Show that the diagonals of the rhombus in question 6 bisect each other at right angles.

13. **Check Your Understanding:** Why is it necessary to show that the properties of shapes are true? List the essential features of a geometric proof using analytic geometry.

C

14. Triangle *ABC* has vertices at *A*(3, 4), *B*(−2, 0), and *C*(5, 0). Prove that the area of the triangle formed by the midsegments of △*ABC* is one-quarter of the area of △*ABC*.

15. Investigate the properties of the line that joins the midpoints of the non-parallel sides of a trapezoid. Prove the properties using analytic geometry.

16. The diagram shows a rectangle with vertices at the origin, (*a*, 0), and (0, *b*).

(a) State the coordinates of the fourth vertex.

(b) Show that the diagonals are equal in length.

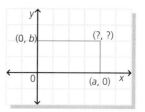

17. Given △*ABC* as shown,

(a) find the coordinates of the midpoints of sides *AB* and *AC*

(b) show that the midsegment joining the midpoints in (a) is parallel to side *BC* and half its length

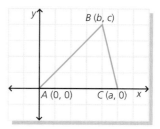

18. **Thinking, Inquiring, Problem Solving:** Draw a parallelogram with one vertex at the origin and one vertex at (*a*, 0). Define variable coordinates for the other vertices. Prove that the diagonals bisect each other.

19. A quadrilateral has vertex coordinates *A*(*a*, *b*), *B*(*c*, *d*), *C*(*e*, *f*), *D*(*g*, *h*). *P*, *Q*, *R*, and *S* are the midpoints of sides *AB*, *BC*, *CD*, and *DA*, respectively.
(a) Find the coordinates of *P*, *Q*, *R*, and *S*.
(b) Prove that *PQRS* is a parallelogram.

The Chapter Problem—Placing the Surveyor's Stakes

In this section, you verified geometric properties. Apply what you learned to answer these questions about the chapter problem on page 140.

1. Verify that the corner stakes really do mark out a rectangle.
2. Check that the dimensions of the rectangle are correct.

Coordinates and Geometry: Where Shapes Meet Symbols

Check Your Understanding

1. What is a line segment and what properties of line segments are used in analytic geometry?

2. **(a)** How would you determine which of two given points is closer to the origin? State the formula you would use.
   (b) Repeat (a) to determine which of the two points is closer to a third given point.

3. What equation can you use to model the path a satellite takes as it orbits the Earth? Explain the variables and form of the equation.

4. How can you find the midpoint of a line segment, if you know the coordinates of the end points? How can you find the coordinates of an end point of a line segment, if you know the midpoint and the other end point?

5. What is a perpendicular bisector of a line segment? How would you find the equation of the perpendicular bisector of a line segment, if you know the coordinates of the end points?

6. What is the difference between a median and an altitude? How would you find the equation of a median in a triangle whose vertex coordinates are known? How would you find the equation of an altitude?

7. Describe two methods you could use to determine if a triangle whose vertex coordinates are given is a right triangle.

8. How does analytic geometry make it possible to determine if a triangle is isosceles, equilateral, or scalene?

9. What properties of line segments would you use to determine whether a given quadrilateral is a parallelogram, a rhombus, a rectangle, a square, or none of these? How would these properties help you to classify the quadrilateral?

10. A triangle can be thought of as having three centres. What are the names of these centres? If you know the coordinates of the vertices of a triangle, how would you find the coordinates of each triangle centre?

11. How would you find the distance of a given point from a line whose equation you know?

2.1–2.3 Distance on the Plane—Part I: Distance from the Origin

- The distance, d, from the origin $(0, 0)$ to any point (x, y) is $d = \sqrt{x^2 + y^2}$.

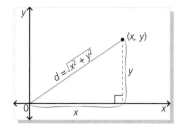

Example

In a game of hide-and-seek, Amy counts to 20 while her three friends find places to hide. Amy is at the origin, $(0, 0)$; Jessica hides at point $(5, -12)$; Pradeep hides at $(-8, 11)$; and Kevin hides at $(3, 13)$. Who is farthest from Amy?

Solution

The distance of a point (x, y) from the origin $(0, 0)$ is given by $d = \sqrt{x^2 + y^2}$.

At $(5, -12)$, Jessica's distance from Amy at $(0, 0)$ is

$$d = \sqrt{5^2 + (-12)^2}$$
$$= 13$$

At $(3, 13)$, Kevin's distance from Amy is

$$d = \sqrt{3^2 + 13^2}$$
$$\doteq 13.3$$

At $(-8, 11)$, Pradeep's distance from Amy is

$$d = \sqrt{(-8)^2 + 11^2}$$
$$\doteq 13.6$$

Pradeep is farthest from Amy.

Extra Practice

1. Which one of these points is closest to the origin: $A(-2, 7)$, $B(5, -5)$, or $C(-4, -6)$?

2. An injured person must be transported from an accident site to the nearest hospital by helicopter. If the accident site is at $(0, 0)$ and hospitals are at $P(27, -55)$, $Q(-19, 59)$, and $R(34, 51)$, which hospital (P, Q, or R) should the pilot head for?

3. A triangle has vertices at $M(24, -7)$, $N(24, 18)$, and $O(0, 0)$. Find the lengths of its sides. What type of triangle is $\triangle MNO$? Explain your answer.

2.4 The Equation of a Circle

- A circle is the set of all points in a plane that are the same distance from a fixed point, the centre. The distance from any point on the circle to the centre is called the **radius**.

- If the centre of the circle is at the origin of the x-y plane and the radius is r units, then $r = \sqrt{x^2 + y^2}$, which is equivalent to $x^2 + y^2 = r^2$. This equation, $x^2 + y^2 = r^2$, is the equation of a circle with centre $(0, 0)$ and radius r.

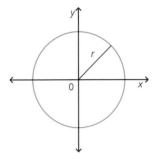

Example

A ruptured oil tanker at $(0, 0)$ starts to leak oil in a circular pattern. If the radius of the circle of oil increases steadily at 3 m/min, what equation would represent the perimeter of the oil slick exactly 5 min after the rupture? How long does it take for the oil slick to reach a seagull swimming at $(-12, 25)$? (Grid units are metres.)

Solution

Exactly 5 min after the rupture, the radius is $5 \times 3 = 15$ m.

The equation of a circle with centre at $(0, 0)$ and radius r is $x^2 + y^2 = r^2$.

Exactly 5 min after the rupture, the perimeter of the oil slick is modelled by a circle with centre at $(0, 0)$ and radius 15 m. The equation is

$$x^2 + y^2 = 15^2$$
$$x^2 + y^2 = 225$$

The distance of the seagull at $(-12, 25)$ from the tanker at $(0, 0)$ is

$$d = \sqrt{(-12)^2 + 25^2}$$
$$\doteq 28$$

The oil slick will reach the seagull when its radius is about 28 m.

Since the radius is increasing at 3 m/min, this will take about $28 \div 3 \doteq 9.3$ min.

Extra Practice

4. i. For each circle, state the coordinates of the centre, the radius, the diameter, and the x- and y-intercepts.
   ii. Sketch a graph of each circle.
   (a) $x^2 + y^2 = 169$ (b) $x^2 + y^2 = 2.89$ (c) $x^2 + y^2 = 98$

5. Find the equation of the circle, with centre at $(0, 0)$, that passes through each point.

(a) $(-5, 0)$ (b) $(0, 7)$ (c) $(-3, -8)$ (d) $(4, -9)$

6. A raindrop falls into a puddle and causes a circular ripple to spread out. The radius of the ripple grows at a steady rate of 5 cm/s. What equation would model the ripple exactly 6 s after the raindrop lands in the puddle?

2.5 Distance on the Plane—Part II

- The distance between points $A(x_1, y_1)$ and $B(x_2, y_2)$ in the coordinate plane is

$$d = \sqrt{(\Delta x^2) + (\Delta y^2)}$$
$$= \sqrt{(x_2 - x_1)^2 + (y_2 - y_1)^2}$$

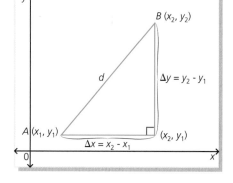

- A **line segment** is the part of a line between two specific points, including the points themselves.

- The slope of a line segment is the same as the slope of the line containing the line segment.

- Parallel line segments have the same slope.

- The slopes of two perpendicular line segments are negative reciprocals. (Their product is -1.) For example, $\frac{5}{4}$ and $-\frac{4}{5}$ are negative reciprocals.

Example

A triangle has vertices at $A(-2, 6)$, $B(-5, 1)$, and $C(3, -1)$. By finding the lengths of its sides, determine if the triangle is isosceles, equilateral, or scalene.

Solution

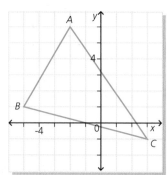

Use the distance formula to find the length of each side of the triangle.

Length of AB	Length of BC	Length of CA
$= \sqrt{(-5-(-2))^2 + (1-6)^2}$	$= \sqrt{(3-(-5))^2 + (-1-1)^2}$	$= \sqrt{(-2-3)^2 + (6-(-1))^2}$
$= \sqrt{34}$	$= \sqrt{68}$	$= \sqrt{74}$
$\doteq 5.8$ units	$\doteq 8.2$ units	$\doteq 8.6$ units

Since the sides all have different lengths, the triangle is scalene.

Extra Practice

7. Find the distance between each pair of points.

    (a) $(2, 2)$ and $(7, 4)$ **(b)** $(-3, 0)$ and $(8, -5)$

    (c) $(9, -3)$ and $(12, -4)$

8. A triangle has vertices at $A(1, 1)$, $B(-2, -1)$, and $C(3, -2)$. Find the lengths of its sides to determine if the triangle is isosceles, equilateral, or scalene.

9. A power line is to be laid from point $A(-22, 15)$ to $B(7, 33)$ to $C(10, 18)$ to $D(-1, 4)$. If the units are metres, what length of cable is required to complete the job?

2.6–2.7 Finding the Midpoint of a Line Segment

- The coordinates of the midpoint of a line segment are the means of the coordinates of the end points.

- Given the line segment with end points $A(x_1, y_1)$ and $B(x_2, y_2)$, the midpoint is the point with coordinates $M\left(\frac{x_1 + x_2}{2}, \frac{y_1 + y_2}{2}\right)$.

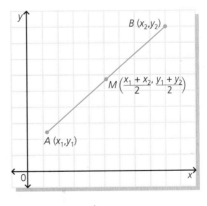

- A **median** (in geometry) is a line that joins a vertex of a triangle to the midpoint of the opposite side. For example, in $\triangle ABC$, CM is a median.

- The **perpendicular bisector** of a line segment is the line that is perpendicular to the line segment and passes through the midpoint of the line segment. For example, in $\triangle ABC$, CM is the perpendicular bisector of AB.

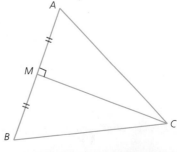

Example

Find the lengths of the midsegments of $\triangle ABC$ with vertex coordinates $A(-2, 10)$, $B(-9, 2)$, and $C(3, -3)$.

Solution

Draw a diagram, labelling the midpoints of sides BC, AC, and AB, as M, N, and P, respectively. Draw the midsegments MN, NP, and PM.

Midpoint M has coordinates $\left(\frac{(-9) + 3}{2}, \frac{2 + (-3)}{2}\right)$ or $(-3, -0.5)$.

Midpoint N has coordinates $\left(\frac{(-2) + 3}{2}, \frac{10 + (-3)}{2}\right)$ or $(0.5, 3.5)$.

Midpoint P has coordinates $\left(\frac{(-2) + (-9)}{2}, \frac{10 + 2}{2}\right)$ or $(-5.5, 6)$.

The distance from M to N is

$$\begin{aligned} d &= \sqrt{(0.5 - (-3))^2 + (3.5 - (-0.5))^2} \\ &= \sqrt{3.5^2 + 4^2} \\ &\doteq 5.3 \end{aligned}$$

The distance from N to P is

$$\begin{aligned} d &= \sqrt{(-5.5 - 0.5)^2 + (6 - 3.5)^2} \\ &= \sqrt{(-6)^2 + 2.5^2} \\ &\doteq 6.5 \end{aligned}$$

The distance from P to M is

$$\begin{aligned} d &= \sqrt{(-3 - (-5.5))^2 + (-0.5 - 6)^2} \\ &= \sqrt{2.5^2 + (-6.5)^2} \\ &\doteq 7.0 \end{aligned}$$

The midsegments of $\triangle ABC$ are 5.3 units, 6.5 units, and 7.0 units, to one decimal place.

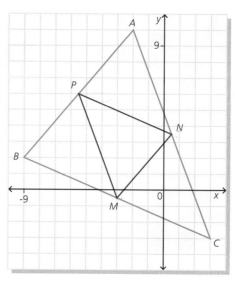

Extra Practice

10. Find the coordinates of the midpoint of the line segment with these end points.

    (a) $(-1, -2)$ and $(-7, 10)$ **(b)** $(6, 4)$ and $(0, 0)$

    (c) $(5, -1)$ and $(-2, 9)$ **(d)** $(4, -5)$ and $(9, -6)$

    (e) $(0, -4)$ and $(12, 0)$ **(f)** $(-2, 3)$ and $(3, 5)$

11. A diameter of a circle has end points $A(9, -4)$, and $B(3, -2)$. Find the centre and the radius of the circle.

12. $\triangle PQR$ has vertices $P(12, 4)$, $Q(-6, 2)$, and $R(-4, -2)$. Find

    (a) the coordinates of the midpoints of its sides

    (b) the length of the median from vertex Q

    (c) the equation of the perpendicular bisector of side PQ

2.8 Classifying Shapes on a Coordinate Plane

- If you know the coordinates of the vertices of a triangle, then

  - you can use the formula for the length of a line segment to determine the lengths of the sides of the triangle, and decide if the triangle is scalene (no sides equal), isosceles (two sides equal), or equilateral (all sides equal)

  - you can use the slopes of the sides to determine if the triangle has a right angle

- If you know the coordinates of the vertices of a quadrilateral, you can determine the length and slopes of the sides and use the information to classify the quadrilateral as

  - a parallelogram, if both pairs of opposite sides are parallel

  - a rectangle, if the quadrilateral is a parallelogram and adjacent sides are perpendicular

  - a square, if the quadrilateral is a rectangle and all sides are the same length

  - a rhombus, if both pairs of opposite sides are parallel and all sides are the same length

Example

Is $\triangle PQR$, with vertices $P(2, 1)$, $Q(-1, -3)$, and $R(6, -2)$, an isosceles, equilateral, scalene, or right triangle? (More than one classification can apply.)

Solution

Draw a diagram of $\triangle PQR$.

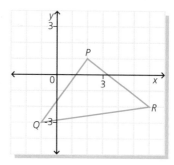

Find the length and the slope of each side of the triangle, using the formulas

$$\text{slope} = \frac{y_2 - y_1}{x_2 - x_1} \qquad\qquad \text{length} = \sqrt{(x_2 - x_1)^2 + (y_2 - y_1)^2}$$

For PQ,

$$\text{slope} = \frac{-3 - 1}{-1 - 2}$$
$$= \frac{-4}{-3}$$
$$= \frac{4}{3}$$

$$\text{length} = \sqrt{(-1 - 2)^2 + (-3 - 1)^2}$$
$$= \sqrt{9 + 16}$$
$$= \sqrt{25}$$
$$= 5 \text{ units}$$

For QR,

$$\text{slope} = \frac{-2 - (-3)}{6 - (-1)}$$
$$= \frac{1}{7}$$

$$\text{length} = \sqrt{(6 - (-1))^2 + (-2 - (-3))^2}$$
$$= \sqrt{49 + 1}$$
$$= \sqrt{50}$$
$$\doteq 7.1 \text{ units}$$

For RP,

$$\text{slope} = \frac{1 - (-2)}{2 - 6}$$
$$= \frac{3}{-4}$$
$$= -\frac{3}{4}$$

$$\text{length} = \sqrt{(2 - 6)^2 + (1 - (-2))^2}$$
$$= \sqrt{16 + 9}$$
$$= \sqrt{25}$$
$$= 5 \text{ units}$$

Since the slopes of PQ and RP are negative reciprocals, PQ is perpendicular to RP. $\triangle PQR$ is a right triangle.

Side PQ and side RP are both 5 units long, so $\triangle PQR$ is isosceles.

Extra Practice

13. If you know the vertex coordinates of a triangle, what calculations do you need to make to determine what type of triangle it is?

14. Show that $\triangle ABC$, where $A(1, 1)$, $B(2, 5)$, and $C(6, 6)$, is isosceles.

15. Write the names of the various types of quadrilaterals along with their special properties. If you know the coordinates of the vertices of a quadrilateral, what calculations can you make to determine what type of quadrilateral it is?

16. Show that the quadrilateral with vertices $J(-1, 1)$, $K(3, 4)$, $L(8, 4)$, and $M(4, 1)$ is a rhombus.

17. What type of quadrilateral(s) is (are) defined by each set of vertices? Explain your choices.

    (a) $A(-5, 3)$, $B(-4, -2)$, $C(7, -1)$, $D(6, 4)$

    (b) $E(-1, 0)$, $F(1, -8)$, $G(9, -6)$, $H(7, 2)$

2.9–2.10 Using the Point of Intersection to Solve Problems

- For a triangle with known vertices on a coordinate plane, the centroid, the circumcentre, and orthocentre can be located using properties of lines and line segments.

- The **centroid** of a triangle can be determined by finding the equations of two of the median lines, then finding the point of intersection of those two lines. It can also be found by calculating the mean of the x- and y-coordinates of all three vertices.

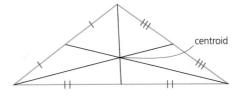

- The **circumcentre** can be determined by finding the equations of the perpendicular bisectors of two sides, then finding the point of intersection of those two lines.

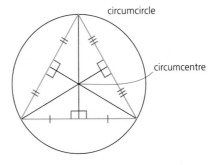

- The **orthocentre** can be determined by finding the equations of two of the altitude lines, and then finding the point of intersection of those two lines.

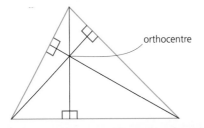

Example

On a design plan, the vertices of a thin triangular component are $A(-2, 4)$, $B(6, 2)$, and $C(-4, -2)$. Find the centre of mass.

(a) Find the midpoints of two sides.

(b) Find the equations of the lines containing the medians.

(c) Find the point of intersection of these lines.

(d) What other name does this point have?

(e) Is there another way to find the centre of mass?

Solution

(a) Draw a sketch.

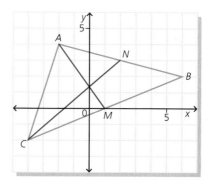

In the sketch, M and N are the midpoints of BC and AB, respectively.

(b) M has coordinates $\left(\dfrac{-4 + 6}{2}, \dfrac{-2 + 2}{2}\right) = (1, 0)$.

Slope of median AM

$$= \frac{0 - 4}{1 - (-2)}$$

$$= \frac{-4}{3}$$

The equation of the line containing AM is
$y = -\dfrac{4}{3}x + b.$

Substitute the coordinates of $A(-2, 4)$ into this equation to find b.

$$4 = -\frac{4}{3}(-2) + b$$

$$4 = \frac{8}{3} + b$$

$$4 - \frac{8}{3} = b$$

$$\frac{4}{3} = b$$

The equation is $y = -\dfrac{4}{3}x + \dfrac{4}{3}.$

N has coordinates $\left(\dfrac{6 + (-2)}{2}, \dfrac{2 + 4}{2}\right) = (2, 3)$.

Slope of median CN

$$= \frac{3 - (-2)}{2 - (-4)}$$

$$= \frac{5}{6}$$

The equation of line containing CN is
$y = \dfrac{5}{6}x + b.$

Substitute the coordinates of $C(-4, -2)$ into this equation to find b.

$$-2 = \frac{5}{6}(-4) + b$$

$$-2 = -\frac{10}{3} + b$$

$$-2 + \frac{10}{3} = b$$

$$\frac{4}{3} = b$$

The equation is $y = \dfrac{5}{6}x + \dfrac{4}{3}.$

(c) Since both lines have the same y-intercept, that must be where they intersect. The centre of mass is at $\left(0, \frac{4}{3}\right)$.

(d) The centre of mass is also the centroid.

(e) The point is also found by computing the means of the vertices.

$$\left(\frac{-2 + 6 + (-4)}{3}, \frac{4 + 2 + (-2)}{3}\right) = \left(0, \frac{4}{3}\right)$$

Extra Practice

18. A new lookout tower is to be equidistant from three ranger stations. If the stations are at positions $A(-90, 28)$, $B(0, -35)$, and $C(125, 20)$, find the coordinates of the point where the new tower should be built.

19. Find the orthocentre of the triangle with vertices at $P(-3, 4)$, $Q(10, -3)$, and $R(3, -2)$.

20. Find the distance of point $S(3, 8)$ from the line that passes through $T(-2, -2)$ and $U(5, 4)$.

2.11 Verifying Geometric Properties

- If geometric figures are placed on a coordinate plane and the coordinates of the vertices are known, then it is possible to verify many of the properties of the figures using the properties of lines and line segments.

- Statements about the lengths of line segments can be verified using the distance formula $d = \sqrt{(x_2 - x_1)^2 + (y_2 - y_1)^2}$.

- Statements about whether line segments are parallel or perpendicular can be verified using the slope formula.

- You may have to determine the coordinates of a point of intersection before you can use the distance formula and the slope formula $m = \left(\frac{y_2 - y_1}{x_2 - x_1}\right)$ to verify a geometric property.

Example

Show that the midsegments of the square with vertices $A(-1, 0)$, $B(1, -8)$, $C(9, -6)$, and $D(7, 2)$ form a square.

Solution

Draw a sketch.

Given: A square with vertices at $A(-1, 0)$, $B(1, -8)$, $C(9, -6)$, and $D(7, 2)$.

The midsegments of square $ABCD$ form a square. To show this, we need to show that all sides are equal and that the corner angles are $90°$.

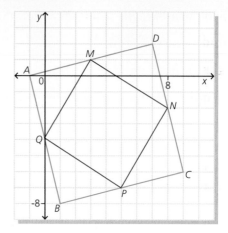

Label the midpoints of sides AD, CD, BC, AB with letters M, N, P, Q, respectively.

M is at $\left(\dfrac{-1 + 7}{2}, \dfrac{0 + 2}{2}\right) = (3, 1)$. $\qquad$ N is at $\left(\dfrac{7 + 9}{2}, \dfrac{2 + (-6)}{2}\right) = (8, -2)$.

P is at $\left(\dfrac{9 + 1}{2}, \dfrac{-6 + (-8)}{2}\right) = (5, -7)$. $\qquad$ Q is at $\left(\dfrac{1 + (-1)}{2}, \dfrac{-8 + 0}{2}\right) = (0, -4)$.

For MN, $\quad$ slope $= \dfrac{-2 - 1}{8 - 3}$ $\qquad\qquad$ length $= \sqrt{(8 - 3)^2 + (-2 - 1)^2}$

$\qquad\qquad\qquad = -\dfrac{3}{5}$ $\qquad\qquad\qquad\qquad\qquad = \sqrt{34}$

For NP, $\quad$ slope $= \dfrac{-7 - (-2)}{5 - 8}$ $\qquad\qquad$ length $= \sqrt{(5 - 8)^2 + (-7 - (-2))^2}$

$\qquad\qquad\qquad = \dfrac{5}{3}$ $\qquad\qquad\qquad\qquad\qquad = \sqrt{34}$

For PQ, $\quad$ slope $= \dfrac{-4 - (-7)}{0 - 5}$ $\qquad\qquad$ length $= \sqrt{(0 - 5)^2 + (-4 - (-7))^2}$

$\qquad\qquad\qquad = -\dfrac{3}{5}$ $\qquad\qquad\qquad\qquad\qquad = \sqrt{34}$

For QM, $\quad$ slope $= \dfrac{1 - (-4)}{3 - 0}$ $\qquad\qquad$ length $= \sqrt{(3 - 0)^2 + (1 - (-4))^2}$

$\qquad\qquad\qquad = \dfrac{5}{3}$ $\qquad\qquad\qquad\qquad\qquad = \sqrt{34}$

The slope calculations prove that all sides are equal in length and all intersecting sides are perpendicular.

All angles in quadrilateral $MNPQ$ are right angles, and opposite sides are parallel.

The lengths of sides MN, NP, PQ, and QM are equal.

Therefore, in quadrilateral $MNPQ$,

- both pairs of opposite sides are parallel

- adjacent sides are perpendicular

- all sides are of equal length

MNPQ is a square. The midsegments of *ABCD* form a square.

Extra Practice

21. A quadrilateral has vertices at $A(-3, 1)$, $B(-5, -9)$, $C(7, -1)$, and $D(3, 3)$. Prove that the midsegments form a parallelogram.

22. Prove that points $(10, 10)$, $(-7, 3)$, and $(0, -14)$ lie on a circle with centre at $(5, -2)$.

23. A triangle has vertices at $P(-2, 7)$, $Q(-4, 2)$, and $R(6, -2)$.
   (a) Prove that $\triangle PQR$ is a right triangle.
   (b) Prove that the circumcentre is at the midpoint of the hypotenuse.

Chapter 2 Summary

In this chapter, you used coordinates to describe the positions of points on maps, plans, and on calculator or computer screens. You developed a formula for the distance of a point from the origin that led you to an equation for the relationship between the *x*- and *y*-coordinates of points that lie on a circle. Using this model of a circle, you solved problems involving circular motion and circular design.

You investigated the straight-line distance between two points on a map. Using the Pythagorean theorem, you developed a formula for this distance, and used the name **line segment** to describe the part of a straight line that joins two points. You examined the slopes of line segments and found that the midpoint of a line segment is located by taking the means of the coordinates of its end points.

You also constructed geometric figures, such as triangles and quadrilaterals, from line segments. By using the properties of line segments you were able to identify what type of triangle or quadrilateral was defined by a set of points with known coordinates. You located the positions of important points of intersection within geometric figures, such as the centroid and other triangle centres, and this allowed you to solve design and layout problems.

Finally, you were able to verify some of the polygon properties you discovered in grade 9 by using the properties of line segments. This work, which has important implications for designers, engineers, and anyone who uses geometric figures in their jobs, allowed you to start to develop proofs of mathematical concepts.

Coordinates and Geometry: Where Shapes Meet Symbols

1. An underground cable is to be laid between points $A(-6, 23)$ and $B(14, -12)$, with the units in metres.

    (a) What length of cable will be needed? Give your answer to the nearest metre.

    (b) An access point will be located halfway between the end points of this cable. At what coordinates should the access point be built?

2. A crow flying overhead drops a small piece of bread into a pond, causing a circular ripple whose radius increases by 12 cm/s. Use the point at which the bread enters the water as the origin.

    (a) Write an equation that describes the ripple exactly 3 s after the bread lands in the water.

    (b) A water beetle is leaning on a bulrush at point $(-36, 48)$. When will the beetle feel the ripple?

3. Show that the triangle with vertex coordinates $A(1, 2)$, $B(-3, -1)$, and $C(0, -5)$ is an isosceles right triangle.

4. The positions for the corners of a building are staked out on a lot at $P(-39, 39)$, $Q(-78, -13)$, $R(26, -91)$, and $S(65, -39)$, with the units in metres.

    (a) Verify that $PQRS$ is a rectangle.

    (b) What will the perimeter of the building be if the rectangle $PQRS$ lies outside the building by 1 m on every side?

5. Quadrilateral $JKLM$ has vertex coordinates $J(2, 4)$, $K(6, 1)$, $L(2, -2)$, and $M(-2, 1)$. What type of quadrilateral is $JKLM$?

6. Three straight paths in a park form a triangle with vertices at $A(-24, 16)$, $B(56, -16)$, and $C(-72, -32)$.

    (a) Determine the coordinates, to an accuracy of one decimal place, of the point that is the same distance from each of A, B, and C.

    (b) State the mathematical name for the point you found in (a). Explain the meaning of this name.

    (c) Determine the area of $\triangle ABC$. **Hint:** You will have to find the length of an altitude.

7. Find the coordinates of the centroid of the triangle with vertex coordinates $D(4, 7)$, $E(6, -1)$, and $F(-2, 3)$. Explain the significance of this point for a thin triangular component for a computer.

8. Given a quadrilateral with vertices at $S(-3, 4)$, $T(1, 2)$, $U(3, -4)$, and $V(-5, -2)$, prove that the midsegments of the quadrilateral form a parallelogram.

Analytic Geometry

1. Solve using the elimination method.

$$3x + 4y = -10$$
$$5x - 2y = 18$$

2. Solve using the substitution method.

$$x = -2y + 3$$
$$y = -3x + 4$$

3. Raj needs to rent a car to drive to Woodstock and back. Cars-To-Go rents cars for $42 per day, plus $0.12/km. Cheapo Rentals rents cars for $30 per day, plus $0.15/km.

(a) Write linear equations to represent the prices of a one-day rental from each company.

(b) Use a graph, or a table of values, or both, to locate the point where the graphs of the two equations cross.

(c) Interpret the coordinates of the point of intersection in terms of the problem situation.

(d) Suppose Raj lives 220 km from Woodstock. Write a detailed explanation that shows how much he will save each day if he chooses the cheaper rental option.

4. The Sweet Tooth candy store sells hard candy for $6/kg and soft candy for $12/kg. The store manager mixes the two kinds of candy to create a 60 kg mixture that sells for $8/kg. How much of each type of candy is in the mixture?

5. Melanie saved $1200 from working last summer. She invested some of the money in a guaranteed investment certificate that paid 4.5% interest. Melanie deposited the rest in a savings account that paid only 2% interest. The total interest for the year was $40. How much money did Melanie invest in each?

6. This table shows how much Canadians spent on furniture and clothing from 1995 to 1999.

Year	Clothing (millions $)	Furniture (millions $)
1995	4.9	5.4
1996	5.1	5.6
1997	5.3	5.8
1998	5.5	6.0
1999	5.5	6.0

Source: Statistics Canada, CANSIM, Matrix *2400*

(a) Create a scatter plot and the graph of best fit that compares both sets of data.

(b) When will Canadians spend equal amounts of money on furniture and clothing?

(c) Suppose you are planning to open a new retail business and are considering these two areas. Which type of store would you open based on this data? Explain.

7. The vertices of a triangle are $(-1, -1)$, $(8, 3)$, and $(4, 7)$.

(a) Is the triangle scalene, isosceles, or equilateral?

(b) What is the equation of the median through point $(-1, -1)$?

8. Points $A(1, 1)$, $B(6, 2)$, $C(8, 5)$, and $D(3, 4)$ form the vertices of a quadrilateral.

(a) Show that the diagonals of the quadrilateral $ABCD$ bisect each other.

(b) Show that $ABCD$ is a parallelogram.

9. Points $D(-3, 2)$, $E(4, -5)$, and $F(6, 2)$ form the vertices of a triangle. The midpoint of EF is G and the midpoint of DF is J. Prove that $JG = \frac{1}{2}DE$ and that $JG \parallel DE$.

10. Triangle ABC is formed using $A(0, 0)$, $B(0, 5)$, and $C(4, 0)$. Squares $ABDE$ and $ACFG$ are drawn on the outside of the triangle as shown. The lines through D and C and through B and F intersect at H. Show that $AH \perp BC$.

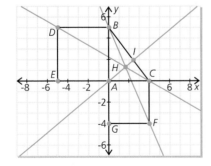

11. A circle is defined by $x^2 + y^2 = 25$. On the circumference of the circle lie points $A(-3, 4)$, $B(4, 3)$, $C(3, -4)$, and $D(-4, 3)$.

(a) Graph the circle and plot the given points.

(b) Verify algebraically that the quadrilateral formed by joining all four points is a square.

(c) Determine the coordinates of the vertices of the smallest square that contains the circle $x^2 + y^2 = 25$. Draw the square on your graph and label it $QRST$.

(d) Verify that the area of square $ABCD$ $= \frac{1}{2}$ area of square $QRST$.

Performance Tasks for Chapters 1 and 2

Analytic Geometry

THE FOLLOWING ACTIVITIES SHOULD EACH TAKE LESS THAN A PERIOD TO COMPLETE

1. Can You See the Light?

An ordinary 60-watt light bulb costs $0.75 to buy and $0.0085/h to operate. A compact fluorescent light bulb that produces the same amount of light costs $12 to buy and $0.0021/h to operate. The fluorescent bulbs last about 4000 h, compared to 800 h for the ordinary bulbs. In a test, the two types of bulbs are operated side by side, and replaced with the same type of bulb whenever one burns out.

(a) From the start of the test, when is the cost to operate both bulbs the same? Justify your answer.

(b) State the conditions under which one lighting system is better than the other.

(c) Which type of light bulb is more cost-effective in the long run? Explain and justify your reasoning.

(d) Write a newspaper article that encourages your readers to switch to the more cost-effective light source. Use charts, diagrams, or graphs to illustrate your argument.

2. Water Consumption

Between 1981 and 1991, water use in Canada increased for some purposes and decreased for others. The following table provides a summary.

Category of Use	Water Consumption (millions of m³)		
	1981	1986	1991
Agriculture	3 125	3 559	3 991
Mining	648	593	363
Manufacturing	9 937	7 984	7 282
Thermal Power	19 281	25 364	28 357
Municipal	4 263	4 717	5 102
Other	3 892	4 279	5 367
Total	41 146	46 496	50 462

Source: Environment Canada

(a) Use linear models to predict water consumption in 1999, by category and total. Explain how you arrived at your models.

(b) The use of water for manufacturing seems to be declining, while municipal use is increasing. Predict the year in which they will be the same. Justify your answer.

(c) Discuss how well a linear model actually represents the data. How does the quality of fit between the model and the data affect the confidence you have in your predictions?

Research Extension (Extra Time)

(d) Do some research on water consumption for the years after 1991. Use the new information to improve your models and refine your predictions for 1999.

(e) Discuss how the new data either supports or weakens the case for using linear models.

(f) If the data for 1999 is available, compare your original predicted values with the actual data. Discuss why the predicted and actual values may not match.

3. Triangle Areas

Sean asked Sara to help him compute the area of a triangle whose vertex coordinates are given.

Sara said that she had discovered a shortcut way to find the area of a triangle. She showed Sean this example. To find the area of $\triangle ABC$ with $A(2, 5)$, $B(6, 5)$, and $C(3, 10)$, first write the vertices in a table like the one at right.

A	B	C
2	6	3
5	5	10

Go "down and right" to find the products:

$$2 \times 5 = 10$$
$$6 \times 10 = 60$$
$$3 \times 5 = 15$$

A	B	C
2	6	3
5	5	10

Then find the sum of the products: $10 + 60 + 15 = 85$.

Now, go "up and right" to find the products and their sum:

$$5 \times 6 = 30$$
$$5 \times 3 = 15$$
$$10 \times 2 = 20$$
$$30 + 15 + 20 = 65$$

A	B	C
2	6	3
5	5	10

The area of the triangle is one-half of the difference between the sums.

$$Area = \frac{1}{2}(85 - 65)$$
$$= \frac{1}{2}(20)$$
$$= 10$$

(a) Verify that Sara's method gives the correct area.

(b) Show that the method also works for $\triangle DEF$ with vertices at $D(2, 5)$, $E(6, 8)$, and $F(3, 10)$.

4. Piecing Things Together (The Centre of a Circle)

A broken piece of a car's circular side mirror has been found at a crime scene. Forensic mathematicians want to determine the original size of the circular mirror to help identify the getaway vehicle. They place the broken mirror on a grid and find that the points $A(1, 10)$, $B(-4, 3)$, and $C(8, 5)$ are on the circumference of the circle.

Find the radius of the circle and explain how you found it. (Do not assume that the centre is at the origin.)

5. The Middle of a Triangle?

Triangle PQR is given by the vertices $P(1, 4)$, $Q(-5, 2)$, and $R(-1, -4)$.

(a) Verify algebraically that the three medians intersect at a single point.

(b) Show that each median is divided in the ratio 1 : 2 at the point of intersection.

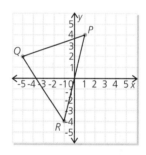

6. Tire Skid Marks

In a "panic stop," the brakes lock the wheels of a car, causing the tires to leave skid marks on the road. Police use the length of the skid marks to determine how fast the vehicle was travelling when the brakes were applied.

The table illustrates the relationship between the vehicle's speed and the length of the skid.

Road Conditions	Speed (km/h)	Length of Skid (m)
	80	31.0
Dry	60	17.5
	40	8.0
	60	28.0
Damp	50	20.0
	40	12.5

(a) Discuss whether an algebraic model that computes speed based on skid length is linear. Do the road conditions have any effect?

(b) Use the data to develop linear algebraic models to predict the vehicle speed from the skid length, for both sets of road conditions.

(c) Suppose a driver locks the wheels in a panic stop at 100 km/h on dry pavement. What speed would produce a skid of the same length on wet pavement? Justify your answer.

THE FOLLOWING ACTIVITIES SHOULD EACH TAKE MORE THAN ONE PERIOD TO COMPLETE

7. The Shin Bone's Connected to the …

When archeologists discover ancient human remains, they often find only a few bones. They want to know as much as possible about the deceased person from the small amount of evidence that is available.

Archeologists use math too! From the length of an adult's tibia (shin bone), they can make quite an accurate prediction of how tall that person was. Archeologists use the following formulas to predict a person's height:

Adult males	$H = 81.7 + 2.4T$
Adult females	$H = 72.6 + 2.5T$

where H = height in centimetres and T = length of tibia in centimetres

(a) For what height do males and females have the same tibia length?

(b) The formulas above work best for adults. Find formulas that are suitable for males and females in your age group. Then use the models to make some predictions.

   i. Measure the tibia length and the height of each person in your class. Record this data in a table and share your results with the class. Keep the data for males and females separate.

   ii. Construct algebraic models for the male and female data.

   iii. Use your models to determine the height for which males and females in your age group have the same tibia length. Discuss whether a graphical solution or an algebraic solution is more accurate and more appropriate, based on your data.

   iv. Compare your results with the models for adults. Explain the differences.

8. Comparing Athletic Performance: Male vs. Female

Many Olympic sports have both male and female competitors. Since the inception of the Olympic Games in 1896, the performances of athletes of both genders have steadily improved. When will the performances of the best female athletes in an Olympic sport meet or surpass those of their best male counterparts? Will it ever happen?

Select two events in which both males and females compete. Choose one event where it seems likely that female athletes will match or exceed the performance of males. Choose another event where that seems unlikely.

Locate data on the performance of both males and females in those Olympic events over several Olympiads, including the most recent. Construct both graphical and algebraic models for the male and the female performances and use the models to answer the following questions.

(a) When, if ever, will the performances of females in the events you have chosen match the performance of the males? Explain in terms of your models.

(b) Discuss how confident you are about your models and your prediction in (a).

(c) List the factors that may cause your models to produce an incorrect prediction.

9. Napoleon's Theorem

The centroid of a triangle is also the triangle's centre of mass or "balance point." This fact can be used to design a mobile or hanging sculpture. If a string is attached at the centroid, the triangle will hang horizontally. When a complex shape is used, its balance point can be found by first locating the centroids of all of the triangles that make up the shape.

Suppose that you are using a piece of graph paper to make a star-shaped mobile by constructing equilateral triangles on the exterior sides of an existing $\triangle ABC$.

(a) The vertices of $\triangle ABC$ are $A(-3, 1)$, $B(-4, -3)$, and $C(6, -1)$. Construct an equilateral triangle on each exterior side of $\triangle ABC$.

(b) Find the coordinates of the centroid of each equilateral triangle.

(c) Show that the centroids form the vertices of a new equilateral triangle.

(d) Find the coordinates of the centroid of this triangle.

(e) Construct the star using rigid construction paper or cardboard. Use the shape to verify whether or not the centroid of the new triangle is the balance point for the star.

(Historical note: The result concerning equilateral triangles constructed on the sides of an arbitrary triangle has been associated with Napoleon Bonaparte, but there is little evidence that he actually had anything to do with either stating or proving the relationship.)

Research Extension (Extra Time)

(f) The constructed triangles do not have to be equilateral. The result can be generalized to triangles with different shapes. Conduct some research to determine the most general form of Napoleon's theorem and verify that it works using $\triangle ABC$ above.

Getting Ready for Quadratic Functions

Exponent Laws

5^3 is called a power. 5 is the base and 3 is the exponent.

$5^3 = \underbrace{5 \times 5 \times 5}_{\text{expanded form}} = 125$

Rule	Written Description	Algebraic Description	Example
Multiplication	To multiply powers with the same base, keep the base the same and add the exponents.	$a^m \times a^n = a^{(m+n)}$	$3^5 \times 3^6 = 3^{(5+6)} = 3^{11}$
Division	To divide powers with the same base, keep the base the same and subtract the exponents.	$a^m \div a^n = a^{(m-n)}$	$4^5 \div 4^2 = 4^{(5-2)} = 4^3$
Power of a power	To simplify a power of a power, keep the base the same and multiply the exponents.	$(a^m)^n = a^{(m \times n)}$	$(2^5)^3 = 2^{(5 \times 3)} = 2^{15}$
Zero as an exponent	When an exponent is zero, it gives a value of 1.	$a^0 = 1$	$7^0 = 1$
Negative exponents	When a power with a base greater than 1 has a negative exponent, it gives a fractional value.	$a^{-n} = \dfrac{1}{a^n}$	$5^{-2} = \dfrac{1}{5^2} = \dfrac{1}{25}$

Practise

1. Simplify.

    (a) $(x^2)(x^4)$ **(b)** $(c^4)(c^6)$

    (c) $(y^3)(y^{-5})$ **(d)** $(g^{-4})(g^{-4})$

    (e) $(x^3)(x^{-2})(x^4)$

2. Simplify.

    (a) $c^5 \div c^3$ **(b)** $d^6 \div d^{-2}$

    (c) $x^{-6} \div x^{-2}$ **(d)** $b^{-7} \div b^4$

    (e) $(x^5)(x^3) \div x^{-5}$

3. Simplify.

    (a) $(f^3)^2$ **(b)** $(k^{-2})^4$ **(c)** $(m^{-3})^{-4}$

    (d) $(n^5)^{-1}$ **(e)** $((x^{-3})^4)^{-2}$

4. Evaluate.

    (a) 4^3 **(b)** 6^0 **(c)** 5^{-2}

    (d) -3^2 **(e)** $(-3)^2$ **(f)** -5^0

    (g) 2^{-3} **(h)** $\left(\frac{1}{2}\right)^4$ **(i)** $\left(\frac{2}{3}\right)^{-2}$

    (j) $(0.55)^3$ **(k)** $(-1)^{100}$ **(l)** $(-1)^{97}$

    (m) $(-4)^{-3}$ **(n)** $(-2)^5$ **(o)** $-(-2)^2$

5. Simplify.

    (a) $(x^3)(x^2)$ **(b)** $(a^4)(a^3)$

    (c) $(x^4)^2$ **(d)** $a^5 \div a^2$

    (e) $(mn)^5$ **(f)** $\left(\frac{x}{y}\right)^3$

    (g) $b^7 \div b^{-3}$ **(h)** $(d^{-4})(d^{-5})$

    (i) $(g^{-3})^{-2}$ **(j)** $(a^{-3}b^5)^{-2}$

    (k) $x^{-6} \div x^5$ **(l)** $\left(\frac{a^2}{b^3}\right)^3$

6. Evaluate for $a = -3$, $b = -2$, and $c = -1$.

    (a) $a^2 - b^2$ **(b)** a^b

    (c) c^{ab} **(d)** $(a^{-1} + b^c)$

    (e) $c^b + b^a$ **(f)** $(a^b)^c$

7. Express each power with a positive exponent, then simplify.

    (a) $2^0 + 4^0$ **(b)** $4^{-1} + 3^{-1}$

    (c) $3 + 2^{-1}$ **(d)** $5^0 + 3^{-1}$

    (e) $(-4^{-2})^{-1}$ **(f)** $\left(\frac{1}{2}\right)^{-1}\left(\frac{2}{3}\right)^{-1}$

    (g) $5^3 \times 5^{-3}$ **(h)** $4^2 \times 2^{-2}$

    (i) $\left(\frac{-4}{3}\right)^{-1}$ **(j)** $(-2)^3$

8. Evaluate each expression.

    (a) $2^{-2} + 2^{-3}$ **(b)** $6(2^{-1} + 3^{-1})$

    (c) $\left(\frac{1}{2}\right)^{-1} + \left(\frac{1}{3}\right)^{-1}$ **(d)** $2^{-1} + \left(\frac{1}{3}\right)^2$

9. Simplify each expression.

    (a) $\dfrac{2^{-1} - 3^{-1}}{3}$

    (b) $(4^2 \div 4^{-2})^{-1}$

    (c) $(5^3 \div 5^2)^{-2}$

    (d) $(2^3 + 3^2)^{-1}$

Simplifying Algebraic Expressions

Algebraic expressions can be multiplied together. This is done by expanding using the **distributive property**:

$$a(b + c) = ab + ac$$

Sometimes it is necessary to express an algebraic expression as the product of two or more polynomials. This is done by **factoring**. Factoring is the opposite of expanding.

expanding $\rightarrow$

$$2x(5x^2 + 3x - 4) = 10x^3 + 6x^2 - 8x$$

$\leftarrow$ factoring

Example 1

Multiply $(3x)(-5yx)(-2z)$.

Solution

$(3x)(-5yx)(-2z) = 30x^2yz$

Example 2

Expand $-3x(5x - 7y + 3)$.

Solution

$-3x(5x - 7y + 3)$
$= -3x(5x) - 3x(-7y) - 3x(3)$
$= -15x^2 + 21xy - 9x$

Example 3

Expand and simplify
$-4x(x - 2y) - 3x(5y + 2x)$.

Solution

$-4x(x - 2y) - 3x(5y + 2x)$
$= -4x(x) - 4x(-2y) - 3x(5y) - 3x(2x)$
$= -4x^2 + 8xy - 15xy - 6x^2$
$= -10x^2 - 7xy$

Example 4

Factor
$15x^3y - 20x^2y^2 + 35x^4y^3$.

Solution

$15x^3y - 20x^2y^2 + 35x^4y^3$
$= 5x^2y(3x - 4y + 7x^2y^2)$

$\uparrow$
common factor

Practise

1. Multiply.
   (a) $(3x)(4y)$ (b) $(2x)(3x)$
   (c) $(-5a)(-4b)$ (d) $(-x)(-3x^2)$
   (e) $(12a)(3a^2)$ (f) $(-2xy)(6x^2y)$
   (g) $(6)(-3xyz)$ (h) $(7ab)(-3abc)$
   (i) $(3x)(5y)(6z)$ (j) $(-x^2y)(xy^3)$

2. Expand.
   (a) $-3x(x^2 - x + y)$
   (b) $-2y(xy + z)$
   (c) $-7b(a - 2b + 3c)$
   (d) $4p(2p - 5q)$
   (e) $-4a(5a - 3a^2 - a^3)$

3. Find each product.
   (a) $-3x(x - 2y)$
   (b) $-2m(m + n)$
   (c) $4x^2(x - 3xy)$
   (d) $-6y(-3x^2 + 2y^2)$
   (e) $5xy(2x - 3y + 4xy)$

4. Expand and simplify.
   (a) $5x(x + 2) + 6x(3x - 2)$
   (b) $-7y(2y - 5) - 3y(4y + 3)$
   (c) $-(3x - 5y) - (4x - 2y)$
   (d) $3y + 2(y + 1)$
   (e) $3x^2 - 3x(2x - 1)$
   (f) $-y(3y - 2) - 5y^2$

5. Find each unknown factor.
   (a) $6 + 8x = (\blacksquare)(3 + 4x)$
   (b) $2xr + 4x = (\blacksquare)(r + 2)$
   (c) $6y - 12y^2 = (6y)(\blacksquare)$
   (d) $4y^3 + 8y^2 - 16y = (4y)(\blacksquare)$
   (e) $6x^2y - 4xy^2 + 10x^2y^2 = (-2xy)(\blacksquare)$
   (f) $9a^2m^2 - 6am^2 - 18a^2m = (-3am)(\blacksquare)$

6. Factor each expression.
   (a) $6 - 12x$ (b) $5x^2 - 3x$
   (c) $9y - 12x$ (d) $5xy - 3xy^2$
   (e) $2x^2 - 6x$ (f) $a^2 - 2a$
   (g) $4ab - b^2$ (h) $4y^2 - 16$
   (i) $28a^2 - 14ab$ (j) $36mn - 25m^2n^2$
   (k) $6x^2 - 12x + 15$
   (l) $5m^3 - 25m^2 + 15$
   (m) $50a^2 + 75ab + 25b^2$
   (n) $10x^3y^3 + 20x^2y^2 - 10xy$
   (o) $x^2y - x^2y^2 - xy^2$
   (p) $2p^2q - 4pq + 8q^2$
   (q) $3k^2 - 9k + 12k^4$
   (r) $3m^2n^3 - 27m^3n^4$

7. Evaluate each expression for $x = 4$ and $z = 3$.
   (a) $2(x - 2z) - 4(3z - 2x)$
   (b) $2z(z - 3x) - 3z(z + 2x)$

Transformations of Two-Dimensional Shapes

A **translation** slides a figure up, down, or diagonally along a straight line.

Triangle *ABC* has been translated right 1 unit and down 3 units to create the image triangle *A′B′C′*.

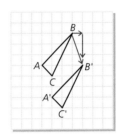

A **reflection** flips a figure about a line of reflection to create a mirror image.

Pentagon *ABCDE* has been reflected through the *y*-axis to create the image pentagon *A′B′C′D′E′*. The *y*-axis is the line of reflection.

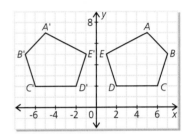

A **rotation** turns a figure around a centre of rotation either clockwise (CW) or counterclockwise (CCW). The amount of rotation is often indicated by an angle.

Rectangle *ABCD* has been rotated clockwise by $\frac{1}{4}$ turn about point (0, 0) to create the image rectangle *A′B′C′D′*. The centre of rotation is (0, 0).

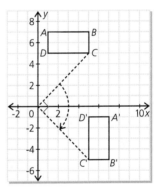

Example 1

Describe the transformations that have been performed on Figures 1, 2 and 3.

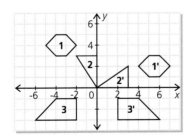

Solution

Figure 1 has been translated 9 units to the right and 2 units down [R9, D2].

Figure 2 has been rotated about the origin. The angle of rotation is either 90° cw or 270° ccw.

Figure 3 has been reflected about the *y*-axis.

Example 2

Triangle ABC has vertices $A(-5, 3)$, $B(-2, 3)$, and $C(-2, 1)$.

State the coordinates of $\Delta A'B'C'$, if ΔABC is:

(a) translated right 8, up 3 [R8, U3]

(b) reflected about the x-axis

(c) reflected about the y-axis

(d) rotated 180° counterclockwise about the origin

Solution

(a) When ΔABC is translated [R8, U3], the x-coordinate of each vertex increases by 8 and the y-coordinate increases by 3. The coordinates of the image are $A'(3, 6)$, $B'(6, 6)$, and $C'(6, 4)$.

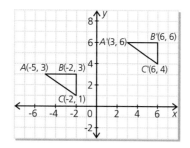

(c) When ΔABC is reflected about the y-axis, the y-coordinates remain the same but the signs of the x-coordinates change. The coordinates of the image are $A'(5, 3)$, $B'(2, 3)$, and $C'(2, 1)$.

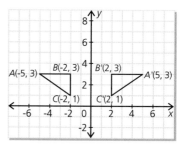

(b) When ΔABC is reflected about the x-axis, the x-coordinates remain the same but the signs of the y-coordinates change. The coordinates of the image are $A'(-5, -3)$, $B'(-2, -3)$, and $C'(-2, -1)$.

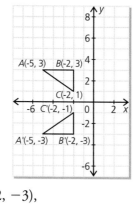

(d) When ΔABC is rotated 180° counterclockwise about the origin, the x- and y-coordinates both change signs. The coordinates of the image are $A'(5, -3)$, $B'(2, -3)$, and $C'(2, -1)$.

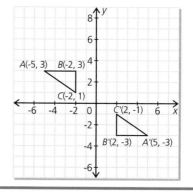

Practise

1. In what ways does the image differ from the original when each transformation is performed?

   (a) translation   (b) reflection

   (c) rotation

2. Identify the transformation.

   (a) 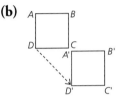   (b)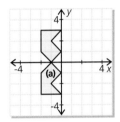

   (c)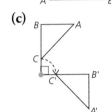

3. State the transformation that was performed on the object to create each image.

   (a)   (b)   (c)

   (d)   (e)   (f)

4. Write the translation rule that was used to create each image.

   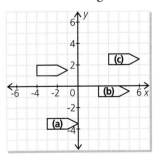

5. The coordinates of △*JKL* are *J*(−4, 5), *K*(−4, 2), and *L*(−1, 2). State the coordinates of △*J′K′L′*, if △*JKL* is

   (a) translated [R2, D5]

   (b) reflected about the *x*-axis

   (c) reflected about the *y*-axis

   (d) rotated 90° cw about the origin

6. Describe how the object was reflected to create each image.

   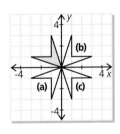

7. Identify the two possible angles of rotation and the centre of rotation that were used to create each image.

   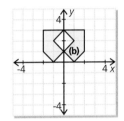

Finite Differences and Rate of Change

When the values of the independent variable increase by the same increment throughout a table of values, the differences between successive values of y form a table of **finite differences** called a **difference table**.

A table of values represents a **linear relationship** if

- a single straight line can be drawn through all of the plotted points

- the finite differences are the same for every row in the difference table

- for all pairs of points in the table, the ratio formed from the differences between the values of x and corresponding differences between the values of y is the same. This ratio represents the **rate of change** between the variables and is equivalent to the slope of the line.

$$\text{Rate of change} = \text{slope} = \frac{\Delta y}{\Delta x} = \frac{y_2 - y_1}{x_2 - x_1}$$

A table of values represents a **nonlinear relationship** if

- a single smooth curve can be drawn through every point

- the finite differences are variable; that is, they are not the same for every row in the difference table

Example 1

The table shows the cost to rent a cement mixer for different lengths of time.

Time (h)	0	1	2	3	4
Cost ($)	45	60	75	90	105

(a) Is the relationship linear or nonlinear?

(b) Graph the data.

(c) What does the slope represent in this situation?

Solution

Time (h)	Cost ($)	First Difference
0	45	
1	60	60 – 45 = 15
2	75	75 – 60 = 15
3	90	90 – 75 = 15
4	105	105 – 90 = 15

(a) The first differences are constant, so the relationship is linear.

(b)

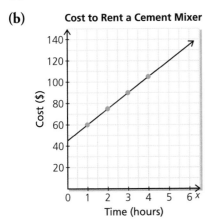

Cost to Rent a Cement Mixer

(c) The rate of change is equivalent to the slope of the line.

The rate of change is

$$m = \frac{65 - 40}{1 - 0}$$

$$m = \frac{15}{1}$$

$$m = 15$$

This rate represents the rate at which the cost changes as time changes. In this case the cost increases $15 for every additional hour.

Example 2

The table shows the population of field mice over several months.

Month	0	1	2	3	4	5
Population	130	286	629	1384	3044	6698

(a) Is the relationship linear or nonlinear?

(b) Graph the data.

Solution

Time (h)	Cost ($)	First Difference
0	130	
1	286	286 − 130 = 156
2	629	629 − 286 = 343
3	1384	1384 − 629 = 755
4	3044	3044 − 1384 = 1660
5	6698	6698 − 3044 = 3654

(a) The first differences are not all the same, so the relationship is nonlinear.

(b)

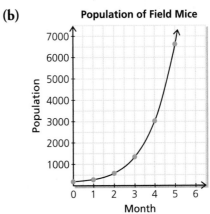

Population of Field Mice

Practise

1. For each set of data,
   i. create a first differences table
   ii. determine whether the relation is linear or nonlinear
   iii. graph the relationship
   (a) Speed of a falling ball

Time from Release (s)	0	1	2	3	4	5	6	7	8
Velocity (m/s)	0	9.8	19.6	29.4	39.2	49	58.8	68.6	78.4

   (b) Volumes of various cones with a height of 1 cm

Radius of Base (cm)	1	2	3	4	5	6	7	8
Volume of Cone (cm³)	1.047	4.189	9.425	16.755	26.180	37.699	51.313	67.021

   (c) Cost of renting a car for a day

Distance Driven (km)	0	10	20	30	40	50	60	70	80
Cost ($)	45	46.50	48	49.50	51	52.50	54	55.50	57

   (d) Value of a photocopier after several years

Age (years)	0	1	2	3	4	5	6	7
Value of photocopier ($)	6750	5800	4850	3900	2950	2000	1050	100

   (e) Population of Totemville

Year	1991	1992	1993	1994	1995	1996	1997	1998
Population	1560	1716	1888	2077	2285	2514	2765	3042

   (f) Height of a model rocket at various times during its flight

Time (s)	0	1	2	3	4	5	6
Height (m)	0	33.1	56.4	69.9	73.6	67.5	51.6

2. Determine the rate of change of each linear relationship in question 1.

Interpolating and Extrapolating

A graph can be used to make predictions for values not actually recorded and plotted. When the prediction involves a point within the range of the values of the independent variable, this is called **interpolating**. When the value of the independent variable falls outside the range of recorded data, it is called **extrapolating**. With a scatter plot, estimates are more reliable if the data shows a strong positive or negative correlation.

Example 1

The Summer Olympics were cancelled in 1940 and 1944 because of World War II. Estimate what the 100 m run winning times might have been in these years if the Olympics had been held as scheduled.

Winning Times of 100 m Run

Year	Name (Country)	Time (s)
1928	Williams (Canada)	10.80
1932	Tolan (U.S.)	10.30
1936	Owens (U.S.)	10.30
1948	Dillard (U.S.)	10.30
1952	Remigino (U.S.)	10.40
1956	Morrow (U.S.)	10.50
1960	Hary (Germany)	10.20
1964	Hayes (U.S.)	10.00
1968	Hines (U.S.)	9.95
1972	Borzov (USSR)	10.14
1976	Crawford (Trinidad)	10.06
1980	Wells (Great Britain)	10.25
1984	Lewis (U.S.)	9.99
1988	Lewis (U.S.)	9.92
1992	Christie (Great Britain)	9.96
1996	Bailey (Canada)	9.84

Solution

Draw a scatter plot and find the line of best fit.

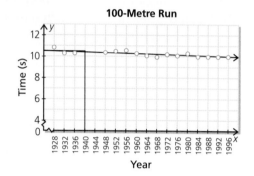

100-Metre Run

Find 1940 on the *x*-axis. Follow the vertical line for 1940 up until it meets the line of best fit. This occurs at about 10.8 s. For 1944 a reasonable estimate would be about 10.7 s.

Example 2

Use the table from Example 1 to predict what the winning time might be in 2044.

Solution

Extend the *x*-axis to 2044. Then extend the line of best fit to the vertical line through 2044.

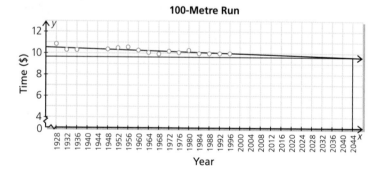

100-Metre Run

The vertical line for 2044 crosses the line of best fit at about 9.5, so the winning time in 2044 might be about 9.5 s.

It would be difficult to forecast much further into the future, since the winning times cannot continue to decline indefinitely. For example, a runner would likely never be able to run 100 m in 1 s, and would certainly never run it in less than 0 s.

Practise

1. The scatter plot shows the gold medal throws in the discuss competition in the Summer Olympics for 1908 to 1992.

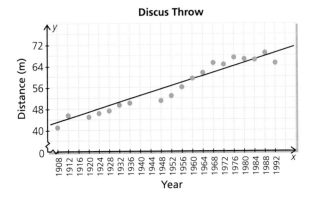

Discus Throw

(a) Estimate the winning distance for 1940 and 1944.

(b) Estimate the winning distance for 1996 and 2000.

2. As an object falls freely toward the ground, it accelerates at a steady rate due to gravity. The data shows the speed, or velocity, an object would reach at one-second intervals during its fall.

Time from Start (s)	Velocity (m/s)
0	0
1	9.8
2	19.6
3	29.4
4	39.2
5	49

(a) Graph the data.

(b) Determine the object's velocity at 2.5 s, 3.5 s, and 4.75 s.

(c) Find the object's velocity at 6 s, 9 s, and 10 s.

3. Explain why values you find by extrapolation are less reliable than those found by interpolation.

4. Explain how you would predict a value of x if you were given a value of y and a scatter plot showing the line of best fit.

5. In question 2, you discovered a way to calculate the speed of a falling object. Once you know this speed, you can determine the force with which the object will strike the ground (called kinetic energy, KE). The relationship used to calculate this force is $KE = \frac{1}{2}mv^2$, where m is the mass of the object, and v is its speed. Use this relationship to find the missing data for a fall lasting 1 s.

Mass of Object (kg)	Kinetic Energy (J)
0	0
1	48.02
2	96.04
3	
4	
6	288.12
	480.2
12	

(a) Complete the table of values.

(b) Graph the data.

(c) Use the graph to determine the kinetic energy of an object with a mass of 5 kg.

(d) Use the graph to determine the mass of an object which hits the ground with a kinetic energy of 550 J.

6. A school principal wants to know if there is a relationship between attendance and marks. You have been hired to collect data and analyze the results. You start by taking a sample of 12 students.

Days Absent	0	3	4	2	0	6	4	1	3	7	8	4
Average (%)	93	79	81	87	87	75	77	90	77	72	61	80

(a) Create a scatter plot. Draw the line of best fit.

(b) What appears to be the average decrease in marks for one day's absence?

(c) Predict the average of a student who is absent for six days.

(d) About how many days could a student likely miss before getting an average below 50%?

Chapter 3

Analyzing and Applying Quadratic Models

This photograph shows the interior of BCE Place in Toronto. The arches are in the form of a quadratic curve. Many buildings use this curve because it combines strength with elegance.

Architects and engineers design and study structures used in transportation, communication, business, and recreation. Many of these structures involve quadratic models in their design and construction. You will learn more about quadratic models in this chapter.

In this chapter you will

- use tables of values to graph quadratic relations

- write algebraic expressions for quadratic relationships and interpret the terms of the expressions in the context of the underlying real-world situations

- identify and apply the relationship between the roots of a quadratic relationship and its graph

- graph quadratic relations, by hand and with graphing technology

- by hand and with technology, develop quadratic models for data and discuss "goodness of fit"

- determine the equation of a quadratic relation from the properties of its graph

- explore the properties of parabolas and their application to optimization problems

- develop the algebraic skills to expand and factor a variety of polynomial expressions

- use your algebraic skills to solve problems involving quadratic relations

For connections to this chapter, visit **www.math.nelson.com**.

The Chapter Problem

Setting the Best Ticket Price

The management of an older movie theatre, without modern sound equipment, decides to start showing second-run movies and classic films at the theatre. Because the films are not first-run movies, the management can experiment with the price they charge for admission. After several months of experimenting, they find that for every 20¢ increase in ticket price, the number of tickets sold for each showing will decrease by 10. Similarly, for every 20¢ decrease in price, the number of tickets sold will increase by 10. On an average evening, the theatre sells 500 tickets at $8 each.

How much should the management charge for tickets to bring in the most revenue? Explain how the ticket price is related to total revenue to someone who is not familiar with these mathematical concepts.

For help with this problem, see pages 260, 269, 286, 301, and 309.

Challenge 1

Photographers sometimes use small rockets to take aerial photographs. An on-board timer triggers the camera at the appropriate point in the flight to get the desired image. It is much less expensive to launch and recover an automated camera using one of these hobby rockets than to rent an aircraft and pay the expenses of a pilot.

The camera fits into the nose cone of the rocket, with the lens pointing forward. That means that the rocket has to be descending to get pictures of the ground.

Suppose you want to use one of these devices to take aerial photographs of your neighbourhood. The rocket must be at a height of at least 600 m for you to get the picture you want. After several test flights, you have determined that the average flight duration is 3 min 20 s, and the average maximum altitude is 900 m.

Once the camera is triggered, it automatically takes 20 pictures at a rate of 1 picture every 2 s. Determine the timer setting to trigger the camera to give the largest the number of acceptable photographs.

Challenge 2

A new theme park is in the planning and design stages. You are one of the project engineers, leading a team that is designing a roller coaster ride. While it must be safe, the ride must also give riders a thrilling free-fall feeling.

You have to prepare a computerized design of the profile of the roller coaster. You can begin by designing the ride manually on graph paper. However, your final design must include the mathematical models needed to redraw the profile of the ride using a graphing calculator or graphing software.

Your final report should include estimates of the maximum and minimum speeds of the roller coaster and where these speeds will occur. You could also conduct some research to identify the points on the ride where the greatest g-forces will be felt by the riders, and where the riders will feel weightless.

To complete these Challenges, you may need to discuss a research plan with your teacher or other students. You may also need to research outside the classroom.

In this chapter you will be working with linear and nonlinear models of real-life situations. These exercises will help you warm up for the work ahead.

1. Find the x- and y-intercepts.
   (a) $y = 3x - 5$ (b) $5x - 2y = 10$
   (c) $4x = 2y - 8$ (d) $5x - 4y - 20 = 0$

2. Determine if the given point is on the line.
   (a) $6x - 3y + 9 = 0; (-2, -1)$
   (b) $7y = 14 - 3x; (-1, \frac{17}{7})$
   (c) $5x + 2y = 20; (\frac{16}{5}, 2)$

3. Evaluate each expression.
   (a) $(20 - 2(5))(10 + 3(5))$
   (b) $\frac{6(16 - 2(6))}{2}$
   (c) $(3^2 - 2^2 - 1)(2^2 - 3^2 - 2)$
   (d) $(-3 - (-2)^2 - 4^2)(-2^2 + (-5) - 3^2)$
   (e) $-0.5(10)(10 - 65)$
   (f) $(4 - 0.25(6))(25 + 2(6))$
   (g) $\frac{-7 + 11}{2}$
   (h) $\frac{2.5 - 4.3}{2}$
   (i) $\frac{-4.4 - 5.6}{2}$
   (j) $\left(\frac{-2}{3}\right)\left(\frac{3}{-4}\right)^2$
   (k) $-16 \div \left(\frac{4}{5}\right)^2$
   (l) $\left(-\frac{4}{3}\right) \div \left(\frac{2}{-3}\right)$
   (m) $\left(\frac{3}{8}\right)\left(-\frac{5}{6}\right)\left(\frac{4}{15}\right)$

4. Simplify each expression.
   (a) $2x + 3y - 5x + 2y$
   (b) $-3ab + 2bc - 4ab - 5bc$
   (c) $3x^2 + 5 - (5x^2 - 2)$
   (d) $2(m - 3) + 3(m - 5)$
   (e) $5 - (9y - 15) + 4(y - 2)$
   (f) $w(16 - 2w)$
   (g) $x^2(2x^3 - 5)$
   (h) $5x^2(2x^4 - 3x^3)$
   (i) $-2x^2(5x^4 + 4x^3) - 6x^6$

5. For each set of data,
   i.   use finite differences to determine whether the relation is linear or nonlinear
   ii. graph the relation
   iii. use the graph to find the value of x when $y = 2.5$

(a)

x	y
0	2
1	3
2	4
3	5
4	6
5	7
6	8
7	9
8	10

(b)

x	y
−3	−10
−2	−7
−1	−4
0	−1
1	2
2	5
3	8
4	11

(c)

x	y
−4	14
−3	7
−2	2
−1	−1
0	−2
1	−1
2	2
3	7
4	14

(d)

x	y
0	−2
1	−1
4	0
7	0.646
10	1.162
13	1.606
16	2
19	2.359
22	2.69
25	3

6. Determine the value of y.

   (a) $y = (20 - 2x)(30 + 4x)$, when $x = 6$

   (b) $y = 800 + 60x - 25x^2$, when $x = 3$

   (c) $y = (18 - 2x)x$, when $x = 4.5$

   (d) $y = 15.9\sqrt{D(f + g)}$, when $D = 21$, $f = 0.55$, and $g = 0.04$

   (e) $y = 25t - t^2$, when $t = 4$

   (f) $y = x^2 - x - 6$, when $x = -2$

7. (a) Solve for x.

   i. $3y - 2x = -7$, when $y = 0$

   ii. $2x - y = 3$, when $y = 2$

   iii. $3y = 2(5 - x)$, when $y = -4$

   iv. $3x + 4y = -11$, when $y = 2$

  (b) Solve for a.

   i. $y = a(x + 2)(x - 2)$, when $x = 0$ and $y = -4$

   ii. $y = ax(x - 6)$, when $x = 3$ and $y = 3$

   iii. $y = a(x - 2)(x - 6)$, when $x = 2$ and $y = 3$

   iv. $y = a(x + 6)(x + 1)$, when $x = -3.5$ and $y = -5$

8. Solve the equation. Verify your solution.

   (a) $3a + 1 = 10$

   (b) $-2b - 5 = 20$

   (c) $4c + 7 = 2c + 1$

   (d) $-3d + 1 = 5d - 7$

   (e) $3e + \dfrac{2}{5} = 4$

   (f) $\dfrac{2f - 1}{3} = \dfrac{f + 3}{2}$

9. Factor using a greatest common factor.

   (a) $16w - 2w^2$

   (b) $4x^2 + 12x - 40$

   (c) $2x^4 + 4x^3 + 8x^2$

   (d) $5x^2y^2 - 15xy + 20x^3y^2$

10. Write an algebraic expression for the relation that models each situation. Clearly define your variables.

   (a) The perimeter of a rectangle is 100 cm.

   (b) The perimeter of a square is 36 m.

   (c) The perimeter of a triangle is 13 cm.

   (d) The area of a rectangle is 40 cm².

   (e) The area of a square is 81 cm².

   (f) The area of a triangle is 14 cm² and the base is equal to the altitude.

   (g) A rectangle has a square hole, 10 cm by 10 cm, cut out of it. What is the area of the remaining material?

   (h) A rectangular floor will be covered with ceramic tiles that are 10 cm squares. Write an expression that can be used to estimate the number of tiles needed.

   (i) Several 5 L gas cans are filled from a large storage tank. Write an expression to represent the total number of gas cans that can be filled.

   (j) A car uses 9 L of gasoline for every 100 km of city driving. If gas costs 65.9¢/L, write an expression for the cost of driving the car in the city.

3.1 Quadratic Relations

Part 1: Linear and Nonlinear Models

Examine each situation and think about the kind of mathematical model that would apply.

Blood Alcohol Content

Drinking and driving is one of the major causes of vehicle accidents. A driver's *blood alcohol content* (BAC) depends on body mass and the amount of alcohol consumed. The table shows the number of standard-size drinks that produce a BAC of 0.05% within a 2 h period.

(Note: One standard-size drink is 30 mL (one ounce) of 80-proof spirits, 90 mL (3 ounces) of wine, or 240 mL (8 ounces) of 5% beer. Also, although the figures shown here are accurate, individual results would vary.)

Alcohol Consumption to Reach 0.05% BAC in 2 Hours

Body Mass (kg)	46	55	64	73	82	91	100	109
Number of Drinks	2.5	2.9	3.3	3.7	4.1	4.5	4.9	5.3

Bacteria Growth

The population of a bacteria colony is measured over a 6 h period, resulting in this data.

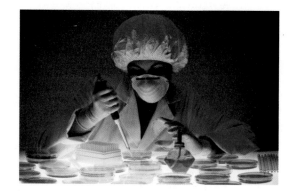

Population of Bacteria

Time (h)	0	1	2	3	4	5	6
Bacteria Count	1900	3900	8000	15 900	31 900	64 100	127 900

Falling Water

A garden hose sprays a stream of water across a lawn. The table records the approximate height of the stream above the lawn at various distances from the nozzle.

Water Height vs. Distance from Nozzle

Distance from Nozzle (m)	0	1	2	3	4	5	6	7	8
Height Above Lawn (m)	0	0.9	1.6	2.1	2.4	2.5	2.4	2.0	1.4

Think, Do, Discuss

1. (a) Draw and label a separate scatter plot for each situation.

    (b) Which situations can be modelled with a linear relation? Justify your answer. Draw the line of best fit for these situations and comment on how well the model fits the data.

    (c) For those situations that require a nonlinear model, use a piece of string to make a curve that matches the pattern of the data points. Some data points may not fit the pattern exactly. Describe how to place the string when this happens.

    (d) Draw the curve of best fit for the nonlinear models by following the shape of the string. How well does the curve fit the data?

2. Use your graphs to answer these questions.

    (a) For an adult with a body mass of 60 kg, how many drinks of alcohol would result in a blood alcohol content of 0.05% after 2 h?

    (b) How many bacteria would there be after 7 h?

    (c) What is the maximum height of the water stream? How far from the nozzle does the water reach this height?

3. (a) The differences between consecutive values of the dependent variable are called **finite differences**, or **first differences**. Calculate the first (or finite) differences for each table of values.

    (b) Explain how the values in the difference tables support your decision about linear and nonlinear models in question 1.

    (c) The value of a first difference represents the amount of change in the dependent variable (Δy) caused by a change in the independent variable (Δx). The ratio of these changes, $\frac{\Delta y}{\Delta x}$, can be used to estimate the rate of change of one quantity relative to the other quantity. For each situation, describe which quantities are changing and what the rate of change means.

    (d) For which of the situations is the rate of change constant? What does this tell you about the relation being modelled?

4. (a) For which of the situations is the rate of change variable? What does this tell you about the relation being modelled?

    (b) How does a variable rate of change affect the graph?

Part 2: Number Patterns

Square Number Patterns

Ancient mathematicians were fascinated by **figurate numbers**: sequences that represent the number of markers needed to construct common geometric shapes. For example, the **square numbers** are 1, 4, 9, 16, and so on.

The first square number (S_1) is 1; the second square number (S_2) is 4, and so on.

$S_4 = 16$

$S_3 = 9$

$S_2 = 4$

$S_1 = 1$

$n = 1$ $n = 2$ $n = 3$ $n = 4$

Complete this table of square numbers.

n	1	2	3	4	5	6	7	8
S_n	1	4	9	16				

Summing Patterns

The great mathematician Karl Friedrich Gauss showed his talents even as a young boy. One day, his teacher, who hoped to keep the class busy, instructed the students to add the whole numbers from 1 to 100. Gauss gave the correct answer almost immediately.

Gauss's reasoning was as follows:

Write out the sequence of numbers (or imagine writing them out). Below the first sequence, write the sequence again, in reverse order.

Karl Friedrich Gauss (1777–1855)

1	2	3	4	...	97	98	99	100
100	99	98	97	...	4	3	2	1

Gauss realized that each vertical pair adds to 101 and that there are exactly 100 pairs. The total, for the two copies of the sequence, is $(100)(101) = 10\ 100$. For one copy of the sequence, the total is half as much.

$$S_{100} = \frac{(100)(101)}{2} = 5050$$

Use Gauss's method to complete this table for values of n from 1 to 20.

n	1	2	3	4	5	6	7	...	20
Sum of numbers from 1 to n	1	3	6						

Surface Area Patterns

The surface area of a 1 cm cube is 6 cm², because the cube has 6 square faces that are each 1 cm × 1 cm. For a 2 cm cube, the 6 faces are 2 cm × 2 cm squares and the surface area is 24 cm².

Copy and complete this table.

Cube Side Length (cm)	1	2	3	4	5	6	7	...	10
Surface Area (cm²)	6	24							

Think, Do, Discuss

1. Refer back to the section Square Number Patterns.
   (a) Write a formula for the nth square number in terms of n.
   (b) Predict the value of the 12th square number. If there was a square number between S_5 and S_6, estimate its value. Explain why such a number is not really possible.
   (c) Draw a scatter plot of the data.

2. Refer back to the section Summing Patterns.
   (a) Write a formula for the sum of the first n whole numbers in terms of n.
   (b) Draw a scatter plot of the data.

3. Refer back to the section Surface Area Patterns.
   (a) Write a formula for the surface area of a cube in terms of its side length l.
   (b) Draw a scatter plot of the data.

4. (a) How are the formulas in questions 1, 2, and 3 similar?
   (b) How are the graphs the same?
   (c) How are they different?

5. (a) Compute the first differences for each table of values.
   (b) Explain how the values of the differences show that the relationships are not linear.
   (c) How is the pattern in the differences the same among these relationships?
   (d) How is the pattern in the differences different?

6. (a) Refer to the sequence of first differences that you found in question 5. Calculate the **second differences**, that is, the differences between consecutive first differences.
   (b) What do you notice about the second differences for all three relationships?

7. Which situations in part 1 have graphs that are similar to those in part 2? What type of mathematical model would best fit those situations? Explain.

8. (a) Calculate the second differences for the relations in part 1.
   (b) Which relations in part 1 have patterns in their second differences similar to those in part 2?
   (c) What does that suggest about the type of mathematical model that would best fit those situations?
   (d) In the formula for the dependent variable, what is the value of the highest exponent when the first differences are constant?
   (e) What is the highest exponent when the second differences are constant?

Focus 3.1

Key Ideas

- Sometimes a **curve of best fit** is a more appropriate model for data than a line of best fit. This is true when the data points seem to fit a recognizable pattern that is not a straight line. In such a case, try to draw a smooth curve that passes through as many of the data points as possible. Visualize where the curve should lie between the actual plotted data points. A piece of string may help you to decide the shape and location of the curve.

- The values of the **first differences** in a table of values determine if the relation is linear.

  ♦ For constant increments of the independent variable, a relation is linear if the first differences of the dependent variable are constant.

  For example, the first differences in this table of values are constant, so the relation is linear.

x	0	1	2	3	4
y	2	3	4	5	6
First Difference	1	1	1	1	

  ♦ For constant increments of the independent variable, a relation is **quadratic** if the second differences of the dependent variable are constant.

  For example, the second differences in this table of values are constant, so the relation is quadratic.

x	0	1	2	3	4
y	2	3	6	11	18
First Difference	1	3	5	7	
Second Difference	2	2	2		

- A linear relation models a phenomenon where the rate of change is constant. A nonlinear relation models a phenomenon with a variable rate of change.

- The **degree** of a one-variable polynomial is the highest exponent that appears in any term of the expanded form of the polynomial.

- A polynomial of degree 2 models a quadratic relation.

Example 1

A car driver puts on the brakes and skids through an intersection. The investigating police officer knows that the distance a car skids depends on the speed of the car just before the brakes are applied. She uses a chart to determine the car's speed before the skid.

Speed (km/h)	0	10	20	30	40	50	60	70	80	90	100
Length of Skid (m)	0	0.7	2.8	6.4	11.4	17.8	25.7	35.0	45.7	57.8	71.4

(a) Draw the curve of best fit for this data.

(b) Use the curve to estimate the initial speed of the car if the skid mark is 104 m long.

(c) Determine if either a linear or a quadratic relation can be used to model the data.

Solution

(a)

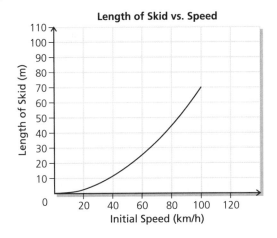

(b)

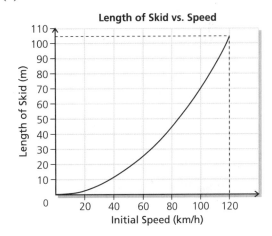

If the car skids 104 m, its initial speed was about 120 km/h.

(c) Compute the first and second differences.

Speed (km/h)	0	10	20	30	40	50	60	70	80	90	100
Length of Skid (m)	0	0.7	2.8	6.4	11.4	17.8	25.7	35.0	45.7	57.8	71.4
First Difference		0.7	2.1	3.6	5.0	6.4	7.9	9.3	10.7	12.1	13.6
Second Difference			1.4	1.5	1.4	1.4	1.5	1.4	1.4	1.4	1.5

The first differences are not the same: the relation is definitely not linear. The second differences are almost the same, so a quadratic model should be suitable for this relation.

Example 2

Two parachutists jump out of a plane at 2000 m. The first opens his parachute almost immediately. The other free-falls for the first 10 s. The table records their height above the ground at different times. Show that the first parachutist has a constant rate of descent and the second has a variable rate of descent during the period of measurement.

Time (s)	0	2	4	6	8	10
Height of Jumper 1 (m)	2000	1980	1960	1940	1920	1900
Height of Jumper 2 (m)	2000	1980	1920	1820	1680	1500

Solution

To determine the rate of descent, examine how the distance each jumper falls during each 2 s interval changes. This is the first difference in the table of values.

Time (s)	0	2	4	6	8	10
Height of Jumper 1 (m)	2000	1980	1960	1940	1920	1900
First Difference		−20	−20	−20	−20	−20

The first jumper has a constant rate of descent of 20 m in each 2 s interval. This could be modelled by a linear relation with a slope of $\frac{-20}{2} = -10$. The rate of descent is -10 m/s.

Time (s)	0	2	4	6	8	10
Height of Jumper 2 (m)	2000	1980	1920	1820	1680	1500
First Difference		−20	−60	−100	−140	−180
Second Difference			−40	−40	−40	−40

The second jumper has a variable rate of descent. During each 2 s interval, the change in height is different. Since the second differences are constant, a quadratic relation could be used to model the situation.

Example 3

Pentagonal numbers are another group of figurate numbers. They are generated in much the same way as square numbers, but are based on pentagons rather than squares.

Determine the kind of relation that would best model the pattern of pentagonal numbers.

Solution

Draw the diagram for the first four pentagonal numbers.

The diagram shows that

$P_1 = 1$

$P_2 = 5$

$P_3 = 12$

$P_4 = 22$

Extend the pattern for P_5 and P_6. Construct a table of values showing the first and second differences.

n		1	2	3	4	5	6
P_n		1	5	12	22	35	51
First Difference		4	7	10	13	16	
Second Difference		3	3	3	3		

Since the second differences are constant, the model should be a quadratic relation.

Practise, Apply, Solve 3.1

1. Examine each pattern. Supply the missing values.

    (a) ■, 4, 1, 0, 1, 4, ■   **(b)** ■, 3, 13, 27, 45, 67, ■

    (c) ■, 1, −2, −11, −26, −47, ■   **(d)** ■, 10, 3, 0, 1, 6, ■

    (e) ■, 5, 7, 5, −1, −11, ■   **(f)** ■, 4, −3, −6, −5, ■

2. i. For each set of data, calculate the first differences and identify the linear and nonlinear relations.

   ii. For the nonlinear relations, determine the second differences and identify the quadratic relations.

(a)

x	10	20	30	40
y	21	41	61	81

(b)

x	1	2	3	4
y	4	7	12	17

(c)

x	5	6	8	11
y	−2	−3	−5	−8

(d)

x	0	1	2	3
y	1	−1	−7	−11

(e)

x	0	1	2	3
y	−2	−1	6	25

(f)

x	0	1	2	3	4
y	1	2	4	8	16

3. For the linear relations in question 2, determine the slope.

4. Follow the pattern and determine the missing values.

(a)

y	■	■	■	−2	■	■
First Difference	−3	−3	−3	−3	−3	

(b)

y	■	■	4	■	■
First Difference	■	■	1	■	
Second Difference	2	2	2		

(c)

y	■	−8	■	■	■	■
First Difference	■	6	■	■		
Second Difference	−1	−1	−1			

5. Determine the degree of each polynomial.

   (a) $3x - 2$ **(b)** $\frac{1}{2}r^2$ **(c)** $2r$

   (d) $-4.9t^2$ **(e)** $x^2 + 3x - 1$ **(f)** $2x^3 - 3x + x - 4$

   (g) $x^2 - 9$ **(h)** $x(x + 2)$ **(i)** $x^2(x^3 - 3)$

   (j) $x(x^2 + 2x + 1)$ **(k)** $ax + b$ **(l)** $ax^2 + bx + c$

6. Identify the polynomials in question 5 that could be used to model a quadratic relation.

7. For each set of data, draw a scatter plot. Depending on the scatter plot, draw either a line of best fit or a curve of best fit.

   (a) The amount of gold produced for several years is estimated.

Year	1977	1978	1979	1980
Gold Produced (t)	1108	1111	1122	1147

   (b) A colony of bacteria is growing in a petri dish. A research scientist estimates the number of bacteria at one minute intervals.

Time (min)	0	1	2	3	4
Bacteria Count (000s)	6	12	23	50	100

   (c) Josh dissolves salt in a pot of water. He finds that as the water gets hotter, more salt will dissolve.

Temperature (°C)	0	20	40	60	80	100
Dissolved Salt (g)	52	62	81	103	131	159

   (d) Each year thousands of tonnes of garbage are produced. Garbage that is not recycled is dumped in a landfill site or burned. The table shows the approximate amount of waste that has been burned in recent years for a large city.

Year	1994	1995	1996	1997	1998	1999
Waste Burned (t)	86 000	90 000	89 000	95 000	89 000	99 000

8. The table represents the average body mass for children up to age 12.

Age (years)	1	2	3	4	5	6	7	8	9	10	11	12
Mass (kg)	11.5	13.7	16.0	20.5	23.0	23.0	30.0	33.0	39.0	38.5	41.0	49.5

(a) Draw a scatter plot.
(b) Draw a best-fit graph.
(c) What type of model best represents the data? Explain.
(d) Describe the goodness of fit of the model, using one of these choices: poor, reasonable, or very good fit. Explain your choice.

9. **Knowledge and Understanding:** A ball is dropped from the roof of a 15-storey building and is timed as it passes various windows. The table shows the results of two repetitions of the experiment.

Height of Ball (storeys)	15	13	11	9	7	5	3	1
Time from 1st Experiment (s)	0	1.1	1.6	2.1	2.3	2.6	2.8	2.9
Time from 2nd Experiment (s)	0	1.0	1.5	2.2	2.3	2.5	2.9	3.0

(a) Draw a scatter plot combining the data from both experiments on the same graph.
(b) Draw a best-fit curve.
(c) Describe the goodness of fit from one of these choices: poor, reasonable, or very good fit. Explain your choice.
(d) Is the data best represented by a linear or nonlinear relation? Explain.

10. A pendulum swings back and forth. The time it takes to make one complete swing and return to the original position is called the **period** of the pendulum. The period changes according to the length of the pendulum.

Length of Pendulum (cm)	6.2	24.8	55.8	99.2	155.0
Period (s)	0.5	1.0	1.5	2.0	2.5

(a) Draw a scatter plot and the curve of best fit.
(b) If a pendulum is 40 cm long, determine its period.
(c) Predict the length of a pendulum if its period is 2.2 s.
(d) Determine the type of model that best describes the relation between the length and the period of a pendulum. Explain.

11. **Communication:** Paymore Shoe Company introduces a new line of neon green high heel running shoes. The table shows the number of pairs sold at one store over an 11-month period.

Month	1	2	3	4	5	6	7	8	9	10	11
Shoes Sold (pairs)	56	60	62	62	60	56	50	42	32	20	6

(a) Draw a scatter plot and the curve of best fit.

(b) When did the number of shoes sold per month reach its peak?

(c) What has happened by month 11? Explain why this might have occurred.

(d) Determine the rate of change in the number of pairs of shoes sold between months 1 and 2, and months 4 and 5. What does this mean?

(e) Compare the rate of change in shoe sales between months 1 and 2, and months 2 and 3. What does this mean?

(f) Compare the rate of change in shoe sales between months 4 and 5, and months 5 and 6. What does this mean?

(g) Show that the relation between the number of pairs of shoes sold and the time the shoes have been on the market is a quadratic relation. Explain why this model is suitable for the fashion business. How is it unsuitable?

12. A ball is tossed straight up in the air. Its height is recorded every quarter second.

Time (s)	0	0.25	0.50	0.75	1.00	1.25	1.50	1.75	2.00
Height (m)	1.5	3.5	4.9	5.7	5.7	5.2	4.1	2.4	0.1

(a) Draw a scatter plot.

(b) What type of model is a reasonable representation of the relationship between the height of the ball and the time in the air? Explain

(c) Draw the graph that best fits the data.

(d) When does the ball reach its highest point above the ground? What is the ball's height at this point? Be as precise as you can, using your graphical model.

(e) About how long is the ball in the air? Explain.

13. A set of rectangles is made from 1 cm squares. The first rectangle is 1 cm × 2 cm. The next is 2 cm × 4 cm, then 3 cm × 6 cm. The pattern continues with the length always twice the width.

(a) Draw the patterns of squares to help you visualize the pattern. Use your diagrams to complete the table.

Shape	Width (cm)	Length (cm)	Area (cm²)
	1	2	2
next shape in pattern			
next shape in pattern			
next shape in pattern			

(b) Determine the first differences for the area of the rectangles. How do these differences tell you whether the relation between width and area is linear or nonlinear?

(c) Determine the second differences for the area. How does this help determine the type of relation between width and area?

(d) Write an algebraic expression that represents the relation between width and area. What is the degree of the expression?

14. Examine these square dot patterns.

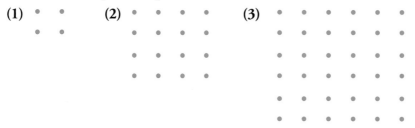

(a) Extend the pattern to form the next two shapes in the sequence.

(b) Complete the table of values in your notebook, where n is the number of each diagram in the pattern and S_n is the total number of dots in each shape.

n	1	2	3	4	5
S_n	4	16	36		

(c) Draw the graph of S_n vs. n.

(d) Does the sequence define a linear or nonlinear relation? Explain.

(e) Determine the second differences. What type of model describes the relationship between the diagram number and the number of dots in each shape? Explain.

(f) Write an algebraic expression that models the relation. What is the degree of the expression?

15. These diagrams show points joined by all possible line segments.

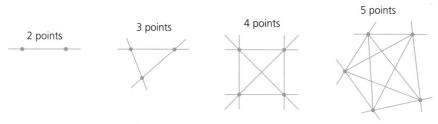

(a) Extend the pattern to include a figure with six points.

(b) Make a table of values that shows the number of points and the number of connecting line segments.

(c) Graph the data.

(d) Does the data represent a linear or nonlinear relation? Explain.

(e) Write an algebraic expression for the number of line segments in terms of the number of points.

(f) Extend the pattern to include a figure with seven points. How many line segments are in this figure?

(g) Use the result from (f) to verify the algebraic expression found in (e).

16. **Application:** When a car is driven, the amount of gas used per kilometre depends on the speed the car is travelling. The table shows an example of this relation.

Speed (km/h)	20	40	60	80	100	120
Cost of Gas (¢/km)	9.1	7.8	7.1	7.1	7.8	9.1

(a) What type of relation seems to be a good model for the data?

(b) Draw the curve of best fit.

(c) What speed is the most cost-efficient?

(d) Explain why lower and higher speeds are not as cost-efficient.

(e) On a 600 km trip, how much money would be saved by driving at the most cost-efficient speed, rather than at 100 km/h? How much longer would the trip take?

17. **Check Your Understanding:** Suppose you are given a table of values representing the results of an experiment. You draw a graph of the data. What kinds of patterns would you look for in the data to decide whether to use a linear model, a quadratic model, or some other nonlinear model to make predictions?

18. Find the sum of all the whole numbers from 200 to 399.

19. **Thinking, Inquiry, Problem Solving:** Nina is an O.P.P. officer. One of her duties is to investigate traffic accidents and to prepare accurate reports for use in court. She uses this formula to estimate the speed of a vehicle, based on the length of the skid mark on the road.

$$s = 15.9\sqrt{Df}$$

where

• f is the drag factor. A more precise name is the frictional coefficient of the road surface.

• D is the length of the skid mark (in metres)

• s is the speed when the skid started (in kilometres per hour)

This table gives typical values of f for a variety of road conditions.

Road Surface	Dry	Wet
concrete	0.70	0.40
asphalt	0.65	0.45
gravel	0.50	0.50
ice	0.07	0.05
snow	0.35	0.30

Source: Huntley, I. D, and D. J. G. James. *Mathematical Modeling.* New York: Oxford University Press, 1990.

(a) Create a table of values and a graph showing how the speed estimate varies with skid length for a concrete surface under dry conditions.

(b) Use the graph to estimate the speed of a car at the time the brakes were applied if the skid mark is 50 m long.

(c) If the speed limit for the road is 80 km/h, what is the longest possible skid mark for a car travelling at or below the limit on dry concrete?

(d) If a car is equipped with an anti-lock braking system (ABS), the skid length is typically 10% less. How would that affect your answer in (c)?

(e) Drivers typically take 1.5 s to react to a dangerous situation. How far from an intersection would a driver have to be to safely stop a car travelling at 80 km/h?

(f) Show how the road surface material and moisture conditions affect your answer to (e).

The Chapter Problem—Setting the Best Ticket Price

In this section you used nonlinear models. Apply what you learned to answer these questions about the chapter problem on page 242.

1. Prepare a table of values to show how a decrease in ticket price affects the attendance and the revenue.

2. Prepare another table to show how an increase in ticket price affects attendance and revenue.

3. Draw scatter plots of the data, showing revenue vs. change in price.

4. Draw the curve of best fit for each scatter plot.

Properties of Quadratic Relations

Part 1: Maximizing the Area Enclosed by a Fence

Wanda and Louise raise puppies. They need a rectangular fenced enclosure for the puppies to run and play in. A contractor said it will cost $30/m of fence, and they have $480 to spend.

Think, Do, Discuss

1. **(a)** What variables in a rectangular design will Wanda and Louise have to consider?
   (b) Draw a sketch that includes all the information you have been given.
   (c) Indicate on your sketch any relationships that exist between the variables.

2. **(a)** Write an algebraic expression for the area of the fenced enclosure. There should be only one independent variable.
   (b) What is the independent variable in the expression? What is the dependent variable?
   (c) Write the expression in both factored form and expanded form.

3. **(a)** Use your model to find the dimensions of a rectangular enclosure that will provide the maximum area for the puppies and meet the budget limitations. Use a series of sketches of rectangular designs, a table of values, and a graph to demonstrate that the dimensions you have found are the best for this solution.
   (b) Use first and second differences to decide what type of relation the algebraic expression represents.

4. Refer to the graph and your table of values from step 3. Locate the point that represents the dimensions that give the maximum area.
   (a) Find two points on the curve that are the same distance to the right and to the left of this point. Compare their y-coordinates.
   (b) Repeat (a) for several similar pairs of points.
   (c) Draw a vertical line through the highest point of the curve. Compare the shape of the left part of the curve to the right part of the curve.
   (d) What observation can you make about the shape of the graph of this relation?
   (e) Why are there two points on the graph that represent an enclosed area of 0 m²?
   (f) Explain how these two points relate to the factors of the expression in 2(a).

Part 2: Minimizing Costs

Wanda and Louise purchased the fencing material described in part 1, but then they decided to build two separate square enclosures instead of one enclosure. They want to be able to separate the adult dogs from the puppies.

The ground inside each enclosure has to be covered with sod. They want to use all the fencing they purchased, and to minimize the amount of sod they need to buy.

Think, Do, Discuss

1. **(a)** What variables will Wanda and Louise have to consider?
   (b) Draw a sketch that shows all the information available to you.

   (c) Indicate on your sketch any relationships that exist between the variables.

2. **(a)** Develop an algebraic expression with one variable to model the total area of the fenced enclosures.
   (b) Use this model to find the dimensions of the two enclosures that will cover the minimum ground area and still use all the available fencing material. Use a table of values and a graph to demonstrate that the dimensions you have found are the best for this situation.

   (c) Use first and second differences to determine the type of relation represented by the algebraic expression.

3. Refer to the graph and the table of values you created in (2). Locate the point that represents the dimensions that cover the minimum area.
   (a) Find two points that are the same distance to the right and to the left of this optimal point. How do their y-coordinates compare?
   (b) Repeat (a) for several similar pairs of points.
   (c) What can you say about the shape of the graph of this relation?
   (d) The relation in part 1 had points that represented an enclosed area of 0 m². Explain why this graph has no such points.

4. Examine the graphs and the tables of values for parts 1 and 2.
   (a) What relation do you see between the second differences and which way the graphs open?
   (b) Examine the graphs and the tables of values for the quadratic relations in section 3.1. Do they confirm the hypothesis you made in (a) or not?

Focus 3.2

Key Ideas

- The graph of a quadratic relation is called a **parabola.**

- The **vertex** of a parabola is the point on the graph with the greatest y-coordinate if the graph opens down or the least y-coordinate if the graph opens up.

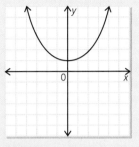

figure 1

- When a quadratic relation is used to model a situation, the y-coordinate of the vertex corresponds to an **optimal value.** Depending on the direction of opening of the parabola, this represents either a **maximum** or a **minimum** value of the quantity being modelled by the dependent variable. The maximum or minimum value is always associated with the vertex.

- The direction of opening of the parabola can be determined from the sign of the second differences in the table of values of the quadratic relation.

  ♦ If the constant value of the second differences is positive, then the parabola opens up (figure 1).

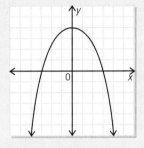

figure 2

  ♦ If the constant value of the second differences is negative, then the parabola opens down (figure 2).

- A parabola is symmetrical with respect to a vertical line through its vertex. The line is called the **axis of symmetry** of the parabola and the vertex lies on the axis of symmetry. If the coordinates of the vertex are (h, k), then the equation of the axis of symmetry is $x = h$ (figure 3).

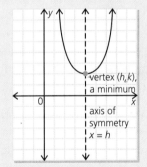

figure 3

- The axis of symmetry is the perpendicular bisector of the segment joining any two points on the parabola that have the same y-coordinates. If the parabola crosses the x-axis, the x-coordinates of these points are called the **zeros**, or **x-intercepts** of the relation, and the vertex is directly above or below the midpoint of the segment joining the zeros (figure 4).

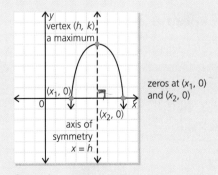

figure 4

Example 1

Phil wants to make the largest possible rectangular vegetable garden using 18 m of fencing. The garden is right behind the back of his house, so he has to fence it on only three sides. Determine the dimensions that maximize the area of the garden.

Solution

First, sketch the situation, showing all the available information. Identify the variables in the problem and state any possible relationships between them. Put these on the diagram as well.

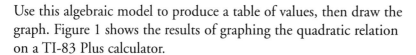

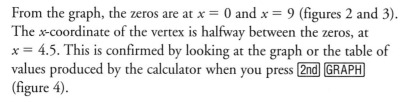

The total length of fencing to be used is 18 m. Therefore,

$$\text{length} + 2(\text{width}) = 18$$

or
$$L + 2W = 18$$

Solving for L,
$$L = 18 - 2W$$

The area of the enclosure is

$$A = LW \qquad \text{Substitute } L = 18 - 2W.$$
$$A = (18 - 2W)W$$

Use this algebraic model to produce a table of values, then draw the graph. Figure 1 shows the results of graphing the quadratic relation on a TI-83 Plus calculator.

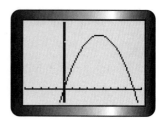

figure 1

From the graph, the zeros are at $x = 0$ and $x = 9$ (figures 2 and 3). The x-coordinate of the vertex is halfway between the zeros, at $x = 4.5$. This is confirmed by looking at the graph or the table of values produced by the calculator when you press [2nd] [GRAPH] (figure 4).

The maximum area enclosed by the fence is 40.5 m², when the width, W, is 4.5 m. The length is 9 m.

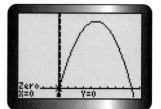

figure 2

Example 2

Consider the quadratic relation $y = x(6x - 18)$.
Without making a table of values or drawing the graph, give

(a) the coordinates of the vertex of the parabola
(b) the direction of opening
(c) the axis of symmetry

figure 3

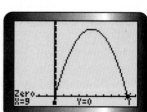

figure 4

Solution

(a) The zeros of the parabola are found where it crosses the x-axis, at the points where $y = 0$. Substitute $y = 0$ in the relation $y = x(6x - 18)$.

$$0 = x(6x - 18)$$

$$x = 0 \text{ or } 6x - 18 = 0$$

The zeros of the parabola are at $x = 0$ and $6x = 18$, or $x = 3$.

The x-coordinate of the vertex is halfway between the zeros. So, the vertex must have $x = \dfrac{0 + 3}{2}$ or $\dfrac{3}{2}$. To find the y-coordinate of the vertex, substitute $x = \dfrac{3}{2}$ in the relation.

$$y = x(6x - 18)$$

$$y = \frac{3}{2}\left(6\left(\frac{3}{2}\right) - 18\right)$$

$$y = \frac{3}{2}(9 - 18)$$

$$y = \frac{-27}{2} \text{ or } -13.5$$

The vertex of the parabola is at $\left(\dfrac{3}{2}, -\dfrac{27}{2}\right)$ or $(1.5, -13.5)$.

(b) Direction of Opening

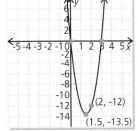

Since the x-coordinate of the vertex is known, you can substitute a value for x on either side of the vertex and determine whether the vertex is lower or higher than that point.

For example, substituting $x = 2$ in $y = x(6x - 18)$ gives $y = 2(6(2) - 18) = -12$. The y-coordinate of the vertex is $-\dfrac{27}{2}$ or -13.5, which is less. That means the vertex is a minimum and the graph opens up.

(c) The x-coordinate of the vertex is $\dfrac{3}{2}$. Therefore, the equation of the axis of symmetry is $x = \dfrac{3}{2}$.

Did You Know?

Before electronic calculators came into common use, people used other tools to perform complex mathematical operations, such as the slide rule and the abacus.

The abacus was invented in China centuries ago, and continues to be used widely today. In fact, expert abacus users often calculate long, involved answers faster than people who use electronic calculators.

Do some research. How do slide rules and abacuses work? Why are decimals important in the operation of these calculators?

Practise, Apply, Solve 3.2

1. Which graphs appear to represent quadratic relations?

(a)

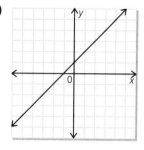

(b)

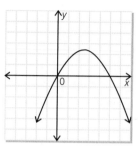

(c)

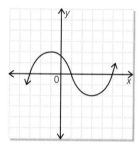

(d)

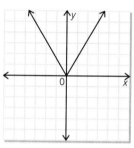

(e)

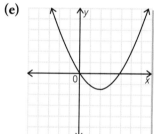

(f)

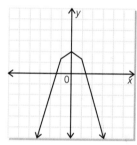

(g)

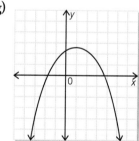

(h)

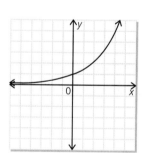

2. Each table of values represents data of a quadratic relation. Decide, without graphing, whether the parabola opens up or down.

(a)

x	−3	−2	−1	0
y	2.5	5	6.5	7

(b)

x	−2	−1	0	1	2
y	0	−5	0	15	40

(c)

x	−2	−1	0	1	2
y	−3	3	5	3	−3

(d)

x	0	1	2	3	4
y	−1	4	15	32	55

3. Examine this parabola.
   (a) What are the coordinates of the vertex?
   (b) What is the optimum value?
   (c) What is the equation of the axis of symmetry?
   (d) What are the zeros of the relation?
   (e) If you calculated the second differences, what would their sign be? Explain.

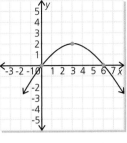

4. Examine this parabola.
   (a) What are the coordinates of the vertex?
   (b) State the optimum value. Is it a minimum or a maximum?
   (c) What is the equation of the axis of symmetry?
   (d) What are the zeros of the relation?
   (e) If you calculated the second differences, what would their sign be? Explain.

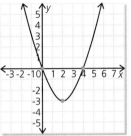

5. The x-intercepts of a quadratic relation are 0 and 5. The second differences are positive.
   (a) Explain whether the optimum value is a maximum or a minimum.
   (b) What value of the independent variable produces the optimum value?
   (c) Is the optimum value a positive or negative number? Explain.

6. The zeros of a quadratic relation are 0 and 15, and the second differences are negative.
   (a) Explain how you can tell whether the optimum value is a maximum or minimum.
   (b) What value of the independent variable produces the optimum value?
   (c) Is the optimum value positive or negative?

7. Determine the zeros of each quadratic relation.
   (a) $A = w(20 - w)$
   (b) $A = L(12 - L)$
   (c) $y = x(3x - 6)$
   (d) $A = 2w(18 - w)$
   (e) $y = 2x(5x + 6)$
   (f) $y = x(16 - 3x)$

8. Two parabolas have the same x-intercepts, 0 and 10. One has a maximum value of 2. The other has a minimum value of -4. Sketch the graphs on the same axes.

B

9. For each relation
   i.   write it in factored form by removing a common factor
   ii. determine the zeros
   iii. state the equation of the axis of symmetry of the parabola
   (a) $A = 15w - w^2$
   (b) $A = 24L - L^2$
   (c) $y = 2x^2 - 10x$
   (d) $y = 15x - 2x^2$

10. Each pair of points (x, y) is located on opposite sides of the same parabola. Determine the equation of the axis of symmetry of the parabola.

    (a) $(3, 2)$, $(9, 2)$ **(b)** $(-18, 3)$, $(7, 3)$

    (c) $(-2, -5)$, $(-5, -5)$ **(d)** $(6.5, -4)$, $(9.0, -4)$

    (e) $(-5.25, -2.5)$, $(3.75, -2.5)$ **(f)** $(-4\frac{1}{2}, 5)$, $(-1\frac{1}{2}, 5)$

    (g) $(-3\frac{1}{8}, -2)$, $(7\frac{3}{8}, -2)$ **(h)** $(s, 0)$, $(t, 0)$

11. **Knowledge and Understanding:** A football is kicked straight up in the air. Its height above the ground is approximated by the relation $h = 25t - 5t^2$, where h is the height in metres and t is the time in seconds.

    (a) What are the zeros of the relation? When does the football hit the ground?

    (b) What are the coordinates of the vertex?

    (c) Use the information you have found to graph the relation.

    (d) What is the maximum height reached by the football? After how many seconds does that occur?

12. The zeros of a quadratic relation are 0 and 6. The relation has a minimum value of -9.

    (a) Sketch the graph of the parabola that satisfies these conditions.

    (b) Find the equation of the parabola.

13. **Communication:** The underside of a bridge is a parabolic arch defined by the equation $y = -0.1x^2 + 2x$ with x and y measured in metres. Explain how to sketch the graph of the structure without using a table of values or graphing technology.

14. Two quadratic relations have the same x-intercepts, 0 and 8. One has a minimum value of -10. The other has a maximum value of 10.

    (a) Sketch both relations on the same axes.

    (b) Determine the equation of each relation. Write the expressions as polynomials of degree 2.

    (c) Compare the coefficients of the x^2-terms. How do the coefficients relate to the direction of opening of the parabola?

15. Two parabolas are defined by $y = 10x - x^2$ and $y = 3x^2 - 30x$ respectively, with both x and y measured in metres. What is the difference between their optimum values?

16. Application: Wanda and Louise consider using 30 m, 50 m, or 70 m of fencing to build their puppy run. They want it to be rectangular, using one wall of the kennel instead of fencing on one side. Set up the required relations to model their options and determine the maximum area for each option.

17. Check Your Understanding

  (a) Describe how the symmetry of a parabola allows you to find the coordinates of the vertex if you know the zeros.

  (b) Explain how the second differences can be used to determine if a quadratic relation has a maximum or a minimum value.

  (c) Explain how the zeros of a parabola can be determined from the factored form of the quadratic relation.

  (d) Describe the relation between the coordinates of the vertex and the optimal value of a quadratic relation.

C

18. Thinking, Inquiry, Problem Solving
Canada Post will deliver parcels only if they are less than a certain maximum size: the combined length and girth cannot exceed 297 cm. (*Girth* is the total distance around the cross-section of the parcel.)

girth = distance around the box

length of the box

Canada Post delivers a crate with the largest possible surface area to your house. What is the surface area of the crate in square metres?

The Chapter Problem—Setting the Best Ticket Price

In this section you used quadratic relations to maximize different situations. Apply what you learned to answer these questions about the chapter problem on page 242.

  1. For each table of values that you found when you worked on the chapter problem in section 3.1, calculate the first and second differences. What type of relation does the data represent?

  2. Extend the graphs using symmetry to determine where each graph meets the horizontal axis.

  3. Using the graph, determine the maximum revenue and the change in price that corresponds to it.

3.3 Finding the Zeros of a Quadratic Relation Using a TI-83 Plus Calculator

Approximating the Zeros by Repeated Zooming

The graph of a quadratic relation can be drawn with the TI-83 Plus graphing calculator. The procedure is the same as for linear relations.

1. To graph $y = (x - 3)(x + 2)$, first enter the equation in the equation editor. (Press $\boxed{Y=}$ to access the equation editor.)

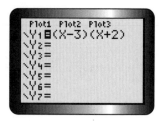

step 1

2. Press $\boxed{GRAPH}$ followed by $\boxed{ZOOM}\boxed{6}$ to display the graph in a window that covers the range from -10 to 10 on both axes.

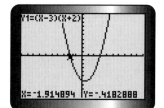

step 2

3. Press $\boxed{TRACE}$ followed by the left or right arrow keys to position the cursor near one of the zeros. The coordinates of the cursor are displayed at the bottom of the window.

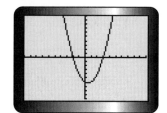

step 3

4. You can get a better approximation of the zero by zooming in. Press $\boxed{ZOOM}\boxed{2}\boxed{ENTER}$, then reposition the cursor to the new location using $\boxed{TRACE}$ and the arrow keys.

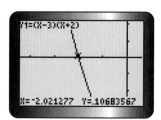

step 4

5. The accuracy of your approximation improves each time you zoom in and trace.

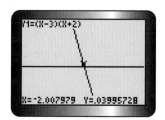

step 5

6. To find the other zero, go back to the original graph (ZOOM 6), move the cursor close to the desired point, then zoom in as before to improve the accuracy.

step 6

7. To check an approximate zero, press 2nd TRACE 1 and enter your estimated value for x.

 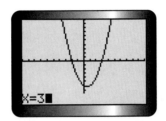 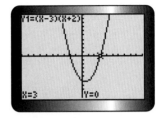

If you have the correct zero, the y-value will be zero. If not, you should repeat the process to improve your estimate for x. Do the same to check your approximation for the second zero.

Finding the Zeros with the Zero Command

The zeros can also be determined using the **zero** command.

1. To demonstrate, start by entering $y = -(x + 3)(x - 5)$ in the equation editor, then press GRAPH ZOOM 6. Adjust the window so that Ymax $=20$. Then press GRAPH.

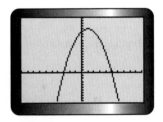

step 1

2. To access the **zero** command, press 2nd TRACE 2.

step 2

3. Use the left and right arrow keys to move the cursor along the curve to a position just to the left of one of the zeros. Press ENTER to set the **Left Bound**.

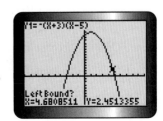

step 3

4. Move the cursor along the curve to a point to the right of the zero. Press ENTER to set the **Right Bound**.

5. You can enter a guess, then see the actual zero by pressing ENTER again.

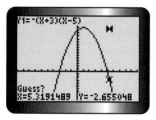

step 4

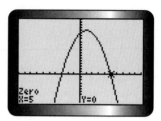

step 5

6. The coordinates of the zero point (the *x*-intercept) are displayed.

7. Repeat this process to find the second zero.

step 6

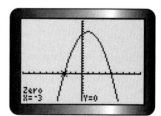

step 7

Practise 3.3

Find the zeros of each quadratic relation by repeated zooming. Verify your approximations using the **zero** operation.

(a) $y = (x + 4)(x + 1)$

(b) $y = -(x - 9)(x + 7)$

(c) $y = (x - 3)(x + 3)$

(d) $y = (-3x + 2)(x + 6)$

(e) $y = (4x - 1)(5x - 3)$

(f) $y = -(2x - 1)(x + 5)$

Euclid (c. 300 B.C.E.)

Euclid is the most prominent mathematician of Greco-Roman antiquity. During the reign of the Egyptian ruler Ptolemy I, Euclid founded, and taught at, a school in Alexandria. Euclid is best known for his textbook on geometry, *Elements,* which he wrote when he was about 40. This illustration shows Euclid presenting *Elements* to Ptolemy I.

Euclidean geometry includes the study of points, lines, angles, surfaces, and solids on the basis of the ten axioms and postulates that Euclid selected. Euclidean geometry is important, not so much because of the mathematics that it contains, but because of the systematic method that Euclid used to present and develop that mathematics.

The Role of the Zeros of 3.4
a Quadratic Relation

Part 1: A Retailing Problem: Maximizing
T-Shirt Revenue

Mirna operates her own store, Mirna's Fashion. A popular style of T-shirt sells for $10. At that price, Mirna sells about 30 T-shirts a week.

Experience has taught Mirna that changing the price of an article has an effect on sales. For example, she knows that a $1 increase in the price of the T-shirt means that she will sell about one less T-shirt per week. Similarly, a $1 decrease in price generally results in one more T-shirt being sold per week. Increasing the price reduces total unit sales, while reducing the price increases unit sales.

Mirna wants to find the price that will maximize her revenue from the sale of T-shirts.

Think, Do, Discuss

1. **(a)** Determine the weekly revenue for several different T-shirt prices.

   (b) Set up a table of values that shows how unit price affects the number of T-shirts sold and the total weekly revenue from T-shirt sales.

   (c) Use a difference table to determine whether the data would be modelled better by a linear relationship or nonlinear relationship.

   (d) List the variables that should be included in an algebraic model of the situation. How will the variables be related?

   (e) Write down any relationships that exist between the variables.

   (f) Write an algebraic expression to model the total weekly revenue in terms of one of the variables.

2. **(a)** Graph the algebraic relation.

   (b) Explain why there are two points on the graph that correspond to a weekly revenue of $0.

   (c) Why does only one of these $0 points make sense in the context of the problem?

   (d) How does knowing both points help you solve the problem?

   (e) Use the table of values and the algebraic model to find the unit price that maximizes Mirna's total weekly revenue.

3. Suppose Mirna's original weekly sales were 35 T-shirts instead of 30.

   (a) Explore how this would affect the price that maximizes her weekly revenue.

   (b) In this situation, is the graph more or less useful than a table of values? Explain.

4. Suppose the original weekly sales base is still 30 T-shirts, but that each $0.50 change in price (instead of $1) causes a change of one T-shirt in weekly sales.

   (a) Explore how this would affect the unit price that maximizes weekly revenue.

   (b) In this situation, is the graph more or less useful than a table of values? Explain.

Part 2: A Retailing Problem: Maximizing CD Revenue

Max operates a store, part of a national chain, that sells CDs in a mall. Max has a one-price-for-all policy: all single CDs sell for $20 each. The national sales manager has given Max permission to change his pricing in an attempt to increase revenue.

Max knows that, over the last six months, he has sold an average of 280 CDs a day at $20 each. The company's market research indicates that for every $0.50 increase in unit price, daily sales will drop by five units.

What unit price will maximize Max's daily revenues?

Think, Do, Discuss

1. **(a)** Determine the daily revenue for several different CD prices.

   (b) Set up a table of values that shows how price affects the number of CDs sold and the total daily revenue from CD sales.

   (c) Use a difference table to determine whether the data would be modelled better by a linear relationship or a nonlinear relationship.

   (d) List the variables that should be included in an algebraic model of the situation. How will the variables be linked?

   (e) Write down any relationships that exist between the variables.

   (f) Write an algebraic expression to model the total weekly revenue in terms of one of the variables.

2. **(a)** Graph the algebraic relation.

   (b) Explain why there are two points on the graph that correspond to a daily revenue of $0.

(c) Why does only one of these $0 points make sense in the context of the problem?

(d) How does knowing both points help you solve the problem?

(e) Use the table of values and the algebraic model to find the price that maximizes Max's total daily revenue.

3. Suppose that every $0.25 increase in price causes a corresponding decrease of two CDs in daily sales.

(a) Explore how this would affect the unit price that maximizes daily revenue.

(b) In this situation, is the graph more or less useful than a table of values? Explain.

Part 3: Projectile Motion: Finding the Model —

The graph shows the trajectory of a water balloon launched from a catapult at a recent university Science Day. The objective was to hit a target 55 m from the launch point. The balloon's path was tracked using a stop-motion camera, and the data was then entered into a graphing program that plotted the height of the balloon against its horizontal distance.

Balloon Trajectory—Height vs. Distance

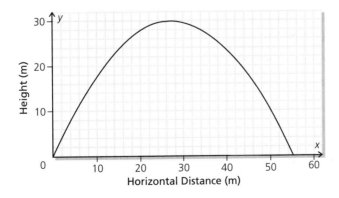

As part of the activity, the engineering students were asked to analyze the graph. They had to find an algebraic model that would predict the height of the balloon at various horizontal distances.

Think, Do, Discuss

1. Use values from the graph to show that the most appropriate model is quadratic.

2. **(a)** Use the zeros from the graph to write an algebraic expression for the quadratic relation that models the trajectory of the balloon.

   (b) Why is a model that is based only on the zeros not complete?

   (c) What additional information do you need to complete the algebraic expression?

   (d) Modify the algebraic expression of the model by including a variable that represents the missing quantity.

3. Locate a point on the graph whose coordinates can be determined easily and accurately.

   (a) Substitute the coordinates for this point into the partial model in 2(d).

   (b) Solve the resulting equation to find the value of the quantity needed to complete the model.

   (c) Check your model by substituting various values for the independent variable and comparing the predicted results to the graph.

4. **(a)** Explain why it is possible to find the x-coordinate of the vertex very precisely using your model.

   (b) Why is the y-coordinate of the vertex harder to determine?

   (c) Use the complete model to give a more precise estimate of the maximum height reached by the balloon.

Part 4: Investigating the Graphs of Quadratic Relations ———————————

All of the quadratic relations presented so far have been in the form $y = a(x - s)(x - t)$. How do the values of a, s, and t affect the graph?

Think, Do, Discuss

1. Use a graphing calculator to graph $y = a(x - 2)(x + 3)$ when $a = 3$. Describe what happens to the graph as you change the value of a to 2, 1, -1, -2, and -3.

2. Graph $y = 2(x - 2)(x - t)$ when $t = -3$. Describe what happens to the graph as you change the value of t to -2, -1, 0, 1, 2, and 3.

3. Which of the quantities a, s, or t affects whether the graph has a maximum or a minimum value? How can you predict if the relation has a maximum or a minimum?

4. What does the equation of a quadratic relation look like if it has two zeros? one zero? no zeros?

Focus 3.4

Key Ideas

- Relations in the form $y = a(x - s)(x - t)$ are quadratic, provided that $a \neq 0$.

- A quadratic relation is said to be in **factored form** if its algebraic expression appears in the form $y = a(x - s)(x - t)$.

- If $a > 0$, the parabola opens up and has a minimum.
  If $a < 0$, the parabola opens down and has a maximum.

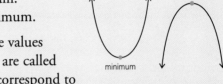

- When a quadratic relation is in factored form, the values of x that are the solutions to $0 = a(x - s)(x - t)$ are called the **zeros** of the quadratic relation. These values correspond to the x-intercepts of the graph of the relation. The zeros can be determined by setting each factor equal to 0 and solving the resulting equation for x. In $y = a(x - s)(x - t)$, the zeros are $x = s$ and $x = t$.

This quadratic relation has two zeros.

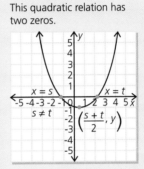

This quadratic relation has one zero.

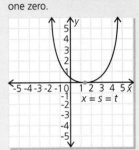

- If $s \neq t$, then the relation has two distinct zeros. If $s = t$, the relation has only one zero at $x = s = t$.

- If the zeros of a quadratic relation are s and t, then the x-coordinate of the vertex is $\dfrac{s + t}{2}$.

- When the zeros of a quadratic relation are known, the value of a can be determined if some other point (x_1, y_1) on the graph is known. Substitute the coordinates of the point in the factored form, giving $y_1 = a(x_1 - s)(x_1 - t)$, then solve for a.

Example 1

Consider the relation $y = (x + 3)(x - 4)$.

(a) Without graphing, show that the relation is quadratic.

(b) Without using graphing technology, sketch the graph, showing the zeros and vertex.

Solution

(a) Use the relation to set up a table of values and compute the first and second differences.

x	−3	−2	−1	0	1	2	3	4
$y = (x + 3)(x - 4)$	0	−6	−10	−12	−12	−10	−6	0
First Difference		−6	−4	−2	0	2	4	6
Second Difference			2	2	2	2	2	2

Since the second differences are constant, the relation is quadratic.

(b) The second differences are positive. Therefore, the parabola opens up.

The zeros of the quadratic relation are the solutions to the equation $0 = (x + 3)(x - 4)$. The values are $x = -3$ and $x = 4$.

The x-coordinate of the vertex is $\frac{-3 + 4}{2} = \frac{1}{2}$.

Substitute this x-value in $y = (x + 3)(x - 4)$:

$$y = \left(\frac{1}{2} + 3\right)\left(\frac{1}{2} - 4\right)$$
$$y = \left(\frac{7}{2}\right)\left(\frac{-7}{2}\right)$$
$$y = -\frac{49}{4}$$

The coordinates of the vertex are $\left(\frac{1}{2}, -\frac{49}{4}\right)$.

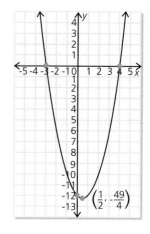

Example 2

The zeros of a parabola are -3 and 5. The parabola crosses the y-axis at -75.

(a) What is the equation of the quadratic relation?

(b) What are the coordinates of the vertex?

Solution

(a) Develop the factored form of the quadratic relation, $y = a(x - s)(x - t)$. Since the zeros are known, -3 and 5, substitute their values to obtain

$$y = a(x + 3)(x - 5)$$

The parabola crosses the y-axis at -75. This occurs when $x = 0$.

Substitute point $(0, -75)$ in the equation above:

$$-75 = a(0 + 3)(0 - 5)$$
$$-75 = a(3)(-5)$$
$$-75 = -15a$$
$$\frac{-75}{-15} = \frac{-15a}{-15}$$
$$5 = a$$

Substitute $a = 5$ to complete the expression:

$$y = 5(x + 3)(x - 5)$$

(b) Since the zeros are -3 and 5, the vertex has x-coordinate $\frac{-3 + 5}{2} = 1$.

Substitute this into the expression found in (a):

$$y = 5(x + 3)(x - 5)$$
$$y = 5(1 + 3)(1 - 5)$$
$$y = -80$$

The vertex is at $(1, -80)$.

Example 3

This data describes the flight of a plastic glider launched from a tower on a hilltop. The height values are negative whenever the glider was below the height of the hilltop.

(a) How tall is the tower?

(b) Find an equation to model the flight of the glider.

(c) Find the lowest point in the glider's flight.

Time (s)	Height (m)
0	9
1	5.5
2	2.5
3	0
4	–2
5	–3.5
6	–4.5
7	–5
8	–5
9	–4.5
10	–3.5

Time (s)	Height (m)
11	–2
12	0
13	2.5
14	5.5
15	9
16	13
17	17.5
18	22.5
19	28
20	34

Solution

(a) In this table, a height of 0 represents ground level of the top of the hill. When $t = 0$, the height is 9 m. Therefore, the tower must be 9 m tall.

(b) Graph the flight to see if the graph looks like a parabola. Since it does, locate the zeros and use them to get the equation in factored form.

Let t represent the time in seconds and h the height in metres.

From the table of values, one of the zeros is at $t = 12$ and the other is $t = 3$.

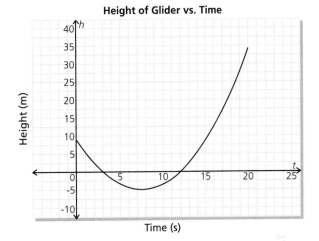

Height of Glider vs. Time

The factored form equation of the parabola must be $h = a(t - 3)(t - 12)$.

Substitute one of the known points, say $(4, -2)$, into this equation to find the value of a.

$$h = a(t - 3)(t - 12)$$
$$-2 = a(4 - 3)(4 - 12)$$
$$-2 = a(1)(-8)$$
$$-2 = -8a$$
$$\frac{-2}{-8} = \frac{-8a}{-8}$$
$$\frac{1}{4} = a$$

The equation of the quadratic model for the flight is $h = \frac{1}{4}(t - 3)(t - 12)$.

(c) The vertex must have a *t*-coordinate halfway between the zeros, at $t = 7.5$. Substitute $t = 7.5$ into the equation to find the value of *h* at the vertex.

$$h = \tfrac{1}{4}(t - 3)(t - 12)$$
$$h = \tfrac{1}{4}(7.5 - 3)(7.5 - 12)$$
$$h = 0.25(4.5)(-4.5)$$
$$h = -5.0625$$

The glider reaches its lowest point, about 5.1 m below the hilltop height, at 7.5 s into the flight.

Practise, Apply, Solve 3.4 ——————

A

1. Examine each parabola. What are the zeros of the quadratic relation?

(a)

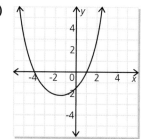

(b)

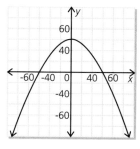

(c)

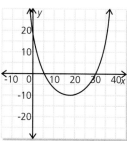

(d)

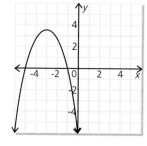

(e)

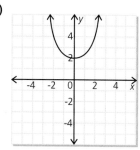

(f)

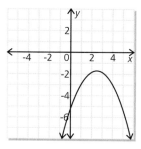

2. Find the equation of the axis of symmetry for each parabola in question 1.

3. Match each factored form equation to the appropriate graph.

(a) $y = (x - 2)(x + 3)$ (b) $y = (x - 3)(x + 2)$

(c) $y = (x + 2)(x + 3)$ (d) $y = (3 - x)(2 + x)$

(e) $y = (3 + x)(2 - x)$ (f) $y = (x - 2)(x - 3)$

i.
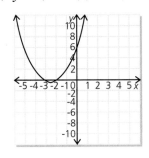

ii.
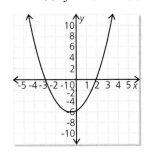

iii.
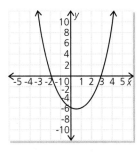

iv.
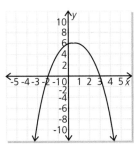

v.
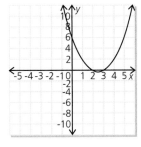

vi.
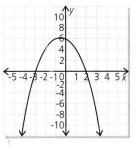

4. Each quadratic relation has zeros and an optimal value as shown. Sketch the graph. State whether the optimal value is a maximum or a minimum.

	Zeros	Optimal Value
(a)	3 and 7	6
(b)	−6 and −1	−2
(c)	−1 and 7	5
(d)	−9 and 0	−4

5. For each relation, state
i. the x-intercepts
ii. the equation of the axis of symmetry
iii. the coordinates of the vertex

(a) $y = (x + 4)(x + 2)$ (b) $y = (x + 5)(2 - x)$

(c) $y = (4 + x)(1 + x)$ (d) $y = (1 - x)(3 + x)$

(e) $y = (x - 3)(2 - x)$ (f) $y = (x + 1)(x - 4)$

(g) $y = 3(x + 1)(x - 3)$ (h) $y = -2(x + 3)(x - 3)$

6. Mirna's Fashion Shoppe is holding a sale. Mirna knows that a decrease in price usually means an increase in sales. These relations are models for expected revenue, based on the selling price x in dollars. Determine the zeros and optimal value.

	Article	Expected Revenue
(a)	sweatshirts	$R = (20 - 2x)(30 + 3x)$
(b)	pants	$R = (30 - 4x)(16 + 2x)$
(c)	socks	$R = (4 - 0.25x)(25 + 2x)$
(d)	suits	$R = (200 - 25x)(9 + 3x)$
(e)	sweaters	$R = (40 - 5x)(20 + 5x)$

B

7. Sketch a graph for each relation. Do not make a table of values or use graphing technology.

(a) $y = (x + 3)(x + 5)$ **(b)** $y = (x - 3)(x - 5)$

(c) $y = (x - 6)(x - 2)$ **(d)** $y = -(x - 1)(x - 2)$

(e) $y = 3(x - 5)(x + 1)$ **(f)** $y = -2(x + 2)(x + 1)$

(g) $y = \frac{1}{2}(x - 4)(x - 2)$ **(h)** $y = -2(3 - x)(5 - x)$

(i) $y = 10(x - 1)(x + 6)$

8. A quadratic relation has the equation $y = a(x - s)(x - t)$. Find the value of a when

(a) $y = a(x - 2)(x + 6)$ and $(3, 5)$ is a point on the graph

(b) the parabola has zeros of 4 and -2 and a y-intercept of 1

(c) the parabola has x-intercepts of 4 and -2 and a y-intercept of -1

(d) the parabola has zeros of 5 and 0 and a minimum value of -10

(e) the parabola has x-intercepts of 5 and -3 and a maximum value of 6

9. Determine the equation (in factored form) of the quadratic relation and the direction of opening of the parabola.

	x-Intercepts	y-Intercept
(a)	−2 and 4	5
(b)	−2 and 4	−5
(c)	−5 and −2	4
(d)	−5 and −2	−4
(e)	3 and 8	6
(f)	3 and 8	−6

10. Sketch the graphs in question 9. Put any graphs that have the same axis of symmetry on the same axes.

Determine the equation of each parabola in question 4.

12. **Knowledge and Understanding:** A parabola has zeros at (5, 0) and (−3, 0) and passes through point (6, 18).

(a) Determine the equation of the axis of symmetry.

(b) Determine the equation of the parabola.

(c) Determine the coordinates of the vertex.

(d) Sketch the graph of the parabola.

13. A ball is thrown upward from the roof of a 25 m building. The ball reaches a height of 45 m above the ground after 2 s and hits the ground 5 s after being thrown.

(a) Use the fact that the relation between the height of a projectile and time is quadratic to draw an accurate graph of the relation on graph paper.

(b) Carefully fold the graph along the axis of symmetry and extend the short side of the parabola to match the long side.

(c) Where does the extended graph cross the time axis?

(d) What are the zeros of the relation?

(e) What are the coordinates of the vertex of the parabola?

(f) Determine the algebraic expression that models this situation.

(g) What is the meaning of each zero?

14. **Application:** Angus is playing golf. The diagram (not to scale) shows him making a perfect shot to the pin. Determine the height of the ball when it is 15 m from the hole by using the information in the diagram to determine a quadratic relation for height vs. distance travelled.

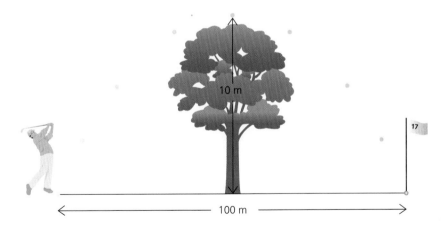

10 m

17

100 m

15. A parabolic arch is used to support a bridge. Vertical support columns set in the ground reinforce the arch every 2 m along its length.

This table of values shows the length of the columns in terms of their placement relative to the centre of the arch. Negative values are to the left of the centre point. Write an algebraic model that relates the length of each column to its horizontal placement.

Distance from Centre of Arch (m)	Length of Support Column (m)
−10	70.0
−8	80.8
−6	89.2
−4	95.2
−2	98.8
0	100.0
2	98.8
4	95.2
6	89.2
8	80.8
10	70.0

16. The second span of the Bluewater Bridge, in Sarnia, Ontario, is supported by a pair of steel parabolic arches. The arches are set in concrete foundations that are on opposite sides of the St. Clair River 281 m apart. The top of each arch rises 71 m above the river. Determine the algebraic expression that models the arch.

the Bluewater Bridge

17. This table gives the height of a golf ball at different times during its flight.
 (a) Create a scatter plot and draw a graph of best fit.
 (b) Use the graph to approximate the zeros of the relation.
 (c) Find an algebraic expression that models the flight of the ball.
 (d) Use the expression to determine the maximum height of the ball.

Time (s)	Height (m)
0.0	0.000
0.5	10.175
1.0	17.900
1.5	23.175
2.0	26.000
2.5	26.375
3.0	24.300
3.5	19.775
4.0	12.800
4.5	3.375

18. A ball is thrown up into the air from the top of a building. This table gives the height of the ball at different times during its flight.

(a) How tall is the building?

(b) How high is the ball at 2.5 s? 3.5 s?

(c) After many seconds does the ball reach its maximum height?

(d) When does the ball hit the ground?

Time (s)	Height (m)
0	10
1	35
2	50
3	55
4	50
5	35
6	10

19. Neil sets the prices in the Hardware To Go store. His research shows that an increase of 10¢ in the price of a package of batteries causes a drop in sales of 10 packages per day. The stores normally sell 600 packages of batteries per day, at $4.95 per package.

(a) What is the maximum revenue Neil can expect on the sale of batteries?

(b) How many packages of batteries must be sold to generate the maximum revenue?

(c) What is the optimum pricing strategy in this model?

20. Communication: A car manufacturer decides to change the price of its new luxury sedan (LS) model to increase sales. The graph shows the relation between revenue and the amount of the price change, as suggested by the marketing department.

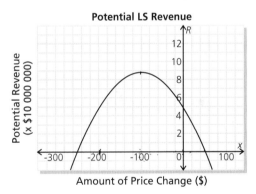

(a) Determine the algebraic model that is a reasonable representation for this graph.

(b) Maximum revenue is not the same as maximum profit. What else should the marketing department consider?

21. Check Your Understanding

(a) Explain how knowing the zeros of a quadratic relation and the coordinates of one additional point allows you to completely determine the algebraic expression for the relation.

(b) What information about the graph can be read directly from the factored form of a quadratic relation?

(c) If the factors of an expression multiply to give zero, how do you know that either factor can equal zero?

22. For each factored form equation in column 1, find the corresponding expanded and simplified equation in column 2. How did you decide?

Column 1

(a) $y = (2x - 3)(x + 4)$

(b) $y = (3x + 1)(4x - 3)$

(c) $y = (3 - 2x)(4 + x)$

(d) $y = (3 - 4x)(1 + 3x)$

Column 2

(1) $y = 12x^2 - 5x - 3$

(2) $y = -2x^2 - 5x + 12$

(3) $y = 2x^2 + 11x - 12$

(4) $y = 2x^2 + 5x - 12$

(5) $y = -12x^2 + 5x + 3$

(6) $y = 12x^2 + 5x - 3$

23. **Thinking, Inquiry, Problem Solving:** For a school experiment, Marcus had to record the height of a model rocket during its flight. However, during the experiment he discovered that the motion detector he was using had stopped working. Before the detector quit, it collected this data.

Time (s)	0	0.5	1.0	1.5	2.0
Height (m)	1.5	12.525	21.1	27.225	30.9

(a) The trajectory of the rocket is quadratic. Complete the table to the time when the rocket hit the ground.

(b) Determine an expression that models the height of the rocket.

(c) Use your expression to find the rocket's height at 3.8 s.

(d) What is the maximum height of the rocket?

The Chapter Problem—Setting the Best Ticket Price

In this section, you found the zeros and optimal value of a quadratic relation. Apply what you have learned to answer these questions about the chapter problem on page 242.

1. Write a formula for the ticket price, based on the change in price.

2. Write a formula for the attendance, based on the change in ticket price.

3. (a) State the algebraic relation for revenue that models the change in ticket price and the corresponding change in attendance. Is there more than one relation? Explain.

(b) Determine the zeros of the relation.

(c) Where does the optimal value occur?

(d) What is the optimal value?

(e) Without using a graphing calculator or a table of values, sketch the graph of the relation.

(f) Compare the graph from (e) to the plots and curves you drew in section 3.1.

Multiplying Binomials
Using Algebra Tiles

The **distributive property** allows you to simplify expressions, like $3(x + 5)$ and $2x(2x + 3)$, that consist of a binomial multiplied by a monomial. Algebra tiles can be used to demonstrate how the distributive property works in these algebraic operations.

Algebra Tile Demonstration

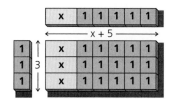

Algebraic Operations using the Distributive Property

$$3(x + 5) = 3x + 3(5)$$
$$= 3x + 15$$

$$2x(2x + 3)$$
$$= 2x(2x) + 2x(3)$$
$$= 4x^2 + 6x$$

$$2x(3x - 4) = 2x(3x) - 2x(4)$$
$$= 6x^2 - 8x$$

Practise 3.5

1. Write the algebraic operations that are demonstrated by the algebra tile diagrams.

(a)

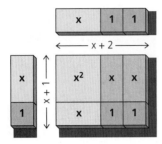

(b)

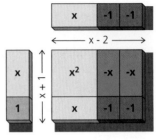

(c)

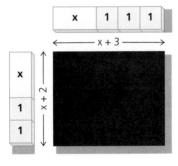

(d)

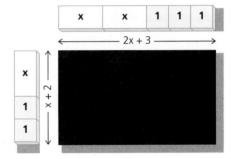

2. Fill in the missing algebra tiles.

(a)

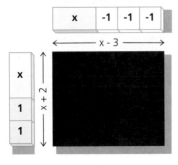

(b)

(c)

(d)

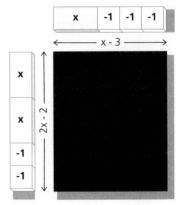

3. Sometimes the process of multiplying one binomial expression by another is referred to as "using the distributive property twice." Explain how the algebra tile diagrams in question 2 support this statement.

4. Use real algebra tiles or sketches of algebra tiles to illustrate each expression.

(a) $(x + 4)(x + 3)$ (b) $(2x + 1)(x + 2)$ (c) $(3x + 1)(2x + 1)$

(d) $(x + 2)(x - 1)$ (e) $(2x - 3)(x - 1)$ (f) $(3x - 1)(2x + 1)$

5. Write a simplified polynomial expression for each illustration in question 4.

Joseph Louis Lagrange (1736-1813)

You have seen that many problems can be solved either by using algebra tiles or diagrams, or with equations. Analysis is the name given to a branch of mathematics that uses equations in algebra or calculus.

Lagrange could be called the first true analyst. He wrote clearly and concisely, developing a modern style of mathematics. His work had a huge influence on the way mathematics was done.

He wrote several great works and was influential in the establishment of the metric system. Napoleon Bonaparte, who himself was very gifted in trigonometry, said, "Lagrange is the lofty pyramid of the mathematical science."

Did You Know?

India has made important contributions to mathematics for many centuries. One example is the introduction of sine values to replace an older Greek table of values.

The earliest documentation of the sine relationship is found in the *Siddhantas,* written between 290 and 400, and the *Aryabhatiya*, written in 499 by the scholar Aryabhata (born 476). In the *Aryabhatiya*, sine values up to 90° are given at 24 equal intervals of 3.75° each.

One of India's greatest mathematicians was Srinivasa Ramanujan (1887–1920). He contributed greatly to the studies of infinite series, continued fractions, and the theory of numbers. A famous story tells that one day, the English mathematician G. H. Hardy visited Ramanujan when he was sick in a London hospital. Hardy mentioned that the number of his taxi was 1729, which he thought was a dull number. "Nonsense," said Ramanujan immediately. "The number isn't dull at all. It's quite interesting. It's the smallest number that can be expressed as the sum of two cubes in two different ways." What are the two different ways?

3.6 Using Quadratic Regression to Find a Curve of Best Fit with a TI-83 Plus Calculator

The TI-83 Plus can draw a curve of best fit for data on a scatter plot. The calculator can also provide the equation of the quadratic relation for this curve.

This table gives the height of a baseball above the ground, from the time it was hit until it touched the ground.

Height of a Baseball After Being Hit

Time (s)	0	1	2	3	4	5	6
Height (m)	2	27	42	48	43	29	5

1. Create a scatter plot by entering the time values into L1 and the corresponding height values into L2. Press $\boxed{\text{STAT}}$ $\boxed{1}$ to edit the lists.

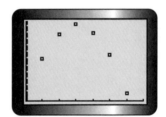

step 1

2. Once you have entered all the values into the appropriate lists, create a scatter plot by turning on the first Stat Plot: press $\boxed{\text{2nd}}$ $\boxed{\text{Y=}}$ $\boxed{1}$ followed by $\boxed{\text{ENTER}}$.
   Make sure that you have the Type set for a scatter plot ($\llcorner$) and that Xlist is L1 and Ylist is L2 as shown.

step 2

3. To see the graph press $\boxed{\text{ZOOM}}$ $\boxed{9}$.

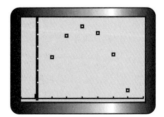

step 3

4. The data is clearly nonlinear. To find the equation of the curve of best fit you can use **quadratic regression**.
Press STAT and scroll over to CALC.
Press 5 to enable QuadReg.

step 4

5. Enter the names of the lists you wish to analyze. Press 2nd 1 , 2nd 2 , VARS. Scroll over to Y-VARS, then press 1 followed by 1 again. This stores the equation of the curve of best fit in the equation editor under $Y_1 =$. Press ENTER to display the results.

step 5

6. To display the curve of best fit press GRAPH. The coefficients *a*, *b*, and *c* define the general quadratic equation $y = ax^2 + bx + c$ for the curve of best fit. R^2 indicates the percentage of the data that is represented by this model.

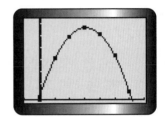

step 6

For this relation, the approximate equation is $y = -4.90x^2 + 29.93x + 1.98$.

Practise 3.6

For each set of data, create a scatter plot and use quadratic regression to determine the equation of the curve of best fit.

(a)

x	−2	−1	0	1	2	3	4	5	6
y	4	1	0	1	4	9	16	25	36

(b)

x	−4	−3	−2	−1	0	1	2	3	4
y	44	23	8	−1	−4	−1	8	23	44

(c)

x	−1	0	1	2	3	4	5	6	7
y	−12	−6	−2	0	0	−2	−6	−12	−20

(d) Time spent every day by teenagers watching television

Year	1989	1990	1991	1992	1993	1994	1995	1996	1997
Time (min)	189	195	196	190	187	185	182	169	174

Source: Nielsen Media Research

3.7 Standard Form of a Quadratic Relation

Part 1: More About the Balloon Catapult ——

Recall the projectile motion problem from section 3.4 on page 275. The projectile was a water balloon launched from a catapult.

The graph was drawn with a graphing program, using data from a stop-motion photograph of the balloon's flight. The table of values is reproduced below.

Horizontal Distance (m)	Height (m)	Horizontal Distance (m)	Height (m)
0	0.0	28	29.9
2	4.2	30	29.7
4	8.1	32	29.1
6	11.6	34	28.3
8	14.9	36	27.1
10	17.8	38	25.6
12	20.4	40	23.8
14	22.7	42	21.6
16	24.7	44	19.2
18	26.4	46	16.4
20	27.7	48	13.3
22	28.7	50	9.9
24	29.5	52	6.2
26	29.9	54	2.1

Think, Do, Discuss

1. **(a)** Enter the data into the lists of a graphing calculator.

   (b) Use the quadratic regression feature of the calculator to determine the algebraic expression for the curve of best fit for this data. Remember to activate DiagnosticOn if need be. If necessary, refer to page 106 of section 1.10. Your display should look similar to the sample shown. This form of a quadratic relation, $y = ax^2 + bx + c$, is called **standard form**.

(c) Plot this quadratic relation and comment on how closely the curve fits the data.

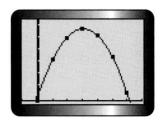

(d) Examine the value of R^2. Give some reasons why the fit might not be exact.

2. Working from the graph in section 3.4, one group of students came up with the equation $y = -0.04x(x - 55)$ for the same situation.

(a) Demonstrate that this equation and the equation found in step 1 are both quadratic models for the same situation.

(b) Use both algebraic models to test the value for the maximum height of the balloon.

(c) Which produces a value closer to the value in the original graph in section 3.4?

(d) Check how well each model predicts values from the original graph or from the table of values above. Use several different data points.

(e) Which algebraic expression is a more accurate model of the flight trajectory of the balloon?

(f) Is one model better than the other? Explain.

Part 2: Comparing Standard Form and Factored Form

Can an equation in factored form, $y = a(x - s)(x - t)$, be equivalent to a quadratic equation in standard form, $y = ax^2 + bx + c$?

Think, Do, Discuss

1. In section 3.4, Mirna used the quadratic relation $R = (10 - 0.1x)(30 + x)$ as a model for her revenue from T-shirt sales.

(a) Graph the factored form of the relation.

(b) Use this equation to create a table of values for the relation with at least 10 ordered pairs.

(c) Enter the ordered pairs into the list editor of a graphing calculator, perform a quadratic regression, and graph the result.

(d) Compare the graph in (a) with the graph of the quadratic regression relation in (c). How closely do they match?

2. Compare the standard form of the equation, produced by the calculator's QuadReg operation, to the factored form.

(a) What is the coefficient of the x^2-term in the standard form of the equation? Describe how its value can be computed from the terms in the factored form.

(b) What is the constant term in the standard form of the equation? Describe how its value can be computed from the terms in the factored form.

(c) What is the coefficient of the x-term in the standard form of the equation? Describe how it can be calculated from the factored form.

Part 3: Expanding and Simplifying Using the Distributive Property

In your previous mathematics studies, you learned about the distributive property for multiplying a polynomial and a monomial. This property can be used to convert the factored form of a quadratic relation to standard form.

Think, Do, Discuss

1. Recall the factored form of Mirna's T-shirt relation, $R = (10 - 0.1x)(30 + x)$. Rewrite the factors as shown.

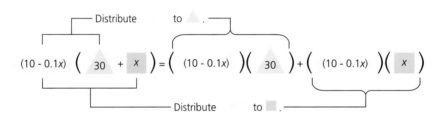

(a) Describe how the distributive property lets you multiply the first binomial, $(10 - 0.1x)$, by each term in the second binomial.

(b) Examine the two products on the right side of the equation in the diagram. Explain how applying the distributive property again allows you to expand each of those products.

(c) Simplify the expression by collecting like terms.

(d) Write the final expanded and simplified form of $R = (10 - 0.1x)(30 + x)$.

(e) Explain how you could use the steps above to express the relation $R = 2.5(10 - 0.1x)(30 + x)$ in standard form.

2. Recall Max's CD store from section 3.4. The quadratic relation Max used as a model for revenue from CD sales was $R = (20 + 0.5x)(280 - 5x)$. Follow the process in step 1 to rewrite this expression in standard form.

Focus 3.7

- The **factored form** of a quadratic relation, $y = (x - s)(x - t)$, $y = a(x - s)(x - t)$, or $y = (ax - s)(bx - t)$, can be expanded using the distributive property and simplified to give a **standard form** trinomial, $y = ax^2 + bx + c$. Standard form is often called **expanded form**.

- Equivalent factored and standard forms

Factored Form	Standard (or Expanded) Form
$y = (x - s)(x - t)$	$y = x^2 - (s + t)x + st$
$y = a(x - s)(x - t)$	$y = ax^2 - a(s + t)x + ast$
$y = (ax - s)(bx - t)$	$y = abx^2 - (at + bs)x + st$

- The **quadratic regression** feature of a graphing calculator provides the algebraic expression for a curve of best fit in **standard** (or **expanded**) **form**, $y = ax^2 + bx + c$.

Example 1

Expand these expressions.

(a) $(x + 3)(x - 4)$

(b) $(x - 4)^2$

(c) $(x - 5)(x + 5)$

(d) $(2x + 3)(3x - 7)$

Solution

(a) $(x + 3)(x - 4)$ Apply the distributive property.

$= (x + 3)(x) + (x + 3)(-4)$ Multiply $(x + 3)$ by x and $(x + 3)$ by -4.

$= x^2 + 3x + x(-4) + 3(-4)$ Multiply.

$= x^2 + 3x - 4x - 12$ Collect like terms.

$= x^2 - x - 12$ Simplify.

(b) $(x - 4)^2$

$= (x - 4)(x - 4)$ Apply the distributive property.

$= (x - 4)(x) + (x - 4)(-4)$ Multiply $(x - 4)$ by x and $(x - 4)$ by -4.

$= x^2 - 4x + x(-4) - 4(-4)$ Multiply.

$= x^2 - 4x - 4x + 16$ Collect like terms.

$= x^2 - 8x + 16$ Simplify.

(c) $(x - 5)(x + 5)$ Apply the distributive property.

$\quad = (x - 5)(x) + (x - 5)(5)$ Multiply $(x - 5)$ by x and by 5.

$\quad = x^2 - 5x + 5x - 25$ Multiply.

$\quad = x^2 + 0x - 25$ Collect like terms.

$\quad = x^2 - 25$ Simplify.

(d) $(2x + 3)(3x - 7)$ Apply the distributive property.

$\quad = (2x + 3)(3x) + (2x + 3)(-7)$ Multiply $(2x + 3)$ by $3x$ and by -7.

$\quad = 2x(3x) + 3(3x) - 2x(7) + 3(-7)$ Multiply.

$\quad = 6x^2 + 9x - 14x - 21$ Collect like terms.

$\quad = 6x^2 - 5x - 21$ Simplify.

Example 2

Find the values of a and b.

$(x + a)(x + 3) = x^2 + 5x + b$

Solution

Expand the left side using the distributive property.

$$x^2 + ax + 3x + 3a = x^2 + 5x + b$$

$$x^2 + (3 + a)x + 3a = x^2 + 5x + b \qquad \text{Collect like terms on the left side.}$$

The coefficients of corresponding like terms must be equal, so

$$3 + a = 5 \qquad \text{(from the } x\text{-terms)}$$

which gives $\qquad\qquad\qquad a = 2$

and $\qquad\qquad\qquad\qquad 3a = b \qquad \text{(from the constant terms)}$

Substituting $a = 2$ gives $3(2) = b$ or $b = 6$.

Therefore, $a = 2$ and $b = 6$.

Example 3

Find the standard form algebraic model that represents a parabola with zeros at 2 and -4 and a y-intercept of 16.

Solution

In factored form, the quadratic relation describing the parabola must be

$$y = a(x - 2)(x + 4)$$

Since the *y*-intercept is 16, you can substitute $(0, 16)$ into this equation and solve for *a*.

$$y = a(x - 2)(x + 4)$$
$$16 = a(0 - 2)(0 + 4)$$
$$16 = -8a$$
$$\frac{16}{-8} = \frac{-8a}{-8}$$
$$-2 = a$$

The factored form of the relation is $y = -2(x - 2)(x + 4)$.

Apply the distributive property to convert the equation to standard form.

$$y = -2(x - 2)(x + 4)$$
$$y = -2[(x - 2)(x + 4)] \qquad \text{Multiply the binomials together.}$$
$$y = -2[(x - 2)x + (x - 2)4] \qquad \text{Expand.}$$
$$y = -2(x^2 - 2x + 4x - 8) \qquad \text{Simplify.}$$
$$y = -2(x^2 + 2x - 8) \qquad \text{Multiply by } -2.$$
$$y = -2x^2 - 4x + 16$$

Practise, Apply, Solve 3.7 ————————

Ⓐ

1. Fill in the missing terms.
   (a) $(m + 3)(m + 2) = \blacksquare + 3m + 2m + \blacksquare$
   (b) $(k - 2)(k + 1) = \blacksquare - 2k + \blacksquare - 2$
   (c) $(r + 4)(r - 3) = r^2 + \blacksquare - 3r - \blacksquare$
   (d) $(x - 5)(x - 2) = x^2 - \blacksquare - \blacksquare + 10$
   (e) $(2n + 1)(3n - 2) = \blacksquare + 3n - \blacksquare - 2$
   (f) $(5m - 2)(m - 3) = 5m^2 - \blacksquare - 2m + \blacksquare$

Ⓑ

2. Expand and simplify each expression.
   (a) $(d + 2)(d + 1)$ **(b)** $(h + 3)(h - 2)$ **(c)** $(p - 3)(p + 4)$
   (d) $(a - 2)(a - 3)$ **(e)** $(w - 3)(w - 3)$ **(f)** $(t + 4)(t + 4)$

3. Expand and simplify each expression.
   (a) $(2n + 1)(n + 3)$ **(b)** $(q - 2)(3q + 1)$ **(c)** $(3x + 1)(2x - 1)$
   (d) $(5m - 1)(2m + 3)$ **(e)** $(2r + 3)(2r + 3)$ **(f)** $(4m + 2)(4m - 2)$
   (g) $2(a + 5)(a - 3)$ **(h)** $-2(m - 4)(m - 3)$ **(i)** $5(7h + 6)(4h - 3)$
   (j) $-2(3 - 8f)(7 - 6f)$ **(k)** $3(3h - k)(5h + 2k)$ **(l)** $6(4x + 3y)(5x - 2y)$

4. Expand and simplify each expression.

   (a) $(x + 3)^2$ **(b)** $(x - 7)^2$ **(c)** $(x + 8)^2$

   (d) $(2x + 1)^2$ **(e)** $(4x - 3)^2$ **(f)** $(5x + 7)^2$

5. Find the unknown value or expression.

   (a) $x^2 + 8x + 12 = (x + 6)(x + \blacksquare)$ **(b)** $x^2 - 3x - 10 = (x - 5)(x + \blacksquare)$

   (c) $x^2 - 6x + 8 = (\blacksquare)(x - 2)$ **(d)** $x^2 - 11x + 30 = (x - 5)(\blacksquare)$

   (e) $x^2 + 4x - 21 = (x + 7)(\blacksquare)$ **(f)** $5x^2 - 17x + 6 = (\blacksquare - 3)(\blacksquare - 2)$

   (g) $6x^2 - 16x + 6 = (\blacksquare - 2)(\blacksquare - 3)$ **(h)** $6x^2 + 29x - 5 = (\blacksquare - 1)(\blacksquare + 5)$

   (i) $2y^2 - 7y - 15 = (y - 5)(\blacksquare)$ **(j)** $6y^2 + 19y + 15 = (\blacksquare)(3y + 5)$

   (k) $9x^2 - 25 = (3x + 5)(\blacksquare)$ **(l)** $25x^2 + 10x + 1 = (\blacksquare)(5x + 1)$

6. **Communication:** Explain why it is **not** possible to fill in the unknown values in each of the following.

   (a) $(a + 5)(a + \blacksquare) = a^2 + 8a + 10$

   (b) $(b - 2)(b + \blacksquare) = b^2 + 6b - 8$

   (c) $(2c + 5)(\blacksquare c + 3) = 6c^2 + 19c + 15$

   (d) $(2d - 5)(5d + \blacksquare) = 10d^2 - 19d + 15$

7. Write an expression for each area.

   (a)
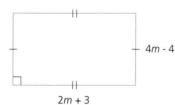
4m - 4

2m + 3

   (b)
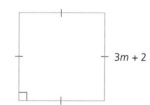
3m + 2

8. Examine each graph. Determine the expanded form of the algebraic relation that defines each parabola.

   (a)
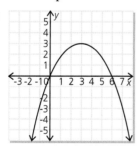

   (b)
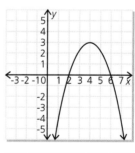

   (c)
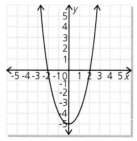

   (d)
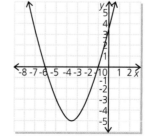

9. The area and one side of a rectangle are given. What is the unknown side?

(a)

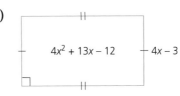

$m^2 + 5m + 6$

$m + 3$

(b)

$4x^2 + 13x - 12$ $4x - 3$

10. For each quadratic relation, write the equation in standard form and tell which way the graph opens.

	Zeros	A Point on the Graph
(a)	−1 and 7	(3, 5)
(b)	−1 and −5	(−3, −4)
(c)	3 and 7	(0, 3)
(d)	−2 and 6	(−1, −1)
(e)	−2 and 8	(3, 7)

11. **Knowledge and Understanding:** Marnie threw a bean bag over a motion detector and it recorded this data.

Time (s)	Height Above Ground (m)
0.00	0.0000
0.25	2.1875
0.50	3.7500
0.75	4.6875
1.00	5.0000
1.25	4.6875
1.50	3.7500
1.75	2.1875
2.00	0.0000

(a) Create a scatter plot and hand draw the curve of best fit.

(b) Determine an algebraic expression that models the data. Express the relation in standard form.

(c) Use a graphing calculator and enter the data into a list. Use quadratic regression to find the equation of the curve of best fit.

(d) Which expression is the better model for the data? Explain.

12. A stone is dropped from a bridge that is 20 m above the river below. This table gives the height of the stone as it falls.

Time (s)	0.00	0.50	1.00	1.50	2.00
Height (m)	20.000	18.775	15.100	8.975	0.400

(a) Create a scatter plot and hand draw the graph of best fit.

(b) Find the approximate time when the stone hits the water.

(c) Point (0, 20) represents the maximum height of the stone. Use this and the value you found in (b) to approximate the other zero of the relation.

(d) Determine an algebraic expression, in standard form, that models the data.

(e) Use a graphing calculator to determine the quadratic regression equation for the data.

13. The Golden Gate Bridge, in San Francisco, is a suspension bridge. It is supported by a pair of cables that are parabolic in appearance. The cables are attached at either end to a pair of towers at points 152 m above the roadway. The towers are 1280 m apart and the cable reaches its lowest point when it is 4 m above the roadway. Determine an algebraic expression that models the cable as it hangs between the towers. **Hint:** Transfer the data to a graph where the parabola lies below the *x*-axis.

the Golden Gate Bridge

14. Application: The manager of the Hardware To Go store knows that if a package of batteries is priced at $4.95, he will sell about 600 packages a week. He knows that for every 10¢ increase in price, his weekly sales will decrease by 10 packages.

(a) Find the algebraic expression, in standard form, that models this relation.

(b) Graph the relation and use the graph to find the price that generates the most revenue.

(c) Use the factored form of the expression to find the optimal value.

(d) Compare the values obtained using the standard form plus graph and the factored form. Which is easier to use? Which gives a more accurate answer?

15. Thinking, Inquiry, Problem Solving
The stainless steel Gateway Arch in
St. Louis, Missouri, is parabolic in shape.
It is 192 m from the base of the north leg
to the base of the south leg. The arch is
192 m high. Determine an algebraic
expression, in standard form, that models
the shape of the arch.

the Gateway Arch

16. Check Your Understanding

(a) Explain how to change a quadratic
relation from factored form into standard form.

(b) If you want to sketch the graph of a quadratic relation, which form of the
algebraic expression is more helpful, factored form or standard form? Why?

(c) Explain why $y = x^2 + 3x + 4$ cannot be expressed in factored form. What
does this tell you about the zeros of this relation?

C

17. Expand and simplify each expression.

(a) $(2x + 3)(3x - 1) + x(2x + 4)$

(b) $(2x - 5)(3x + 4) - (4x + 1)(x - 2)$

(c) $(3x - 4)(x + 5) + 2((2x - 3)(x - 5)$

(d) $2(x + 3)(x - 5) - 4(2x + 1)(3x + 6)$

(e) $3(2x + 1)^2 - 5(x - 4)^2$

(f) $-3(2x - 3)^2 + 4(x + 2)^2$

18. Expand and simplify each expression.

(a) $(x + 3)^3$ (b) $(2x - 2)^3$

(c) $(4x + 2y)^3$ (d) $[(x + 2)(x - 2)]^2$

(e) $(x + 6)(x + 3)(x - 6)(x - 3)$ (f) $(3x^2 + 6x - 1)^2$

(g) $(x - 1)^4$

The Chapter Problem—Setting the Best Ticket Price

In this section, you expressed quadratic relations in standard form. Apply
what you learned to answer these questions about the chapter problem on
page 242.

What is the ticket price that will produce the most revenue for the theatre?
In sections 3.2, 3.4, and 3.7, you had enough information to answer this
question. Which section provided the most efficient way to find the answer?
Explain.

3.8 Extending Algebra Skills: Factoring Quadratic Expressions

Part 1: Factoring a Quadratic Expression in Standard Form

Earlier in this chapter, you learned that having a quadratic relation in factored form permits you to quickly find the zeros and the vertex of the parabola. Factored form is very useful for modelling situations with quadratic expressions and for solving maximum or minimum problems.

You saw that a factored expression like $(2x - 5)(3x + 2)$ can be expanded using the distributive property. The resulting quadratic expression is said to be in standard or expanded form.

You also used the distributive property to find missing values in expressions like

$(x + 5)(x - \blacksquare) = x^2 + \blacksquare x - 15$

What if you start with a quadratic expression in standard form? Can you use the distributive property to convert it to factored form?

Think, Do, Discuss

1. Consider the quadratic expression $x^2 + 8x + 15$.

   (a) If the expression can be factored, will the form be $(x - s)(x - t)$ or $a(x - s)(x - t)$?

   (b) Apply the distributive property. What does the result tell you about the value of st? of $s + t$?

   (c) Explain how you can use the results from (b) to find the values of s and t. What are the values?

   (d) Verify the values of s and t by graphing the relation $y = x^2 + 8x + 15$.

   (e) Explain how the graph verifies the factored form.

2. (a) Explain why the expression $x^2 + 8x + 20$ cannot be factored.

   (b) Does this mean that the expression has no zeros? How do you know?

3. Think about the expression $6x^2 + 24x - 72$.

   (a) If this expression can be factored, the factored form must be either $a(x - s)(x - t)$ or $(ax - s)(bx - t)$. How can you tell that the form $a(x - s)(x - t)$ is most likely to work?

   (b) If the form is $a(x - s)(x - t)$, what must the value of a be?

   (c) What must the value of st be? Why?

   (d) What information does the coefficient of x tell you about s and t?

   (e) Use the results from (b), (c), and (d) to find the factors of the expression.

   (f) How is factoring this expression similar to factoring the expression in question 1? How is it different?

4. Consider the quadratic expression $6x^2 + 25x - 9$.

   (a) If this expression can be factored, the factored form must be either $a(x - s)(x - t)$ or $(ax - s)(bx - t)$. How can you determine that the form $(ax - s)(bx - t)$ is most likely to work?

   (b) If the form is $(ax - s)(bx - t)$, what must ab and st be equal to?

   (c) What information does the coefficient of x tell you about a, b, s, and t?

   (d) Use all the information from (b) and (c) to find the factors using a guess-and-check strategy.

Part 2: Some Special Factoring Patterns ———

Some types of products reveal special patterns when they are expanded using the distributive property. If you can recognize these special patterns, it will be much easier to factor many polynomial expressions.

Think, Do, Discuss

1. Use the following expressions for this question.

   i. $(a + 1)(a - 1)$ **ii.** $(b + 2)(b - 2)$ **iii.** $(c - 10)(c + 10)$

   iv. $(2d + 1)(2d - 1)$ **v.** $(3e + 5)(3e - 5)$ **vi.** $(6 - 5f)(6 + 5f)$

   (a) Apply the distributive property to expand each expression. Describe the pattern that all of the expanded products have in common.

   (b) Explain why the phrase "difference of squares" is a good way to describe this pattern.

   (c) If the trinomial $x^2 + ax + b$ can be factored using the same pattern, what must be true about the values of a and b?

   (d) If the trinomial $ax^2 + bx + c$ can be factored using the same pattern, what must be true about the values of a, b, and c?

2. Examine how the following products can be expanded using the distributive property.

i. $(a + 1)(a + 1)$ ii. $(b - 2)(b - 2)$ iii. $(c - 10)^2$

iv. $(2d + 1)^2$ v. $(3e - 5)^2$ vi. $(6 - 5f)^2$

(a) Describe the pattern that all of the expanded products have in common.

(b) Explain why the phrase "perfect square" is a good way to describe this product pattern.

(c) If the trinomial $x^2 + ax + b$ can be factored using the same pattern, what must be true about the values of a and b?

(d) If the trinomial $ax^2 + bx + c$ can be factored using the same pattern, what must be true about the values of a, b, and c?

Focus 3.8

Key Ideas

- Many quadratic relations in standard form $y = ax^2 + bx + c$ can be expressed as the product of two binomial factors. Finding this product is called **factoring.**

- Factoring is the opposite operation of expanding.

- If the quadratic expression $x^2 + bx + c$ can be factored, the factors are of the form $(x - s)(x - t)$, where $b = -(s + t)$ and $c = st$.

- If the quadratic expression $ax^2 + bx + c$ (where $a \neq 1$) can be factored, the factors can be found using a guess-and-check strategy.

  ◆ Choose factors that produce the correct first and last term of the quadratic (the x^2-term and the constant term) when multiplied.

  ◆ The middle (x) term of the quadratic comes from multiplying the outside terms of the binomial factors together, then the inside terms, then adding the results. For example, $6x^2 - 23x + 20 = (3x - 4)(2x - 5)$, since $(3x)(2x) = 6x^2$, $(-4)(-5) = 20$, and $(3x)(-5) + (-4)(2x) = (-15x) + (-8x)$ or $-23x$. Check that the factors you choose give the correct x-term in the standard form.

  ◆ Sometimes quadratics in the form $ax^2 + bx + c$ have a common factor. If the trinomial remaining after a common factor is removed is in the form $x^2 + bx + c$, you may be able to factor it as above. For example, $5x^2 - 5x - 150 = 5(x - 6)(x + 5)$, since $5x^2 - 5x - 150 = 5(x^2 - x - 30)$ and $(x^2 - x - 30) = (x - 6)(x + 5)$.

- If a trinomial is in the form $a^2x^2 - b^2$, then it is a **difference of squares** and can be factored as $(ax + b)(ax - b)$.

- If a trinomial is in the form $a^2x^2 + 2abx + b^2$, then it is a **perfect square** and can be factored as $(ax + b)(ax + b) = (ax + b)^2$.

Example 1

Factor each expression.

(a) $x^2 - 14x + 45$

(b) $4x^2 + 12x - 40$

Solution

(a) The trinomial $x^2 - 14x + 45$ can be factored if there are two numbers which multiply to give 45 and add to give -14.

Using guess-and-check, the numbers -5 and -9 are found to satisfy these conditions, since $(-5)(-9) = 45$ and $(-5) + (-9) = -14$.

Therefore, $x^2 - 14x + 45 = (x - 5)(x - 9)$.

(b) The trinomial $4x^2 + 12x - 40$ has a common factor, 4, in each term.

$$4x^2 + 12x - 40 \qquad \text{Remove the common factor.}$$
$$= 4(x^2 + 3x - 10) \quad \text{Find two numbers that multiply to give } -10 \text{ and}$$
$$= 4(x + 5)(x - 2) \quad \text{add to give 3. The numbers 5 and } -2 \text{ work, since}$$
$$(5)(-2) = -10 \text{ and } (5) + (-2) = 3.$$

Example 2

Factor each expression.

(a) $x^2 - 9$ **(b)** $4x^2 - 12x + 9$ **(c)** $3x^2 + 8x + 4$

Solution

(a) $x^2 - 9 = (x + 3)(x - 3)$ You can recognize this expression as a difference of squares and factor it immediately using the pattern discussed above.

$$x^2 - 9 = x^2 + 0x - 9$$
$$= (x + 3)(x - 3)$$

Or you can use the general approach and look for two numbers that multiply to give -9 and add to give 0, since the coefficient of the x-term is 0. The required numbers are 3 and -3.

(b) $4x^2 - 12x + 9$

The coefficient of the x^2-term is not 1 and there is no common factor. The factors of the trinomial will be two binomials. Try visualizing the distributive property of two binomials to determine the factors.

The first term and last term are perfect squares:

$$4x^2 = (2x)(2x) \text{ and } 9 = (3)(3) \text{ or } (-3)(-3)$$

The middle term is composed of the factors of the first and last terms:

$$-12x = (2x)(-3) + (2x)(-3) \quad \text{Select the } -3, \text{ so the sum of products is negative.}$$

Following the pattern discussed above, this expression is a perfect square.

$$4x^2 - 12x + 9 = (2x - 3)(2x - 3)$$
$$= (2x - 3)^2$$

Check: $(2x - 3)(2x - 3) = 4x^2 - 6x - 6x + 9$
$$= 4x^2 - 12x + 9$$

(c) $3x^2 + 8x + 4$

The coefficient of the x^2-term is not 1 and there is no common factor. The factors of the trinomial will be two binomials. Try visualizing the distributive property of two binomials to determine the factors.

First term: $3x^2 = (3x)(x)$

Last term: $4 = (2)(2)$ or $(-2)(-2)$

The middle term is composed of the factors of the first and last terms:

$$8x = (3x)(2) + (2)(x) \quad \text{Select 2 so the sum of the}$$
$$3x^2 + 8x + 4 = (3x + 2)(x + 2) \quad \text{products is positive.}$$

Check: $(3x + 2)(x + 2) = 3x^2 + 6x + 2x + 4$
$$= 3x^2 + 8x + 4$$

Example 3

For a set of experimental data, the QuadReg function of a graphing calculator has given the curve of best fit as $y = -2x^2 + 8x + 42$. Find the vertex of the parabola.

Solution

The expression has a common factor, -2. Remove it to give $y = -2(x^2 - 4x - 21)$. Now try to factor the trinomial $x^2 - 4x - 21$.

To factor as $(x - s)(x - t) = x^2 - 4x - 21$, you must find s and t such that $st = -21$ and $s + t = 4$. Two numbers that multiply to -21 and add to 4 are 7 and -3.

Therefore, $x^2 - 4x - 21 = (x - 7)(x + 3)$.

The factored form of the relation is $y = -2(x - 7)(x + 3)$.

The vertex is on the perpendicular bisector of the zeros. Since the zeros are at $x = 7$ and $x = -3$, the vertex occurs on the line $x = \frac{7 - 3}{2}$, or $x = 2$.

Substitute $x = 2$ in the equation to find the y-coordinate of the vertex.

$$y = -2(x - 7)(x + 3)$$
$$y = -2(2 - 7)(2 + 3)$$
$$y = -2(-5)(5)$$
$$y = 50$$

The vertex of the parabola is at $(2, 50)$.

Practise, Apply, Solve 3.8

A

1. Find two numbers with these properties.
   (a) product is 56 and sum is 15
   (b) product is -16 and sum is -6
   (c) product is -12 and sum is -1
   (d) product is -35 and the sum is 2

2. Factor each expression.
   (a) $x^2 + 3x + 2$
   (b) $x^2 + 5x + 4$
   (c) $f^2 - 6f + 9$
   (d) $c^2 + 2c - 15$
   (e) $g^2 + 3g - 18$
   (f) $r^2 - 2r - 8$
   (g) $m^2 - 5m - 14$
   (h) $n^2 - 9n + 20$
   (i) $x^2 - 10x + 16$
   (j) $a^2 - 6a + 9$
   (k) $x^2 - 9x + 20$
   (l) $y^2 + 8y + 16$
   (m) $x^2 + 5x - 36$
   (n) $b^2 - 4b - 32$
   (o) $x^2 - 15x + 56$
   (p) $v^2 + 6v - 27$
   (q) $t^2 + 2t - 48$
   (r) $p^2 - 17p + 72$

B

3. Factor each expression. Remember to look for common factors first.
   (a) $3x^2 + 24x + 45$
   (b) $2y^2 - 2y - 60$
   (c) $3a^2 + 9a + 6$
   (d) $5x^2 - 10x + 5$
   (e) $6x^2 + 24x - 30$
   (f) $x^3 + 5x^2 + 4x$
   (g) $8m^2 - 104m + 336$
   (h) $21x^2 + 21x - 42$
   (i) $7x^2 + 28x - 147$

4. Factor each expression.
   (a) $x^2 - 25$
   (b) $c^2 - 49$
   (c) $a^2 - 36$
   (d) $x^2 - 81$
   (e) $d^2 - 121$
   (f) $b^2 - 64$
   (g) $9x^2 - 4$
   (h) $64a^2 - 1$
   (i) $25p^2 - 49$
   (j) $16c^2 - 81$
   (k) $50r^2 - 72$
   (l) $7y^2 - 28$

5. Factor each expression.
   (a) $9x^2 - 6x + 1$
   (b) $25x^2 + 20x + 4$
   (c) $4a^2 - 20a + 25$
   (d) $49c^2 + 42c + 9$
   (e) $100x^2 - 180x + 81$
   (f) $36g^2 + 60g + 25$
   (g) $9v^2 - 12v + 4$
   (h) $64c^2 + 16c + 1$
   (i) $16d^2 - 24d + 9$

6. Factor each expression.
   (a) $2t^2 + t - 6$
   (b) $3m^2 - 11m - 4$
   (c) $10x^2 + 3x - 1$
   (d) $9x^2 + 12x + 4$
   (e) $9x^2 - 12x + 4$
   (f) $4x^2 - 16x + 15$
   (g) $2y^2 + 3y + 1$
   (h) $3b^2 - 5b - 2$
   (i) $2c^2 + 5c - 12$
   (j) $6x^2 + 5x + 1$
   (k) $5a^2 - 11a + 2$
   (l) $6m^2 - 11m - 10$
   (m) $2d^2 + 5d + 2$
   (n) $6w^2 - 13w + 6$
   (o) $10b^2 + b - 3$

7. Factor each expression.

(a) $3a^2 + 6a$

(b) $2x - 8xy$

(c) $25a^2 - 9$

(d) $x^2 + 7x + 12$

(e) $y^2 - 11y + 28$

(f) $16a^2 - 8a + 1$

(g) $8 + 6x + x^2$

(h) $5b^2 - 14b + 8$

(i) $10x^2 - 28x + 16$

(j) $3d^2 - 432$

(k) $6d^2 + 5d + 1$

(l) $56c^2 + 9c - 2$

(m) $2g^2 - 2g - 24$

(n) $-16 + 9x^2$

(o) $x^2y^3z - 2xy^2$

8. Knowledge and Understanding: For each relation

i.   express it in factored form

ii. determine its zeros

iii. determine the coordinates of its vertex

iv. graph the relation

(a) $y = x^2 - 4$

(b) $y = x^2 + 6x + 8$

(c) $y = x^2 - 6x + 5$

(d) $y = -x^2 + 2x + 24$

(e) $y = x^2 + 2x + 1$

(f) $y = -x^2 + 3x + 18$

9. A rectangular enclosure has an area in square metres given by $A = -2w^2 + 36w$, where w is the width of the rectangle in metres. What is the maximum area of the enclosure?

10. Communication: Can all equations of parabolas be expressed in factored form? Explain.

11. A model rocket is shot into the air and its path is approximated by $h = -5t^2 + 30t$, where h is the height of the rocket above the ground in metres and t is the elapsed time in seconds.

(a) When will the rocket hit the ground?

(b) What is the maximum height of the rocket?

12. A baseball is thrown from the top of a building and falls to the ground below. Its path is approximated by the relation $h = -5t^2 + 5t + 30$, where h is the height above ground in metres and t is the elapsed time in seconds.

(a) How tall is the building?

(b) When will the ball hit the ground?

(c) When does the ball reach its maximum height?

(d) How high above the building is the ball at its maximum height?

13. Application: A small company that manufactures snowboards uses the relation $P = 162x - 81x^2$ to model its profit. In the model, x represents the number of snowboards in thousands, and P represents the profit in thousands of dollars.

(a) What is the maximum profit the company can earn?

(b) How many snowboards must it produce to earn this profit?

(c) The company breaks even when there is neither a profit nor a loss. What are the break-even points for the company?

14. A computer software company models the profit on its latest game using the relation $P = -2x^2 + 28x - 90$, where x is the number of games it produces in hundred thousands and P is the profit in millions of dollars.

(a) What is the maximum profit the company can earn?

(b) How many games must it produce to earn this profit?

(c) What are the break-even points for the company?

15. Check Your Understanding

(a) Explain how to change a quadratic relation from standard form into factored form.

(b) Describe the advantages of working with a quadratic relation in factored form compared with standard form.

C

16. The path of a shot put is given by $h = -0.0502(d^2 - 20.7d - 26.28)$ where h is the height and d is the horizontal distance in metres.

(a) Rewrite the relation in the form $h = a(d - s)(d - t)$ where s and t are the zeros of the relation.

(b) What is the significance of s and t in this question?

17. Factor completely. Identify the expressions that cannot be factored.

(a) $4x^4 - 36x^2 + 9$ (b) $4x^4 + 24x^2 + 9$

(c) $8x^2 - 50$ (d) $\frac{a^2}{64} - \frac{b^2}{49}$

(e) $\frac{c^4}{16} - \frac{d^4}{81}$ (f) $625m^8n^4 - 16p^8$

(g) $100 - (w - 4)^2$ (h) $4x^2 + y^2$ (i) $x^2 - 2xy + y^2 - 9z^2$

(j) $a^2 + 6a + 9 - b^2$ (k) $4a^2b^2 + 12abc + 9c^2$ (l) $1 - 6x + 9x^2 - 4y^2$

18. **Thinking, Inquiry, Problem Solving**: Soundz Inc. makes CD players. Last year, accountants modelled the company's profit by $P = -5x^2 + 60x - 135$. Over the course of the year, in an effort to become more efficient, Soundz Inc. restructured its operation, eliminating some employees and reducing costs. This year, accountants are using $P = -7x^2 + 70x - 63$ to project the company's profit. In both models, P is the profit in hundreds of thousands of dollars and x is the number of CD players made, in hundreds of thousands. Was Soundz Inc.'s restructuring effective? Justify your answer.

The Chapter Problem—Setting the Best Ticket Price

In this section you changed quadratic relations from standard form into factored form. Apply what you learned to answer these questions about the chapter problem on page 242.

1. The relation $R = 4000 + 20x - 2x^2$, where x is the amount of the price change and R is the revenue in dollars, is a model that predicts revenue from ticket sales. What is the maximum revenue predicted by this model?

2. Revisit section 3.1 and use the table of values and the quadratic regression feature of a graphing calculator to draw the scatter plots and the curves of best fit. Compare these graphs to the hand-drawn graphs. How can they be used to solve the original problem?

3.9 Solving Problems with Quadratic Equations

Part 1: Solving a Quadratic Equation Graphically

Trendy Fashion Shop sells blouses. Over the last season, the manager used the quadratic relation $R = 300 + 20x - x^2$ to model the effect on revenue of raising or lowering the price. Here, R is the revenue in dollars and x is the price change in dollars.

Think, Do, Discuss

1. Graph the relation.

2. Use the graph to determine the price change that produces the maximum revenue.

3. **(a)** What is the price change that results in revenue of $375?

   (b) What is the price change that results in revenue of $300?

   (c) At what amount of increase or decrease does the shop get no revenue?

4. Each question in step 3 corresponds to an equation that must to be solved.

   (a) Write the equation that matches each question.

   (b) Why can't these equations be solved using the methods for solving linear equations that you learned in your previous mathematics courses?

Did You Know?

Are humans the only animals that count? No, say Nobuyuki Kawai and Tetsuro Matsuzawa of the Kyoto Research Institute of Japan. In April 2000, they reported in *Nature* that a 14-year-old chimpanzee named Ai has learned to use Arabic numerals to count from 0 to 9. Ai can also remember a five-digit sequence of numbers. Do some research. How do Ai's math skills compare to those of a preschool child? What other evidence is there that chimpanzees plan ahead?

Part 2: Solving a Quadratic Equation Algebraically

The earlier sections of this chapter focused on the zeros or x-intercepts of quadratic relations.

For a quadratic relation in standard form $(y = ax^2 + bx + c)$ or in factored form $(y = a(x - s)(x - t))$ the zeros are found by solving for x when $y = 0$.

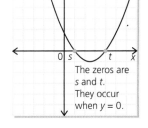

The zeros are s and t. They occur when $y = 0$.

If $0 = a(x - s)(x - t)$, then $x = s$ and $x = t$ are the solutions of the equation.

In this section, you will learn to solve quadratic equations for *any* value of y, including zero.

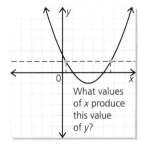

What values of x produce this value of y?

Think, Do, Discuss

1. Consider the quadratic relation $y = x^2 - 8x + 12$.

   (a) Graph the relation. Use factoring to determine the zeros exactly.

   (b) Use the graph to find the value of x for which the value of the relation is -3. How accurate is your answer? How can you check?

   (c) Write the equation that corresponds to the relation you found in (b).

   (d) Rewrite the equation so that 0 is on one side and all the other terms on the other.

   (e) Graph the relation that corresponds to this new equation. Use factoring to determine the zeros exactly.

   (f) How does finding the zeros for this quadratic relation also answer the problem in (b)? Why is it possible to find an exact answer to the problem?

2. Why is solving $x^2 - 8x + 12 = -3$ the same as solving $x^2 - 8x + 15 = 0$?

3. Describe the key steps that you followed in question 1 to find the exact solution to an equation involving a quadratic expression.

4. Use this procedure to find exact values of x for which the relation has a value of 12, 5, and -4.

5. Try to use the procedure to find the exact value of x for which the relation has a value of 1. Why does the method not work in this case?

6. Under what circumstances will this procedure work to find the exact solution to an equation involving a quadratic expression?

Focus 3.9

Key Ideas

- If the value of y is known for the relation $y = ax^2 + bx + c$, then the corresponding values of x can be found either graphically or algebraically.

- If the quadratic relation $y = ax^2 + bx + c$ is graphed, then for any value of the dependent variable, y, the values of the independent variable, x, can be read from the graph.

- In a quadratic relation, when y is replaced with a number, the result is a **quadratic equation**. For example, $y = x^2 - 9$ is a quadratic relation and $72 = x^2 - 9$ is a quadratic equation.

- In some cases, quadratic equations can be solved by factoring. Follow this procedure:

◆ Replace y with the given value.	For example, to solve $x^2 - x = 6$,
◆ Rearrange the quadratic equation to the form $ax^2 + bx + c = 0$.	$x^2 - x = 6$
	$x^2 - x - 6 = 0$
◆ Factor the quadratic expression, if possible.	$(x + 2)(x - 3) = 0$
◆ Set each factor equal to zero and solve the resulting equations.	$x + 2 = 0$ or $x - 3 = 0$
	$x = -2$ or $x = 3$

- The solutions to a quadratic equation are often called the **roots** of the equation.

Example 1

A ball is thrown straight down from a 180 m high cliff.

The relation $h = -5t^2 - 5t + 180$ is a model that gives the approximate height of the ball h, in metres, at t seconds after it is thrown. How long does it take the ball to reach a ledge 80 m from the base of the cliff? Check the answer using a graphing calculator.

Solution

Since $h = -5t^2 - 5t + 180$, then for $h = 80$

$$80 = -5t^2 - 5t + 180$$

$$0 = -5t^2 - 5t + 180 - 80 \qquad \text{Subtract 80 from both sides of the equation.}$$

$$0 = -5t^2 - 5t + 100 \qquad \text{Remove the common factor.}$$

$$0 = -5(t^2 + t - 20) \qquad \text{Factor } t^2 + t - 20.$$

$$0 = -5(t + 5)(t - 4) \qquad \text{Since } (5)(-4) = -20 \text{ and } 5 + (-4) = 1.$$

So $t + 5 = 0$ or $t - 4 = 0$. The roots are $t = -5$ and $t = 4$.

The value $t = -5$ has no meaning in this context, since the ball only started moving at $t = 0$.

Therefore, after 4 s the ball reaches a height of 80 m from the base of the cliff.

Check with a graphing calculator. Graph the parabola and adjust the window. Use the **1:value** command from the CALCULATE menu ([2nd] [TRACE]), enter $x = 4$, and press [ENTER].

 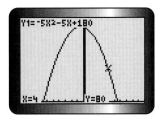

The result shows that the answer is correct.

Example 2

The population of a city is modelled by the relation $P = 0.5t^2 + 10t + 200$, where P is the population in thousands and t is the time in years. **Note:** $t = 0$ corresponds to the year 2000.

(a) What is the population in 2000?

(b) What is the population in 2002?

(c) When is the population 350 000? Explain your answer.

(d) Use a graphing calculator to check the answers.

Solution

Use a graphing calculator to check each of (a), (b), and (c) as they are completed.

(a) When $t = 0$, the year is 2000. Substitute $t = 0$ in the equation.

$P = 0.5t^2 + 10t + 200$

$P = 0.5(0)^2 + 10(0) + 200$

$P = 200$

Since P is measured in thousands, the population in 2000 is 200 000. This screen capture shows the result is correct.

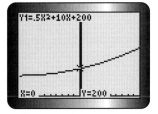

(b) The year 2002 corresponds to $t = 2$.
Substitute $t = 2$.

$P = 0.5(2)^2 + 10(2) + 200$

$P = 0.5(4) + 20 + 200$

$P = 222$

In 2002, the population is 222 000.

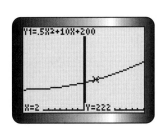

(c) To calculate when the population reaches 350 000, substitute $P = 350$ in the equation and solve for t.

$$P = 0.5t^2 + 10t + 200$$

$350 = 0.5t^2 + 10t + 200$	Substitute $P = 350$.
$0 = 0.5t^2 + 10t + 200 - 350$	Subtract 350 from both sides of the equation.
$0 = 0.5t^2 + 10t - 150$	Remove the common factor.
$0 = 0.5(t^2 + 20t - 300)$	Factor $t^2 + 20t - 300$.
$0 = 0.5(t + 30)(t - 10)$	Factor as a product of binomials.

So $t + 30 = 0$ or $t - 10 = 0$. The zeros are $t = -30$ and $t = 10$ as shown.

The population will reach 350 000 in 2010. According to the model, the population was also 350 000 in 1970 (at $t = -30$). The relation models a city whose population decreased to a minimum and is now increasing.

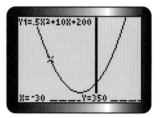

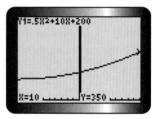

Example 3

Solve the equation $18y - 14 = 4y^2$. Check your solution.

Solution

$$4y^2 = 18y - 14$$

$4y^2 - 18y + 14 = 0$	Rewrite the equation in the form $ax^2 + bx + c = 0$.
$2(2y^2 - 9y + 7) = 0$	Remove the common factor.
$2(2y - 7)(y - 1) = 0$	Factor the trinomial as you have learned in this chapter. Check your factoring by expanding using the distributive property: $2y(y) + (-7)y + 2y(-1) + (-7)(-1)$ $= 2y^2 - 7y - 2y + 7$ $= 2y^2 - 9y + 7$
$2y - 7 = 0$ or $y - 1 = 0$	Set the factors equal to zero and solve.
$y = \dfrac{7}{2}$ or $y = 1$	The roots are $\dfrac{7}{2}$ and 1.

Check $y = \frac{7}{2}$:

L. S.	R. S.
$4y^2$	$18y - 14$
$= 4\left(\frac{7}{2}\right)^2$	$= 18\left(\frac{7}{2}\right) - 14$
$= 4\left(\frac{49}{4}\right)$	$= 9(7) - 14$
$= 49$	$= 63 - 14$
	$= 49$

left side $=$ right side

Check $y = 1$:

L. S.	R. S.
$4y^2$	$18y - 14$
$= 4(1)^2$	$= 18(1) - 14$
$= 4$	$= 4$

left side $=$ right side

The solutions to $18y - 14 = 4y^2$ are $y = \frac{7}{2}$ and $y = 1$.

Practise, Apply, Solve 3.9

A

1. Solve each equation.

(a) $(x + 5)(x - 2) = 0$

(b) $3y(y - 5) = 0$

(c) $(2m + 1)(m - 3) = 0$

(d) $(3t - 2)(t + 3) = 0$

(e) $(2x - 1)(3x - 2) = 0$

(f) $(r - 3)(r + 2) = 0$

(g) $a(a - 5) = 0$

(h) $(4x + 3)(5x - 2) = 0$

(i) $(3 - 4p)(2 - 7p) = 0$

2. Factor each expression. Then find the roots of each equation.

(a) $n^2 + 7n - 30 = 0$

(b) $2y^2 + 9y + 4 = 0$

(c) $m^2 + 8m + 15 = 0$

(d) $y^2 - y - 6 = 0$

(e) $x^2 - 2x - 15 = 0$

(f) $m^2 - 1 = 0$

(g) $4n^2 - 1 = 0$

(h) $16x^2 - 25 = 0$

(i) $9n^2 - 6n + 1 = 0$

(j) $3x^2 + 9x - 30 = 0$

(k) $5x^2 + 25x + 30 = 0$

(l) $4x^2 - 14x - 8 = 0$

3. Solve each equation.

(a) $42 = x^2 - x$

(b) $x^2 - 4x = 21$

(c) $a^2 = 2a + 48$

(d) $m^2 = 30 - 7m$

(e) $3 = 6x^2 - 7x$

(f) $15 + x = 2x^2$

(g) $2y^2 + 4 = -9y$

(h) $17x + 5x^2 = -6$

(i) $2m^2 = 3 - 5m$

4. Wanda and Louise determine that the expression $A = -2w^2 + 36w$ models the area of a rectangular puppy run, where w is the width in metres and A is the area in square metres. What dimensions produce an area of 112 m²?

5. Mirna's Fashion store determined that each relation below modelled expected revenue for an article of clothing. R is the revenue in dollars and x is the amount of the change in price. Solve for x. Interpret each answer in the context of the question.

(a) Sweatshirts $R = (20 - 2x)(30 + 3x)$ when $R = \$594$

(b) Suits $R = (200 - 25x)(9 + 3x)$ when $R = \$2250$

(c) Pants $R = (30 - 4x)(16 + 2x)$ when $R = \$396$

B

6. Determine all values of x that satisfy the equation.

(a) $y = x^2 - x - 30$, when $y = -24$ (b) $y = x^2 - 3x - 28$, when $y = -10$

(c) $y = x^2 - 7x + 12$, when $y = 2$ (d) $y = 2x^2 - 9x + 10$, when $y = -6$

(e) $y = 6x^2 - x - 1$, when $y = 50$ (f) $y = x^2 - 8x + 16$, when $y = 4$

7. Graph each relation in question 6 using a graphing calculator and confirm the values of x that you found.

8. A pair of skydivers jump out of an airplane 5.5 km above the ground. The equation $H = 5500 - 5t^2$ is an approximate model for the divers' altitude in metres at t seconds after jumping out of the plane.

(a) After 10 s how far have the divers fallen?

(b) They open their chutes at an altitude of 1000 m. How long did they free-fall?

(c) If a parachute does not open at 1000 m, how much time is left to use the emergency chute?

9. A professional stunt performer at a theme park dives off a tower 21 m high into the water. His height above the ground at time t seconds is given by the equation $h = -4.9t^2 + 21$.

(a) How long does it take to reach the halfway mark?

(b) How long does it take to reach the water?

(c) Compare the times in (a) and (b). Explain why the time at the bottom is not twice the time at the halfway point.

10. Sasha works at the Botanical Gardens and is planning a new rectangular rose garden 20 m by 30 m. She plans to build a walkway, with a uniform width, all around the garden. Her budget is $6000 and she knows it will cost $10/m² to construct the walkway. How wide can the walkway be?

11. Sasha's budget in question 10 is reduced by $1000. How will this affect the width of the walkway?

12. Knowledge and Understanding: Suppose that the population of a town is described by $P = 0.16t^2 + 7.2t + 100$, where P is the population in thousands and t is the time in years, with $t = 0$ representing the year 2000.
(a) What will the population be in 2010?
(b) What was the population in 1995?
(c) When will the population reach 52 000?
(d) Will the population ever reach zero under this model? Explain.

13. A model rocket is shot straight up from the roof of a school. The height at any time t is approximated by the model $H = 15 + 23t - 5t^2$, where H is the height in metres and t is the time in seconds.
(a) What is the height of the school?
(b) How long does it take for the rocket to pass a window 10 m above the ground?
(c) When does the rocket hit the ground?
(d) What is the maximum height the rocket reaches above the roof of the school?

14. Communication: Water from a fire hose is sprayed on a fire 15 m up the side of a wall. The equation $H = -0.011x^2 + x + 1.6$ models the height of the jet of water and the horizontal distance from the nozzle in metres. What is the farthest distance back from the building that a firefighter could stand and still reach the fire? Explain. Include a diagram with your explanation.

15. The safe stopping distance, d, in metres, for a boat travelling at v km/h in calm water is determined to be $d = 0.002(2v^2 + 10v + 3000)$.
(a) What is the safe stopping distance if the speed is 12 km/h?
(b) What is the initial speed of the boat if it takes 15 m to stop?

16. Application: A Zamboni is resurfacing the ice on a rectangular ice rink 25 m wide by 40 m long. The operator starts at the centre of the rink and makes uniform rectangular passes over the surface, gradually working outward in a concentric way. After only ten percent of the surface is complete, the machine breaks down. Find the width of the remaining strip of unfinished ice surface.

17. Nancy walks 15 m diagonally across a rectangular field. She then returns to her starting position along the outside of the field. The total distance she walks is 36 m. What are the dimensions of the field?

18. Raj and his sister cut the lawn. The lawn is a square and Raj says he will cut a path around the outside 3 m wide. His sister will cut the remaining lawn. If the part he cuts is the same area as the part she cuts, what are the dimensions of the lawn?

19. Check Your Understanding
   (a) Explain in detail how to determine the value of the independent variable in a quadratic relation if the value of the dependent variable is known.
   (b) What is the greatest number of solutions a quadratic equation can have? Explain, with an example, why all of the solutions to the equation may not be reasonable answers to the original problem.

20. Thinking, Inquiry, Problem Solving
Nicole is doing a project on the planets in the solar system. She wants to show the different effect of gravity on each planet and decides to examine the flight of an imaginary arrow that is shot straight up from the surface of the planet.

The table shows how the pull of gravity on each planet compares with gravity on Earth.

The equation $H = 2.3 + 50t + \frac{1}{2}gt^2$ models the height of the arrow in metres at time t seconds. The pull of gravity is g and is different for each planet. On Earth, $g = -9.8$ m/s².

Planet	Relative Gravity (% of Earth's Gravity, g)
Earth ($g = -9.8$ m/s²)	100%
Mercury	38%
Venus	81%
Mars	40%
Jupiter	254%
Saturn	108%
Uranus	91%
Neptune	190%
Pluto	8%

   (a) Determine the equation that models the height of the arrow at time t on each planet.
   (b) What is the maximum height the arrow would reach on each planet?
   (c) How long would the arrow be in flight on each planet?
   (d) At what time would the arrow reach a distance halfway between the ground and its maximum height?
   (e) Account for the different forces of gravity on each planet.

21. A new children's play area will be a square 40 m by 40 m. Inside the playground will be four square sand boxes each with a side length of 4 m. How must they be placed so that the distance between the sand boxes and between the outside boundary and the sand boxes is the same?

Analyzing and Applying Quadratic Models
Check Your Understanding

1. When is it more appropriate to use a curve of best fit rather than a line of best fit to model a set of data?

2. Suppose a set of data is best modelled using a smooth curve.
   (a) How can you tell from the scatter plot whether a quadratic relation is the most appropriate model?
   (b) How can you use a finite difference table to determine whether a quadratic model is most appropriate?

3. What is the least amount of information you need about a parabola to find its equation in factored form?

4. Suppose you have a set of data that can be modelled very closely using a hand-drawn parabola.
   (a) Describe the relationship between the zeros of the parabola and the algebraic expression that represents it.
   (b) What is the degree of the algebraic expression?
   (c) Describe the relationship between the location of the optimal point on the curve and the x-intercepts.
   (d) Explain how to use the zeros to find the location of the vertex of the parabola.
   (e) What is the relationship between the vertex and the optimal value of the relation?
   (f) How can you find the equation of the axis of symmetry of the parabola if you know the zeros?
   (g) What information would you need to know about a parabola if you wanted to find the equation of the axis of symmetry but did not know the zeros?

5. Imagine that you have used the quadratic regression feature of a graphing calculator to find the equation of a curve of best fit for a set of data.
   (a) What information would the calculator provide that is a measure of how well the equation fits the data?
   (b) What form will the equation be in?
   (c) What are the disadvantages of this form of equation compared to the factored form?

6. Describe how to convert the equation of a parabola from factored form to standard form.

7. (a) Create an example of a quadratic expression in standard form that can be factored as a product like $(x - s)(x - t)$. Explain how the coefficients in the terms are related to the values of s and t.

   (b) Create an example of a quadratic expression in standard form that can be factored as a product like $a(x - s)(x - t)$. Explain how the coefficients in the terms are related to the values of a, s, and t.

   (c) Create an example of a quadratic expression in standard form that can be factored as a product like $(ax - s)(bx - t)$. Explain how the coefficients in the terms are related to the values of a, b, s, and t.

   (d) Create an example of a quadratic expression that cannot be factored as a product of two binomials. Explain why it cannot be factored.

8. Suppose you are solving an equation in the form $ax^2 + bx + c = 0$. How can you use factoring to find the solutions? How many solutions are possible?

9. Suppose you are solving an equation in the form $ax^2 + bx + c = d$. What do you need to do in order to be able to apply the procedure in question 8 to this equation?

3.1 Quadratic Relations

- Sometimes a **curve of best fit** is a more appropriate model for data than a line of best fit. This is true when the data points seem to fit a recognizable pattern that is not a straight line. In such a case, try to draw a smooth curve that passes through as many of the data points as possible. Visualize where the curve should lie between the actual plotted data points. A piece of string may help you to decide the shape and location of the curve.

- The values of the **first differences** in a table of values determine if the relation is linear.

  ♦ For constant increments of the independent variable, a relation is linear if the first differences of the dependent variable are constant.

  For example, the first differences in this table of values are constant, so the relation is linear.

x	0	1	2	3	4
y	2	3	4	5	6
First Difference	1	1	1	1	

  ♦ For constant increments of the independent variable, a relation is **quadratic** if the second differences of the dependent variable are constant.

  For example, the second differences in this table of values are constant, so the relation is quadratic.

x	0	1	2	3	4
y	2	3	6	11	18
First Difference	1	3	5	7	
Second Difference	2	2	2		

- A linear relation models a phenomenon where the rate of change is constant. A nonlinear relation models a phenomenon with a variable rate of change.

- The **degree** of a one-variable polynomial is the highest exponent that appears in any term of the expanded form of the polynomial.

- A polynomial of degree 2 models a quadratic relation.

Example

A model rocket is shot straight up into the air. The table shows its height, h, in metres, at t seconds.

t (s)	0	1	2	3	4	5	6
h (m)	0.0	25.1	41.5	40.4	45.9	27.5	3.6

(a) Draw the curve of best fit.

(b) Identify the type of relationship between time and height. Explain.

(c) Estimate the height after 4.5 s.

(d) When does the rocket reach 20 m?

Solution

(a)

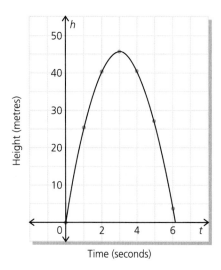

Time (seconds)

(b) To identify the relationship between time and height, examine the first and second differences.

t (s)		0	1	2	3	4	5	6
h (m)		0.0	25.1	40.4	45.9	41.6	27.5	3.6
First Difference			25.1	15.3	5.5	4.3	−14.1	−23.9
Second Difference				−9.8	−9.8	−9.8	−9.8	−9.8

The first differences are not constant, so the relationship is nonlinear.

The second differences are constant, so the relationship is quadratic.

(c) Reading the graph tells you that at 4.5 s, the rocket is about 34 m high.

(d) The rocket reaches 20 m at two different times. Once on the way up, at about 0.8 s, and again on the way down, at 5.2 s.

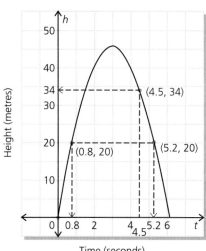

Time (seconds)

Extra Practice

1. In each case,
   i. use finite differences to determine whether the relationship is best represented by a linear expression, a quadratic expression, or another type of expression
   ii. draw a curve of best fit to verify your answer in (i)

   (a)

x	−3	−2	−1	0	1
y	−7	−4	−1	2	5

   (b)

x	−1	0	1	2	3
y	−1	0	1	8	27

   (c)

x	−2	−1	0	1	2
y	0.25	0.5	1	2	4

   (d)

x	−2	−1	0	1	2
y	−7.5	−4.5	−1.5	1.5	4.5

   (e)

x	0	1	2	3	4
y	8	10	12	14	16

2. Examine the pattern of numbers, $N_1 = 6$, $N_2 = 20$, $N_3 = 42$, $N_4 = 72$, and $N_5 = 110$.
   (a) Find the next three terms in the sequence.
   (b) Use finite differences to show that the relationship between n and the value of N_n is quadratic.

3. Over the ocean, a sandbag is dropped from a hot air balloon, so the balloon will rise. The table shows the height of the sandbag at different times as it falls.

t (s)	0	1	2	3	4	5	6	7	8	9	10
h (m)	1200	1195	1180	1155	1120	1075	1020	955	880	795	700

   (a) Draw the scatter plot of the data.
   (b) What type of model represents the relationship between the height of the sandbag and time?
   (c) Follow the pattern and extend the table of values until the sandbag hits the water.
   (d) Draw the curve of best fit.
   (e) About how long does it take for the sandbag to reach the water?

3.2 Properties of Quadratic Equations

- The graph of a quadratic relation is called a **parabola.**

- The **vertex** of a parabola is the point on the graph with the greatest y-coordinate if the graph opens down or the least y-coordinate if the graph opens up.

- When a quadratic relation is used to model a situation, the y-coordinate of the vertex corresponds to an **optimal value**. Depending on the direction of opening of the parabola, this represents either a **maximum** or a **minimum** value of the quantity being modelled by the dependent variable. The maximum or minimum value is always associated with the vertex.

- The direction of opening of the parabola can be determined from the sign of the second differences in the table of values of the quadratic relation.

  - If the constant value of the second differences is positive, then the parabola opens up (figure 1).

  - If the constant value of the second differences is negative, then the parabola opens down (figure 2).

- A parabola is symmetrical with respect to a vertical line through its vertex. The line is called the **axis of symmetry** of the parabola and the vertex lies on the axis of symmetry. If the coordinates of the vertex are (h, k), then the equation of the axis of symmetry is $x = h$ (figure 3).

- The axis of symmetry is the perpendicular bisector of the segment joining any two points on the parabola that have the same y-coordinates. If the parabola crosses the x-axis, the x-coordinates of these points are called the **zeros**, or **x-intercepts** of the relation, and the vertex is directly above or below the midpoint of the segment joining the zeros (figure 4).

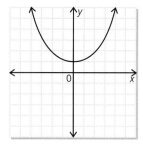

figure 1

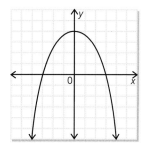

figure 2

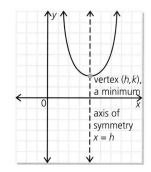

figure 3

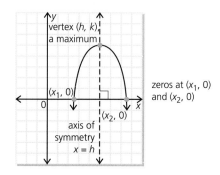

figure 4

Example

A golf ball is hit and its height is given by $h = 29.4t - 4.9t^2$, where h is its height in metres and t is the time in seconds.

(a) When is the golf ball on the ground?

(b) At what time does the golf ball reach its maximum height?

(c) What is the ball's maximum height?

(d) What will be the shape of the graph of this relation?

(e) Sketch the graph.

Solution

(a) The zeros of the relation occur when the height is zero, that is, when the ball is on the ground. Then,

$$h = 29.4t - 4.9t^2 \text{ or}$$
$$0 = 29.4t - 4.9t^2$$
$$0 = t(29.4 - 4.9t) \qquad \text{The common factor is } t.$$

So either $t = 0$ or $29.4 - 4.9t = 0$.

$$29.4 = 4.9t$$
$$\frac{29.4}{4.9} = \frac{4.9t}{4.9}$$
$$6 = t$$

The zeros are 0 and 6. The ball is on the ground at 0 s and 6 s.

(b) The golf ball reaches its maximum height at a value of the independent variable that is midway between 0 and 6. This value is $\frac{0 + 6}{2} = 3$. The golf ball reaches its maximum height at 3 s.

(c) To find the maximum height, substitute $t = 3$ into the equation.

$$h = 29.4t - 4.9t^2$$
$$h = 29.4(3) - 4.9(3)^2$$
$$h = 88.2 - 44.1$$
$$h = 44.1$$

The maximum height is 44.1 m.

(d) The relation $h = 29.4t - 4.9t^2$ is a polynomial of degree 2, which means it is a quadratic relation. The graph of a quadratic relation is a parabola. Since the coefficient of the t^2 term is negative, the parabola opens downward.

(e) The parabola has zeros, or x-intercepts, at 0 and 6. The vertex is at $(3, 44.1)$

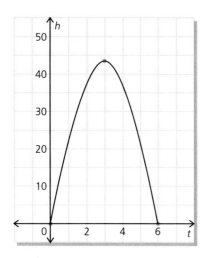

Extra Practice

4. Each pair of points lies on a different parabola. Determine the axis of symmetry of each parabola.

(a) $(-5, 4)$ and $(-9, 4)$

(b) $(2.5, 3.5)$ and $(3.7, 3.5)$

(c) $(16, -2)$ and $(-18, -2)$

(d) $(\frac{3}{4}, -5)$ and $(-\frac{1}{2}, -5)$

(e) $(5\frac{5}{8}, -5)$ and $(4\frac{1}{4}, -5)$

(f) $(-3\frac{2}{3}, 7)$ and $(5\frac{1}{6}, 7)$

5. The zeros of a quadratic relation are -2 and 5, and the second differences are all negative.

(a) Explain whether the optimal value will be a maximum or a minimum.

(b) What value of the independent variable will produce the optimal value?

(c) Will the optimal value be positive or negative? Explain.

6. For each parabola,

i. find where it crosses the x-axis

ii. state the equation of the axis of symmetry

iii. without graphing, determine whether the vertex represents a maximum or a minimum value

iv. find the coordinates of the vertex

(a) $A = 18w - w^2$

(b) $A = -L^2 + 10L$

(c) $y = 4x - 16x^2$

(d) $h = 25t - 5t^2$

(e) $y = 15x + 6x^2$

(f) $A = 42w - 6w^2$

3.3–3.4 The Role of the Zeros of a Quadratic Relation

- Relations in the form $y = a(x - s)(x - t)$ are quadratic, provided that $a \neq 0$.

- A quadratic relation is said to be in **factored form** if its algebraic expression appears in the form $y = a(x - s)(x - t)$.

- If $a > 0$, the parabola opens up and has a minimum. If $a < 0$, the parabola opens down and has a maximum.

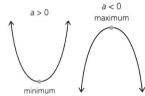

- When a quadratic relation is in factored form, the values of x that are the solutions to $0 = a(x - s)(x - t)$ are called the **zeros** of the quadratic relation. These values correspond to the x-intercepts of the graph of the relation. The zeros can be determined by setting each factor equal to 0 and solving the resulting equation for x. In $y = a(x - s)(x - t)$, the zeros are $x = s$ and $x = t$.

This quadratic relation has two zeros.

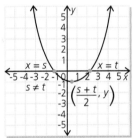

- If $s \neq t$, then the relation has two distinct zeros. If $s = t$, the relation has only one zero at $x = s = t$.

- If the zeros of a quadratic relation are s and t, then the x-coordinate of the vertex is $\dfrac{s + t}{2}$.

This quadratic relation has one zero.

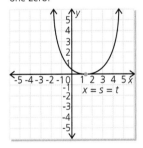

- When the zeros of a quadratic relation are known, the value of a can be determined if some other point (x_1, y_1) on the graph is known. Substitute the coordinates of the point in the factored form, giving $y_1 = a(x_1 - s)(x_1 - t)$, then solve for a.

Example

The zeros of a parabola are -2 and 7, and it crosses the y-axis at -28.

(a) What is the equation of the quadratic relation?

(b) What are the coordinates of the vertex?

Solution

(a) The factored equation of any parabola is in the form $y = a(x - s)(x - t)$, where s and t are the zeros. In this case, $s = -2$ and $t = 7$. Substitute these values.

$$y = a(x - s)(x - t)$$
$$y = a(x - (-2))(x - 7)$$
$$y = a(x + 2)(x - 7)$$

The y-intercept of -28 occurs when $x = 0$. Then,

$$-28 = a(0 + 2)(0 - 7)$$
$$-28 = a(2)(-7)$$
$$-28 = -14a$$
$$a = \frac{-28}{-14}$$
$$a = 2$$

The equation of the quadratic relation is $y = 2(x + 2)(x - 7)$.

(b) The vertex occurs midway between -2 and 7, so

$$x = \frac{-2 + 7}{2}$$
$$x = \frac{5}{2}$$
$$x = 2\frac{1}{2}$$

Substitute this value into the equation.

$$y = 2(2\tfrac{1}{2} + 2)(2\tfrac{1}{2} - 7)$$
$$y = 2\left(4\tfrac{1}{2}\right)\left(-4\tfrac{1}{2}\right)$$
$$y = 2\left(\tfrac{9}{2}\right)\left(-\tfrac{9}{2}\right)$$
$$y = -\frac{81}{2}$$
$$y = -40\frac{1}{2}$$

The coordinates of the vertex are $(2\tfrac{1}{2}, -40\tfrac{1}{2})$.

Extra Practice

7. Determine the equation of each parabola.

(a)

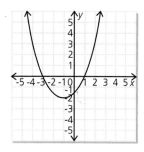

(b)

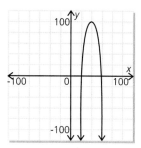

(c)

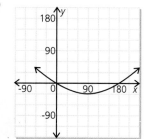

(d)

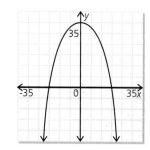

8. **(a)** Determine the zeros for each parabola in question 7.

   (b) What is the value of the independent variable at the optimal point on each curve?

9. Determine the quadratic equation for a parabola with

   (a) zeros at 5 and 9, and an optimal value of -2

   (b) zeros at -3 and 7, and an optimal value of 4

   (c) zeros at -6 and 2, and a y-intercept of -9

   (d) zeros at -9 and -5, and a y-intercept of 8

10. The city bus company usually transports 12 000 riders per day at a ticket price of $1. The company wants to raise the ticket price and knows that for every 10¢ increase the number of riders decreases by 400.

    (a) What price for a ticket will maximize revenue?

    (b) What other factors can influence the number of people who use public transportation?

    (c) How might the company use the answers from (a) and (b) in its decision to set ticket prices?

3.5–3.7 Standard Form of a Quadratic Relation

- The **factored form** of a quadratic relation, $y = (x - s)(x - t)$, $y = a(x - s)(x - t)$, or $y = (ax - s)(bx - t)$, can be expanded using the distributive property and simplified to give a **standard form** trinomial, $y = ax^2 + bx + c$. Standard form is often called **expanded form**.

- Equivalent factored and standard forms

Factored Form	Standard (or Expanded Form)
$y = (x - s)(x - t)$	$y = x^2 - (s + t)x + st$
$y = a(x - s)(x - t)$	$y = ax^2 - a(s + t)x + ast$
$y = (ax - s)(bx - t)$	$y = abx^2 - (at + bs)x + st$

- The **quadratic regression** feature of a graphing calculator provides the algebraic expression for a curve of best fit in **standard** (or **expanded**) **form**, $y = ax^2 + bx + c$.

Example

A pizza company's research shows that a 25¢ increase in the price of a pizza results in 50 fewer pizzas being sold. The usual price of $15 for a three-item pizza results in sales of 1000 pizzas.

(a) Write the algebraic expression that models the revenue for this situation.

(b) Expand and simplify the expression in standard form.

(c) Graph the expressions in (a) and (b). Compare the graphs.

Solution

(a) Revenue = price of one pizza × number of pizzas sold

Let x be the number of 25¢ price increases and R be the revenue in dollars. Then, the price of one pizza is $15 + 0.25x$ and the number of pizzas sold is $1000 - 50x$. So, the expression for revenue is $R = (15 + 0.25x)(1000 - 50x)$.

(b) $R = (15 + 0.25x)(1000 - 50x)$

$R = (15)(1000) + (0.25x)(1000) + (15)(-50x) + (0.25x)(-50x)$

$R = 15\,000 + 250x - 750x - 12.5x^2$

$R = 15\,000 - 500x - 12.5x^2$

(c)

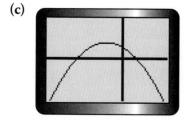 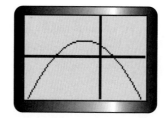

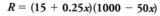

$R = (15 + 0.25x)(1000 - 50x)$ $R = 15\,000 - 500x - 12.5x^2$

Although the algebraic expressions for both graphs look different, the graphs are the same and represent the same relation.

Extra Practice

11. Expand and simplify these expressions.

(a) $(x + 5)(x + 4)$

(b) $(x - 2)(x - 5)$

(c) $(x + 6)(x - 7)$

(d) $(2x - 3)(2x + 3)$

(e) $(4x + 5)(3x - 2)$

(f) $(6x - 2)(5x + 7)$

(g) $(5 - 3x)(6 + 2x)$

(h) $(4a - 2b)(5a + 3b)$

(i) $(2m + 3n)(2m + 3n)$

(j) $-3(2x - 1)(x + 4)$

(k) $5(3u + 2v)(2u - 5v)$

(l) $-2(5 - 2x)(3x + 4)$

12. Determine the equation of each parabola in standard form. Verify your answer using the quadratic regression function of a graphing calculator.

(a)

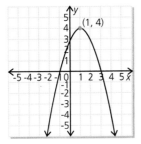

(b)

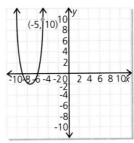

(c)

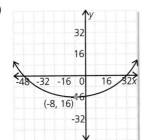

(d)

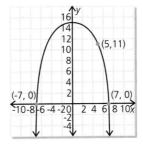

13. Express, in standard form, the equation of the parabola

(a) that has zeros at 4 and -2, and whose optimal value for y is 12

(b) that has zeros at -4 and 8, and goes through $(2, 18)$

3.8 Extending Algebra Skills: Factoring Quadratic Expressions

- Many quadratic relations in standard form $y = ax^2 + bx + c$ can be expressed as the product of two binomial factors. Finding this product is called **factoring**.

- Factoring is the opposite operation of expanding.

- If the quadratic expression $x^2 + bx + c$ can be factored, the factors are of the form $(x - s)(x - t)$, where $b = -(s + t)$ and $c = st$.

- If the quadratic expression $ax^2 + bx + c$ (where $a \neq 1$) can be factored, the factors can be found using a guess-and-check strategy.

    ◆ Choose factors that produce the correct first and last term of the quadratic (the x^2-term and the constant term) when multiplied.

- Sometimes quadratics in the form $ax^2 + bx + c$ have a common factor. If the trinomial remaining after a common factor is removed is in the form $x^2 + bx + c$, you may be able to factor it as above. For example, $5x^2 - 5x - 150 = 5(x - 6)(x + 5)$, since $5x^2 - 5x - 150 = 5(x^2 - x - 30)$ and $(x^2 - x - 30) = (x - 6)(x + 5)$.

- The middle (x) term of the quadratic comes from multiplying the outside terms of the binomial factors together, then the inside terms, then adding the results. For example, $6x^2 - 23x + 20 = (3x - 4)(2x - 5)$, since $(3x)(2x) = 6x^2$, $(-4)(-5) = 20$, and $(3x)(-5) + (-4)(2x) = (-15x) + (-8x)$ or $-23x$. Check that the factors you choose give the correct x-term in the standard form.

- If a trinomial is of the form $a^2x^2 - b^2$, then it is a **difference of squares** and can be factored as $(ax + b)(ax - b)$.

- If a trinomial is of the form $a^2x^2 + 2abx + b^2$, then it is a **perfect square** and can be factored as $(ax + b)(ax + b) = (ax + b)^2$.

Example

Factor completely.

(a) $x^2 - 13x + 42$

(b) $6x^2 + x - 15$

(c) $4x^2 - 25$

(d) $9x^2 - 12x + 4$

Solution

(a) $x^2 - 13x + 42 = (x - 6)(x - 7)$

(b) $6x^2 + x - 15 = (3x + 5)(2x - 3)$

(c) $4x^2 - 25 = (2x + 5)(2x - 5)$

(d) $9x^2 - 12x + 4 = (3x - 2)(3x - 2)$
$= (3x - 2)^2$

Extra Practice

14. Factor each expression.

(a) $x^2 + 2x - 15$

(b) $m^2 + 3m - 4$

(c) $r^2 - 4r + 4$

(d) $q^2 - 3q - 10$

(e) $6x^2 + 5x - 1$

(f) $6d^2 - d - 2$

(g) $x^2 - 9$

(h) $4x^2 - 25$

(i) $9x^2 + 12x + 4$

(j) $3m^2 + 3m - 18$

(k) $8p^2 + 8p - 6$

(l) $27x^2 - 48$

15. The Wheely Fast Co. makes custom skateboards for professional riders. They model their profit with the relation $P = -2b^2 + 14b - 20$, where b is number of skateboards they produce (in thousands), and P is the company's profit in hundred thousands of dollars.

(a) When does Wheely Fast break even? That is, when is their profit 0?

(b) How many skateboards does Wheely Fast need to produce to maximize profit?

3.9 Solving Problems with Quadratic Equations

- If the value of y is known for the relation $y = ax^2 + bx + c$, then the corresponding values of x can be found either graphically or algebraically.

- If the quadratic relation $y = ax^2 + bx + c$ is graphed, then for any value of the dependent variable, y, the values of the independent variable, x, can be read from the graph.

- In a quadratic relation, when y is replaced with a number, the result is a **quadratic equation**.

- In some cases, quadratic equations can be solved by factoring. Follow this procedure:

◆ Replace y with the given value.	For example, to solve $x^2 - x = 6$,
◆ Rearrange the quadratic equation to the form $ax^2 + bx + c = 0$.	$x^2 - x = 6$
	$x^2 - x - 6 = 0$
◆ Factor the quadratic expression, if possible.	$(x + 2)(x - 3) = 0$
◆ Set each factor equal to zero and solve the resulting equations.	$x + 2 = 0$ or $x - 3 = 0$
	$x = -2$ or $x = 3$

- The solutions to a quadratic equation are often called the **roots** of the equation.

Example

The population, P, of an Ontario city is modelled by $P = 14t^2 + 820t + 42\ 000$, where t is the time in years. When $t = 0$, the year is 2000.

(a) What will the population be in 2008?

(b) What was the population in 1991?

(c) In which year(s) was the population 30 000?

(d) Determine the year when the fewest people lived in the town.

Solution

(a) In 2008, $t = 8$. Substitute $t = 8$ into the model.

$P = 14t^2 + 820t + 42\,000$

$P = 14(8)^2 + 820(8) + 42\,000$

$P = 49\,456$

In 2008, the population will be 49 456.

(b) In 1991, $t = -9$. Substitute $t = -9$ into the model.

$P = 14t^2 + 820t + 42\,000$

$P = 14(-9)^2 + 820(-9) + 42\,000$

$P = 35\,754$

In 1991, the population was 35 754.

(c) To find the year in which the population is 30 000, substitute $P = 30\,000$ into the model.

$$P = 14t^2 + 820t + 42\,000$$
$$30\,000 = 14t^2 + 820t + 42\,000$$
$$0 = 14t^2 + 820t + 42\,000 - 30\,000$$
$$0 = 14t^2 + 820t + 12\,000$$
$$0 = (2t + 60)(7t + 200)$$

Then $2t + 60 = 0$ or $7t + 200 = 0$.

Solve to get

$$2t = -60 \quad \text{or} \quad 7t + 200 = 0$$
$$t = -30 \qquad\qquad t = -\frac{200}{7}$$
$$t \doteq -28.5$$

The population was 30 000 twice, once in 1970 (2000 − 30) and once again around 1971 (2000 − 28.5).

(d) The population of the city is at its lowest point on the vertex of the parabola. In this example, we will use a graphing calculator to find this point.

This graph is drawn using the TI-83 Plus and the vertex is determined by tracing. The vertex is at $(-29.3, 29\,993)$. So, the population was at its lowest level around 28.8 years before 2000, or around 1971.

Extra Practice

16. Solve each equation.

(a) $x^2 - x - 30 = 0$ (b) $x^2 - 4x - 32 = 0$ (c) $x^2 + 12x + 35 = 0$

(d) $x^2 + 4x = 21$ (e) $-5x = x^2 - 36$ (f) $x^2 = 10x - 25$

(g) $6x^2 + 2 = 7x$ (h) $9x - 4 = -9x^2$ (i) $3x^2 - 39x = -126$

17. Determine all the values of x for each value of y.

(a) $y = x^2 + x - 3$ for $y = 27$ (b) $y = x^2 + 7x - 9$ for $y = -21$

(c) $y = 2x^2 - x + 20$ for $y = 23$ (d) $y = 6x^2 - 13x + 1$ for $y = -5$

18. Graph each relation in question 17 and confirm the values of x that you found for the given values of y.

19. Boris throws a ball vertically upward from the top of a cliff. The height of the ball above the base of the cliff is approximated by the model $h = 65 + 10t - 5t^2$, where h is the height in metres and t is the time in seconds.
(a) How high is the cliff?
(b) How long does it take for the ball to reach a height of 50 m above the base of the cliff?
(c) After how many seconds does the ball hit the ground?

20. Helga owns a campground, and she has installed a rectangular swimming pool measuring 10 m by 20 m. She wants to put a wooden deck of uniform width around the pool.
(a) Helga has budgeted $1920 to spend on the deck and knows that construction costs are $30/m². What is the widest that the deck can be?
(b) Helga decides that the deck she can build with $1920 is not big enough, so she budgets $6000 for the deck. How wide can the deck be now?

Chapter 3 Summary

In this chapter you studied quadratic relationships and saw that they are better described by a curve of best fit than a line of best fit. You can use finite difference tables to determine whether a relationship is best represented by a linear expression, a quadratic expression, or some other type of algebraic expression.

The graph of a quadratic relationship is called a **parabola**. The axis of symmetry of a parabola passes through its vertex, and is the perpendicular bisector of the line segment that joins the zeros. If the relationship is quadratic and the zeros and optimal value are known, the algebraic relationship can be determined. The relationship's equation can be expressed in factored form $y = a(x - s)(x - t)$, where s and t are the zeros, or x-intercepts of the parabola.

To find a quadratic curve of best fit for a set of data, you can use the quadratic regression feature of a graphing calculator. The calculator will give the regression equation in standard form, $y = ax^2 + bx + c$. An equation in standard form can be converted into factored form if it can be factored.

Analyzing and Applying Quadratic Models

1. Determine, without graphing, which type of relationship best models each table of values: linear, quadratic, or neither.

(a)

x	−1	0	1	2	3
y	1	2	−3	−14	−31

(b)

x	−2	−1	0	1	2
y	−10	−2	−4	4	22

(c)

x	0	2	4	6	8
y	3	4	5	6	7

(d)

x	0	1	2	3	4
y	10	7	3	5	−1

2. The zeros of a quadratic relation are −3 and 9. The second differences are positive.
  (a) Explain whether the optimal value will be a maximum or a minimum.
  (b) What value of the independent variable will produce the optimal value?
  (c) Explain whether the optimal value is a negative or positive value.

3. (a) Points $(-9, 0)$ and $(19, 0)$ lie on the curve of a parabola. What is the axis of symmetry for the parabola?
  (b) What are the zeros of the parabola?
  (c) The optimal value of the parabola is -28. Write the algebraic expression of the parabola in standard form.

4. Sketch each graph, using the x-intercepts and the optimal value as reference points. Clearly identify the x-intercepts and vertex.
  (a) $y = (x - 6)(x + 2)$ **(b)** $y = (4 + x)(6 - x)$

5. Expand and simplify each expression.
  (a) $(2x - 3)(5x + 2)$ **(b)** $(5a + 2b)(3a - 4b)$ **(c)** $-5(x - 6)(2x + 7)$

6. Factor each expression.
  (a) $x^2 - 9x + 14$ **(b)** $16x^2 - 25$
  (c) $6x^2 + 5x - 4$ **(d)** $2x^2 + 10x + 12$

7. Solve each equation.

    (a) $x^2 + 4x - 21 = 0$ **(b)** $x^2 + 12 = -8x$ **(c)** $6x^2 = 5 - 13x$

8. A toy rocket sitting on a tower is launched vertically upward. The table shows its height, h, in metres, at t seconds.

t (s)	0	1	2	3	4	5	6	7	8
h (m)	16	49	57	85	88	81	64	37	0

    (a) Justify the choice of a quadratic expression to model this data.

    (b) Without graphing technology, make a scatter plot for the data. Manually fit a quadratic curve of best fit to the data. Use the graph to write a quadratic expression to model the data.

    (c) Use your expression from (b) to answer these questions.

        i. How high is the tower?

        ii. When does the rocket reach its maximum height?

        iii. What is the maximum height that the rocket reaches?

        iv. How long did the flight last?

    (d) Use graphing technology to find an equation for the curve of best fit for the data. Compare the answers for (b) to the answers found using technology.

9. The population of Steelsville is modelled by the equation $P = 6t^2 + 110t + 3000$, where P is the population and t is the time in years. When $t = 0$, the year is 2000.

    (a) What was the population in 2000?

    (b) What will be the population in 2020?

    (c) What was the population in 1994?

    (d) When will the population be 32 000?

    (e) Explain why the population can never be 0 under this model.

10. A ticket to the school dance is $6 and usually 250 students attend. The dance committee knows that for every $1 increase in the price of a ticket, 25 fewer students attend the dance. What ticket price maximizes revenue?

Chapter

4

Graphing Quadratic Relations and Using Them as Models

Quadratic relations are used as mathematical models for many real-life situations, such as the design of satellite dishes, headlights, and bridge supports. Quadratic models can show trends and provide predictions about data relationships. They are also used to solve problems of maximizing a quantity such as revenue or area, or minimizing the amount of material used or the cost of production.

For example, the path of any projectile, whether it is a tennis ball, a baseball, or a model rocket is a parabola. With quadratic modelling, you can find the maximum height of the projectile or the time when it will hit the ground.

In this chapter you will

- investigate properties of quadratic relations and how they relate to graphs

- use the symmetry properties of a parabola to write its equation in vertex form

- use the algebraic method called *completing the square* to write a quadratic relation in vertex form

- graph quadratic relations

- solve quadratic equations that cannot be factored using the quadratic formula

- find the roots of quadratic equations and the maximum or minimum values of quadratic relations

- learn how to choose the best method to solve a quadratic problem

For connections to this chapter, visit **www.math.nelson.com**.

339

The Chapter Problem

Trends in the Smoking Habits of Canada's Youth

Health Canada is a branch of the federal government that develops health policy, enforces health regulations, and promotes disease prevention and healthy living. One of the responsibilities of Health Canada is to conduct research into areas that affect the health of all Canadians. Researchers collect data about important health issues, such as smoking. Then the data must be analyzed so that a plan of action can be developed. In analyzing the data, statisticians use their knowledge of mathematical relations to draw conclusions and make predictions about the future.

Scientists have found more than 4000 different chemicals in tobacco smoke, more than 50 of which are known to cause cancer. Smoking kills more than 38 000 Canadians each year—four times more than AIDS, traffic accidents, suicide, murder, fires, and accidental poisoning combined. A person who smokes a pack a day will have spent $30 000 on cigarettes by the time they are 30, and over $100 000 by the time they are 65.

In recent years, Health Canada has tried to increase awareness of the health risks involved in smoking. Cigarette packages now carry information about the hazards of smoking, but do these messages have any impact on young people?

From the table, answer the following questions about smoking among 15- to 19-year-olds.

(a) When was smoking among males at a minimum?

(b) When was smoking among females at a minimum?

(c) When were there equal percentages of male and female smokers?

(d) What is the current trend in the smoking habits of Canadian youth?

(e) Is Health Canada's initiative of warning labels on cigarette packages having an impact?

After certain lessons, you will be asked questions about this problem to help you develop your solution. Keep a record of your work in a project folder or computer file, so that you can provide a full solution at the end of the chapter.

For help with this problem, see pages 356, 381, 394, and 407.

Percentage of 15- to 19-Year-Old Canadians Who Smoke

Year	Males (%)	Females (%)
1981	43.4	41.7
1983	39.6	40.5
1985	26.7	27.7
1986	25.2	27.0
1989	22.6	23.5
1991	22.6	25.6
1994	27.3	28.9
1995	28.5	29.5
1996	29.1	31.0

Source: Health Canada

Challenge 1

The world population is growing quickly. This table shows the world population for each decade during the 20th century. Many organizations, like the United Nations, make predictions about what the population will be in the future. Construct an algebraic model of population growth and use it to predict the population in 2050. Do some research to compare your prediction with those of the United Nations and other organizations.

Year	World Population (billions)
1900	1.65
1910	1.75
1920	1.86
1930	2.07
1940	2.30
1950	2.52
1960	3.02
1970	3.70
1980	4.44
1990	5.27
1998	5.90
1999	6.00

Source: United Nations Population Division

Challenge 2

A **locus** is a set of points that satisfy one or more conditions. For example, the locus of points that are 5 units from the fixed point $Q(0, 0)$ is the set of all points $P(x, y)$ that are on the circle with centre $Q(0, 0)$ and a radius of 5. In chapter 2, using the distance formula and the Pythagorean theorem, you found the algebraic relation that models this locus of points: $x^2 + y^2 = 25$.

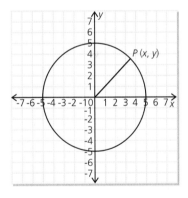

For this challenge, investigate the locus of points $P(x, y)$ that are the same distance from the point $Q(0, 4)$ and from the line $y = 0$ (the x-axis). The special fixed point, $(0, 4)$ in this case, is called the **focus,** and the fixed line $y = 0$ is called the **directrix**. The focus plays an important role in mirrors, telescopes, satellite dishes, light reflectors, and lenses. The focus and directrix are shown on this graph, along with locus points P_1, $P_2(0, 2)$, and $P(x, y)$. Find the algebraic relation that models this locus.

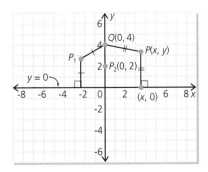

To complete these Challenges, you may need to discuss a research plan with your teacher or other students. You may also need to research outside the classroom.

In this chapter, you will

- factor and expand algebraic expressions
- solve second-degree equations
- graph parabolas by hand using several techniques
- model situations using algebraic expressions
- draw the curve of best fit for a set of data
- find the equation of the curve in various forms

These exercises will help you warm up for the work ahead.

1. Verify whether the point is on the graph of $y = -2x^2 - 5x + 22$.
   (a) $(-4, 10)$ (b) $(-1, 29)$ (c) $(\frac{3}{2}, 10)$

2. How is the quadratic equation $0 = (x - 2)(x + 2)$ related to the quadratic relation $y = (x - 2)(x + 2)$?

3. The zeros of a quadratic relation are given. Find the x-coordinate of the vertex.
   (a) $1, 5$ (b) $-2, 8$
   (c) $3, 8$ (d) $-2.3, 8.4$
   (e) $-\frac{4}{3}, -\frac{5}{2}$ (f) $-7, -7$

4. Express each quadratic relation in standard (expanded) form.
   (a) $y = (x + 4)(x + 5)$
   (b) $y = (2x - 3)(x + 2)$
   (c) $y = -3(x - 4)(x + 7)$
   (d) $y = (x + 5)^2$
   (e) $y = -5x(x - 1)$
   (f) $y = 2(x + 3)^2 - 6$

5. State if the relation is linear, quadratic, or neither. Justify your answer.
   (a) $y = 2x - 7$
   (b) $y = 3x^2 + 5$

   (c) $y = -2x^2 - 4x + 9$
   (d) $3x - 4y = 12$
   (e) $y = 2^x + 3$
   (f) $y = (x - 4)(x + 2)$
   (g) $y = -3x(x - 4)$
   (h) $y = \sqrt{x} + 2$
   (i) $x^2 + y^2 = 36$

6. Express each quadratic relation in fully factored form.
   (a) $y = 2x^2 - 8x$
   (b) $y = x^2 + 5x + 6$
   (c) $y = x^2 - 4x - 60$
   (d) $y = x^2 - 8x + 16$
   (e) $y = 3x^2 - 9x - 30$
   (f) $y = w^2 - 36$
   (g) $y = 3x^2 + 14x + 8$
   (h) $y = 4x^2 - 10x + 25$
   (i) $y = 50x^2 - 18$

7. Find the roots of each quadratic equation.
   (a) $0 = (x + 5)(x - 3)$
   (b) $0 = 2(x - 4)(x + 1)$
   (c) $0 = -4x(x + 3)$
   (d) $0 = x^2 - 10x$
   (e) $0 = x^2 - 2x - 35$
   (f) $x^2 = 16$
   (g) $0 = (w - 4)^2$
   (h) $x^2 + 3x = 18$
   (i) $0 = x^2 - 10$

8. Find the quadratic relation
   (a) that has zeros at -3 and 7, and passes through $(1, 12)$
   (b) that has zeros at -2 and -2, and passes through $(0, -12)$

9. For each quadratic relation,
   i. find the zeros
   ii. find the coordinates of the vertex
   iii. use the information from (i) and (ii) to sketch the graph of the relation on graph paper
   (a) $y = (x - 2)(x + 4)$
   (b) $y = (x - 1)(x - 4)$
   (c) $y = -2(x + 1)(x - 3)$
   (d) $y = x(x + 3)$
   (e) $y = (x - 2)^2$
   (f) $y = \frac{1}{2}(x + 2)(x + 6)$

10. Find the quadratic relation that models the graph.
   (a)
   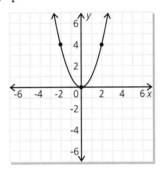
   (b)
   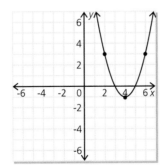

11. A ball bounces off the ground and a sensor records its height from the time it first hits the ground until it returns to the ground again.

Time (s)	0	1	2	3	4	5
Height (m)	0	15	20	20	15	0

(a) Use a difference table to determine if the data represents a linear relation or a quadratic relation.
(b) Create a scatter plot and draw the line or curve of best fit.
(c) What is the maximum height the ball reaches?
(d) When does the ball hit the ground?
(e) Find the algebraic relation that models the data.
(f) What is the ball's height after 2.5 s?

12. A local bowling alley charges $5 and averages 400 customers on Friday nights. Over the past several months, the manager changed the cover charge several times to see how it affected the number of customers. The manager found that for every increase of $0.50 in the cover charge, the number of customers decreased by 25. Write an algebraic expression in terms of one variable to represent the alley's revenue on a Friday night.

13. Write the coordinates of $\triangle A' B' C'$ after each transformation of $\triangle ABC$ has been applied. (Start from the original $\triangle ABC$ each time.)

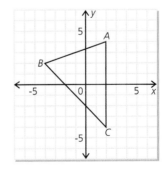

(a) translation 6 units left and 2 units up
(b) reflection in the x-axis
(c) translation 4 units right and 3 units down
(d) reflection in the y-axis

4.1 Quadratic Dental Models

Most mammals, including humans, have four kinds of specialized teeth:

- *incisors,* chisel-like teeth for cutting

- *canines* and *premolars,* for gripping and tearing

- *molars,* for crushing and breaking

Dentists and anthropologists both describe the arrangement of human teeth as a **parabolic dental arcade**.

You can find a quadratic relation for your own dental arcade. To do this, you will need a piece of clean paper, a piece of graph paper, and a graphing calculator that can do quadratic regression.

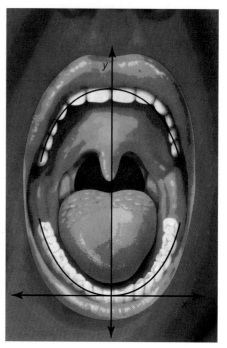

Think, Do, Discuss

1. Carefully put the blank piece of paper in your mouth and bite down to make an impression of your teeth—including both the front and back teeth.

2. On the impression you created, use a dark marker to draw a parabola that passes through the centre of your bite.

3. On a piece of graph paper, create a set of *x-* and *y*-axes. Put the graph paper over the impression of your bite, so that the vertex of the parabola that you drew is at (0, 0). Make the *y*-axis the axis of symmetry. Trace the parabola on the graph paper.

4. Choose ten points on the parabola and estimate their coordinates as accurately as you can.

5. Using a graphing calculator, enter the coordinates of your points into a list. Enter the *x*-coordinates in L1 and the *y*-coordinates in L2

6. Use the calculator to create a scatter plot. Use quadratic regression (**QuadReg**) to find the quadratic relation that best models the data.

7. Describe how well the quadratic model fits the data for your bite.

8. Compare your model with several classmates' models. Are they the same or different?

9. Is "parabolic dental arcade" a good name for your bite? Explain.

Francine manages the community centre, where there is a teen dance every week. The centre holds a maximum of 600 people. Francine knows that if she charges too much, only a few teens will attend, and if she charges too little, more students will attend but the total revenue may decrease. Over a three-month period, she varied the admission price to see what effect it has on the number of teens who attend and the total revenue. Francine collected this data.

Ticket Price, t	Tickets Sold, n	Revenue ($), R
$3.00	420	
$3.50	390	
$4.50	330	
$5.50	270	
$6.00	240	
$6.50	210	
$7.50	150	

What price should Francine charge to maximize her revenue?

Think, Do, Discuss

1. Make a scatter plot showing the relation between the ticket price t and the number of tickets sold n. Which is the independent variable? Which is the dependent variable? What type of algebraic relation seems to exist between the ticket price and the number of tickets sold? Confirm your answer using finite differences.

2. Complete the table in your notebook by calculating the revenue for each ticket price. On a new scatter plot, plot the relation between ticket price t and revenue R. What type of relation seems to exist between the ticket price and the revenue? Confirm your answer using finite differences. Complete the graph by drawing the curve of best fit.

3. How confident are you that your curve of best fit passes through the actual vertex of this relation? Estimate the coordinates (h, k) of the vertex. What do the coordinates represent?

4. How does the graph of this relation differ from the quadratic relations you worked with in chapter 3?

5. What would you have to do to each revenue value in your table of values and to each point on the graph to make the vertex lie on the horizontal axis (the t-axis)? Adjust your table and graph to reflect this.

6. What are the coordinates of the new vertex? What is the axis of symmetry? In chapter 3, you learned that you can find the equation of a quadratic curve of best fit if you know the zeros of the relation and one other point on the curve. What are the zeros of the new graph?

7. Find the equation of this new curve using the zeros and the coordinates of one other point from your adjusted table.

8. Now adjust the table of values so the graph is back to where it started. What can you conclude about the equation of the original graph? Adjust your equation from question 7 to write the equation that would do this.

9. With your graphing calculator, use quadratic regression on the scatter plot to find an algebraic model for the revenue in terms of the ticket price. Is it a good fit? Justify your answer.

10. Expand and simplify the equation you found in question 8 and compare it to the regression equation. What do you notice? What kind of relation is represented by $y = a(x - h)^2 + k$?

11. The equation you found in question 8 represents a quadratic relation.
    (a) What information does this form of the equation give you?
    (b) What information does the factored form give you?
    (c) Which form is more useful in thinking about the relation between revenue and ticket price? Why?

12. What ticket price will produce the greatest revenue for the community centre? What will the revenue be at this price?

Focus 4.2

Key Ideas

- The expression $y = a(x - h)^2 + k$ defines a quadratic relation.

- The graph of $y = a(x - h)^2 + k$ is a vertical translation of $y = a(x - h)^2$ by k units.

- When a quadratic relation is in the form $y = a(x - h)^2 + k$, the coordinates of the vertex of the corresponding parabola are (h, k). As a result, $y = a(x - h)^2 + k$ is called the **vertex form** of a quadratic relation.

- If the coordinates of the vertex (h, k) are known, you can write the quadratic relation in vertex form by substituting h and k into $y = a(x - h)^2 + k$. To find the value of a, substitute the coordinates of another point that satisfies the relation into the equation, then solve for a.

- If $a > 0$, the parabola opens upward. If $a < 0$, the parabola opens downward.

- A quadratic relation in vertex form $y = a(x - h)^2 + k$ can be converted to standard form $y = ax^2 + bx + c$ by expanding and collecting like terms.

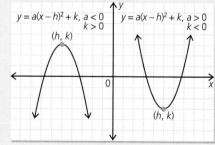

Example 1

Find the vertex, the axis of symmetry, the direction of opening, and the number of zeros for the graph of the quadratic relation.

(a) $y = -\frac{1}{2}(x - 5)^2 - 3$

Solution

The relation is in vertex form. The coordinates of the vertex are $(5, -3)$. The axis of symmetry is $x = 5$, and the parabola opens downward, since $a < 0$. Because the vertex is below the x-axis and the parabola opens downward, the relation has no zeros.

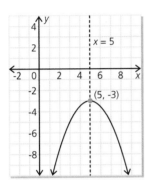

(b) $y = 2(x + 3)^2 - 7$

Solution

First, rewrite the relation in vertex form, $y = 2(x - (-3))^2 - 7$. The coordinates of the vertex are $(-3, -7)$. The axis of symmetry is $x = -3$, and the parabola opens upward, since $a > 0$. The vertex is below the x-axis and the parabola opens upward, so you know the relation has two different zeros.

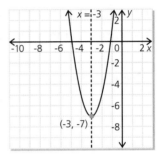

Example 2

A ball is hit into the air. Its height H (in metres) after t seconds is $H = -5(t - 4)^2 + 120$.

(a) In which direction does the parabola open? How do you know?

(b) What are the coordinates of the vertex? What does the vertex represent in this situation?

(c) From what height was the ball hit?

(d) Find one other point on the curve and interpret its meaning.

Solution

(a) The parabola opens downward because $a = -5$, which is negative.

(b) The coordinates of the vertex (h, k) are $(4, 120)$. In this situation, the position of the vertex means that the ball reached its maximum height, 120 m, after 4 s.

(c) The ball was hit at $t = 0$. Substitute this value into the equation and solve for H.

$$H = -5(0 - 4)^2 + 120$$
$$H = -5(16) + 120$$
$$H = -80 + 120$$
$$H = 40$$

The ball was hit from a height of 40 m.

(d) To find another point on the curve, substitute a reasonable value for t and solve for H. At $t = 3$, you know that the ball is still moving up (it has not reached the vertex yet).

$$H = -5(3 - 4)^2 + 120$$
$$H = -5(-1)^2 + 120$$
$$H = -5 + 120$$
$$H = 115$$

After 3 s, the ball is 115 m high.

Example 3

A parabola passes through the point $(-5, 6)$ and has vertex $(-3, -10)$. Find its equation in vertex form and in standard form.

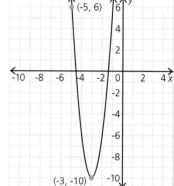

Solution

Since the vertex is given, you can use vertex form:

$y = a(x - h)^2 + k$ Vertex is at $(-3, -10)$, so $h = -3$ and $k = -10$.

$y = a(x - (-3))^2 - 10$ Substitute $h = -3$ and $k = -10$.

$6 = a(-5 + 3)^2 - 10$ Substitute $x = -5$ and $y = 6$ from the given point.

$6 = a(-2)^2 - 10$ Expand and solve for a.

$6 = 4a - 10$

$16 = 4a$

$a = 4$

The equation of the parabola in vertex form is $y = 4(x + 3)^2 - 10$.

Expand to express the equation in standard form.

$y = 4(x + 3)^2 - 10$

$y = 4(x + 3)(x + 3) - 10$ Multiply the binomials.

$y = 4(x^2 + 6x + 9) - 10$ Distribute and collect like terms.

$y = 4x^2 + 24x + 36 - 10$ Simplify.

$y = 4x^2 + 24x + 26$

The equation of the parabola in standard form is $y = 4x^2 + 24x + 26$.

Example 4

The table shows how many new cars were sold in Canada from 1982 to 1992.

Year	1982	1983	1984	1985	1986	1987	1988	1989	1990	1991	1992
New Cars Sold (000s)	718	841	971	1135	1102	1061	1056	985	885	873	798

Source: Statistics Canada

(a) Draw a scatter plot and the curve of best fit.

(b) Estimate the coordinates of the vertex and find an algebraic relation that models the data.

(c) Use the algebraic model to predict how many new cars were sold in 1994.

(d) How well does the model work to predict sales in the year 2000 and beyond?

(e) Check the accuracy of your model using quadratic regression on your graphing calculator.

Solution

(a)

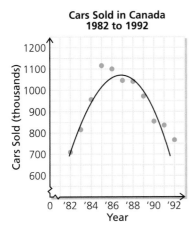

Cars Sold in Canada 1982 to 1992

(b) From the graph, the vertex is close to (1987, 1075). Substitute in the general vertex form:

$$y = a(x - h)^2 + k$$
$$y = a(x - 1987)^2 + 1075$$

Point (1988, 1060) seems to be on the curve of best fit. Use its coordinates to find a.

$$1060 = a(1988 - 1987)^2 + 1075$$
$$1060 = a(1)^2 + 1075$$
$$1060 = a + 1075$$
$$1060 - 1075 = a$$
$$-15 = a$$

The relation $y = -15(x - 1987)^2 + 1075$ models the data.

(c) Substitute $x = 1994$ in the algebraic model.

$$y = -15(x - 1987)^2 + 1075$$
$$y = -15(1994 - 1987)^2 + 1075$$
$$y = -15(7)^2 + 1075$$
$$y = -15(49) + 1075$$
$$y = 340$$

According to the model, 340 000 cars were sold in 1994.

(d) Substitute $x = 2000$ in the algebraic model.

$$y = -15(x - 1987)^2 + 1075$$
$$y = -15(2000 - 1987)^2 + 1075$$
$$y = -15(13)^2 + 1075$$
$$y = -15(169) + 1075$$
$$y = -1460$$

The model indicates that $-1\ 460\ 000$ cars will be sold in 2000. This result is unrealistic; obviously the number of cars sold cannot be negative. The model is only appropriate for the years $1982 - 1992$.

(e) Enter the data into L1 and L2, then create a scatter plot. Now use quadratic regression.

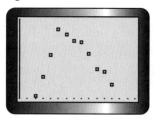 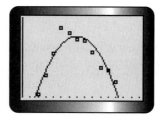

The graphing technology gives the relation $y = -13.4x^2 + 53\ 375.2x - 53\ 026\ 694.7$. In standard form, the model from (b) is $y = -15x^2 - 59\ 610x - 59\ 221\ 460$. These models are similar, so the model drawn from the original scatter plot seems reasonable.

Did You Know?

Combinatorics is a branch of mathematics that often involves finding the best combination of a set of circumstances. For instance, suppose a saleswoman living in city A has to drive to cities B, C, D, E, F, and G, and then return home. The distances between the cities are shown (not to scale). What is the shortest route?

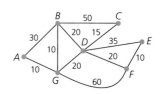

Is there a general formula that could be used for any number of cities and set of distances?

Practise, Apply, Solve 4.2

1. For the relation $y = -3(x + 5)^2 - 4$,
   (a) find the coordinates of the vertex
   (b) find the equation of the axis of symmetry
   (c) find the direction of opening
   (d) sketch the graph

2. For each quadratic relation, find
   i. the coordinates of the vertex
   ii. the equation of the axis of symmetry
   iii. the direction of opening

   (a) $y = (x - 2)^2 + 5$ **(b)** $y = -4(x + 3)^2 - 2$ **(c)** $y = 2(x - 4)^2$

   (d) $y = x^2$ **(e)** $y = -3x^2 + 2$ **(f)** $y = -(x + 7)^2 + 4$

3. Express each quadratic relation in standard form (also called expanded form).

   (a) $y = (x - 2)^2$ **(b)** $y = 3(x + 4)^2$ **(c)** $y = (x - 3)^2 + 3$

   (d) $y = -2(x + 1)^2$ **(e)** $y = 4(x - 1)^2 - 6$ **(f)** $y = -\frac{2}{3}(x + 3)^2 - 5$

4. In each of your answers to question 3, compare the coefficient of the x^2-term in standard form to the coefficient a in vertex form $y = a(x - h)^2 + k$. What do you notice about the coefficients?

5. Find the quadratic relation in vertex form $y = a(x - h)^2 + k$.
   (a) $a = 2$, vertex at $(0, 3)$ **(b)** $a = -3$, vertex at $(2, 0)$
   (c) $a = -1$, vertex at $(3, -2)$ **(d)** $a = 0.5$, vertex at $(-3.5, 18.3)$

6. Which of these points are on the parabola $y = 2(x - 1)^2 + 5$?
   (a) $(2, 7)$
   (b) $(4, 13)$
   (c) $(0, 5)$
   (d) $(-2, 23)$
   (e) $(-1, 13)$

B

7. Find, in vertex form, the equation of the quadratic relation
   (a) with vertex at $(0, 3)$, passing through $(2, -5)$
   (b) with vertex at $(2, 0)$, passing through $(5, 9)$
   (c) with vertex at $(-3, 2)$, passing through $(-1, 14)$
   (d) with vertex at $(5, -3)$, passing through $(1, -8)$

8. Use the symmetric properties of a parabola to find another point that satisfies each relation in question 7.

9. For each equation,
   i. find the vertex
   ii. find two other points that satisfy the equation
   iii. use the information from (i) and (ii) to graph the relation on graph paper

   (a) $y = x^2 - 5$ **(b)** $y = (x + 3)^2$ **(c)** $y = (x - 2)^2 - 5$

   (d) $y = -3x^2 + 12$ **(e)** $y = 2(x + 1)^2 - 5$ **(f)** $y = -\frac{1}{2}(x - 3)^2 + 8$

10. Find the equation of the parabola, in vertex form.

(a)

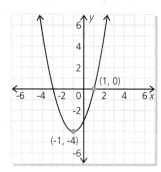

(b)

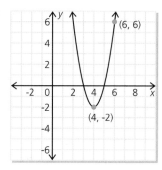

(c)

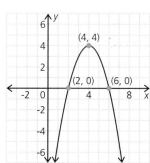

(d)

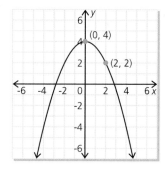

11. A parabola has zeros -3 and 7 and passes through point $(5, 36)$.
   (a) Find the equation of the parabola in the form $y = a(x - s)(x - t)$.
   (b) Write the equation in standard form.
   (c) Find the coordinates of the vertex.
   (d) Write the equation in vertex form.

12. Find the equation, in vertex form, of the quadratic relation with zeros at -2 and 8 and a y-intercept of 8.

13. A rock arch was produced by thousands of years of erosion. It is 10 m across at the base and 8 m high at the centre. Find an algebraic expression, in vertex form, that models the shape of the arch.

14. Create a table of values to help you draw the graph of $y = 2x^2 - 4x$.

    (a) Find the x-intercepts of the parabola.

    (b) Use the graph to find the vertex of the parabola.

    (c) Verify that the midpoint of the zeros gives the x-coordinate of the vertex.

    (d) If the point (4, 16) is on the parabola, what other point has a y-coordinate of 16?

    (e) Write the equation of the parabola in vertex form.

15. **Knowledge and Understanding:** One of the maintenance staff finds a tennis ball on the school roof and throws it to the ground below. The table gives the ball's height above the ground as it moves through the air.

Time (s)	0	0.5	1.0	1.5	2.0	2.5	3.0
Height (m)	5.0	11.25	15.0	16.25	15.0	11.25	5.0

    (a) Does the data appear to be linear or quadratic?

    (b) Create a scatter plot and draw the quadratic curve of best fit.

    (c) Estimate the coordinates of the vertex.

    (d) Find, in vertex form, an algebraic relation that models this data.

    (e) Use your model to predict the height of the ball at 2.75 s and at 1.25 s.

    (f) How effective is the model for values of time greater than 3.5 s? Explain.

    (g) Check the accuracy of your model using quadratic regression.

16. This table shows the TV viewing habits of male adults from 1988 to 1997.

    (a) Does the data appear to be linear or quadratic?

    (b) Create a scatter plot and draw the quadratic curve of best fit.

    (c) Estimate the coordinates of the vertex.

    (d) Find, in vertex form, an algebraic expression that models this relation.

    (e) Use your model to predict how many minutes per day an adult male will watch TV in 2010.

    (f) Use your model to predict how many minutes per day an adult male watched TV in 1970.

    (g) Check the accuracy of your model using quadratic regression.

Average Minutes of TV Viewing Per Day (Male Adults)

Year	TV Viewing Time (min)
1988	239
1989	238
1990	231
1991	241
1992	242
1993	244
1994	242
1995	242
1996	238
1997	236

Source: Nielsen Media Research

17. A chain of ice cream stores sells a total of $840 of ice cream cones per day, at $3.50 each. Market research shows this trend in revenue as the price of an ice cream cone is decreased:

Price ($)	3.50	3.00	2.50	2.00	1.50	1.00	0.50
Revenue ($)	840	2520	3600	4080	3960	3240	1920

(a) Create a scatter plot and draw the quadratic curve of best fit.
(b) Find, in vertex form, an algebraic expression that models this relation.
(c) Use your model to predict the revenue that would be produced at a price of $2.25.
(d) What should the price be set at to maximize revenue?
(e) Check the accuracy of your model using quadratic regression.

18. This table shows how many motorcycles were registered in Canada between 1979 and 1989.

Motorcycles Registered in Canada 1979–1989

Year	Motorcycles (000s)
1979	380
1980	456
1981	431
1982	473
1983	510
1984	507
1985	487
1986	465
1987	448
1988	400
1989	378

Source: Statistics Canada

(a) Create a scatter plot and draw the quadratic curve of best fit.
(b) Find, in vertex form, an algebraic expression that models this relation.
(c) Use your model to predict how many registered motorcycles there were in 1992.
(d) What does the model predict for the year 2000? Is this answer accurate? Explain.
(e) Check the accuracy of your model using quadratic regression

19. Use graphing technology, such as the TI-83 Plus graphing calculator, to graph the parabola $y = -2x^2 + 16x - 24$.

   (a) Find the zeros of the parabola. Describe how you found them.

   (b) Use the zeros and the value of a to express the equation as a product of a and two binomials. Expand and simplify your expression to verify that it is equivalent to the original expression.

   (c) Use your graph to find the coordinates of the vertex. What method did you use?

   (d) Use the vertex and the value of a to express the equation of the relation in vertex form. Expand and simplify your expression to verify that it is equivalent to the original.

20. Communication: What information about the graph do you know immediately when you are given a quadratic relation in

   (a) factored form?   **(b)** vertex form?   **(c)** standard form?

   Justify your answers in each case.

21. A football is punted into the air. Its height h, in metres, after t seconds is $h = -4.9(t - 2.4)^2 + 29$.

   (a) What was the height of the ball when it was kicked?

   (b) What was the maximum height of the ball?

   (c) How high was the ball after 2 s? Was it going up or down at that time? Justify your answer.

   (d) Was the ball still in the air after 5 s? Explain your reasoning.

   (e) Use graphing technology to find the time when the ball hit the ground.

   (f) The ball travelled a horizontal distance d given by $d = 8.3t$. How far down the field did the ball travel?

22. Application: A senior's dance club has a $5 cover charge and averages 300 customers on Friday nights. Over the past several months, the club has changed the cover price several times to see how it affects the number of customers. They have discovered that for every increase of $0.50 in the cover charge, the number of customers decreases by 30.

   Analyze the situation and use an algebraic model to find the cover charge that maximizes revenue.

23. Check Your Understanding: For the quadratic relation $y = a(x - h)^2 + k$,

   (a) what are the coordinates of the vertex?

   (b) what is the equation of the axis of symmetry?

   (c) what will make the graph of the parabola open upward? downward?

C

24. **Thinking, Inquiry, Problem Solving:** Rebecca has a difficult golf shot to make. Her ball is 120 m from the hole. She wants the ball to land 10 m in front of the hole, so it can roll to the hole. A 15 m tree is between her ball and the hole—40 m from the hole and 80 m from her ball.
    (a) With the base of the tree as the origin, write an algebraic expression to model the height of the ball if it just clears the top of the tree.
    (b) Find the coordinates of the vertex of your model. Interpret the position of the vertex.

25. Express the quadratic relation $y = 2x^2 - 8x$ in vertex form.

The Chapter Problem—Trends in the Smoking Habits of Canada's Youth

In this section, you found the connection between the vertex of a quadratic relation and its equation. Apply what you learned to the chapter problem on page 340.

1. Draw a scatter plot of the data for males and another plot for females.
2. Draw a curve of best fit for each scatter plot. What type of curve best fits the data? Check using finite differences.
3. For each graph, estimate the location of the vertex.
4. Write an algebraic expression to model each relation.
5. Determine when the percentage of smokers was at a minimum, for both males and females.

Did You Know?

The Ahmes, or Rhind, Papyrus, from about 1650 B.C.E, is one of the earliest math textbooks. It describes the Egyptian method for multiplying and dividing, solving area problems, and using fractions.

The Ahmes Papyrus has 84 math problems and solutions. It uses a "heap" to refer to an unknown number, or variable. A pair of human legs walking forward represented addition and a pair walking backward meant subtraction.

Using Technology to Investigate Transformations of Quadratics

In this lesson you will investigate how you can transform the graph of $y = x^2$ to obtain the graphs of relations in the form $y = a(x - h)^2 + k$.

Part 1: The Graph of $y = ax^2$ Compared to $y = x^2$

Think, Do, Discuss

1. Press ZOOM 6 to view the standard window on your calculator: the x- and y-axes from -10 to 10.

2. Graph the relation $y = x^2$. What is the axis of symmetry? Where is the vertex? What is the direction of opening?

3. On the same set of axes, graph $y = 2x^2$. How does the shape of the new graph compare to the previous graph of $y = x^2$?

4. Suppose that you are not using graphing technology and you have to create tables of values for the original relation and the new, transformed relation. How will the new table of values differ from the original table of values?

5. Press 2nd GRAPH to examine the tables of values for both graphs. Was your prediction in (4) accurate?

6. Explore what happens to the graph and table of values when you change the coefficient a in ax^2 from 2 to some other number. Try numbers between 0 and 1, greater than 1, and less than 0.

7. (a) What is the same about all of the graphs?

   (b) How can you tell from the equation whether the graph will open upward or downward?

   (c) What values of a make the graph narrower than $y = x^2$? For these cases, would you say that you are vertically stretching or compressing the graph of $y = x^2$ to obtain the graph of $y = ax^2$? Use the table of values to explain why this is so.

   (d) What values of a make the graph of $y = ax^2$ wider than $y = x^2$? For these cases, are you vertically stretching or compressing the graph of $y = x^2$?

Part 2: The Graph of $y = ax^2 + k$
Compared to $y = x^2$

Think, Do, Discuss

1. On your calculator, clear all of the equations from part 1 except $y = x^2$. On the same set of axes as before, graph $y = x^2 - 4$. Compare the shape of this graph to the original.

2. When you subtract 4 from $y = x^2$, what is the effect on the original graph? Examine the tables of values of both relations to see if this is true for every ordered pair.

3. Explore what happens to the graph and the table of values when you change the constant term k in $x^2 + k$ from -4 to other numbers, both positive and negative. What changes on the graph? What stays the same? What effect does the constant term k have on the graph?

4. Explore the effect of varying both a and k on the graph of $y = ax^2 + k$. For each graph done, record the following in your notebook:
   - the equation
   - the direction of opening
   - the width of the parabola opening compared to $y = x^2$
   - whether the graph is stretched or compressed vertically compared to $y = x^2$
   - the vertex
   - the axis of symmetry
   - the number of zeros (x-intercepts)

5. Based on your exploration, how can you use the values of a and k to tell how many x-intercepts the graph of $y = ax^2 + k$ will have?

Part 3: The Graph of $y = a(x - h)^2$
Compared to $y = x^2$

Think, Do, Discuss

1. On your calculator, clear all of the equations from part 2 except $y = x^2$. On the same set of axes, graph $y = (x - 3)^2$. Compare the shape of this graph to the original graph.

2. When you subtract 3 from x in $y = x^2$, what is the effect on the original graph? Examine the tables of values of both relations to see if this is true for every ordered pair.

3. Explore what happens to the graph and the table of values when you change the constant term h in $y = (x - h)^2$ from 3 to several other numbers, both positive and negative. What changes on the graph and what stays the same? What effect does the constant term h have on the graph?

4. Explore the effect of varying both a and h on the graph of $y = a(x - h)^2$. For each graph, record the following in your notebook:

- the equation
- the direction of opening
- the width of the parabola opening compared to $y = x^2$
- whether the graph is stretched or compressed vertically compared to $y = x^2$
- the vertex
- the axis of symmetry
- the number of zeros (*x*-intercepts)

Part 4: The Graph of $y = a(x - h)^2 + k$ Compared to $y = x^2$

1. What would you have to do to the graph of $y = x^2$ to obtain the graph of $y = 3(x - 5)^2 + 4$? Sketch your prediction on a piece of graph paper.

2. On your calculator, clear all of the equations from part 3 except for $y = x^2$. On the same set of axes, graph the relation $y = 3(x - 5)^2 + 4$. Was your prediction correct? How does the shape of the new graph compare to the original graph in step 1?

3. What effect do the three transformations have on the graph of $y = x^2$?

4. Explore the effect of varying a, k, and h in $y = a(x - h)^2 + k$ on the graph of $y = x^2$. For each graph, record the following in your notebook:

- the equation
- the values of a, k, and h
- the direction of opening
- the width of the parabola opening compared to $y = x^2$
- whether the graph is stretched or compressed vertically compared to $y = x^2$
- the vertex
- the axis of symmetry
- the number of zeros (*x*-intercepts)

5. Evaluate the expression $y = 3(x - 5)^2 + 4$ when $x = 7$ and state the order of your calculations. Use this information to list, in the correct order, the three transformations that must be applied to $y = x^2$ to obtain the graph of $y = 3(x - 5)^2 + 4$.

Focus 4.3

Key Ideas

- The relation defined by $y = x^2$ (figure 1) is the simplest quadratic relation. It is the base curve for all quadratic relations.

- The graph of any quadratic relation can be created by altering and repositioning the graph of $y = x^2$. Possible changes include shifting the graph up or down, shifting it left or right, vertically stretching or compressing the graph, or reflecting it about the x-axis. These types of changes are called **transformations.**

- When a quadratic relation is in **vertex form,** $y = a(x - h)^2 + k$, several properties of the graph of the relation are obvious:

  - If $k > 0$, then the graph of $y = x^2$ is translated vertically up by k units. If $k < 0$, then the graph is translated down by k units. If $k = 0$, the graph has one x-intercept (figure 2).

  - If $h > 0$, then the graph of $y = x^2$ is translated horizontally h units to the right. If $h < 0$, then the graph is translated h units to the left (figure 3).

  - If $a > 0$, then the curve opens upward. If $a < 0$, then the graph is reflected about the x-axis and the curve opens downward (figure 4).

  - If $-1 < a < 1$, then the graph of $y = x^2$ is compressed vertically by a factor of $\frac{1}{a}$. The resulting graph has an opening that is wider than $y = x^2$ (figure 5).

  - If $a > 1$ or $a < -1$, then the graph of $y = x^2$ is stretched vertically by a factor of a. The resulting graph has an opening that is narrower than $y = x^2$ (figure 5).

- When you use transformations to graph $y = a(x - h)^2 + k$ from $y = x^2$, apply the transformations in this order:

  (1) translation left or right

  (2) vertical stretch or compression

  (3) reflection about the x-axis

  (4) translation up or down

- If a and k have opposite signs, then the graph has two x-intercepts, or zeros. If a and k have the same signs, then the graph has no x-intercepts.

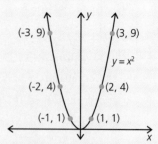

figure 1

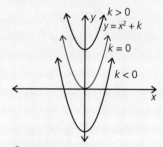

figure 2

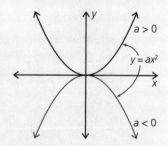

figure 3

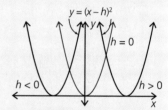

figure 4

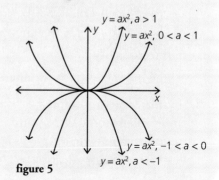

figure 5

Example 1

For each relation,

i. state the vertex

ii. state the axis of symmetry

iii. state the direction in which the parabola opens

iv. use the information from (i) to (iii), plus the properties of $y = x^2$, to graph the relation on graph paper

(a) $y = (x + 2)^2 - 4$ **(b)** $y = -2x^2 + 6$ **(c)** $y = \frac{1}{2}(x - 3)^2 - 1$

Solution

(a) The relation $y = (x + 2)^2 - 4$, or $y = (x - (-2))^2 - 4$, represents a curve with the same shape as $y = x^2$. Each point in the base curve $y = x^2$ has been translated 2 units to the left and 4 units down. The axis of symmetry is $x = -2$; the vertex is at $(-2, -4)$; and the parabola opens upward.

(b) The relation $y = -2x^2 + 6$ represents a curve similar to $y = x^2$, but reflected about the x-axis (so it opens downward). It has been stretched vertically by a factor of 2 and translated up by 6 units. The axis of symmetry is $x = 0$ and the vertex is at $(0, 6)$.

The graph can be drawn from $y = x^2$ by ① multiplying the y-coordinate of each point by -2, and ② translating the resulting point up 6 units.

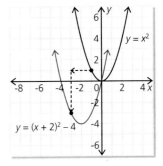
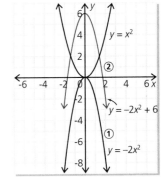

(c) The relation $y = \frac{1}{2}(x - 3)^2 - 1$ represents a parabola that opens upward. Compared to $y = x^2$, it has been compressed vertically by a factor of 2, then translated to the right 3 units and down 1 unit. The axis of symmetry is $x = 3$ and the vertex is at $(3, -1)$.

The graph can be drawn from $y = x^2$ by ① translating each point 3 units to the right, ② multiplying the y-coordinate by $\frac{1}{2}$, then ③ translating the point down 1 unit.

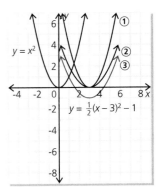

Example 2

(a) Sketch the new graph that results from applying these transformations to
$y = x^2$: ① translate 3 units to the left; ② stretch vertically by a factor of 2;
③ translate up 1 unit.

(b) Find the equation of the new graph.

Solution

(a)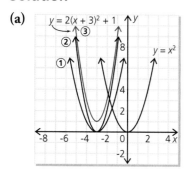

(b) The new parabola has its vertex at $(-3, 1)$. It has been stretched by a factor of 2,
so $a = 2$. The equation is $y = 2(x + 3)^2 + 1$.

Example 3

When a stationary object is released to fall freely, its height h, in
metres, after t seconds is $h = -0.5gt^2 + k$, where g is the
acceleration due to gravity and k is the height from which the object
is dropped. On Earth, $g = 9.8$ m/s². For a charity event, the
principal pays to drop a watermelon from a height of 100 m.

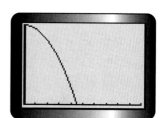

(a) The clock that times the fall of the watermelon runs for 3 s
before the principal releases the watermelon. How does this
change the graph shown? Find the equation of this relation.

(b) On Mars, $g = 3.7$ m/s². Suppose the principal dropped a watermelon from
100 m on Mars. How does the graph for Mars look, compared to the one above?
Find the equation of this relation.

(c) Now, suppose the principal drops another watermelon from a height of 50 m on
Earth. How does the graph change? How does the relation change?

(d) Repeat (c) for Mars.

Solution

(a) Since $g = 9.8$ m/s² on Earth, the basic relation is
$h = -0.5(9.8)t^2 + k$ or $h = -4.9t^2 + k$. If the clock
starts 3 s earlier, the graph shown must be translated 3
units to the right. The new relation is
$h = -4.9(t - 3)^2 + 100$. (It only applies to values of t
that are greater than or equal to 3.)

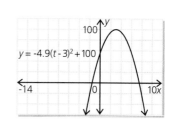

(b) Since $g = 3.7$ m/s^2 on Mars, then $h = -0.5(3.7)t^2 + k$ or $h = -1.85t^2 + k$. The graph shown must be widened, and the object will take longer to hit the ground. The new relation is $h = -1.85t^2 + 100$.

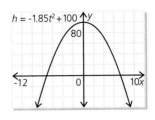
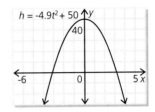

(c) The new graph has the same shape but starts halfway up the vertical axis, at $h = 50$ instead of $h = 100$. The new relation is $h = -4.9t^2 + 50$.

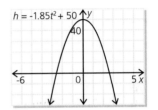

(d) The new graph for Mars is wider than the original and starts at $h = 50$ instead of $h = 100$. The new relation is $h = -1.85t^2 + 50$.

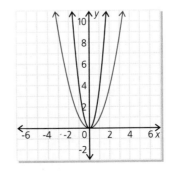

Practice, Apply, Solve 4.3

A

1. Match each graph with the correct equation. The graph of $y = x^2$ is also in each diagram in red.

(a) $y = 4x^2$ **(b)** $y = -3x^2$ **(c)** $y = \frac{2}{3}x^2$ **(d)** $y = -0.4x^2$

i.

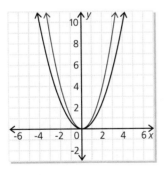

ii.

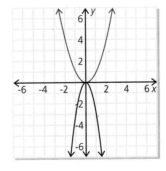

iii.

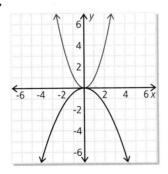

iv.

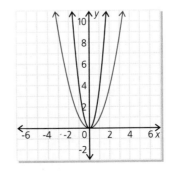

2. Match each graph with the correct equation.

    (a) $y = x^2 + 5$ **(b)** $y = (x + 5)^2$ **(c)** $y = x^2 - 3$ **(d)** $y = (x - 3)^2$

i.

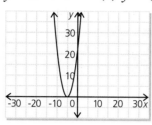

ii.

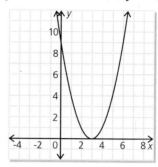

iii.

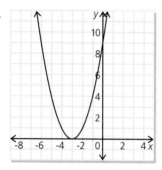

iv.

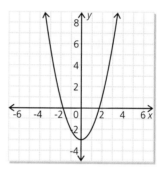

v.

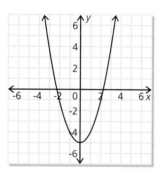

vi.

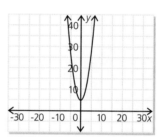

3. Describe the transformations applied to the graph of $y = x^2$ to obtain the graph of each quadratic relation.

    (a) $y = x^2 + 5$ **(b)** $y = (x - 3)^2$ **(c)** $y = -3x^2$

    (d) $y = (x + 7)^2$ **(e)** $y = \frac{1}{2}x^2$

4. Sketch the graph of the relation by hand. Start with the graph of $y = x^2$ and use the appropriate transformations.

    (a) $y = x^2 - 4$ **(b)** $y = (x - 3)^2$ **(c)** $y = x^2 + 2$

    (d) $y = (x + 5)^2$ **(e)** $y = (x + 1)^2 - 2$ **(f)** $y = (x - 5)^2 + 3$

5. The vertex form $y = a(x - h)^2 + k$ was used to graph these screens on the TI-83 Plus. For the set of graphs on each screen, tell which of the variables a, h, and k remained constant and which ones changed. Give possible values for the variables that remained constant.

(a)

h changed

(b)

k + a changed

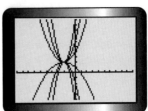

(c)

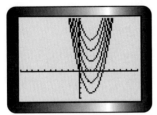

h + k changed

6. Write two different equations, in vertex form, that represent quadratic relations that meet each of the following descriptions.

(a) parabola opens downward

(b) has a narrower opening than $y = x^2$

(c) has a wider opening than $y = -x^2$

(d) axis of symmetry is $x = -5$

B

7. What transformations must you apply to $y = x^2$ to create the new graph? List the transformations in the order you would apply them.

(a) $y = -x^2 + 9$

(b) $y = (x - 3)^2$

(c) $y = (x + 2)^2 - 1$

(d) $y = -x^2 - 6$

(e) $y = -2(x - 4)^2 + 16$

(f) $y = \frac{1}{2}(x + 6)^2 + 12$

(g) $y = -\frac{1}{2}(x + 4)^2 - 7$

(h) $y = 5(x - 4)^2 - 12$

(i) $y = \frac{3}{4}(x - 1)^2 + 5$

8. Sketch the graph of the relation by hand. Start with the graph of $y = x^2$ and use the appropriate transformations. *check key ideas for order*

(a) $y = -x^2 + 4$

(b) $y = -2(x + 3)^2$

(c) $y = \frac{3}{4}x^2 - 7$

(d) $y = \frac{1}{2}(x + 4)^2 - 5$

(e) $y = -3(x - 2)^2 + 12$

(f) $y = -1.5x^2 + 10$

9. Transformations were applied to the graph of $y = x^2$ to obtain the coloured parabolas. Describe the transformations that were applied and use them to write a relation for each coloured parabola.

(a)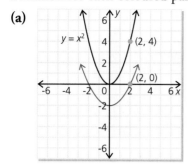

(b)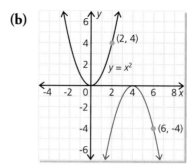

(c)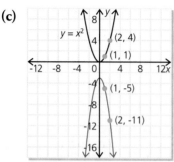

(d)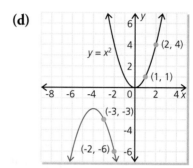

10. Knowledge and Understanding: Find three different equations for parabolas that have a vertex at $(-3, 5)$. Describe how your graphs are different from each other. Sketch graphs of the three relations on the same set of axes.

11. Communication: Without graphing, tell how many zeros (x-intercepts) the quadratic relation has. Explain your answer.

  (a) $y = x^2 - 6$ **(b)** $y = (x + 2)^2 + 4$

  (c) $y = -4(x - 3)^2$ **(d)** $y = \frac{2}{5}(x - 1)^2 - 3$

12. Consider a parabola P that is congruent to $y = x^2$, opens upward, and has its vertex at $(2, -4)$. Now find the equation of a new parabola that results if P is
  (a) stretched vertically by a factor of 5
  (b) compressed by a factor of 2
  (c) translated 2 units to the left
  (d) translated 3 units up
  (e) reflected about the x-axis and translated 2 units to the right and 4 units down

13. Write the relation for a parabola that satisfies each set of conditions.

(a) vertex at $(0, 4)$; opens upward; the same shape as $y = x^2$

(b) vertex at $(5, 0)$; opens downward; the same shape as $y = x^2$

(c) vertex at $(2, -3)$; opens upward; narrower than $y = x^2$

(d) vertex at $(-3, 5)$; opens downward; wider than $y = x^2$

(e) axis of symmetry $x = 4$; opens upward; two distinct zeros; narrower than $y = x^2$

(f) vertex at $(3, -4)$; no zeros; wider than $y = x^2$

14. On a calculator like the TI-83 Plus, enter these equations: $Y_1 = X^2$, $Y_2 = Y_1 - 4$, and $Y_3 = 2*Y_2$.

(a) Use an appropriate WINDOW setting to graph Y_1, Y_2, and Y_3. Find the coordinates of the vertex for Y_3. Write an equation in vertex form for Y_3.

(b) Change Y_2 and Y_3 to $Y_2 = 2*Y_1$ and $Y_3 = Y_2 - 4$. Find the coordinates of the vertex for Y_3. Write an equation in vertex form for Y_3.

(c) Explain why the graph of Y_3 in (a) is different from the one in (b).

(d) Describe the sequence of transformations needed to transform the graph of $y = x^2$ into the graph of $y = 2x^2 - 4$.

15. In chapter 3, you investigated the trajectory of a water balloon launched from a catapult. You were given the height of the balloon at various horizontal distances. In section 3.7, the quadratic regression equation was found to be $y = -0.040x^2 + 2.178x - 0.011$ (rounded to three decimals), where y represents the height of the balloon (in metres) and x represents the horizontal distance. Use a graphing calculator to find the approximate coordinates of the vertex. What do the coordinates of the vertex represent? Express the regression equation in vertex form.

16. Write the relation for a parabola that satisfies each condition.

(a) The graph of $y = x^2$ is reflected about the x-axis, then translated down 7 units.

(b) The graph of $y = x^2$ is stretched vertically by a factor of $\frac{3}{2}$, then translated left 4 units.

(c) The graph of $y = x^2$ is compressed vertically by a factor of 3, then translated up 10 units.

(d) The graph of $y = x^2$ is reflected about the x-axis, stretched vertically by a factor of 2, then translated to the right 5 units and down 8 units.

17. Describe how the graph of $y = 5x^2$ can be translated. For each type of translation, give at least two examples—in different directions—of translated relations derived from $y = 5x^2$. Include examples that show each type of translation by itself and in combination with other translations.

18. Application: The acceleration due to gravity g is 8.9 m/s^2 on Venus, 3.7 m/s^2 on Mars, 10.5 m/s^2 on Saturn, and 11.2 m/s^2 on Neptune. Refer to example 3 and the equation $h = -0.5gt^2 + k$. Describe how the graphs will differ for an object dropped from a height of 200 m on each of the four planets. On which planet will the object be moving fastest when it hits the surface? On which planet will it be moving slowest?

19. Suppose identical objects are released from a height of 500 m on Earth and on Mars. How much longer does it take for the object to descend to 150 m on Mars than it takes on Earth? Remember that acceleration due to gravity is 9.8 m/s^2 on Earth and 3.7 m/s^2 on Mars.

20. Check Your Understanding: If $y = x^2$ is the base curve for these graphs, what equations could be used to produce these screens on a graphing calculator? The scale on both axes is 1 unit per tick mark.

(a)

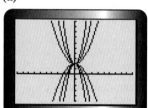

(b)

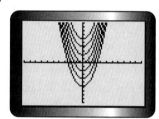

C

21. Thinking, Inquiry, Problem Solving: The equation of a circle with its centre at $(0, 0)$ is $x^2 + y^2 = r^2$.

(a) Explore the effect of varying the constants h and k in the equation $(x - h)^2 + (y - k)^2 = r^2$.

(b) Explore the effect of varying the constants a and b in the equation $ax^2 + by^2 = r^2$.

(c) Explain the roles of a, b, h, and k in determining the shape and position of $a(x - h)^2 + b(y - k)^2 = r^2$.

Did You Know?

Donald W. Foster (b. 1950), an English professor at Vassar College, uses mathematics and probability to identify the authors of literary works. For instance, he has shown that a funeral elegy was probably written by William Shakespeare.

In 1996, the authorship of the anonymous novel *Primary Colors* was hotly debated. Professor Foster used computer analysis to compare writing samples of some 35 journalists and novelists with *Primary Colors*. As he explained in an article in the February 26, 1996, *New York Magazine*, the analysis showed a very high probability that the author was *Newsweek* columnist Joe Klein. At first Klein denied he was the author, but then he admitted that he did write *Primary Colors*, showing that Professor Foster was right.

Using Symmetry to Relate Standard Form to Vertex Form

When you examined the dance problem in section 4.2, you performed a quadratic regression to get an algebraic model of the relationship between the ticket price and revenue. The quadratic regression equation was $y = -60x^2 + 600x$, where y is the revenue and x is the price of a ticket. Using R for revenue and t for ticket price gives $R = -60t^2 + 600t$.

From section 4.3, you know that the vertex form of a quadratic relation, $y = a(x - h)^2 + k$, shows several properties of the graph directly and makes it possible to sketch the graph.

In this section, you will apply factoring and symmetry to a quadratic relation in standard form, $y = ax^2 + bx + c$, so that you can find the vertex and sketch the graph.

Part 1: What the Zeros Tell You About the Vertex

Think, Do, Discuss

1. Consider the revenue equation $R = -60t^2 + 600t$. Compare it to the more general equation $y = ax^2 + bx + c$. In which direction does the graph of this relation open? What is the value of a?

2. Recall that the revenue $R =$ ticket price $\times$ number of tickets sold. If you remove the common factor t from the revenue equation, you get $R = t(-60t + 600)$ or $R = t(600 - 60t)$, where t represents the ticket price in dollars.

   (a) What does the other factor, $600 - 60t$, represent? Recall that the hall holds a maximum of 600 people. What is the significance of the term $-60t$?

   (b) Find the two zeros of the factored revenue equation by letting the revenue equal zero ($R = 0$). What do the two zeros of the revenue equation represent?

   (c) What is the t-coordinate of the point halfway between the two zeros? What is the equation of the axis of symmetry?

3. Use the t-coordinate of the midpoint to find the vertex of $R = -60t^2 + 600t$. What does the R-value represent? What do the coordinates of the vertex represent?

4. Use the vertex and the value of a you found in step 1 to rewrite the revenue equation in vertex form $R = a(t - h)^2 + k$.

5. Verify that the two equations from steps 1 and 4 represent the same graph. (Use a graphing calculator to verify that the maximum revenue is the same as you found in section 4.2.)

Part 2: Finding the Vertex When the Standard Form Can Be Factored ———

The dance organizers want to know what their profit will be. The definition of profit, P, is $P = R - E$, where R is revenue and E is expenses. The revenue equation is $R = -60t^2 + 600t$, where t represents the number of tickets sold. The expenses for each dance are $540, for advertising, printing, security, and staff.

Think, Do, Discuss

1. Express the equation for profit P in terms of ticket price t and the actual expenses.

2. The equation for P has a common factor. Take out the greatest common factor and rewrite the profit equation in fully factored form.

3. Find the zeros. What do the two zeros of the profit equation represent?

4. Find the coordinates of the vertex for this relation, as you did in part 1.

5. Use the vertex, axis of symmetry, and the zeros to draw a sketch of the profit relation.

6. Rewrite the quadratic profit relation in vertex form. Compare this profit equation to the revenue equation. What do you notice?

7. Use technology to graph the revenue equation; the expense equation, $E = 540$; and the profit equation on the same grid. Use the TRACE key on your calculator to find how the y-coordinates are related on the three graphs. Where does the graph of expenses E intersect with the graph of revenue R?

Career: Futurist

Do you ever wonder about the future? As an analyst of world trends, Alvin Toffler (b. 1928) looks at past and present technological developments and tries to predict future trends. In his book *Future Shock,* published in 1970, he predicted a world oil crisis. During the seventies, the world's oil supply was drastically reduced, causing gasoline, home fuel, and oil prices to increase astronomically. He predicted cable TV as well. But not all his predictions were correct; he also thought that people would wear disposable paper clothes.

In *The Third Wave* (1980), Toffler stressed the importance of computers and communications and concluded that information would become more valuable than material resources like oil or iron. How can mathematics help a futurist like Alvin Toffler make predictions?

Part 3: Finding the Vertex by Partial Factoring

The location of the vertex of a quadratic relation is an important piece of information. If the zeros of the quadratic are known, then the vertex can be found. And if a quadratic can be factored, then its zeros are known and therefore the vertex can be found. Can you find the vertex when a quadratic relation cannot be fully factored?

Suppose that the operating expenses for each dance increase from $540 to $817. How does this affect the profit from the dances?

Think, Do, Discuss

1. Find the new profit equation. Can this equation be factored? How can you tell?

2. What effect does changing 540 to 817 have on the graph of the original profit equation?

3. In an earlier revenue problem, you took out a common factor of t from the revenue equation to get $R = t(-60t + 600)$ or $R = t(600 - 60t)$. Do the same thing to the first two terms of the profit equation. This is called taking out a **partial factor**.

4. Recall that for the revenue equation, by letting $R = 0$, you located roots at $t = 0$ and $t = 10$. In the expression $P = t(600 - 60t) - 817$, what is the value of P when t is 0? when t is 10?

5. What do you notice about the value of P when $t = 0$ and $t = 10$? Express this as two points (t_1, P_1) and (t_2, P_2) on the graph. Where is the axis of symmetry in terms of these two points? What do the points represent?

6. What is the t-coordinate of the vertex? What are the coordinates of the vertex and what do they represent?

7. Use the vertex, axis of symmetry, and the two points found in step 5 to draw a rough sketch of the profit equation.

8. What is the coefficient of the t^2 term? Use it, together with the coordinates of the vertex, to rewrite the relation in vertex form.

9. Graph this new profit relation on the graph that you set up in step 7 of part 2. What is common to all three parabolas? What effect does the constant term have on the graphs?

Focus 4.4 ─────────────

Key Ideas

- Given a quadratic relation in the form $y = ax^2 + bx + c$, you can use algebraic techniques to find the vertex and axis of symmetry.

- If the quadratic relation can be **completely factored**, you can find the zeros by setting each of the factors equal to zero, and then solving for x. The axis of symmetry and the x-coordinate of the vertex can be found from the midpoint between the zeros. Substitute this x-value into the relation to find the y-coordinate of the vertex.

- If the quadratic relation $y = ax^2 + bx + c$ cannot be completely factored, you can use **partial factoring** to express it in the form $y = x(ax + b) + c$. This form suggests two points on the graph: $(0, c)$ and $(-\frac{b}{a}, c)$. The axis of symmetry is halfway between these points and has the equation $x = -\frac{b}{2a}$. Substitute $x = -\frac{b}{2a}$ into the relation to find the y-coordinate of the vertex.

- Once you know the coordinates of the vertex, use the value of a from the original equation to express the relation in vertex form $y = a(x - h)^2 + k$.

Example 1

Rewrite the quadratic relation in vertex form, then carefully draw a graph of the relation by hand.

(a) $y = x^2 + 3x - 10$
(b) $y = 2x^2 + 8x + 5$

Solution

(a) The constant a equals 1. The graph will be a parabola that opens upward.

$$y = x^2 + 3x - 10$$
$$y = (x + 5)(x - 2) \quad \text{Factor.}$$
$$0 = (x + 5)(x - 2) \quad \text{Let } y = 0 \text{ to find the zeros.}$$

The zeros are $x = -5$ and $x = 2$.

The equation of the axis of symmetry is $x = \dfrac{-5 + 2}{2} = -\dfrac{3}{2}$.

Substitute $x = -\dfrac{3}{2}$ and solve for y in the original expression.

$$y = \left(-\frac{3}{2}\right)^2 + 3\left(-\frac{3}{2}\right) - 10$$
$$y = \frac{9}{4} - \frac{9}{2} - 10$$
$$y = \frac{9}{4} - \frac{18}{4} - \frac{40}{4}$$
$$y = -\frac{49}{4} \text{ or } -12.25$$

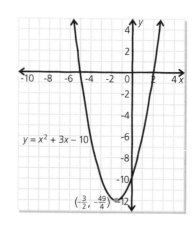

$y = x^2 + 3x - 10$

$\left(-\frac{3}{2}, -\frac{49}{4}\right)$

The vertex is at $\left(-\frac{3}{2}, -\frac{49}{4}\right)$ and the coefficient of x^2 is 1.

In vertex form, the relation is $y = \left(x + \frac{3}{2}\right)^2 - \frac{49}{4}$ or $y = (x + 1.5)^2 - 12.25$.

The parabola has a y-intercept of -10 and zeros at $x = -5$ and $x = 2$.

(b) The expression cannot be completely factored.

$$y = 2x^2 + 8x + 5$$
$$y = x(2x + 8) + 5 \quad \text{Remove a partial factor of } x \text{ from the first two terms.}$$

Find two points with y-coordinate $y = 5$. The points are equidistant from the axis of symmetry.

$$5 = x(2x + 8) + 5$$

Then $x(2x + 8) = 0.$ Solve for x.

$$x = 0 \text{ and } 2x + 8 = 0$$
$$x = 0 \text{ and } x = -4$$

The points $(0, 5)$ and $(-4, 5)$ on the parabola are equidistant from the axis of symmetry, so its equation is

$$x = \frac{0 + (-4)}{2} \qquad \text{To find the axis of symmetry, find the midpoint}$$
$$x = -2 \qquad\qquad \text{between 0 and } -4.$$

Since the parabola is symmetrical, the vertex is on the line $x = -2$.

To find the vertex, substitute $x = -2$ into $y = 2x^2 + 8x + 5$.

$$y = 2(-2)^2 + 8(-2) + 5.$$
$$y = -3$$

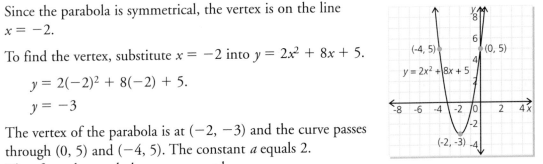

The vertex of the parabola is at $(-2, -3)$ and the curve passes through $(0, 5)$ and $(-4, 5)$. The constant a equals 2. Therefore, the parabola opens upward.

In vertex form, the equation of the parabola is $y = 2(x + 2)^2 - 3$.

Example 2

Find the equation of a parabola with zeros of -3 and 11 and a minimum y-value of -35. Verify your equation by graphing it with technology.

Solution

The zeros are -3 and 11. Therefore, the equation of the axis of symmetry is $x = \frac{-3 + 11}{2}$ or $x = 4$. Since the parabola has a minimum y-value of -35, the vertex is located at $(4, -35)$.

$$y = a(x - 4)^2 - 35$$

To find a, substitute the coordinates of one of the zeros, say $(-3, 0)$.

$$0 = a(-3 - 4)^2 - 35$$
$$0 = 49a - 35$$
$$35 = 49a$$
$$\frac{35}{49} = a$$
$$\frac{5}{7} = a$$

The equation of the parabola is $y = \frac{5}{7}(x - 4)^2 - 35$.

The graph of the equation on a TI-83 Plus calculator confirms that it has a minimum at $(4, -35)$ and x-intercepts at $x = -3$ and $x = 11$.

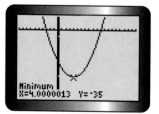

Example 3

The underside of a concrete bridge forms a parabolic arch that is 32 m wide at the water level and 12 m high in the centre. The upper surface of the bridge is horizontal and 48 m wide; the minimum vertical thickness of the concrete is 1.5 m.

(a) Sketch the bridge.

(b) Find an equation that represents the parabolic arch of the bridge.

(c) What is the vertical thickness of the concrete 4 m (horizontally) from the centre of the bridge?

(d) If the water level rises 2 m, how wide will the arch be at the new level?

Solution

(a) To draw the diagram, review the facts.

The top of the road is 1.5 m above the top of the arch, or 13.5 m above the water. The entire bridge is 48 m long or 24 m on each side of the axis. Choose the water level below the bridge as the x-axis and the axis of symmetry of the arch as the y-axis. Since the arch is 32 m wide at the base, the water meets the arch at $(16, 0)$ and $(-16, 0)$. The vertex is 12 m above the water on the y-axis, at $(0, 12)$.

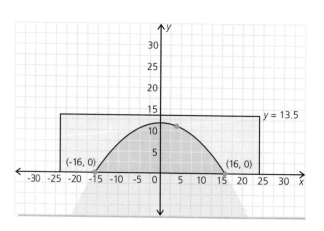

(b) The equation of the arch in vertex form is $y = a(x - 0)^2 + 12$ or $y = ax^2 + 12$.

Point (16, 0) is a point at the base of the arch. Substitute and solve for *a*.

$$0 = a(16)^2 + 12$$
$$0 = 256a + 12$$
$$-12 = 256a$$
$$-\frac{12}{256} = a$$
$$-\frac{3}{64} = a$$

The equation of the arch is $y = -\frac{3}{64}x^2 + 12$.

(c) The height of the top of the bridge is 13.5 m above the water. Find the height of the arch at a point 4 m from the axis of symmetry. Substitute (4, *y*) into the equation.

$$y = -\frac{3}{64}(4)^2 + 12$$
$$y = -\frac{48}{64} + 12$$
$$y = -\frac{3}{4} + 12$$
$$y = 11\frac{1}{4} \text{ or } 11.25$$

The arch at this point is 11.25 m above the water. The vertical thickness of the concrete is $13.5 - 11.25 = 2.25$ m.

(d) If the water level rises 2 m, the *y*-coordinate of a point at the new water level will be 2. Let $y = 2$ and solve for *x*.

$$2 = -\frac{3}{64}x^2 + 12$$
$$-10 = -\frac{3}{64}x^2$$
$$64(-10) = 64\left(-\frac{3}{64}x^2\right)$$
$$-640 = -3x^2$$
$$\frac{640}{3} = x^2$$
$$\sqrt{\frac{640}{3}} = x$$
$$14.6 \doteq x$$

The arch will be 2×14.6 or 29.2 m wide at the new level.

Practise, Apply, Solve 4.4

A

1. Solve the quadratic equation.

    (a) $x(x + 3) = 0$ **(b)** $(w - 2)(w + 7) = 0$

    (c) $(3x - 8)(2x + 5) = 0$ **(d)** $3t(45 - 2t) = 0$

    (e) $4(z - 6)(z + 6) = 0$ **(f)** $-2(x - 3)^2 = 0$

2. Find the zeros of the quadratic relation, then find the x-coordinate of the vertex.

    (a) $y = x^2 + 5x$ **(b)** $y = x^2 - 3x - 10$

    (c) $y = x^2 - 8x + 16$ **(d)** $y = w^2 - 1$

    (e) $E = -t^2 + 19t + 20$ **(f)** $A = 2w^2 - 14w$

    (g) $y = x^2 - 12x - 36$ **(h)** $y = 3x^2 + 6x - 72$

    (i) $y = 4x^2 - 4x - 35$ **(j)** $y = 9x^2 - 18x - 16$

3. For each quadratic relation,

    i. find two points that are equidistant from the axis of symmetry

    ii. find the x-coordinate of the vertex

    iii. find the y-coordinate of the vertex

    iv. use the points and vertices you found to sketch the relation

    (a) $y = (x - 2)(x + 6)$ **(b)** $y = x(x - 2) - 8$

    (c) $y = (x + 3)(x - 2)$ **(d)** $y = x(x + 4) + 2$

    (e) $P = t(-3t + 12) + 5$ **(f)** $y = x(2x - 10) - 3$

B

4. For each quadratic relation,

    i. express the relation in factored form

    ii. find the coordinates of the vertex

    iii. express the relation in vertex form

    iv. sketch the graph

    (a) $y = x^2 - 6x + 5$ **(b)** $y = -2x^2 + 12x - 16$

    (c) $y = \frac{1}{2}x^2 + x - 4$ **(d)** $y = 4x^2 - 12x + 5$

    (e) $y = -3x^2 - 12x$ **(f)** $y = 2x^2 - 4x - 30$

5. For each quadratic relation,

   i. use partial factoring to find two points that are equidistant from the axis of symmetry

   ii. find the coordinates of the vertex

   iii. express the relation in vertex form

   iv. sketch the graph

   (a) $y = x^2 - 6x + 5$ **(b)** $y = x^2 - 4x - 11$

   (c) $y = -2x^2 + 12x - 11$ **(d)** $y = -x^2 - 6x - 13$

   (e) $y = -\frac{1}{2}x^2 + 2x + 3$ **(f)** $y = 2x^2 - 10x + 11$

6. **Communication:** Write down the steps you would take to find the coordinates of the vertex of the quadratic relation $y = -3x^2 + 12x + 29$. Don't actually find the vertex, just explain the steps in your own words.

7. **Knowledge and Understanding:** A ball is tossed into the air. Its height h, in metres, after t seconds is $h = 15t - 5t^2$.

   (a) Find the maximum height of the ball.

   (b) How long is the ball in the air?

   (c) Draw a sketch of the relation.

8. The world production of gold from 1970 to 1990 can be modelled by $G = 1492 - 76t + 5.2t^2$, where G is the number of tonnes of gold and t is the number of years since 1970 ($t = 0$ for 1970, $t = 1$ for 1971, etc.). Source: Energy, Mines and Resources Canada.

   (a) During this period, when was the minimum amount of gold mined?

   (b) What was the least amount of gold mined in one year?

   (c) How much gold was mined in 1985?

9. From 1960 to 1990, the average number of cigarettes C smoked in one year by each Canadian over 18 can be modelled by $C = 4024.5 + 51.4t - 3.1t^2$, where t is the number of years since 1960 ($t = 0$ for 1960). Source: Health Canada.

   (a) When was cigarette consumption highest during this period?

   (b) What was the average per capita consumption of cigarettes in the peak year?

   (c) Since the late 1960s, cigarette packages have carried health warnings. Does the model indicate that this had any effect on cigarette consumption? Explain.

10. From 1995 to 1999, the average ticket price for a regular movie theatre (all ages) can be modelled by the $C = 0.06t^2 - 0.27t + 5.36$, where C is the price in dollars and t is the number of years since 1995 ($t = 0$ for 1995). Source: Canadian Motion Picture Theatres and Drive-Ins.

   (a) When were ticket prices at their lowest during this period?

   (b) What was the average ticket price in 1998?

   (c) What does the model predict the average ticket price will be in 2010?

11. A bridge is to be constructed over a river. The underside of the bridge has the shape of a parabola as in the picture. The river is 18 m wide and the arch of the parabola must be anchored on the ground 3 m back from the riverbanks. The bridge's arch must reach a maximum height of between 22 and 26 m above the surface of the river. Find two different equations to represent arches that satisfy the conditions, then use technology to graph them on the same grid.

12. A movie theatre can accommodate a maximum of 450 moviegoers in a day. The theatre operators have changed admission prices on several occasions to find out how price affects attendance, daily revenue, and profit. Using the formula *profit* = *revenue* − *expenses*, and after reviewing their data, the operators found they could express the relation between profit P and ticket price t as $P = t(450 - 30t) - 790$.

  (a) What does the expression $450 - 30t$ represent? What does the 790 represent?

  (b) What is the ticket price that maximizes the daily profit? What is the maximum profit? About how many tickets will be sold at this price?

  (c) Use graphing technology to find the break-even ticket price and the required minimum ticket sales.

13. Application: In question 12, the theatre operators forgot to consider the revenue from concession sales. They expect this to be $3.50 per ticket. This changes the profit equation to $P = (t + 3.5)(450 - 30t) - 790$.

  (a) What ticket price will maximize this new profit equation? What will that profit be?

  (b) Use graphing technology to find the new break-even ticket price and the required minimum ticket sales.

14. The Sudbury Community Recreation Centre wants to enclose a rectangular swimming area at a public beach on the shores of Ramsey Lake. The city has provided 300 m of rope and buoys to mark off the area. What is the maximum swimming area (in m²) that can be enclosed along the beach with the 300 m of rope?

15. The underside of a bridge has the shape of a parabolic arch. It has a maximum height of 30 m and a width of 50 m. Can a sailboat with a mast 27 m above the water pass under the bridge at a distance of 8 m from the axis of symmetry of the arch? Justify your solution.

16. An arena seats 2000 people and charges $10 per ticket. At this price, all the tickets are sold. The team owners want to increase the ticket prices. A survey indicated that for every one-dollar increase in price, the number of tickets sold will decrease by 100.

(a) Write an equation for the revenue using $R = $ *ticket price* $\times$ *tickets sold.*

(b) In what form is the revenue equation expressed? Use it to help you find the ticket price that will result in the greatest revenue.

(c) Expand and simplify the expression for the equation in (a). Use a partial factor to help you find what ticket price will result in the greatest revenue.

(d) Which method was the easiest way to solve the problem? Which method would you recommend if the revenue equation was given to you in the expanded form you found in (c)? Explain your reasoning.

17. To test a miniature rocket for a science fair, Ben and Andrea launched a prototype from the edge of the escarpment. The rocket's height (in metres above the ground) was recorded using a built-in beacon. This table shows some of the heights recorded after takeoff.

Time (s)	Height Above Escarpment Base (m)
1	127.6
3	178.4
4	189.1
7	162.4
9	95.6

Ben used quadratic regression to find the algebraic model that most closely resembles the flight of the rocket. The expression is $y = -4.9x^2 + 45x + 87.5$, where y represents the rocket's height in metres and x is the elapsed time in seconds.

(a) What is the maximum height of the rocket?

(b) When does the rocket reach its maximum height?

(c) How high above the base of the escarpment were they when they launched the rocket?

18. **Thinking, Inquiry, Problem Solving:**
Many suspension bridges hang from
cables that are supported by two towers.
The shape of the hanging cables is very
close to a parabola. A typical suspension
bridge has large cables that are supported
by two towers that are 20 m high and
80 m apart. The bridge surface is
suspended from the large cables by many
smaller vertical cables. The shortest vertical
cable is 4 m long.

the Lion's Gate Bridge in Vancouver

(a) Using the bridge surface as the *x*-axis,
find a quadratic equation to represent the
parabolic shape of the large cables.

(b) How long are the vertical cables that are 25 m from each tower?

19. A tunnel has a parabolic cross-section. It is 24 m wide at the base. At a point
6 m above the base, the width is 18 m. Find the maximum height of the tunnel.

20. Use the method of partial factoring to express $y = ax^2 + bx + c$ in vertex form.

21. **Check Your Understanding**

(a) A quadratic relation can be changed from standard form to factored form by
complete factoring or by partial factoring. Explain how both of these
methods enable you to find the vertex of the parabola.

(b) Describe the situations in which partial factoring is a better method than
complete factoring for finding the vertex of a quadratic relation.

C

22. A rectangular pool has two rows of water
fountains along the long sides that spray
streams of water into the pool. The two
rows of fountains are 10 m apart. Each
fountain sprays an identical parabolic-
shaped stream of water a total horizontal
distance of 8 m toward the opposite side.
Looking from one end of the pool, the
streams from the left and right sides cross
each other in the middle of the pool at a
height of 3 m.

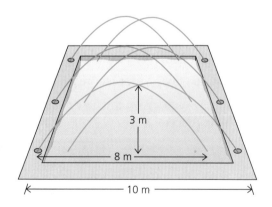

(a) Find two equations that represent the
shapes of the left and right sprays on the same set of axes.

(b) Find the maximum height of the water arches.

The Chapter Problem—Trends in the Smoking Habits of Canada's Youth

In this section you used factoring and symmetry to find a vertex. Apply what you learned to solve these questions about the chapter problem on page 340.

1. Express each algebraic expression you found to model the relations in standard form.
2. Use graphing technology and enter each set of data into a table or lists.
3. Use the technology to obtain a scatter plot of the data.
4. Perform a quadratic regression on each set of data to obtain a second model for the curve of best fit. You now have two algebraic models for each set of data: one developed from your scatter plot and one developed with technology. How do your models compare with the quadratic regression models?
5. Using technology, determine when the percentage of smokers (for both males and females) was at a minimum.

Career: Astrophysicist

Astrophysics involves a wide range of observational and theoretical studies of the planets, stars, galaxies, and the universe, such as

Doug Johnstone

- how atoms combine to form molecules in the near vacuum of space
- how stars form from clouds of gas and dust in a galaxy
- how planets form around stars and the dynamics of planetary systems
- why stars shine, how they age, and why they sometimes explode as supernovae
- what exists in the stellar graveyard—black holes, white dwarfs, and neutron stars
- why galaxies come in different shapes and sizes—spiral, spheroidal, elliptical, and irregular
- how structure formed in the universe—the cosmic web of galaxies, clusters, and voids
- how the universe began, how it evolves, and how the universe will end

Professor Doug Johnstone, in the Department of Astronomy at the University of Toronto, studies the formation of stars and planetary systems. He can often be found at the observatory on Mauna Kea in Hawaii, where he takes pictures of the gases and dust in star-forming regions. He also teaches university students about the physics of stars and planets.

4.5 Finding the Maximum or Minimum Value of a Quadratic Relation Using the TI-83 Plus Calculator

Zooming in on the Optimum Value

After you graph a quadratic relation on the TI–83 Plus calculator, you can find the maximum or minimum value of the relation the same way you found the zeros. Enter the relation $y = 5x^2 + 10x + 3$ and graph it in a standard window by pressing GRAPH ZOOM 6.

Press TRACE followed by ◄ or ► to position the cursor near the maximum or minimum. (In this case, the parabola opens upward, so it has a minimum.) The coordinates of the cursor are displayed at the bottom of the window.

You can improve your approximation of the minimum or maximum by zooming in. To do this, press ZOOM 2 ENTER.

In the new window, use TRACE and ◄ or ► to again move the cursor as close as possible to the minimum or maximum. Your approximation gets better each time you zoom in and trace.

 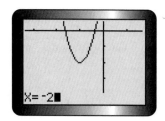 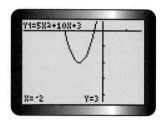

To check your approximation, press 2nd TRACE 1 and enter your guess for the x-coordinate. Press ENTER. The calculator displays the corresponding minimum value for y.

Finding the Optimum Value with the Minimum or Maximum Operation

You can also find the optimum value using the **minimum** or **maximum** operation. Enter the relation $y = -2x^2 - 12x + 30$, then graph it and adjust the window roughly as shown. This graph opens downward and has a maximum.

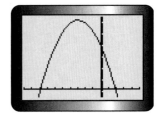

To use the **maximum** operation, press [2nd] [TRACE] [4]. (For parabolas that open upward, press [2nd] [TRACE] [3] to access the **minimum** operation.)

Use the [◄] and [►] keys to move the cursor along the curve so that it is to the left of the optimum value (in this case, the maximum). Then press [ENTER] to set the Left Bound.

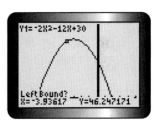

Now move the cursor along the curve so that it is to the right of the optimum value. Press [ENTER] to set the Right Bound.

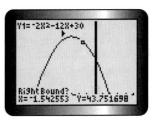

Press [ENTER] again to see the optimum value. The cursor moves to the maximum (or minimum) point and the coordinates are displayed.

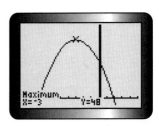

Practise 4.5

Find the optimum value of the quadratic relation by repeated zooming. Note the result, then verify your approximation using the **minimum** or **maximum** operation.

(a) $y = x^2 - 4x + 3$ **(b)** $y = 2x^2 - 12x + 13$ **(c)** $y = -x^2 - 25$

(d) $y = -2x^2 - 3x + 16$ **(e)** $y = -2x^2 + 620x$ **(f)** $y = 2x^2 + 9x - 5$

4.6 Determining Maximum and Minimum Values Algebraically: Completing the Square

In section 4.4 you discovered that a quadratic relation in standard form $y = ax^2 + bx + c$ can be expressed in vertex form using two methods. If the expression can be completely factored, you can find the zeros of the relation. If it cannot be completely factored, you can use a partial factor to find the coordinates of two points. In both cases, you start by

- finding two points on the graph
- using symmetry to calculate the x-coordinate of the midpoint
- then substituting to find the y-coordinate of the vertex

In this lesson, you will learn a more direct method to express a quadratic relation in vertex form.

Part 1: Reversing the Order: Standard Form to Vertex Form

A baseball is hit into the air, and its height is recorded at several different times.

Flight of a Baseball

Time (s)	Height (m)
0	0.491
0.10	2.50
0.75	13.17
1.10	17.20
1.75	21.50
1.95	21.99
2.45	21.50
2.75	20.03
3.10	17.20
3.52	12.22
3.90	6.224

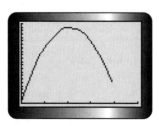

Carol created a scatter plot of the data on a TI-83 Plus calculator using the WINDOW values shown. She studied the data and her scatter plot and concluded that the relation between height and time is quadratic.

Think, Do, Discuss

1. From her graph, Carol estimates that the vertex is at $(2, 22)$. Use graphing technology to create a scatter plot and show that $h = -5(t - 2)^2 + 22$ is a good algebraic model of the data. If you do not have a graphing calculator, you can do this activity using graph paper.

2. Use quadratic regression to show that the best model is
   $h = -4.9t^2 + 20.58t + 0.491$.

3. How close is Carol's model of $h = -5(t - 2)^2 + 22$ to the regression model? Expand Carol's model and compare the two.

4. Carol reasoned that if she can change a quadratic equation from vertex form to standard form by expanding, then she should also be able to change a quadratic equation from standard form to vertex form. She decided to write down—in reverse order—the steps she used to expand the vertex form to standard form.

   (1) $h = -5t^2 + 20t + 2$

   (2) $h = -5t^2 + 20t - 20 + 22$

   (3) $h = -5(t^2 - 4t + 4) + 22$

   (4) $h = -5(t - 2)(t - 2) + 22$

   (5) $h = -5(t - 2)^2 + 22$

   (a) Look closely at the steps Carol wrote down. From step 2 to step 3, what was done to the trinomial $-5t^2 + 20t - 20$?

   (b) From step 3 to step 4, what did Carol do to the trinomial $t^2 - 4t + 4$?

   (c) What is special about the trinomial $t^2 - 4t + 4$?

   (d) This procedure is called **completing the square**. Explain why this name is suitable. In which step is the square completed?

5. To convert a quadratic from standard form to vertex form, you must factor a trinomial. What special factoring pattern is used?

6. Examine these perfect squares to find the relation between the coefficient of the middle term and the last term:

$x^2 + 2x + 1$	$x^2 + 10x + 25$
$x^2 + 4x + 4$	$x^2 - 12x + 36$
$x^2 + 6x + 9$	$x^2 - 14x + 49$

   What is the relation? What constant must you add to $x^2 + 20x$ to create a perfect square?

Part 2: Completing the Square ——————

These steps show how to complete the square to find the vertex form of a trinomial in standard form.

Think, Do, Discuss

1. These steps show how to express Carol's model in vertex form.

   (1) $h = -5t^2 + 20t + 2$

   (2) $h = -5(t^2 - 4t) + 2$ What was done to go from step 1 to step 2?

   (3) $h = -5(t^2 - 4t + 4 - 4) + 2$ Why has 4 been added to $t^2 - 4t$ and then subtracted away again? Can any number be added and then subtracted? Explain.

   (4) $h = -5(t^2 - 4t + 4) + 20 + 2$ What is really being added to the equation in step 3?

   (5) $h = -5(t - 2)(t - 2) + 22$ In step 4, where does the 20 come from? Why was this done?

   (6) $h = -5(t - 2)^2 + 22$ What factoring pattern was used to go from step 4 to step 5?

2. Carol used this technique on the regression equation she found in part 1. Copy Carol's steps. Describe what was done to go from one step to the next.

   (1) $y = -4.90x^2 + 20.580x + 0.491$

   (2) $y = -4.90(x^2 - 4.2x) + 0.491$

   (3) $y = -4.90(x^2 - 4.2x + 4.41 - 4.41) + 0.491$

   (4) $y = -4.90(x^2 - 4.2x + 4.41) + 21.609 + 0.491$

   (5) $y = -4.90(x - 2.1)(x - 2.1) + 22.1$

   (6) $y = -4.90(x - 2.1)^2 + 22.1$

3. Use graphing technology to verify $y = -4.90x^2 + 20.580x + 0.491$ and $y = -4.90(x - 2.1)^2 + 22.1$ represent the same relation.

Career: Land Surveyor

Before construction begins, a land surveyor locates the required points and boundaries. For example, for the building shown here, the land surveyor marked the location of the roads, the boundaries of the lots, and the positions of the fire hydrants and other utilities.

Geometry and bisectors are an integral part of the surveyor's job. Where might a surveyor use bisectors in surveying the land for this building?

Focus 4.6

Key Ideas

- A quadratic relation in standard form $y = ax^2 + bx + c$ can be rewritten in vertex form $y = a(x - h)^2 + k$ by creating a perfect square in the expression, then factoring the square. This technique is called **completing the square**.

- Completing the square involves the following steps:

  Example: $y = 2x^2 + 12x - 3$

  (1) Remove the common constant factor from both the x^2- and x-term

  (1) $y = 2(x^2 + 6x) - 3$

  (2) Find the constant that must be added and subtracted to create a perfect square. This value equals the square of half of the coefficient of the x-term in step 1. Rewrite the expression by adding, then subtracting, this value after the x-term inside the brackets.

  (2) $y = 2(x^2 + 6x + 9 - 9) - 3$

  (3) Group the three terms that form the perfect square. Move the subtracted value outside the brackets by multiplying it by the common constant factor.

  (3) $y = 2(x^2 + 6x + 9) - 18 - 3$

  (4) Factor the perfect square and collect like terms.

  (4) $y = 2(x + 3)^2 - 21$

- Completing the square can be used to find the vertex of a quadratic in standard form without finding the zeros of the relation or two points equidistant from the axis of symmetry.

- Completing the square allows you to find the maximum or minimum value of a quadratic relation algebraically, without using a graph.

Example 1

Rewrite the quadratic relation in vertex form by completing the square.

(a) $y = x^2 + 8x + 15$

(b) $y = -2x^2 + 12x - 7$

Solution

(a) $y = x^2 + 8x + 15$

Decide what must be added and subtracted to make a perfect square, $\left(\frac{8}{2}\right)^2 = 16$.

$y = x^2 + 8x + 16 - 16 + 15$ Add and subtract 16.

$y = (x^2 + 8x + 16) - 16 + 15$ Group the first three terms, which form the perfect square and factor.

$y = (x + 4)(x + 4) - 16 + 15$ Simplify.

$y = (x + 4)^2 - 1$

(b) $y = -2x^2 + 12x - 7$ Factor -2 from $-2x^2 + 12x$.

$y = -2(x^2 - 6x) - 7$ Decide what must be added and subtracted to make a perfect square: $\left(\frac{-6}{2}\right)^2 = 9$.

$y = -2(x^2 - 6x + 9 - 9) - 7$ Add and subtract 9.

$y = -2((x^2 - 6x + 9) - 9) - 7$ Group the first three terms.

$y = -2(x^2 - 6x + 9) + 18 - 7$ Isolate the group with the first three terms and simplify the rest. Factor the perfect square.

$y = -2(x - 3)^2 + 11$

Example 2

A glassworks that makes lead-crystal bowls has a daily production cost C in dollars given by the relation $C = 0.2b^2 - 10b + 650$, where b is the number of bowls made. How many bowls should be made to minimize the production cost? What is the cost when this many bowls are made?

Solution

The graph of this relation is a parabola that opens upward. The vertex corresponds to the minimum. Find the vertex by completing the square.

$y = 0.2b^2 - 10b + 650$ Factor 0.2 from $0.2b^2 - 10b$.

$y = 0.2(b^2 - 50b) + 650$ Determine what must be added and subtracted to make a perfect square: $\left(\frac{-50}{2}\right)^2 = 625$.

$y = 0.2(b^2 - 50b + 625 - 625) + 650$ Add and subtract 625.

$y = 0.2((b^2 - 50b + 625) - 625) + 650$ Group the first three terms.

$y = 0.2(b^2 - 50b + 625) - 125 + 650$ Isolate the group with the first three terms and simplify the rest, then factor.

$y = 0.2(b - 25)^2 + 525$

The vertex is at (25, 525). This means that the cost is minimized when 25 bowls are made. The production cost for 25 bowls is $525.

Example 3

A gardener wants to enclose a rectangular vegetable garden with 60 concrete curbstones, each 1 m long.

(a) Write an expression for the number of curbstones used (the perimeter) and for the total area.

(b) Use the perimeter expression to rewrite the area expression in terms of only one variable.

(c) How should the gardener lay out the curbstones to maximize the total enclosed area?

Solution

Let w represent the width and l the length.

(a) The perimeter is $P = 2w + 2l$ and the area is $A = wl$.

(b)

$$P = 2w + 2l$$

$$60 = 2w + 2l \qquad \text{Isolate } l.$$

$$2l = 60 - 2w$$

$$l = \frac{60 - 2w}{2}$$

$$l = 30 - w$$

$A = wl$ Substitute $l = 30 - w$ from the perimeter calculations.

$A = w(30 - w)$ Expand.

$A = 30w - w^2$

(c) You have to find the maximum area. The expression for the area is a quadratic relation that opens downward, since the coefficient of w^2 is -1. The maximum area or maximum A-coordinate occurs at the vertex. To find the vertex, you can either factor or complete the square.

Factoring

$A = -w^2 + 30w$

$A = w(-w + 30)$

Let $w(-w + 30) = 0$. Then $w = 0$ or $w = 30$. The w-coordinate of the vertex is

$\frac{0 + 30}{2} = 15$

To find the A-coordinate, let $w = 15$ in the formula for A.

$A = -(15)^2 + 30(15)$

$A = -225 + 450$

$A = 225$

The vertex is at $(15, 225)$.

Completing the Square

$A = -w^2 + 30w$

$A = (-1)(w^2 - 30w)$

$A = -(w^2 - 30w + 225 - 225)$, since $\left(\frac{-30}{2}\right)^2 = 225$

$A = -((w^2 - 30w + 225) - 225)$

$A = -(w - 15)^2 + 225$

The vertex is at (15, 225), which means that the maximum area of 225 m² occurs when the width is 15 m. The length of the garden is

$$l = 30 - w$$
$$l = 30 - 15$$
$$l = 15 \text{ m}$$

When the width and length of the garden are both 15 m, the area of the garden is maximized at 225 m².

Practice, Apply, Solve 4.6

(A)

1. Find the value of m that makes the expression a perfect square.
   - **(a)** $x^2 + 4x + \underline{m}$
   - **(b)** $x^2 - 4x + m$
   - **(c)** $x^2 - 6x + m$
   - **(d)** $x^2 + 8x + m$
   - **(e)** $x^2 + 10x + m$
   - **(f)** $x^2 - 12x + m$
   - **(g)** $x^2 - 20x + m$
   - **(h)** $x^2 + 18x + m$
   - **(i)** $x^2 + 14x + m$

2. Each expression is a perfect square. Assuming that $b > 0$, find b.
   - **(a)** $y = x^2 + bx + 49$
   - **(b)** $y = x^2 + bx + 9$
   - **(c)** $y = x^2 + bx + 36$
   - **(d)** $y = x^2 + bx + 81$
   - **(e)** $y = x^2 + bx + 25$
   - **(f)** $y = x^2 + bx + 100$
   - **(g)** $y = x^2 + bx + 1$
   - **(h)** $y = x^2 + bx + 64$
   - **(i)** $y = x^2 + bx + 144$

3. Find the values of h and k that make the equation true.
   - **(a)** $x^2 + 4x = (x - h)^2 + k$
   - **(b)** $x^2 - 6x = (x - h)^2 + k$
   - **(c)** $x^2 - 10x = (x - h)^2 + k$

4. Write the equation in vertex form $y = a(x - h)^2 + k$ by completing the square.
   - **(a)** $y = x^2 + 4x$
   - **(b)** $y = x^2 - 8x$
   - **(c)** $y = x^2 + 6x + 2$
   - **(d)** $y = x^2 + 10x - 12$
   - **(e)** $y = x^2 + 12x - 15$
   - **(f)** $y = x^2 - 14x + 20$
   - **(g)** $y = x^2 - 6x - 8$
   - **(h)** $y = x^2 - 10x - 5$
   - **(i)** $y = x^2 + 20x - 20$

5. Does the quadratic relation have a maximum or a minimum? State the optimum value and the coordinates of the point where it occurs.
   - **(a)** $y = 2(x - 3)^2 + 5$
   - **(b)** $y = -3(x - 2)^2 - 25$
   - **(c)** $y = 6(x + 4)^2 - 7$

(B)

6. What value of c makes the expression a perfect square?
   - **(a)** $x^2 + x + c$
   - **(b)** $x^2 + 3x + c$
   - **(c)** $x^2 + 9x + c$
   - **(d)** $x^2 + 5x + c$
   - **(e)** $x^2 - 15x + c$
   - **(f)** $x^2 - 0.5x + c$
   - **(g)** $x^2 + 0.2x + c$
   - **(h)** $x^2 - 0.16x + c$
   - **(i)** $x^2 + bx + c$

7. Find the values of a, h, and k that make the equation true.

(a) $2x^2 + 8x + 4 = a(x - h)^2 + k$

(b) $-3x^2 - 12x + 5 = a(x - h)^2 + k$

(c) $\frac{1}{2}x^2 - 3x + 5 = a(x - h)^2 + k$

8. Express the equation in vertex form by completing the square.

(a) $y = 2x^2 + 4x$

(b) $y = 3x^2 - 9x$

(c) $y = -x^2 + 6x$

(d) $y = -4x^2 + 8x + 9$

(e) $y = 2x^2 - 4x + 5$

(f) $y = -3x^2 + 6x - 7$

(g) $y = -3x^2 - 12x + 5$

(h) $y = 5x^2 + 10x - 11$

(i) $y = -\frac{1}{2}x^2 + 6x + 5$

(j) $y = 0.2x^2 + 2x + 9$

(k) $y = 0.5x^2 - 4x + 6$

(l) $y = -0.1x^2 - 0.6x - 0.4$

9. For each quadratic relation,

i. complete the square to express the relation in vertex form

ii. graph the relation

(a) $y = x^2 - 4x + 7$

(b) $y = x^2 + 8x + 6$

(c) $y = \frac{1}{2}x^2 - 2x + 5$

(d) $y = -x^2 + 6x - 11$

(e) $y = -3x^2 - 18x + 13$

(f) $y = 2x^2 + 20x + 43$

10. Communication: What transformations must be applied to the graph of $y = x^2$ to produce the graph of $y = 2x^2 - 12x + 7$? Justify your reasoning.

11. A model rocket is launched straight upward with an initial velocity of 200 m/s. The height of the rocket h, in metres, can be modelled by $h = -5t^2 + 200t$, where t is the elapsed time in seconds. What is the maximum height the rocket reaches?

12. Knowledge and Understanding: The cost C, in dollars, of operating a concrete-cutting machine is modelled by $C = 2.2n^2 - 66n + 655$, where n is the number of minutes the machine is run. How long must the machine run for the operating cost to be at a minimum? What is the minimum cost?

13. Find the dimensions of a rectangle that has a perimeter of 40 cm and the largest possible area.

14. A police officer is investigating a crime. He wants to seal the area around the scene with a roll of yellow police tape that is 300 m long. What are the dimensions of the maximum rectangular area? What is the maximum area?

15. Randy is building a fence at the side of his warehouse. He has 120 m of fencing and plans to use the side of the warehouse as one side of the rectangular fenced area. What are the dimensions of the maximum area Randy can enclose?

16. A rectangular field will be fenced on all four sides. There will also be a line of fence across the field, parallel to the shorter side. If 900 m of fencing are available, what dimensions of the field will produce the maximum area?

17. (a) The sum of two numbers is 26. The sum of their squares is a minimum. Find the numbers.

(b) Verify your results using technology. Use technology to find the numbers if the sum of their squares is 442.

18. The city transit system carries 24 800 bus riders per day for a fare of $1.85. The city hopes to reduce car pollution by getting more people to ride the bus, while maximizing the transit system's revenue at the same time. A survey indicates that the number of riders will increase by 800 for every $0.05 decrease in the fare. What fare will produce the greatest revenue?

19. A baseball is hit from a height of 1 m. Its height h, in metres, after t seconds is $h = -5t^2 + 10t + 1$.

(a) Is it better to use the partial factor method or completing the square to find the maximum height of the ball? Justify your answer.

(b) Use one of the methods in (a) to find the maximum height of the ball. Use technology to verify your solution.

(c) Use technology to find out how long the ball is in the air.

20. Application: A farmer has $3600 to spend on fencing for three adjoining rectangular pastures, all with the same dimensions. A local contracting company tells the farmer that they can build the fence for $6.25/m. What is the largest total area that the farmer can have fenced for that price?

21. Hassan used the method of completing the square to express $y = 2x^2 + 3x + 4$ in vertex form. If Hassan's solution is correct, write "Correct." If not, identify the errors and show the correct solution.

(1) $y = 2(x^2 + \frac{3}{2}x) + 4$

(2) $y = 2(x^2 + \frac{3}{2}x + \frac{9}{4} - \frac{9}{4}) + 4$

(3) $y = 2(x + \frac{3}{4})^2 - \frac{9}{2} + 4$

(4) $y = 2(x + \frac{3}{4})^2 - \frac{1}{2}$

22. The amount of gasoline that a car consumes is measured at various speeds. The data is recorded in the form of ordered pairs: (speed in kilometres per hour, gas consumed in litres per 100 km).

(10, 8.2)   (20, 7.9)   (30, 7.5)   (40, 6.9)   (60, 6.4)   (70, 6.2)

(80, 5.9)   (90, 6.1)   (100, 6.7)   (110, 7.8)   (120, 8.4)   (130, 9.9)

(a) A commuter drives 12 000 km on highways in one year. If the average price of a litre of gas is $0.62, how much will this person save in one year by driving at a speed of 90 km/h rather than 110 km/h?

(b) Create a scatter plot for the data on graph paper.

(c) Draw a curve of best fit for the data.

(d) Use a quadratic model to approximate an equation, in vertex form, for the curve of best fit. Use technology to graph your equation and the scatter plot.

(e) Use graphing technology to obtain a quadratic regression curve of best fit.

(f) Discuss the goodness of fit of the regression curve to the data. Find the vertex of the regression curve and use the value of a to express the regression curve as a quadratic in vertex form. Compare it to the equation you approximated in (d).

(g) Based on the regression curve of best fit, what is the most fuel-efficient speed for driving? How does this compare to the data?

(h) What recommendation would you make with respect to driving speed to minimize fuel consumption?

23. i. Which algebraic method would you use to find the coordinates of the vertex of each relation? Justify your answer.

(a) $y = (x + 4)(x - 10)$ **(b)** $y = 3x^2 - 12x$

(c) $y = 2x^2 - 5x$ **(d)** $y = x^2 + 2x - 15$

(e) $y = x^2 + 3x - 11$ **(f)** $y = -4.9x^2 + 34.3x + 8.4$

(g) $R = (3 + t)(660 - 15t)$ **(h)** $y = 3x^2 - 6x + 13$

(i) $y = (2x - 7)(3x + 8) + 11x$ **(j)** $y = -2(x + 3)(x - 1)$

(k) $y = 3.2x^2 - 27.2x + 30.3$

ii. Which method does not work all the time? Which methods give you additional information about the graph?

iii. Find the coordinates of the vertex of each relation in (i).

24. Check Your Understanding: Consider the quadratic relation $y = x^2 - 2x - 35$. Use the three different algebraic methods you have learned to rewrite the relation in vertex form. Which methods enable you to also find points on the graph that are equidistant from the axis of symmetry? Which method also reveals the x-intercepts of the graph? If the graph of the relation is not required, is there an advantage to using one method over another? Explain.

25. A 60 cm length of rope is to be cut into two pieces to form the perimeters of two squares. If the total area of the two squares is to be a minimum, what are the dimensions of the squares?

26. If $y = a(x - 1)^2 + q$, and points $(-1, -9)$ and $(1, 1)$ both lie on the parabola, what is the optimum value of y?

27. Consider a quadratic relation of the form $y = x^2 + bx + c$.

(a) Complete the square to express the relation in vertex form. Write an expression for the coordinates of the vertex. (**Hint**: What would one-half of the coefficient of x be?)

(b) Substitute $b = 10$ and $c = 7$ into the expression you found in (a) for the vertex.

(c) Verify that the answer you found in (b) is correct by substituting $b = 10$ and $c = 7$ in $y = x^2 + bx + c$ and completing the square.

28. Thinking, Inquiry, Problem Solving: Recall that the x-coordinate of the vertex of a quadratic relation in standard form $y = ax^2 + bx + c$ is $-\dfrac{b}{2a}$.

(a) Complete the square on $y = ax^2 + bx$ and express the relation in vertex form. Is your answer consistent with the statement above about the x-coordinate of the vertex? What is the y-coordinate of the vertex of $y = ax^2 + bx$?

(b) Complete the square on $y = ax^2 + bx + c$ and express the relation in vertex form.

The Chapter Problem—Trends in the Smoking Habits of Canada's Youth

In this section you completed the square to find maximum and minimum values. Apply what you learned to answer these questions concerning the chapter problem on page 340.

1. For each quadratic regression model you found at the end of section 4.4 for the chapter problem, use the method of completing the square to express the relation in vertex form.

2. How accurate are your models? Compare the models you developed to the ones found using technology.

Solving Quadratic Equations: 4.7
The Quadratic Formula

Part 1: Solving Quadratic Equations ──────

In the previous section, Carol used a quadratic model to represent the table of values for a ball that was tossed in the air. She found two different forms to represent the equation of this curve: standard form, $h = -5t^2 + 20t + 2$, and vertex form, $h = -5(t - 2)^2 + 22$.

How can you use these equations to find the times at which the ball was at a height of 17 m or at a height of 9.2 m?

Think, Do, Discuss

1. (a) How would you use the graph of $h = -5t^2 + 20t + 2$ to find t when $h = 17$?

   (b) To find the time when $h = 17$, start by substituting 17 for h: $17 = -5t^2 + 20t + 2$. Carol observed that solving this problem is equivalent to solving $0 = -5t^2 + 20t - 15$. How was the second equation obtained from the first? How can it be solved using the graph of $y = -5t^2 + 20t - 15$? How can it be solved algebraically?

2. Factor the new equation $0 = -5t^2 + 20t - 15$ completely.

   (a) What are the roots of this equation? What do they represent in this problem?

   (b) Verify that the midpoint of these roots has the same t-coordinate as the vertex of h computed using both $h = -5t^2 + 20t + 2$ and $h = -5(t - 2)^2 + 27$.

   (c) Why is the ball 17 m high at two different times?

3. Using graphing technology, graph the relation $h = -5t^2 + 20t + 2$. Use TRACE to find the times that correspond to a height of 17 m. Verify, by graphing and tracing, that these time values are also the zeros of the relation $h = -5t^2 + 20t - 15$.

4. To find the times when the height of the ball is 9.2 m, repeat steps 1 and 2, substituting $h = 9.2$.

   (a) Does this expression factor completely?

   (b) Does partial factoring enable you to find the roots of this equation? Would using this method help solve the problem?

5. (a) Suppose you want to find the time when the ball is 9.2 m high. What equation would you have to solve?

(b) What does this equation mean in terms of the graph? To find t algebraically, follow these steps.

$$9.2 = -5(t - 2)^2 + 22$$

(1) $9.2 - 22 = -5(t - 2)^2$ Explain why this equation corresponds to the one in (a).

(2) $-12.8 = -5(t - 2)^2$ How does this lead to isolating t?

(3) $\dfrac{-12.8}{-5} = \dfrac{-5(t - 2)^2}{-5}$ What was done to the equation?

(4) $2.56 = (t - 2)^2$ Why were both sides of the equation divided by -5?

(5) $\sqrt{2.56} = \sqrt{(t - 2)^2}$

(6) $\pm\sqrt{2.56} = t - 2$ What has been done to both sides of the equation?

What has happened on the right side of the equation?

What does the $\pm$ (combined $+$ and $-$) mean? Why is it there?

How does this affect the solution to the equation $\pm\sqrt{2.56} = t - 2$?

What must be done to both sides to isolate t?

6. Find the two values of t that correspond to a height of 9.2 m.

Part 2: Developing a Formula for the Quadratic Model

An object is thrown from the top of a building. Its height h, in metres, after t seconds is $h = -5t^2 + 8t + 10$. When does the object hit the ground?

Review how the questions in part 1 were solved. To solve an equation of the form $at^2 + bt + c = 0$,

(1) complete the square, to express the equation in vertex form
$a(t - h)^2 + k = 0$

(2) isolate $(t - h)^2$

(3) take the square root of both sides of the equation

(4) solve for t

Because the same process can be used for any quadratic equation in standard form $ax^2 + bx + c = 0$, there must be a formula for finding x. In the table below, the same steps are applied to the example $0 = -5t^2 + 8t + 10$ and to the general quadratic equation $ax^2 + bx + c = 0$.

Specific Example	General Equation
1. $-5t^2 + 8t + 10 = 0$	$ax^2 + bx + c = 0$
2. $-5\left(t^2 - \frac{8}{5}t\right) + 10 = 0$	$a\left(x^2 + \frac{b}{a}x\right) + c = 0$
3. $-5\left(t^2 - \frac{8}{5}t + \left(\frac{4}{5}\right)^2 - \left(\frac{4}{5}\right)^2\right) + 10 = 0$	$a\left(x^2 + \frac{b}{a}x + \left(\frac{b}{2a}\right)^2 - \left(\frac{b}{2a}\right)^2\right) + c = 0$
4. $-5\left(t^2 - \frac{8}{5}t + \frac{16}{25} - \frac{16}{25}\right) + 10 = 0$	$a\left(x^2 + \frac{b}{a}x + \frac{b^2}{4a^2} - \frac{b^2}{4a^2}\right) + c = 0$
5. $-5\left(t^2 - \frac{8}{5}t + \frac{16}{25}\right) + \frac{16}{5} + 10 = 0$	$a\left(x^2 + \frac{b}{a}x + \frac{b^2}{4a^2}\right) - \frac{b^2}{4a} + c = 0$
6. $-5\left(t^2 - \frac{8}{5}t + \frac{16}{25}\right) + \frac{16}{5} + \frac{50}{5} = 0$	$a\left(x^2 + \frac{b}{a}x + \frac{b^2}{4a^2}\right) - \frac{b^2}{4a} + \frac{4ac}{4a} = 0$
7. $-5\left(t - \frac{4}{5}\right)^2 + \frac{66}{5} = 0$	$a\left(x + \frac{b}{2a}\right)^2 - \frac{b^2 - 4ac}{4a} = 0$
8. $-5\left(t - \frac{4}{5}\right)^2 = -\frac{66}{5}$	$a\left(x + \frac{b}{2a}\right)^2 = \frac{b^2 - 4ac}{4a}$
9. $\left(t - \frac{4}{5}\right)^2 = \frac{66}{25}$	$\left(x + \frac{b}{2a}\right)^2 = \frac{b^2 - 4ac}{4a^2}$
10. $\sqrt{\left(t - \frac{4}{5}\right)^2} = \sqrt{\frac{66}{25}}$	$\sqrt{\left(x + \frac{b}{2a}\right)^2} = \sqrt{\frac{b^2 - 4ac}{4a^2}}$
11. $t - \frac{4}{5} = \pm\sqrt{\frac{66}{25}}$	$x + \frac{b}{2a} = \frac{\pm\sqrt{b^2 - 4ac}}{2a}$
12. $t = \frac{4}{5} \pm \frac{\sqrt{66}}{5}$	$x = -\frac{b}{2a} \pm \frac{\sqrt{b^2 - 4ac}}{2a}$
13. $t = \frac{4 \pm \sqrt{66}}{5}$	$x = \frac{-b \pm \sqrt{b^2 - 4ac}}{2a}$

Think, Do, Discuss

1. Which steps in the specific case involve completing the square? Which steps in the general case involve completing the square?

2. Which steps in the specific case solve the equation for t? Which steps in the general case solve the equation for x?

3. How many solutions for t are there in the specific case? Find the solutions to the nearest hundredth. What is the significance of the negative solution? Which solution seems to make the most sense for the flight time of the ball?

4. How many solutions are there for the general case? Explain.

5. In the specific case, $-5t^2 + 8t + 10 = 0$, what are the values of a, b, and c?

6. Verify that the formula developed for the general case, $x = \frac{-b \pm \sqrt{b^2 - 4ac}}{2a}$ produces the same solution for t, by replacing a, b, and c with the values from the equation $-5t^2 + 8t + 10 = 0$. Evaluate to the nearest hundredth.

7. Which method produces the solution to a quadratic equation using the least amount of work, completing the square or the formula in the last line of the general case?

Part 3: Connecting the Parabola and Its Zeros to the Quadratic Formula

In part 2, you found that the zeros of a quadratic relation in standard form $y = ax^2 + bx + c$ are given by $x = \dfrac{-b \pm \sqrt{b^2 - 4ac}}{2a}$.

This formula is called the **quadratic formula**. Does every quadratic relation have two zeros? Does every quadratic equation have two roots?

Think, Do, Discuss

1. Graph the quadratic relation.

   (a) $y = x^2 + 2x - 9$ (b) $y = 2x^2 - 12x + 18$ (c) $y = 3x^2 + 4$

2. Copy the table into your notebook. For each relation, use the graphs you made in question 1 and complete the table by adding the following items:
   • a sketch of the graph
   • the number of zeros the relation has
   • the calculation of the zeros using the quadratic formula to the nearest hundredth
   • the quantity under the square root symbol in your formula evaluation: is it positive (> 0), negative (< 0), or zero (0)?

Relation	Graph	How Many Zeros?	Roots, Calculated Using the Quadratic Formula	Quantity Under the Square Root, $b^2 - 4ac$ (> 0, < 0, or 0?)
(a) $y = x^2 + 2x - 9$				
(b) $y = 2x^2 - 12x + 18$				
(c) $y = 3x^2 + 4$				

3. Based on your findings, under what conditions does a quadratic in standard form have two real roots?

4. The three relations that you just examined were all parabolas that opened upward.

   (a) Sketch a quadratic relation that opens downward and has two zeros.

   (b) Sketch a quadratic relation that opens downward and has one zero.

   (c) Sketch a quadratic relation that opens downward and has no zeros.

5. Use graphing technology to find a relation that is an example for each situation in question 4.

Focus 4.7

Key Ideas

- The roots of a quadratic equation in the form $a(x - h)^2 + k = 0$ can be found algebraically without expanding. First, isolate $(x - h)^2$, giving $(x - h)^2 = -\frac{k}{a}$. After taking the square root of both sides, you can solve for x. Remember, the square root has positive and negative values.

- The roots of a quadratic equation in the form $ax^2 + bx + c = 0$ can sometimes be found by factoring.

- The roots of a quadratic equation in the form $ax^2 + bx + c = 0$ can be found using the **quadratic formula**: $x = \dfrac{-b \pm \sqrt{b^2 - 4ac}}{2a}$.

- A quadratic equation must be expressed in standard form $ax^2 + bx + c = 0$ before it can be solved by factoring or by using the quadratic formula.

- The quadratic formula sometimes leads to a negative number under the square root sign. When this happens, the calculation cannot be completed using ordinary numbers (called **real** numbers). In this case, the relation has **no real roots**.

- Numbers such as $\sqrt{-16}$ and $\sqrt{-35}$ are called **imaginary numbers**. They are not real numbers since the square root of a negative number does not exist in the set of real numbers. They are part of a larger set of numbers called complex numbers, which are important in advanced mathematics. When an equation has no real roots, it may have complex or non-real roots.

- In the quadratic formula, the value of $b^2 - 4ac$ determines the number and type of roots a quadratic equation has. This expression is called the **discriminant**.

- When using the quadratic formula,

  - if $b^2 - 4ac > 0$, then the quadratic equation has 2 real roots

  - if $b^2 - 4ac = 0$, then the quadratic equation has 1 real root

  - if $b^2 - 4ac < 0$, then the quadratic equation has no real roots

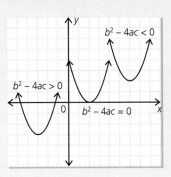

Example 1

Solve the quadratic equation.

(a) $2x^2 + 5 = 167$ **(b)** $4(2x - 1)^2 = 36$

Solution

These equations can be solved by isolating $(x - h)^2$, then taking the square root of both sides.

(a)
$$2x^2 + 5 = 167$$
$$2x^2 = 167 - 5$$
$$2x^2 = 162$$
$$x^2 = 81$$
$$x = \pm\sqrt{81}$$
$$x = \pm 9$$
$$x = 9 \text{ and } x = -9$$

(b)
$$4(2x - 1)^2 = 36$$
$$(2x - 1)^2 = \frac{36}{4}$$
$$(2x - 1)^2 = 9$$
$$\sqrt{(2x - 1)^2} = \pm\sqrt{9}$$
$$2x - 1 = \pm 3$$
$$2x = 1 \pm 3$$
$$x = \frac{1 \pm 3}{2}$$
$$x = \frac{1 + 3}{2} \text{ and } x = \frac{1 - 3}{2}$$
$$x = 2 \text{ and } x = -1$$

Example 2

A digital sensor records the height of a baseball after it is hit into the air. Quadratic regression on the data gives the quadratic relation $y = -4.9x^2 + 20.58x + 0.491$. How long is the ball in the air? Verify your answer using graphing technology.

Solution

The ball hits the ground when its height is zero. Let $y = 0$ and solve the equation.
$$0 = -4.9x^2 + 20.58x + 0.491$$

Substituting -4.9 for a, 20.58 for b, and 0.491 for c into the quadratic formula gives

$$x = \frac{-b \pm \sqrt{b^2 - 4ac}}{2a}$$

$$x = \frac{-20.58 \pm \sqrt{20.58^2 - 4(-4.9)(0.491)}}{2(-4.9)}$$

$$x = \frac{-20.58 \pm \sqrt{423.5364 + 9.6236}}{-9.8}$$

$$x \doteq \frac{-20.58 \pm 20.8125}{-9.8}$$

$$x \doteq 4.22 \text{ and } x \doteq -0.02$$

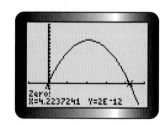

The ball hits the ground about 4.22 s after being hit. Note that at $t = 0$, the ball was 0.491 m above the ground. The negative root found is extraneous to the problem, since negative time is not meaningful in the context of this question.

Example 3

Recall that the dances at the community centre produce revenue $R = -60t^2 + 600t$, where R is the revenue and t the ticket price in dollars. The profit equation is $P = R - E$, where E is the expense equation.

Francine, the manager, found that the expenses for the dances are not really constant. As the ticket price increases, fewer teens attend the dance, and the expenses for cups, cleaning, staffing, and tickets decrease.

She found that $E = 1000 - 90t$ models the expenses for each dance.

(a) Find the break-even price for tickets. Explain your answer.

(b) Find the maximum profit and the ticket price that yields this profit.

Solution

(a) At the break-even point, revenue equals expenses.

$$R = E$$
$$-60t^2 + 600t = 1000 - 90t$$
$$-60t^2 + 600t + 90t - 1000 = 0$$
$$-60t^2 + 690t - 1000 = 0$$

Use the quadratic formula to solve for t.

$$t = \frac{-690 \pm \sqrt{690^2 - 4(-60)(-1000)}}{2(-60)}$$

$$t = \frac{-690 \pm \sqrt{476\,100 - 240\,000}}{-120}$$

$$t \doteq \frac{-690 \pm 485.90}{-120}$$

$$t \doteq 9.80 \text{ and } t \doteq 1.70$$

The break-even prices for the dance tickets are $9.80 or $1.70. A ticket price of $9.80 produces greater revenue per person, but fewer people attend. A price of $1.70 per ticket produces much less revenue per person, although many more people attend. These amounts are the zeros of a profit relation whose graph opens downward, so any ticket price between $1.70 and $9.80 will result in a profit.

One way of finding the break-even points is to use technology to graph the quadratic revenue equation, R, and the linear expense equation, E, and find the points of intersection. A ticket price of $1.70 results in revenue of $846.93 and expenses of $846.93. Similarly, you can find the other point of intersection at a price of $9.80.

(b) The profit equation is $P = R - E$.

$$P = (-60t^2 + 600t) - (1000 - 90t)$$
$$P = -60t^2 + 690t - 1000$$

The graph of P is a parabola that opens downward. The maximum profit occurs at the vertex. The coordinates of the vertex can be found by completing the square on P or by using the roots of the equation in (a). These correspond to the zeros of the graph of P.

Therefore the t-coordinate of the vertex is $t = \dfrac{9.8 + 1.70}{2}$ or 5.75.

A ticket price of $5.75 maximizes the profit.
Substitute $t = 5.75$ to determine the maximum profit:

$$P = -60(5.75)^2 + 690(5.75) - 1000$$
$$P = 983.75$$

A ticket price of $5.75 will produce a profit of $983.75.

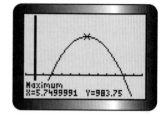

Example 4

Determine how many roots each equation has.

(a) $-5x^2 + 8x - 10 = 0$ **(b)** $2(x - 7)^2 - 12 = 0$

Solution

(a) Evaluate $b^2 - 4ac$ for $a = -5$, $b = 8$, and $c = -10$.

$$b^2 - 4ac = (8)^2 - 4(-5)(-10)$$
$$= 64 - 200$$
$$= -136$$

Since $b^2 - 4ac$ is negative, the equation has no real roots.

(b) The equation comes from the quadratic relation $y = 2(x - 7)^2 - 12$. Because the vertex is below the x-axis (it is at $(7, -12)$) and the parabola opens upward, the relation has two zeros. The equation has two roots. Check using the discriminant.

Did You Know?

Native American weavers range in age from 15 to 90. The involvement of young and old weavers is very important, as most weavers use designs and patterns that have been passed down from generation to generation. These designs often contain diamonds and isosceles triangles like the one shown here.

Practise, Apply, Solve 4.7

Ⓐ

1. Solve the equation. Round your answer to the nearest hundredth.

(a) $x^2 = 16$ (b) $x^2 = 225$ (c) $t^2 = 50$

(d) $2b^2 = 98$ (e) $c^2 - 44 = 100$ (f) $4d^2 - 1 = 11$

(g) $20 = 5 - x^2$ (h) $6f^2 + 32 = 80$

2. Find the roots of the equation by factoring.

(a) $x^2 - 9 = 0$ (b) $x^2 + x - 6 = 0$ (c) $x^2 - 3x = 0$

(d) $x^2 + 7x + 12 = 0$ (e) $x^2 - 10x + 25 = 0$ (f) $x^2 - 13x + 12 = 0$

(g) $2x^2 - 8x = 0$ (h) $2x^2 + x - 15 = 0$ (i) $3x^2 - 75 = 0$

3. Communication

(a) Find the roots of the quadratic equation $x^2 - 6x + 5 = 0$ by using the quadratic formula and by factoring.

(b) Which method do you prefer? Why?

(c) Based on your results in (a), what do you know about the graph of $y = x^2 - 6x + 5$?

4. Solve the equation using the quadratic formula.

(a) $6x^2 - x - 15 = 0$ (b) $x^2 - 16 = 0$ (c) $x^2 + 9x + 20 = 0$

(d) $4x^2 - 10x + 25 = 0$ (e) $5x^2 - 11x = 0$ (f) $12x^2 - 40 = 17x$

(g) $6x^2 - 30x = -36$ (h) $2x^2 - 2x - 24 = 0$ (i) $x^2 - 8x - 24 = 0$

5. Determine how many real roots the equation has.

(a) $x^2 + 9 = 0$ (b) $x^2 + 5x - 8 = 0$ (c) $2x^2 - 12 = 0$

(d) $3x^2 + 2x + 6 = 0$ (e) $9x^2 + 12x + 4 = 0$ (f) $x^2 + 8x - 3 = 0$

(g) $(x - 4)^2 = 0$ (h) $-3(x + 2)^2 + 10 = 0$ (i) $(x - 2)^2 - 5 = 0$

Ⓑ

6. Solve each equation to two decimal places.

(a) $x^2 - 4x - 1 = 0$ (b) $2x^2 - x - 3 = 0$

(c) $5x^2 - 6x - 2 = 0$ (d) $m^2 - 5m + 3 = 0$

(e) $3w^2 + 8w + 2 = 0$ (f) $-3x^2 + 12x - 7 = 0$

(g) $-2x^2 + 8x - 3 = 0$ (h) $16y^2 + 8y + 1 = 0$

(i) $3m^2 + 10m - 7 = 0$

7. Using graphing technology, verify that your solutions in question 6 are correct. Graph the quadratic relation that corresponds to the equation and find the zeros of the graph.

8. A soup company makes cans with a radius of 4.6 cm and a height of 11.5 cm.

   (a) Find the volume of soup in the can.

   (b) The company wants to introduce a new can with a volume of 1.5 L. It decides to make the new cans with the same height, 11.5 cm. What is the radius of the new can? (Recall: $1 \text{ m}L = 1 \text{ cm}^3$.)

9. The surface area of the moon is about 37 939 289 km². Find the radius of the moon to the nearest kilometre.

10. Knowledge and Understanding

   (a) Find the roots of $2(x - 3)^2 - 11 = 0$ to two decimal places by isolating $(x - 3)^2$, then taking the square root of both sides.

   (b) Solve the equation in (a) by expanding $(x - 3)^2$, then using the quadratic formula.

   (c) Which method involves fewer steps?

11. Find the roots of the equation, if possible. Use the most appropriate method.

   (a) $x^2 - 8x = -16$ **(b)** $2x^2 + 3x - 20 = 0$

   (c) $(x - 5)^2 = 16$ **(d)** $x^2 + 10 = 0$

   (e) $-2(x + 1)^2 + 10 = 0$ **(f)** $x^2 = 90 - 6x$

   (g) $-5x^2 + 15x = 11$ **(h)** $3.2w^2 + 28.9w - 8.4 = 0$

   (i) $-4.9(t - 4)^2 + 50 = 0$

12. Communication: A ball is thrown up into the air. Its height h, in metres, after t seconds is $h = -4.9t^2 + 38t + 1.75$.

   (a) What is the height of the ball after 3 s?

   (b) For what length of time is the ball above 50 m?

   (c) What is the maximum height of the ball?

   (d) When does the ball strike the ground?

   (e) Verify your answers using graphing technology.

13. The annual budget B, in $billions, for the National Aeronautics and Space Administration (NASA) is approximated by the quadratic relation $B = -0.1492x^2 + 1.8058x + 9$, where x is the number of years since 1988.

   (a) Use the model to predict NASA's budget in 2001.

   (b) When does the model indicate that NASA's budget was about $12 billion?

   (c) In what year was NASA's budget at its maximum?

14. A cliff diver in Acapulco, Mexico, dives from about 17 m above the water. The diver's height above the water h, in metres, after t seconds is modelled by $h = -4.9t^2 + 1.5t + 17$. How long is the diver in the air?

15. The algebraic relation $d = 0.0056s^2 + 0.14s$ models the relation between a vehicle's stopping distance d, in metres, and its speed s, in kilometres per hour.

    (a) What is the fastest you could drive and still be able to stop within 80 m?

    (b) What is the stopping distance for a car travelling at 120 km/h?

    (c) Estimate the length of an average car. How many car lengths does the stopping distance in (b) correspond to?

16. Application: A rectangle is 3 cm longer than it is wide. The diagonal is 15 cm. Find the dimensions of the rectangle.

17. The altitude of a triangle is 2 m longer than its base. What are the dimensions of the altitude and the base if the area of the triangle is 40 m²?

18. A bus company has 4000 passengers daily, each paying a fare of $2. For each $0.15 increase, the company estimates that it will lose 40 passengers. If the company needs to take in $10 450 per day to stay in business, what fare should be charged?

19. Tickets to a school dance cost $4 and the projected attendance is 300 persons. For every $0.10 increase in ticket price, the dance committee projects that attendance will decrease by 5. What ticket price will generate $1237.50 in revenue?

20. (a) Solve $2x^2 = 20 - 3x$ to two decimal places.

    (b) Sketch the graph of the relation that corresponds to the equation in (a).

    (c) What are the zeros of the graph in (b)?

21. The student council at City High is thinking about selling school T-shirts. To help them decide what to do, they conducted a schoolwide survey. Students were asked, "Would you buy a school T-shirt at this price?" The results of the survey are shown.

T-Shirt Price (t)	Students Who Would Buy (N)	Revenue (R)
$4.00	923	
$6.00	752	
$8.00	608	
$10.00	455	
$12.00	287	
$14.00	139	

    (a) Use the table to find the revenue corresponding to each possible price.

    (b) Draw a scatter plot relating the revenue R to the T-shirt price t. Sketch the curve of best fit.

    (c) Verify that the linear relation $N \doteq 1230 - 78t$ exists.

    (d) Use the equation in (c) to find an algebraic expression for the revenue.

    (e) The student council needs to bring in revenue of at least $4750. What price range can they consider?

(f) What T-shirt price will generate the greatest revenue? What is the greatest revenue possible? Verify your results using technology. The council doesn't want to handle a lot of change. What is the optimum price that is a multiple of $0.25?

22. (a) In the previous question, the student council buys the shirts for $4. The council must also pay a one-time charge of $100 for the printer to set up the school logo. Write an equation for their expenses (E).

(b) Write a simplified equation for the profit P based on $P = R - E$. Calculate the break-even price for selling T-shirts algebraically by finding the roots of $P = 0$. Interpret the results.

(c) Express the profit equation you found in (b) in vertex form, using an algebraic method. What T-shirt price will generate the greatest profit? What is the expected profit at this price? Suggest the price, rounded to the nearest $0.25, that will maximize profit. Is it the same as the price that maximizes revenue?

(d) Use graphing technology to graph the revenue R, expense E, and profit P equations. Use technology to verify the algebraic values you found in (b) and (c).

23. Repeat the steps in question 22, using a T-shirt cost of $3.50 and a set-up charge of $150.

24. At Bell Park, a landscaper wishes to plant a uniform border of tulips on the inside of a rectangular garden with dimensions of 18 m by 12 m. The garden will look best if the area of the tulip border is half the area of the garden. How wide should the inside border of tulips be, to one decimal place?

25. A framer at a photo gallery wants to frame a print with a matte of uniform width all around the print. To make it pleasing to the eye, the area of the matte should equal the area of the print. If the print measures 40 cm by 60 cm, how wide should the matte be?

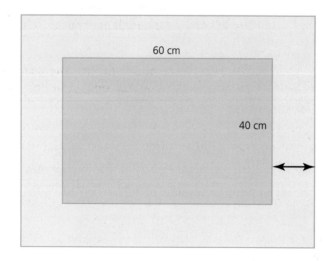

26. A box with no top is to be made by cutting a 10 cm square from each corner of a square sheet of metal. After bending up the sides, the volume of the box must be 64 000 cm³. How large must the original piece of metal be? Round to the nearest hundredth.

27. A right triangle has a perimeter of 36 units. If the hypotenuse is 15 units, how long are the other two sides?

28. The Acme circular sprinkler waters a lawn out to a radius of 8 m. Watts Water Ways, a rival company, claims that their circular sprinkler waters an area 100% larger than the Acme sprinkler. What radius would their sprinkler have to reach for this claim to be true?

29. Check Your Understanding

(a) Solve $4x^2 - 10x - 24 = 0$ in three different ways. State the advantages and disadvantages of each method.

(b) Create a flow chart to help you decide which approach to use when you want to find the roots of a quadratic equation.

30. Find an algebraic expression for the solution to $0 = a(x - h)^2 + k$, without expanding.

31. Thinking, Inquiry, Problem Solving: Find the points of intersection of $y = x^2 + 9x + 18$ and $y = -2x^2 - 12x - 9$.

32. Find the point of intersection of $y = 3x + 5$ and $y = 3x^2 - 2x - 9$.

The Chapter Problem—Trends in the Smoking Habits of Canada's Youth

Cigarettes caus\
fatal lung diseas\
Health Canada

s are addictive\
Health Canada

Cigarettes c\
rokes and heart\
Health Can

In this section you solved quadratic equations using the quadratic formula. Apply what you learned to answer these questions about the chapter problem introduced on page 340.

1. Using the equations of your curves of best fit, find the year when there were equal percentages of male and female smokers in the population. (Hint: Use substitution.)

2. Using the quadratic regression equations you found in section 4.4, find the year when there were equal percentages of male and female smokers.

3. Use graphing technology to verify the results found in (2).

4. Comment on the trend in the smoking habits of Canadian youth. Discuss whether Health Canada's initiative of warning labels on cigarette packages is having an impact on this age group.

5. Do some research to investigate if the trend in adults (male and females over 20 years old) is similar.

4.8 Investigating Quadratic Relations

In this section you will perform several practical experiments that will enable you to apply the skills and understanding you learned in this chapter. In each case, you will

- conduct the experiment
- collect and record the appropriate data
- create a scatter plot and find the quadratic curve of best fit
- find a quadratic relation that models the relation in the data
- use the model to make predictions and answer questions

Experiment 1: Pendulum Length and Period—

In this activity, you will create pendulums of different lengths and develop algebraic models of the relation between the length of the pendulum and its period.

Equipment

- a piece of string about 1.5 m long
- two or three metal washers
- stopwatch or watch with a second hand

Procedure

1. Fasten the top of the string to a fixed location so that the bottom is free to swing. Tie or fasten the washers to the string 40 cm from the top.

2. One person will act as the timer. The timer will say when to release the pendulum.

3. Pull the washers back 20 cm from vertical. Measure to make sure that you always release the washers from the same spot. When the timer is ready, start timing as the washers are released.

4. Allow the pendulum to swing back and forth five times. Stop timing on the return of the fifth swing.

5. Calculate the average time of the five swings by dividing the recorded time by 5. This is your measurement that approximates the period of the pendulum. Enter the value in the table.

6. Repeat for the other pendulum lengths in the table.

Length of Pendulum (cm)	40	50	60	70	80	90	100
Period (s) (Measured Time ÷ 5)							

Analyzing the Data

1. Create a scatter plot of the data from the completed table.

2. Create a table of first differences based on the period measurements. What happens to the first differences as the length of the pendulum increases? What does this mean?

3. Model the data.

   (a) Find the linear regression model and the value of r^2.

   (b) Find the quadratic regression model and the value of r^2.

   (c) Which model seems to fit the data the best?

Experiment 2: Exploring Gravity and Acceleration

In this activity, you will explore how the time it takes for a ball to roll down a ramp is related to the length of the ramp. You will also investigate the effect of the angle of the ramp and the mass of the ball.

Equipment

- two metre sticks
- masking tape
- several books
- protractor
- golf ball, marble, or ping-pong ball
- stopwatch

Procedure

1. Make a ramp by taping two metre sticks together, side by side, in a V-shape.

2. Place one end of the ramp on a stack of books so that the other end forms an angle of about 10° with the floor. Measure the angle with a protractor.

3. Use a stopwatch or a watch with a second hand to measure the time it takes the ball to roll down to the end of the ramp from a marked starting point. Record the time and the distance for ten different starting points.

Time (s)	Distance Rolled (cm)

Analyzing the Data

1. Make a scatter plot of the data.

2. Does the data appear to show a linear or nonlinear relation?

3. Draw the curve of best fit and find a quadratic relation that models the data.

4. Use the model to predict how long the ball would take to roll 55 cm.

5. If you double the time the ball rolls, how does the distance change?

Repeat the experiment to answer the following:

6. If you change the angle of the ramp how does the algebraic model change?

7. Are the results of the experiment different if you use a lighter or heavier ball?

Experiment 3: Walk This Way —————

Equipment

- TI CBR (Calculator-Based Ranger)
- TI-83 Plus graphing calculator

Procedure

1. Be sure that the CBR and calculator are both OFF.

2. Connect the CBR to the calculator using the unit-to-unit connector cable. Connect the cable firmly to the INPUT/OUTPUT (I/O) port on the bottom of the calculator (see photograph).

3. Place the motion detector on a desk or chair or hold it steady. Place it so that it can detect the motion of a student walking directly toward or away from the detector.

4. Run the RANGER program. Turn the calculator ON and press APPS. Choose **2:CBR/CBL**, then press ENTER. Press any key. Choose **3:RANGER**, then press ENTER. Select **2: SET DEFAULTS**. The SETUP screen is now displayed. Press ENTER to choose START NOW.

5. Have a walker ready to walk in a such a way that the graph created is a parabola opening up. When the walker is ready, press ENTER on the calculator to begin collecting the data. You may need to repeat this step several times until you have a good example of a parabola.

Analyzing the Data

1. Press ENTER, then choose SELECT DOMAIN to eliminate any unwanted data.

2. Use TRACE to find the coordinates of the vertex and the coordinates of another point on the graph.

3. Use the information you found in step 2 to find an algebraic expression that models the path of the walker.

4. Check the accuracy of your model using quadratic regression on the data that was collected. Quit the RANGER program and then perform a quadratic regression analysis using the data stored in L1 and L2. How good is the fit of the model to the data? Explain

5. Repeat the experiment and have the walker walk so that the parabola created is

   (a) wider than the original parabola

   (b) narrower than the original parabola

6. Describe how the walker had to walk in terms of the original parabola to create the graphs in step 5.

7. Find algebraic expressions that model the parabolas in step 5.

8. How is the width of each parabola represented in your algebraic models?

9. How would the walker have to walk to create a parabola that is as wide as possible?

10. How would this be reflected in the algebraic model?

Experiment 4: What Goes Up Must Come Down

Equipment

- TI CBR (Calculator-Based Ranger)

- small exercise book, wad of crumpled paper, playground ball, hat, or some other light object to drop

- TI-83 Plus graphing calculator

Procedure A – Dropping Objects

1. Follow steps 1–4 of the procedures steps of Experiment 3 to set up the CBR and the calculator.

2. Place the motion detector on the floor (facing up) in an open spot in the classroom.

3. Three students are needed for this experiment: The catcher catches the dropped objects before they hit the motion detector. The dropper holds and drops the object. The CBR operator controls the calculator.

4. When you are ready, position the object to be dropped directly over the motion detector. When the calculator operator is ready, that person presses ENTER on the calculator to begin collecting data. When the motion detector begins to click, the dropper releases the object and the catcher catches it before it hits the motion detector.

Helpful Hints

- The catcher should move into position to catch the falling object, keeping his or her hands clear of the motion detector's beam.

- The dropper should hold the object about 1.5 m above the motion detector.

Analyzing the Data

1. The plot contains data points before the object was released and after it was caught. These should be removed before you begin your analysis. To do this, press ENTER on the calculator and select SET DOMAIN. Move the cursor to the position where the object starts its motion. Press ENTER. This marks the lower bound. Move the cursor to where the object stopped its motion. Press ENTER. This marks the upper bound. The program removes all the points outside the bounds and plots the new data. The new set of data is now stored in L1 (time) and L2 (distance).

2. Use TRACE to find the coordinates of the point that represents the object's maximum height. Does this graph represent a parabola or part of one? Explain.

3. What are the coordinates of the vertex?

4. Use TRACE to find the coordinates of another point on the graph.

5. Use the information you found to find a quadratic expression that models the path of the object.

6. Check the accuracy of your model using quadratic regression on the data that was collected.

7. How good is the fit of the model to the data?

8. What is the significance of the numbers in the model?

9. Repeat the experiment using a heavier object and a lighter object than the original. Try to drop these objects from the same height as the original.

10. Find algebraic models for these other objects. How do these compare to the original model?

Procedure B – Tossing Objects

1. Set up the equipment as in Procedure A, except this time place the motion detector facing up on the seat of a chair so that it can detect an object being tossed up over it.

2. Turn on the CBR and start the RANGER program on the calculator. The motion detector will start clicking.

3. Have the dropper hold the object over the motion detector so that the dropper's hands and arms are not detected by the sensor. The dropper then tosses the object directly above the motion detector (straight up and not at an angle).

4. This may need some practice. Repeat step 2 and 3 until you have a good set of data to analyze.

Analyzing the Data

1. Remove any points that do not correspond to the object's motion.

2. Use TRACE to find the coordinates of the point that represents the objects maximum height.

3. Use TRACE to find the coordinates of another point on the graph.

4. Use the information you found to find a quadratic expression that models the path of the object.

5. Check the accuracy of your model using quadratic regression on the data that was collected.

6. How good is the fit of the model to the data?

7. Repeat the experiment using a heavier object and a lighter object than the original. Try to toss these objects from the same height as the original.

8. Find algebraic models for these other objects. How do these compare to the original model?

9. If you used the same objects as in Procedure A, compare the models and comment on any similarities that you find.

Experiment 5: Car on a Ramp

Equipment

- TI CBR (Calculator-Based Ranger)

- TI-83 Plus graphing calculator

- several books, suitable material such as a piece of plywood to create a ramp, and a toy car, ball, or child's toy with wheels

Procedure

1. Make sure that the CBR and calculator are both OFF.

2. Follow steps 1–4 of the procedure in Experiment 3 to set up the CBR and the calculator.

3. Connect the motion detector to the SONIC port on the CBR. This port is on the left side of the unit.

4. Arrange the ramp so that it rests at an incline of no more than 3°. Steeper tracks will make the car move too quickly to study.

5. Place the motion detector so that it is about 50 cm from the end of the track.

6. Practise rolling the car up the ramp. You want to give it just the needed push to send it freely rolling up the ramp but not off the top. Catch the car before it returns to the bottom.

7. Turn the CBR unit and the calculator ON.

8. Start the RANGER program. When the motion detector starts clicking, have the pusher roll the car up the ramp.

9. Repeat step 8 until you have a good set of data to analyze.

Analyzing the Data

1. What x- and y-intercepts did you obtain?

2. Use the zeros to express the relationship between the position and time as an algebraic model in the form $y = a(x - s)(x - t)$.

3. Express your model in standard form.

4. Find the quadratic regression equation for your data. How does it compare to the model you found?

5. Find the coordinates of the vertex of your equation and TRACE to find the vertex of the regression equation. Compare these to the scatter plot and find which gives the best estimate for the maximum distance (minimum distance from the motion detector) the car actually reached.

6. What effect will increasing/decreasing the incline of the ramp have on your model?

7. Repeat the experiment to justify your predictions made in question 6.

Graphing Quadratic Relations and Using Them as Models
Check Your Understanding

1. How can you test whether the graph of a given quadratic relation passes through a given point?

2. What information can be determined about the graph of a quadratic relation when it is expressed in the form $y = ax^2 + bx + c$?

3. If the zeros of a parabola are s and t, and you are given the coordinates of another point on the curve, describe how you would find the equation for the curve.

4. Describe all the information that can be determined directly about the graph of a quadratic relation when it is expressed in the form $y = a(x - h)^2 + k$.

5. Using $y = 3x^2 + 12x - 15$ as an example of a quadratic relation in standard form show how to find the vertex using each technique below. Include any additional information that the technique gives about the graph of the relation.

   (a) factoring completely

   (b) using partial factors

   (c) completing the square

6. List any disadvantages of the techniques in question 5.

7. (a) What transformations are needed to obtain the graph of $y = a(x - h)^2 + k$ from the graph of $y = x^2$ under each of the following conditions?

   i. $a > 1,\ h < 0,\ k > 0$ **ii.** $0 < a < 1,\ h > 0,\ k < 0$

   iii. $-1 < a < 0,\ h = 0,\ k = 0$ **iv.** $a < -1,\ h < 0,\ k > 0$

   (b) Does the order in which the transformations are applied make a difference? Explain.

8. Using $y = 3x^2 + 12x - 15$ as an example of a quadratic relation in standard form, show the steps needed to find the zeros of the graph using each of the following techniques.

   (a) factoring completely

   (b) using graphing technology

   (c) completing the square

9. Draw a sketch to show examples of a relation $y = a(x - h)^2 + k$ that has

   (a) no zeros

   (b) one zero

   (c) two zeros

10. Give an example of a quadratic equation that has

    (a) no real roots

    (b) one real root

    (c) two real roots

11. Describe several ways that you can find the roots of a quadratic equation in the form $a(x - h)^2 + k = 0$.

4.1–4.2 The Vertex Form of a Quadratic Relation

- The expression $y = a(x - h)^2 + k$ defines a quadratic relation.

- The graph of $y = a(x - h)^2 + k$ is a vertical translation of $y = a(x - h)^2$ by k units.

- When a quadratic relation is in the form $y = a(x - h)^2 + k$, the coordinates of the vertex of the corresponding parabola are (h, k). As a result, $y = a(x - h)^2 + k$ is called the **vertex form** of a quadratic relation.

- If the coordinates of the vertex (h, k) are known, you can write the quadratic relation in vertex form by substituting h and k into $y = a(x - h)^2 + k$. To find the value of a, substitute the coordinates of another point that satisfies the relation into the equation, then solve for a.

- If $a > 0$, the parabola opens upward. If $a < 0$, the parabola opens downward.

- A quadratic relation in vertex form $y = a(x - h)^2 + k$ can be converted to standard form $y = ax^2 + bx + c$ by expanding and collecting like terms.

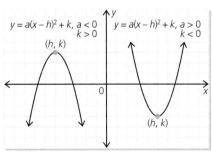

Example

When Homer Simmons hits a baseball, its height h, in metres, after t seconds is $h = -5.2(t - 3)^2 + 48$.

(a) What is the height of the ball at the instant it is hit?

(b) Find the maximum height of the ball and the time when this height is reached.

(c) The ball hits the outfield wall at $t = 5.9$ s. How high up the wall does the ball hit?

Solution

(a) When Homer makes contact with the ball, $t = 0$.

$$h = -5.2(0-3)^2 + 48$$
$$h = -5.2(9) + 48$$
$$h = 1.2$$

The initial height of the ball is 1.2 m.

(b) The equation is in vertex form. Since $a = -5.2$, the graph opens downward. The ball reaches its maximum height, 48 m, 3 s after it is hit.

(c) Let $t = 5.9$ and solve for h.

$$h = -5.2(5.9 - 3)^2 + 48$$
$$h = -5.2(8.41) + 48$$
$$h = 4.3$$

The ball hits the wall at a height of 4.3 m.

Extra Practice

1. Find the vertex and direction of opening of the graph of the quadratic relation.

   (a) $y = 2(x - 4)^2$ **(b)** $y = (x + 2)^2 - 5$ **(c)** $y = -3x^2 + 6$

2. Find, in vertex form, the equation of the quadratic relation

   (a) with vertex at $(0, 7)$, passing through $(-2, -3)$

   (b) with vertex at $(3, 0)$, passing through $(1, -8)$

   (c) with vertex at $(-1, -4)$, passing through $(3, 4)$

3. For each quadratic relation you found in question 2,

   (a) is the point $(2, -3)$ on the graph?

   (b) find one other point on the graph

4. (a) Find the relation in the form $y = a(x - s)(x - t)$ for a parabola that has zeros -1 and 5 and passes through $(3, 16)$.

(b) Express the relation you found in (a) in vertex form $y = a(x - h)^2 + k$.

5. A rock is tossed into the air from a bridge over a river. Its height h above the water, in metres, after t seconds is $h = -4.9(t - 2)^2 + 29$.

(a) From what height above the water is the rock tossed?

(b) Find the maximum height of the rock and the time when this height is reached.

(c) Is the ball still in the air after 4.5 s?

4.3 Using Technology to Investigate Transformations of Quadratics

- The relation defined by $y = x^2$ (figure 1) is the simplest quadratic relation. It is the base curve for all quadratic relations.

- The graph of any quadratic relation can be created by altering and repositioning the graph of $y = x^2$. Possible changes include shifting the graph up or down, shifting it left or right, vertically stretching or compressing the graph, or reflecting it about the x-axis. These types of changes are called **transformations.**

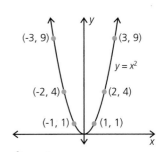

figure 1

- When a quadratic relation is in **vertex form**, $y = a(x - h)^2 + k$, several properties of the graph of the relation are obvious:

  ◆ If $k > 0$, then the graph of $y = x^2$ is translated vertically up by k units. If $k < 0$, then the graph is translated down by k units. If $k = 0$, the graph has one x-intercept (figure 2).

  ◆ If $h > 0$, then the graph of $y = x^2$ is translated horizontally h units to the right. If $h < 0$, then the graph is translated h units to the left (figure 3).

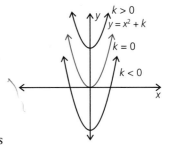

figure 2

  ◆ If $a > 0$, then the curve opens upward. If $a < 0$, then the graph is reflected about the x-axis and the curve opens downward (figure 4).

  ◆ If $-1 < a < 1$, then the graph of $y = x^2$ is compressed vertically by a factor of $\dfrac{1}{a}$. The resulting graph has an opening that is wider than $y = x^2$ (figure 5).

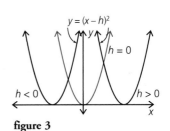

figure 3

- ♦ If $a > 1$ or $a < -1$, then the graph of $y = x^2$ is stretched vertically by a factor of a. The resulting graph has an opening that is narrower than $y = x^2$ (figure 5).

- When you use transformations to graph $y = a(x - h)^2 + k$ from $y = x^2$, apply the transformations in this order:

  (1) translation left or right

  (2) vertical stretch or compression

  (3) reflection about the x-axis

  (4) translation up or down

- If a and k have opposite signs, then the graph has two x-intercepts, or zeros. If a and k have the same signs, then the graph has no x-intercepts.

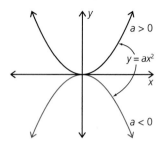

figure 4

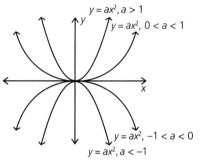

figure 5

Example

(a) Describe the transformations that must be performed on the graph of $y = x^2$ to obtain the graph of $y = -2(x + 3)^2 + 10$.

(b) Sketch a graph of the transformed curve.

Solution

(a) Express the equation in vertex form: $y = -2(x - (-3))^2 + 10$.

Stretch the graph of $y = x^2$ vertically by a factor of 2.

Reflect the graph about the x-axis.

Translate the graph 3 units to the left and 10 units up.

(b) Plot the vertex at $(-3, 10)$. Substitute a value for x, close to the x-coordinate of the vertex, into the equation and solve for y. For example, choose $x = -1$ and solve

$$y = -2(2)^2 + 10$$
$$= -8 + 10$$
$$= 2$$

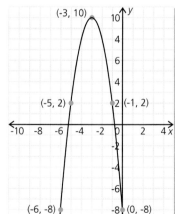

Plot the point $(-1, 2)$. Use symmetry to find and plot a second point $(-5, 2)$ on the other side of the axis of symmetry. Choosing $x = 0$, solve $y = -2(3)^2 + 10 = -8$. Plot point $(0, -8)$ and (by symmetry) point $(-6, -8)$. Draw a curve through these points.

Extra Practice

6. Find the vertex, axis of symmetry, and direction of opening of the parabola. Use this information to sketch the graph.

(a) $y = (x - 2)^2 + 1$ (b) $y = -\frac{1}{2}(x + 4)^2$ (c) $y = 2(x + 1)^2 - 8$

7. Describe, using transformations, how the graph of $y = x^2$ can be transformed into the graph of the quadratic relation. How many x-intercepts does the graph have?

(a) $y = 5x^2 - 4$ (b) $y = -\frac{1}{4}(x - 5)^2$ (c) $y = -3(x + 2)^2 - 7$

8. Recall that the height of an object, in metres above the ground, t seconds after it is dropped is $h = -0.5gt^2 + k$, where g is the acceleration due to gravity and k is the height from which the object is released. If an object is released from a height of 400 m, how much longer does it take to descend to a height of 75 m on the Moon compared to on Earth? The acceleration due to gravity is 9.8 m/s^2 on Earth and 1.6 m/s^2 on the Moon.

4.4 Using Symmetry to Relate Standard Form to Vertex Form

- Given a quadratic relation in the form $y = ax^2 + bx + c$, you can use algebraic techniques to find the vertex and axis of symmetry.

- If the quadratic relation can be **completely factored**, you can find the zeros by making each of the factors equal to zero. The axis of symmetry and the x-coordinate of the vertex can be found from the midpoint between the zeros. Substitute this x-value into the relation to find the y-coordinate of the vertex.

- If the quadratic function $y = ax^2 + bx + c$ cannot be completely factored, you can use **partial factoring** to express it in the form $y = x(ax + b) + c$. This form suggests two points on the graph: $(0, c)$ and $\left(-\frac{b}{a}, c\right)$. The axis of symmetry is halfway between these points and has the equation $x = -\frac{b}{2a}$.

  Substitute $x = -\frac{b}{2a}$ into the relation to find the y-coordinate of the vertex.

- Once you know the vertex, and using the value of a from the original equation, you can express the relation in vertex form $y = a(x - h)^2 + k$.

Example

Find the minimum value of the graph of $y = 3x^2 - 9x - 30$ and use it to express the equation in vertex form.

Solution

The method of complete or partial factors can be used. The parabola opens upward.

Using complete factoring,

$$y = 3x^2 - 9x - 30$$
$$y = 3(x^2 - 3x - 10)$$
$$y = 3(x - 5)(x + 2)$$

The zeros are $x = 5$ and $x = -2$.

The axis of symmetry is $x = \frac{(-2 + 5)}{2} = \frac{3}{2}$.

Using partial factors,

$$y = 3x^2 - 9x - 30$$
$$y = x(3x - 9) - 30 \text{ or}$$
$$y = 3x(x - 3) - 30$$

Therefore $(0, -30)$ and $(3, -30)$ are on the graph. The axis of symmetry passes through the midpoint, so $x = \frac{(0 + 3)}{2} = \frac{3}{2}$.

Alternatively, the x-coordinate of the vertex is $x = -\frac{b}{2a}$.

In all three cases $x = \frac{3}{2}$ or 1.5.

Substitute $x = \frac{3}{2}$ or 1.5 and solve for the y-coordinate of the vertex.

$$y = 3(1.5 - 5)(1.5 + 2)$$
$$y = 3(-3.5)(3.5)$$
$$y = -36.75$$

The minimum value of the graph is -36.75 or $-\frac{147}{4}$.

The equation in vertex form is $y = 3(x - 1.5)^2 - 36.75$ or $y = 3\left(x - \frac{3}{2}\right)^2 - \frac{147}{4}$.

Extra Practice

9. For each quadratic relation,

   i. find the coordinates of two points on the graph

   ii. find the axis of symmetry

   iii. find the coordinates of the vertex

   iv. rewrite the relation in vertex form

   (a) $y = (x - 1)(x + 7)$ **(b)** $y = x(x - 6) - 8$

   (c) $y = -2(x + 3)(x - 7)$ **(d)** $y = x(3x + 12) + 2$

   (e) $y = x^2 + 5x$ **(f)** $y = x^2 - 11x + 21$

   (g) $y = 4x^2 - 4x - 35$ **(h)** $y = x^2 + 10x - 6$

   (i) $y = -2x^2 + 12x - 11$

10. A punter kicks a football. Its height h, in metres, after t seconds is
$h = -4.9t^2 + 22.54t + 1.1$.

  (a) What was the height of the ball when the punter kicked it?

  (b) To one decimal place, find the maximum height of the football and the time when it reached this height.

11. The city transit system carries an average of 9450 bus riders a day, for a fare of $1.75 each. The city wants to reduce car pollution by increasing ridership and to maximize the transit system's revenue at the same time. A survey indicates that the number of riders will increase by 150 for every $0.05 decrease in fare.

  (a) Write an equation to represent the total daily revenue, using f to represent the fare for one passenger, in dollars. Remember that
  revenue = fare × number of passengers.

  (b) What fare will result in the greatest revenue?

  (c) Find the expected number of riders and the total daily revenue at this fare.

4.5–4.6 Determining Maximum and Minimum Values Algebraically: Completing the Square

- Quadratic relations in standard form $y = ax^2 + bx + c$ can be rewritten in vertex form $y = a(x - h)^2 + k$ by creating a perfect square in the expression, then factoring the square. This technique is called **completing the square**.

- Completing the square involves the following steps:

  Example: $y = 2x^2 + 12x - 3$

  (1) Remove the common constant factor from both the x^2- and x-term.

  (1) $y = 2(x^2 + 6x) - 3$

  (2) Find the constant that must be added and subtracted to create a perfect square. This value equals the square of half of the coefficient of the x-term in step 1. Rewrite the expression by adding, then subtracting, this value after the x-term inside the brackets.

  (2) $y = 2(x^2 + 6x + 9 - 9) - 3$

  (3) Group the three terms that form the perfect square. Move the subtracted value outside the brackets by multiplying it by the common constant factor.

  (3) $y = 2(x^2 + 6x + 9) - 18 - 3$

  (4) Factor the perfect square and collect like terms.

  (4) $y = 2(x + 3)^2 - 21$

- Completing the square can be used to find the vertex of a quadratic in standard form without finding the zeros of the relation or two points equidistant from the axis of symmetry.

- Completing the square allows you to find the maximum or minimum value of a quadratic relation algebraically, without using a graph.

Example

The organizing committee of the Snowflake Winter Carnival found that the profit P from the carnival depends on the ticket price t and the number of people who attend (which also depends on the ticket price). The estimated profit is given by the relation $P = -37t^2 + 1258t - 7700$. Complete the square to find the ticket price that will maximize the profit. Find the expected profit at this price.

Solution

$P = -37t^2 + 1258t - 7700$ Factor -37 from $-37t^2 + 1258t - 7700$.

$P = -37(t^2 - 34t) - 7700$ Determine what to add and subtract to make

$P = -37(t^2 - 34t + 289 - 289) - 7700$ a perfect square: $\left(-\dfrac{34}{2}\right)^2 = 289$.

$P = -37(t^2 - 34t + 289) + 10\ 693 - 7700$ Group the first three terms. Expand, then

$P = -37(t - 17)^2 + 2993$ factor the perfect square, and simplify.

A ticket price of $17 is expected to produce a profit of $2993.

Extra Practice

12. Express the quadratic relation in vertex form by completing the square.

(a) $y = x^2 + 6x - 3$ (b) $y = -2x^2 - 8x - 11$

(c) $y = \dfrac{1}{2}x^2 + 5x - 7$ (d) $y = 3x^2 + 6x - 5$

13. A baseball is hit from a height of 0.8 m. After t seconds, its height h, in metres, is $h = -5t^2 + 20t + 0.8$.

(a) Use the method of completing the square to find the maximum height of the ball.

(b) Describe a second method you could use to find the maximum height.

14. In the example above, the Snowflake Winter Carnival committee did not include the revenue from sales of Snowflake toques and scarves in their profit estimate. Taking the expected sales into account, the new estimated profit is given by $P = -37t^2 + 1110t - 4368$.

(a) Find the new ticket price that maximizes the profit.

(b) Find the expected profit at this new price.

(c) Explain how it is possible for the committee to make a greater profit even though the ticket price is less.

4.7 Solving Quadratic Equations: The Quadratic Formula

- The roots of a quadratic equation in the form $a(x - h)^2 + k = 0$ can be found algebraically without expanding. First, isolate $(x - h)^2$, giving $(x - h)^2 = -\frac{k}{a}$. After taking the square root of both sides, you can solve for x.

- The roots of a quadratic equation in the form $ax^2 + bx + c = 0$ can sometimes be found by factoring.

- The roots of a quadratic equation in the form $ax^2 + bx + c = 0$ can be found using the **quadratic formula**: $x = \dfrac{-b \pm \sqrt{b^2 - 4ac}}{2a}$.

- A quadratic equation must be expressed in standard form $ax^2 + bx + c = 0$ before it can be solved by factoring or by using the quadratic formula.

- The quadratic formula sometimes leads to a negative number under the square root sign. When this happens, the calculation cannot be completed using ordinary numbers (called **real** numbers). In this case, the relation has **no real roots**.

- Numbers such as $\sqrt{-16}$ and $\sqrt{-35}$ are called **imaginary numbers**. They are not real numbers since the square root of a negative number does not exist in the set of real numbers. They are part of a larger set of numbers called complex numbers, which are important in advanced mathematics. When an equation has no real roots, it may have complex or non-real roots.

- In the quadratic formula, the value of $b^2 - 4ac$ determines the number and type of roots a quadratic equation has. This expression is often called the **discriminant.**

- When using the quadratic formula,

  ♦ if $b^2 - 4ac > 0$, then the quadratic equation has 2 real roots

  ♦ if $b^2 - 4ac = 0$, then the quadratic equation has 1 real root

  ♦ if $b^2 - 4ac < 0$, then the quadratic equation has no real roots

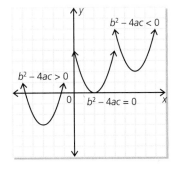

Example

A school photographer conducted a survey to evaluate the demand for school pictures at different prices. He found that as the price t for a package of pictures increased, student demand for the packages decreased. If N represents the number of packages sold, he decided that $N = 600 - 30t$ would be a good model for the demand. It costs the photographer \$2 to produce each package plus \$180 in fixed costs.

(a) Find the revenue equation R in terms of the package price t.

(b) Find the maximum revenue possible under this model.

(c) Find a simplified expression for the expected profit P.

(d) Calculate the prices and expected sales needed to break even.

(e) What price will maximize the profit?

Solution

(a) $R = price \times sales$

$R = t \times N = t(600 - 30t)$

(b) The expression in (a) is already partially factored, so it can be used to find the vertex. Points $(0, 0)$ and $(20, 0)$ are on the graph of R.

The maximum occurs at $t = \dfrac{(0 + 20)}{2} = 10$ and

$$R = 10(600 - 30(10))$$
$$= 10(300)$$
$$= 3000$$

The maximum possible revenue is \$3000, with a package selling for \$10. (He expects to sell 300 packages at this price.)

(c) $P = revenue - expenses$

$P = revenue - (\$2 \times sales \text{ plus } \$180 \text{ fixed cost})$

$P = t(600 - 30t) - (2(600 - 30t) + 180)$

$P = 600t - 30t^2 - 1200 + 60t - 180$

$P = -30t^2 + 660t - 1380$

(d) The break-even price is the price where $revenue = expenses$ or $P = 0$. P does not factor fully, but you can use the quadratic formula to find the roots of P.

$$t = \frac{-660 \pm \sqrt{660^2 - 4(-30)(-1380)}}{2(-30)}$$

$$t = \frac{-660 \pm \sqrt{270\,000}}{-60}$$

$$t \doteq \frac{-660 \pm 519.615\ 24}{-60}$$

$t \doteq 19.66$ and $t \doteq 2.34$

The number of sales is given by $N = 600 - 30t$. Substitute the values of t that have been found.

$N = 600 - 30(19.66) = 10.2$ and $N = 600 - 30(2.34) = 529.8$

The photographer will break even with a price of $19.66 and about 10 sales or a price of $2.34 and about 530 sales. Any price between these prices will result in a profit.

(e) The maximum profit occurs midway between 19.66 and 2.34, at

$\frac{19.66 + 2.34}{2} = 11.00$. A price of $11 will maximize the profit. Expected

sales will be $N = 600 - 30(11) = 270$ and the maximum profit will be
$P = 11(270) - (2(270) + 180) = \$2250$.

Extra Practice

15. Find the x-intercepts for the graph of the quadratic relation. Use the most appropriate method.

(a) $y = x^2 - 25$

(b) $y = 3x^2 - 12x$

(c) $y = x^2 - 2x - 35$

(d) $y = (x - 3)^2 - 16$

(e) $y = 6x^2 - x - 15$

(f) $y = -2(x + 5)^2 + 18$

16. Without finding the roots, determine how many real roots the quadratic equation has.

(a) $-2x^2 - 11 = 0$

(b) $x^2 - 7x - 10 = 0$

(c) $-3x^2 + 5x - 6 = 0$

(d) $(x + 7)^2 = 0$

(e) $-2(x - 3)^2 + 13 = 0$

(f) $3x - 8 + 2x^2 = 0$

17. Find the roots, if any, of the equation, using the most appropriate method. Round the answers to two decimal places.

(a) $x^2 - 6x = -9$

(b) $(x - 5)^2 = 36$

(c) $m^2 - 4m + 3 = 0$

(d) $-3x^2 - 2x + 10 = 0$

(e) $2x^2 - 5x + 6 = 0$

(f) $x^2 + 7x + 2 = 0$

(g) $4x^2 - 20x + 25 = 0$

(h) $3(t - 4)^2 = 30$

(i) $4.9t^2 + 21.5t - 10.2 = 0$

18. A water balloon is catapulted into the air so that its height h, in metres, after t seconds is $h = -4.9t^2 + 27t + 2.4$.

   (a) How high is the balloon after 1 s?

   (b) For how long is the balloon more than 30 m high?

   (c) What is the maximum height of the balloon?

   (d) When will the balloon burst as it hits the ground?

   (e) Verify your work using graphing technology.

19. (a) In the example above, find a new simplified expression for the photographer's expected profit P if it costs $3 to produce each package plus $150 in fixed costs.

   (b) Calculate the new prices and expected sales needed to break even.

   (c) What price will maximize the profit?

   (d) Use graphing technology to graph the revenue R, profit P, and the expense equation, all in terms of the package price t. Verify your solutions from (b) and (c).

Chapter 4 Summary

In this chapter, you used quadratic relations to answer questions about gravity and acceleration, the height of projectiles, the shapes of parabolic structures, and how to maximize revenue and profit. Through transformations of the base graph of $y = x^2$, you discovered the vertex form of a quadratic relation.

To get an accurate graph of a quadratic relation or to answer questions about maxima or minima, you need to find the coordinates of the vertex. You can find the vertex using several methods. If the relation factors completely, the roots of the relation are easy to find and can be used to locate the axis of symmetry. When the relation doesn't factor completely, the method of partial factors can be used to find two points on the graph that are equidistant from the axis of symmetry. A third method, called completing the square, was developed; it does not require you to find the x- and y-coordinates of the vertex before expressing a relation in vertex form. Completing the square was also used to develop the quadratic formula, which enables you to find the roots of a quadratic relation that cannot be solved by factoring.

Learning to use the most appropriate method to find the vertex or the roots of a quadratic relation is an important step in becoming a good problem solver.

Graphing Quadratic Relations and Using Them as Models

1. Find the vertex, axis of symmetry, and direction of opening of the parabola. Use this information to sketch the graph.

   (a) $y = x^2 - 7$
   (b) $y = (x - 3)^2$
   (c) $y = -(x + 1)^2 + 10$

   (d) $y = 3x^2 - 12$
   (e) $y = -\frac{1}{2}(x + 2)^2 - 3$
   (f) $y = -2(x - 5)^2 + 6$

2. Describe how the graph of $y = x^2$ can be transformed, step by step, to obtain the graph of each quadratic relation in question 1.

3. Find the quadratic relation in vertex form that
   (a) has its vertex at $(-6, 0)$ and passes through $(-3, 27)$
   (b) has its vertex at $(3, 7)$ and passes through $(-1, -17)$
   (c) has its vertex at $(-4, -2)$ and has a y-intercept of -8
   (d) has zeros -3 and 5 and passes through $(3, 6)$

4. Express each relation you found in (3) in standard form $y = ax^2 + bx + c$.

5. Without graphing, tell how many zeros (x-intercepts) the quadratic relation has. Justify your answers.

   (a) $y = x^2 + 3$
   (b) $y = -3(x + 5)^2$
   (c) $y = \frac{2}{3}(x - 2)^2 - 7$

6. A concrete bridge over a river has an underside in the shape of a parabolic arch. At the water level, the arch is 30 m wide. It has a maximum height of 10 m above the water. The minimum vertical thickness of the concrete is 1.5 m.

   (a) Find an algebraic relation that represents the shape of the arch.
   (b) What is the vertical thickness of the concrete 3 m from the centre of the arch?
   (c) If the water level rises 2 m, how wide will the arch be at this new level?

7. A baseball is hit into the air by the Blue Jays' batting coach. Its height h, in metres, after t seconds is $h = -4.9(t - 2.8)^2 + 39$.

   (a) How high off the ground was the ball when it was hit?
   (b) What is the maximum height of the ball?
   (c) What is the height of the ball after 2.5 s? Is it on the way up or down? Justify your answer.
   (d) Is the ball still in the air after 6 s? Explain how you know.
   (e) To one decimal place, when does the ball hit the ground?

8. Find the coordinates of the vertex of the quadratic relation using the most appropriate method. List two other points that lie on the graph of the relation. Express the relation in vertex form.

(a) $y = 2(x - 3)(x + 7)$

(b) $y = x(2x + 6) - 11$

(c) $y = -3x^2 + 12x + 15$

(d) $y = x^2 - 6x - 4$

(e) $y = 4x^2 - 11x - 55$

(f) $y = 5x^2 + 20x - 11$

9. A farmer has $2400 to spend to fence two rectangular pastures as shown in the diagram. The local contractor will build the fence at a cost of $6.25/m. What is the largest total area that the farmer can have fenced for that price?

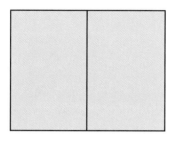

10. Write the quadratic equation in vertex form $y = a(x - h)^2 + k$ by completing the square.

(a) $y = x^2 - 6x + 11$

(b) $y = -3x^2 + 18x + 29$

11. Without finding the roots, determine how many real roots the quadratic equation has.

(a) $4x^2 - 20x + 25 = 0$

(b) $-3(x - 7)^2 + 18 = 0$

(c) $2x^2 + 8 = 5x$

12. Target-shooting disks are launched into the air from a machine 12 m above the ground. The height h, in metres, t seconds after launch is $h = -5t^2 + 30t + 12$.

(a) Describe two algebraic methods that you can use to find the maximum height of the discs.

(b) Select one of these methods and use it to find the maximum height of the discs.

(c) Assuming a disc hits the ground, use the quadratic formula to find when this happens. Answer to the nearest tenth of a second.

13. Explain how the method of partial factors enables you to find the vertex of a quadratic relation. Discuss why you cannot use this method to find the zeros of a quadratic relation.

Cumulative Review Test 2

Quadratic Functions

1. Using finite differences, determine whether the data represents a linear or quadratic relation.

(a)

Radius (cm)	1	2	3	4	5
Area (cm²)	3.14	12.56	28.26	50.24	78.5

(b)

Radius (m)	10	20	30	40	50
Circumference (m)	62.8	125.6	188.4	251.2	314

2. Examine this parabola.

    (a) State the coordinates of its vertex.

    (b) What is the optimal value?

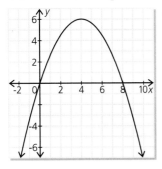

    (c) What is the equation of the axis of symmetry?

    (d) State the zeros of the relation.

    (e) Find the equation of this parabola.

3. A student running a ski trip over March Break determined that his break-even point (zero profit) occurs if he can sell ski packages to 12 students. He also knows that when he sells 16 ski packages he will maximize his profit at $2000.

    (a) Assume that the relation for his profit is quadratic. Sketch a graph that models his situation.

    (b) Determine the algebraic expression in standard form that models his profit.

    (c) What is his profit if he sells 18 packages?

(d) How many students were on the trip if his profit is $875?

4. Expand and simplify.

    (a) $(2x - 3)(4x + 1)$ **(b)** $(5h - 2k)(3h - k)$

    (c) $(3x - 5)^2$ **(d)** $(g - 4)(g - 4)$

5. Factor.

    (a) $x^2 + 2x - 15$ **(b)** $3x^2 + 15x + 18$

    (c) $9x^2 - 12x + 4$ **(d)** $16a^2 - 25b^2$

    (e) $12x^2 - 5x - 2$

6. A model rocket is launched from the roof of a building. Its flight path through the air is modelled by $h = -5t^2 + 30t + 10$, where h is the height of the rocket above ground in metres and t is the time after the launch in seconds.

    (a) Sketch a graph that represents the flight of the rocket.

    (b) How high is the building?

    (c) When will the rocket hit the ground?

    (d) What is the rocket's maximum height?

    (e) When is the rocket 45 m off the ground?

7. **(a)** Identify the transformations and the sequence in which they must be applied to the graph of $y = x^2$ to obtain $y = -2(x + 5)^2 - 3$.

    (b) Graph $y = x^2$, then apply the transformations in (a) to graph $y = -2(x + 5)^2 - 3$.

8. Graph $y = 2x^2 - 4x + 7$, by first expressing it in vertex form.

9. Solve.

    (a) $x^2 + 6x = 72$

    (b) $(2x + 1)(3x - 5) = 15$

10. The average ticket price to see a Drive-in movie between 1993 and 1998, is modelled by $C = 0.075t^2 - 0.25t + 5.85$, where C is the cost of the ticket in dollars and t is the number of years after 1993 ($t = 0$ in 1993) (Source: Motion Picture Theatre Association of Canada).

(a) What will be the admission cost in 2005?

(b) When will the admission cost be $7.75?

(c) Determine the minimum admission. When will this occur?

11. This table shows how many domestic and imported passenger cars were bought in Canada from 1995 to 1999.

Sales of Passenger Cars in Canada, 1995–1999

	1995	1996	1997	1998	1999
Domestic	553 265	572 581	629 488	590 667	625 393
Imported	116 925	88 188	109 062	150 142	181 158

Source: Statistics Canada, CANSIM, Matrix 64

Here is a linear and quadratic model for each type of vehicle.

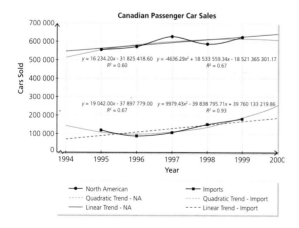

Canadian Passenger Car Sales

$y = 16\ 234.20x - 31\ 825\ 418.60$ $R^2 = 0.60$
$y = -4636.29x^2 + 18\ 533\ 559.34x - 18\ 521\ 365\ 301.17$ $R^2 = 0.67$
$y = 19\ 042.00x - 37\ 897\ 779.00$ $R^2 = 0.67$
$y = 9979.43x^2 - 39\ 838\ 795.71x + 39\ 760\ 133\ 219.86$ $R^2 = 0.93$

North American
Quadratic Trend - NA
Linear Trend - NA
Imports
Quadratic Trend - Import
Linear Trend - Import

(a) Use both models to project purchases in 2000 and 1994.

(b) Discuss which predictions you feel more confident in. Justify your choice.

12. This table shows how many injuries resulted from motor vehicle accidents in Canada from 1984 to 1998.

Year	Injuries
1984	237 455
1986	264 481
1988	278 618
1990	262 680
1992	249 821
1994	245 110
1996	230 890
1998	217 614

Source: Transport Canada

(a) Create a scatter plot and draw the graph of best fit.

(b) Determine the equation of the graph of best fit.

(c) Check the accuracy of your model using quadratic regression.

(d) Use one of your models to predict how many accidents will result in injury in 2002. Explain why you chose the model you did.

(e) According to the quadratic regression model, when were accidents that resulted in injury at their maximum levels?

Quadratic Functions

THE FOLLOWING ACTIVITIES SHOULD EACH TAKE LESS THAN A PERIOD TO COMPLETE

1. The Rabbit Colony

The population of a colony of rabbits on an isolated island is recorded below.

Time t (weeks)	5	10	15	20	25	30
Rabbit Population R	140	200	280	400	570	800

Scientists studying the colony have found that the food supply after t weeks is enough to feed N rabbits, according to this table.

Time t (weeks)	5	10	15	20	25
Food Supply (enough to feed N rabbits)	440	480	520	560	600

(a) When is the population of the rabbit colony balanced with the available food supply?

(b) Based on the available data, discuss possible changes in the rabbit population over time.

2. To Fill or Not to Fill

As part of your job with the Ministry of the Environment, you monitor the amount of waste material received at the Barnesdale landfill site. Your records show how much waste has been handled in recent years.

Year	Waste (tonnes)
1991	523
1992	528
1993	534
1994	542
1995	551
1996	562
1997	574
1998	583
1999	594

(a) Determine an algebraic expression that models the amount of waste received at the Barnesdale site each year.

(b) Use your model to predict how much waste the site will receive in 2000.

(c) Use your model to make a historical prediction of the last year that the landfill site handled less than 500 t of waste.

(d) During this period, the city of Barnesdale conducted an extensive recycling campaign. Using the predictions of your model, write a short newspaper article on the effectiveness of the recycling campaign.

3. Designing a Football Field

Have you ever walked on a football field covered with artificial turf? If so, you probably noticed that the field is not flat. The profile of the surface is arched and highest in the centre, permitting rainwater to drain away quickly.

45.75 cm
50 m

(a) The diagram shows the profile of an actual field, viewed from the end of the field. Assuming that the cross-section is a parabola, find the algebraic model that describes this shape.

(b) Use your equation to determine the distance from the sidelines where the field surface is 20 cm above the base line.

Research Extension (Extra Time)

(c) Civil engineers and road builders use a similar design for roadways. The height of the arch or "crown" on the roadway depends on the width of the road, the construction materials, and the intended use of the road. Research the requirements for the crown for various types of roads in your area. Use an algebraic model to determine the height of the road surface above the base level 2 m from the sidewalk in each case.

4. Personal Computer Sales: Linear or Quadratic?

U.S. Domestic Sales of Personal Computers

Year	1988	1989	1990	1991	1992	1993	1994	1995	1996	1997
PCs Sold (millions)	6.8	7.2	9.0	9.8	12.1	15.2	17.9	22.0	26.4	31.9

Source: Information Technology Industry Board

(a) Create a table that shows the first and second differences for this data.

(b) Discuss whether a linear or quadratic model is a better representation of this data.

(c) Explain how you can use graphing technology to support your conclusion in (b).

(d) Use your model to predict when computer sales in the U.S. will exceed 50 million per year. Discuss the probable accuracy of your prediction.

Research Extension (Extra Time)

(e) Find similar data for the Canadian personal computer market. Compare the rate of increase in computer sales in Canada with computer sales in the United States.

5. Every Picture Tells a Story

For each graph, make up a story that describes the situation being graphed. The *h*-axis represents height and the *t*-axis represents time.

(a)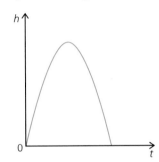

(b)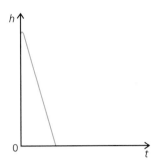

(c)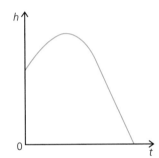

(d)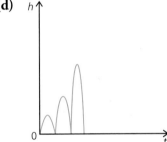

6. The Drinking Fountain Model

Designers use computer-aided drafting and design (CADD) software to represent real objects on a computer display. CADD software lets them experiment with various shapes and designs without having to construct real, physical models. When the designer is satisfied, the software prints out detailed plans that a machinist or carpenter can use to build the real object.

How is a real object represented mathematically in the CADD software?

(a) Bend a piece of wire so that it has the same shape as the stream of water from a drinking fountain.

(b) Trace the shape of the wire onto a piece of graph paper.

(c) Use the graph to find an algebraic model for the bent wire.

(d) Use graphing technology to verify that your algebraic model accurately represents the wire model of the water flow.

(e) Explain how you would adjust your model to reflect higher or lower water pressure at the fountain.

7. Leapfrog

The game of leapfrog involves moving pegs along a line of holes in a wooden board. Equal numbers of pegs of two different colours (e.g., red and blue) are placed in the holes. To start, all the red pegs are together on the left, separated by one empty hole from all the blue pegs on the right. The object of the game is to move the red pegs to the holes initially occupied by the blue pegs, and vice versa.

The rules allow only two types of moves:

- A peg can be moved to an adjacent hole.

- A peg of one colour can jump over a peg of the other colour to get to an empty hole on the other side.

You can simulate this game using markers or coins and a grid drawn on paper. For example, to play with 6 pegs, you could use 3 dimes and 3 pennies to represent the two different groups of pegs. You would draw the game board and position the markers like this:

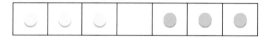

(a) Play this game using different numbers of markers. Remember that you must use equal numbers of markers of each colour or type. Construct a table that relates the number of markers of each type, N, to the minimum number of moves, M, required to interchange the markers.

(b) Determine the algebraic relationship between M and N.

(c) What is the minimum number of moves required to interchange 100 markers of each type?

(d) If a game takes 670 moves and this is the least number of moves possible, how many markers of each type are involved?

8. Investigating Water Flow

In many towns in Ontario, you can see a tall water tower proudly displaying the name of the town. The tower stores water for all the residents of the town. The higher the tower, the higher the water pressure at the base of the tower and in the underground water pipes that supply the town.

This situation can be modelled using a can filled with water. If there is a hole in the bottom of the can, the water will flow out, decreasing the pressure at the hole as the water level drops. How does this decrease in pressure affect the rate at which the water flows out of the can?

(a) Use a large juice can to act as the water tower and a pail to catch the water as it flows out of the can. Punch a small hole near the base of the can with a nail and hammer. (You will be blocking this hole with your finger, so make sure that any sharp edges are on the inside of the can.)

Block the hole with your finger while someone else fills the can with water. Then let the water run out and record the height of the water remaining in the can at regular intervals (every 5 or 10 seconds, for example). You can block the hole and stop the clock while you measure. Restart the timer when you unblock the hole again.

(b) Discuss whether a linear model, a quadratic model, or neither best represents the data.

(c) Develop a quadratic model for the data. Use the model to predict how long it would take to empty a full can of water that is twice as tall as the one you used, but has the same size base.

(d) Engineers use a theoretical model, based on physics, to represent this type of situation. The model is

$$h = \left(\sqrt{h_0} - \frac{70d^2}{D^2}t \right)^2$$

where h is the height of the water at elapsed time t seconds
   h_0 is the initial height of the water
   D is the diameter of the can
   d is the diameter of the hole (All lengths in centimetres.)

   i.   Use the dimensions of your can to apply this model to your experiment.

   ii. Compare the predicted values from this model with the observed values from your experiment. How closely do they match?

   iii. Compare the predicted values from this model with those of the model you created in (c). Which model more closely matches your data?

9. Simulating a Bouncing Ball

David used a software program called *Interactive Physics* to simulate rolling a ball off an elevated ramp onto a wooden floor. The resulting computer display shows the position of the ball in metres every 0.1 s.

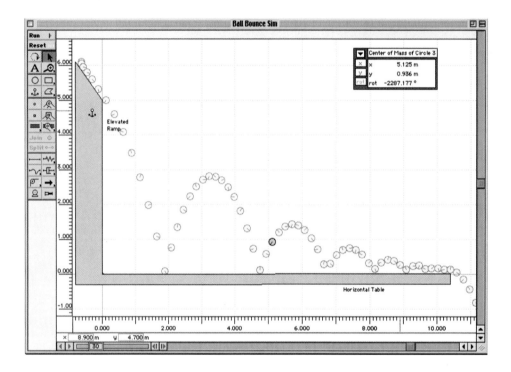

(a) Construct tables of values that show the height of the ball and the horizontal distance travelled vs. elapsed time

(b) Discuss whether a linear, quadratic, or some other kind of algebraic relation best fits each set of data. Develop the best algebraic models you can.

(c) Use your models to predict the time of the third bounce of the ball. How far from the base of the ramp does it occur? Discuss whether the computer image confirms your answer.

(d) As accurately as you can, determine the times when the height of the ball is the same as the distance from the ramp. Can you answer this question directly from your algebraic models?

Getting Ready for Trigonometry

Rate, Ratio, and Proportions

A **ratio** compares two or more quantities measured with the same unit, so units are not specified.

A ratio can be written in three different forms: $\frac{3}{4}$, 3 : 4, or 3 to 4.

A **rate** compares different quantities, so units must be included.

Both rates and ratios are simplified by dividing all terms by the greatest common factor.

When two ratios are equivalent, they form a proportion. $\frac{a}{b} = \frac{c}{d}$.

When one of the terms of a proportion is unknown it can be found by

- inspection, using a multiplication or division relationship between terms of the numerators and denominators.

- cross multiplication, $ad = bc$ then solving the resulting equation.

Example 1

In a class of 16 girls and 12 boys, what is the ratio of boys to girls?

Solution

$$\text{boys to girls} = 12 : 16$$
$$= \frac{12}{4} : \frac{16}{4}$$
$$= 3 : 4$$

Example 2

A bouquet of 25 flowers cost $20. What is the cost per flower?

Solution

$$\text{Cost/flower} = \$20 \div 25/\text{flower}$$
$$= \$0.80/\text{flower}$$

Example 3

Find x.

$$\frac{4}{x} = \frac{14}{21}$$

Solution

$$\frac{4}{x} = \frac{14}{21}$$
$$= \frac{2}{3}$$
$$4 = 2 \times 2, \text{ so}$$
$$x = 2 \times 3$$
$$= 6$$

Or, use algebra.

$\frac{4}{x} = \frac{14}{21}$ is the same as

$$\frac{x}{4} = \frac{21}{14}$$
$$4 \times \frac{x}{4} = \frac{21}{14} \times 4$$
$$x = \frac{84}{14} = 6$$

Practise

1. Express each situation as a ratio.
   (a) 4 pucks to 5 sticks
   (b) 5 markers to 3 pens
   (c) 6 boys to 1 girl
   (d) 7 rabbits to 3 puppies
   (e) 4 elephants to 7 lions

2. Write the ratio smaller to greater, in lowest terms, to compare each quantity.
   (a) 10 cm, 8 cm
   (b) 5 km, 3000 m
   (c) 30 s, 1.5 min
   (d) 400 g, 3 kg
   (e) 5 L, 2500 mL
   (f) 40 weeks, 1 year

3. The scale on a diagram is 1 cm represents 2 m. Calculate the actual length of each length on the diagram.
   (a) 2 cm   (b) 9 cm
   (c) 12.25 cm   (d) 24.2 cm
   (e) 13.5 cm

4. Express each situation as a rate.
   (a) Your heart beats 40 times in 30 s.
   (b) Your aunt drove 120 km in 1.5 h.
   (c) You bought 3.5 kg of ground beef for $17.33.
   (d) You typed 360 words in 8 min.

5. Solve.
   (a) $\dfrac{2}{5} = \dfrac{x}{20}$ (b) $\dfrac{4}{7} = \dfrac{36}{x}$
   (c) $\dfrac{9}{12} = \dfrac{24}{x}$ (d) $\dfrac{25}{x} = \dfrac{5}{2}$
   (e) $\dfrac{9}{x} = \dfrac{15}{20}$ (f) $\dfrac{x}{15} = \dfrac{64}{24}$
   (g) $\dfrac{20}{65} = \dfrac{16}{x}$ (h) $\dfrac{x}{7} = \dfrac{6}{21}$

6. Write the missing term(s) for each ratio
   (a) $2 : 3 = \blacksquare : 6$
   (b) $3 : 8 = \blacksquare : 24$
   (c) $8 : 5 = 16 : \blacksquare$
   (d) $1 : \blacksquare : 8 = 3 : 12 : \blacksquare$
   (e) $2 : 5 : \blacksquare = 6 : \blacksquare : 9$

7. Solve. Evaluate all answers to the nearest hundredth.
   (a) $\dfrac{x}{14} = \dfrac{8}{40}$ (b) $\dfrac{36}{x} = \dfrac{10}{3}$
   (c) $\dfrac{5}{7} = \dfrac{x}{95}$ (d) $\dfrac{13}{42} = \dfrac{55}{x}$
   (e) $\dfrac{x}{12} = \dfrac{25}{65}$ (f) $\dfrac{18}{24} = \dfrac{x}{84}$
   (g) $\dfrac{21}{35} = \dfrac{40}{x}$ (h) $\dfrac{152}{240} = \dfrac{x}{6}$

8. The ratio of boys to girls at Highland Secondary School is 3 to 4. If there are 435 boys at the school, determine the school's entire population.

9. A lawnmower engine requires oil and gas to be mixed in the ratio of 2 to 5. If John has 3.5 L of gas in his can, how much oil should he add?

Angle Relationships 2

Here is a review of special angle relationships.

Complementary angles
$a + b = 90°$

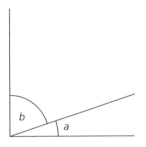

Isosceles triangle
$a = b$

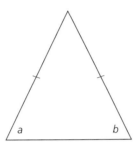

Transversal parallel lines
Alternate angles are equal.
$c = f, d = g$

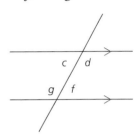

Supplementary angles
$a + b = 180°$

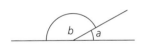

Sum of the angles of a triangle
$a + b + c = 180°$

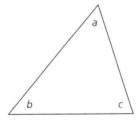

Corresponding angles are equal.
$b = f, a = e, d = h, c = g$

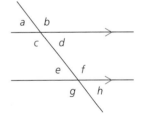

Vertically opposite angles
$a = b$
$c = d$

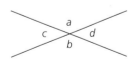

Exterior angle of a triangle
$a + b = c$

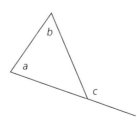

Co-interior angles are supplementary.
$d + f = 180°, c + e = 180°$

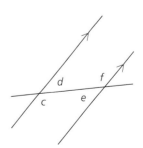

Practise

Determine the values of x, y, and z in each diagram.

(a)

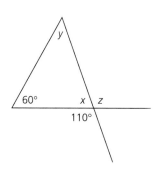

(b)

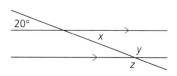

(c)

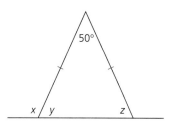

(d)

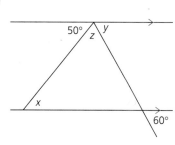

(e)

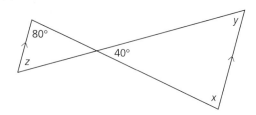

(f)

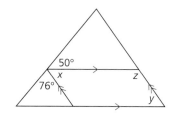

(g)

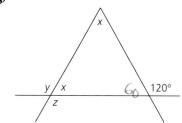

(h)

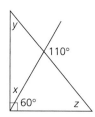

Congruent Figures

Two figures are congruent if they are the same size and shape. This relationship is only true when all corresponding angles and all corresponding sides are equal in measure. The symbol for congruency is ≅.

If $\triangle ABC \cong \triangle LMN$, then the following is true.

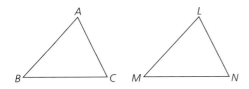

Sides	Angles
$AB = LM$	$\angle ABC = \angle LMN$
$BC = MN$	$\angle BCA = \angle MNL$
$CA = NL$	$\angle CAB = \angle NLM$

Example 1

Are quadrilaterals *AMPJ* and *RWZE* congruent? Give reasons for your answer.

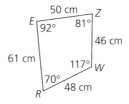

Solution

Use the diagram to decide which corresponding parts are equal.

Corresponding Angles
$\angle A = \angle R$, $\angle M = \angle W$,
$\angle J = \angle E$, $\angle P = \angle Z$

Corresponding Sides
$JA = ER$, $AM = RW$, $PM = WZ$, $JP = EZ$

Quadrilateral $AMPJ \cong$ Quadrilateral $RWZE$

Example 2

Pentagon *PQMNO* is congruent to pentagon *RSTUV*. Find the value of *x*.

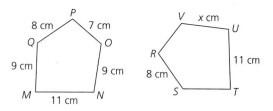

Solution

If pentagon *RSTUV* is rotated 90° clockwise it will fit exactly over pentagon *PQMNO*.

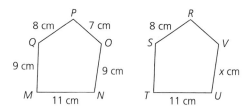

Side *VU* corresponds to side *ON*. Since the two figures are congruent

$$VU = ON$$
$$VU = 9 \text{ cm}$$

Practise

1. Draw two congruent rectangles on a coordinate grid. Explain how you know the figures are congruent.

2. Quadrilaterals *JKLM* and *SPQR* are congruent. List all pairs of equal

    (a) angles   **(b)** sides

3. These two quadrilaterals are congruent. Find the values for *x*, *y*, and *z*.

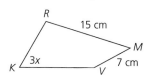

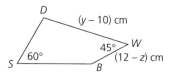

4. Rectangle *ABCD* ≅ rectangle *LMNO*. Complete each statement.

    (a) $AB = \blacksquare$ **(b)** $\angle C = \blacksquare$

    (c) $AD = \blacksquare$ **(d)** $\angle M = \blacksquare$

    (e) $\angle O = \blacksquare$ **(f)** $MN = \blacksquare$

    (g) $\angle A = \blacksquare$ **(h)** $CD = \blacksquare$

Chapter 5

Introduction to Trigonometry

Trigonometry deals with the relationships between the sides and angles in triangles. Trigonometry was developed thousands of years ago, to solve problems in astronomy and geography such as measuring the diameter of the Earth. Over time, people found it could be used in other areas as well.

Today trigonometry is used to solve problems in physics, chemistry, architecture, navigation, and engineering. We use trigonometry to construct buildings, make machines, plan space missions, and navigate boats, airplanes, and even cars. On a daily basis, trigonometry is probably used more than any other branch of mathematics to model and solve real-world problems.

In this chapter, you will

- compute the angle of inclination or declination that corresponds to the slope of a line

- use dynamic geometry software to investigate the properties of triangles

- use analytic geometry to solve problems and prove conjectures involving angles, area, and perimeter of similar triangles

- use the properties of similar right triangles to solve practical problems

- develop the three primary trigonometric ratios and use them to solve practical problems

For connections to this chapter, visit **www.math.nelson.com**.

The Chapter Problem

Mechanical Engineering

Mechanical engineers design, test, build, and operate many kinds of machines, such as bicycles. When designing a bicycle, the engineer must consider not only the physical design of the bike, but also how its components work. The engineer is responsible for steering, braking, and the gear system. Consider this typical problem.

Building a Bicycle

You are the mechanical engineer on a team that is designing a new bike. You have decided that the distance between the sprocket wheel centres, as measured along the frame, should be 420 mm. The diameter of the smaller sprocket wheel will be 90 mm and the diameter of the larger sprocket wheel will be 175 mm.

How long, to the nearest millimetre, should the chain be? This length must be accurate. If the chain is too short, it will be too tight and will break. If the chain is too long, it will be loose and will fall off the sprocket wheels.

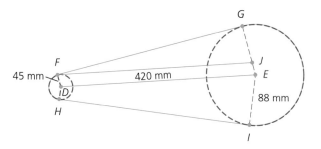

For help with this problem, see pages 464, 478, 489, and 511.

Challenge 1

Find a building in your community without wheelchair access. Design a wheelchair ramp that satisfies the building codes of your community. Pay attention to the legal slope of the ramp. Present the plan as an accurate scale drawing. Include a materials list and cost estimate.

Challenge 2

Weather satellites have special cameras that take images of large areas of the globe. These images are sent to Earth, where they are used to forecast the weather. Some satellites are in stationary orbit, which means they orbit Earth at the same speed that Earth rotates. These satellites are always above the same spot on Earth. A camera is on a weather satellite that is in stationary orbit above Earth at an altitude of 100 km. Find:

(a) the distance to the horizon that the camera can view
(b) the distance along Earth's surface that the camera can view
(c) the fraction of Earth's surface that the camera can view
(d) the minimum altitude needed for the camera to view all of Canada
(e) the latitude and longitude of the location in Canada above which the satellite would have to be positioned at the altitude in (d)

To complete these Challenges, you may need to discuss a research plan with your teacher or other students. You may also need to research outside the classroom.

In this chapter, you will be working with triangles. You will need to be familiar with

- basic geometric properties
- equations of lines
- the Pythagorean theorem
- ratio operations

These exercises will help you warm up for the work ahead.

1. Find the unknown measures in each diagram.

(a)

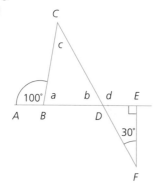

(b)

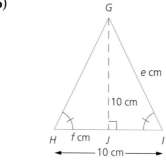

(c)

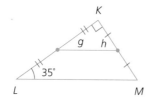

(d)

(e)

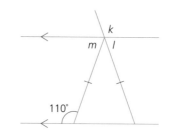

(f)

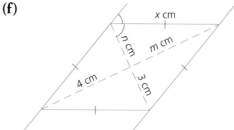

2. Draw each triangle. Measure the remaining sides and angles.

(a) $\triangle ABC$, $\angle B = 90°$, $AB = 3$ cm, and $BC = 4$ cm

(b) $\triangle DEF$, $\angle E = 30°$, $\angle F = 50°$, and $DE = 2$ cm

(c) $\triangle GHI$, $\angle H = 90°$, $GH = 5$ cm, and $GI = 13$ cm

(d) $\triangle JKL$, $\angle L = 30°$, $JL = 5$ cm, and $JK = 4$ cm
Explain why two triangles are possible.

3. Compute each value. Indicate which values are rational numbers (exact) and which are irrational (approximate).

(a) $\sqrt{100}$ (b) $\sqrt{42}$

(c) $\sqrt{36^2}$ (d) $\sqrt{10^2 - 8^2}$

(e) $\sqrt{5^2 - 1}$ (f) $\sqrt{\dfrac{4}{9}}$

4. Sketch each figure. Then compute its area and perimeter.
  (a) a regular hexagon with a side length of 6.0 cm and an **apothem** of 7.2 cm
  (b) a circle with a radius of 10 cm
  (c) a rhombus with a long diagonal of 16 cm and a short diagonal of 12 cm
  (d) a right-angled trapezoid with parallel sides of 4 cm and 7 cm, and an altitude of 4 cm

5. Find the slope and the equation of the line
  (a) that is parallel to $y = 2x + 4$ and has a y-intercept of -4
  (b) that passes through $A(-1, 4)$ and $B(-3, 8)$
  (c) that is perpendicular to $y = \frac{2}{3}x - 5$ and passes through $(0, 4)$
  (d) with a y-intercept of -3 and an x-intercept of 10
  (e) that is parallel to the x-axis and passes through $(4, 4)$

6. Express each ratio in simplest form.
  (a) $10 : 12$ **(b)** $15 : 30$
  (c) $\frac{12.5}{25}$ **(d)** $\frac{-5}{15}$

7. Find the unknown value in each expression.
  (a) $\frac{x}{4} = \frac{12}{16}$ **(b)** $\frac{y}{5} = \frac{17}{20}$
  (c) $\frac{12.5}{50} = \frac{13}{w}$ **(d)** $\frac{-5}{8} = \frac{a}{24}$
  (e) $\frac{6}{-7} = \frac{8}{b}$ **(f)** $\frac{-3}{4} = \frac{x-5}{8}$

8. (a) Are the quadrilaterals $ABCD$ and $WXYZ$ congruent? Give reasons for your answer.

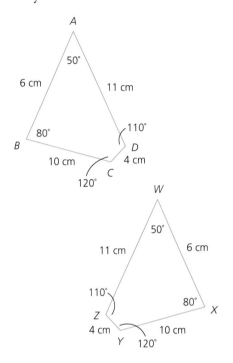

  (b) Use the diagram to show the corresponding sides that are equal.
  (c) Use the diagram to show the corresponding angles that are equal.

9. Triangle ABC is congruent to $\triangle LMN$.
  (a) List all pairs of equal angles.
  (b) List all pairs of equal sides.

10. These two quadrilaterals are congruent. Find x, z, and y.

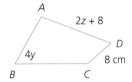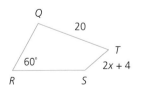

11. Two figures are congruent if they have the same ■ and ■.

5.1 Constructing Triangles with *The Geometer's Sketchpad*

TECHNOLOGY

The drawing tools in *The Geometer's Sketchpad* help you create two-dimensional geometric shapes. The measurement tools measure side length, angle size, and area of the shapes.

You can use *The Geometer's Sketchpad* to construct triangles from a list of measurements.

Sketch 1: A Triangle, Given the Lengths of Three Sides

Use *The Geometer's Sketchpad* to construct a triangle with sides 5 cm, 8 cm, and 10 cm.

1. **Draw the base of the triangle.**
   Draw one side of the triangle using the **Segment**

   tool ![] in the tool bar. Select the line and
   measure its length. Adjust the length using the

   Selection arrow tool ![] to match the length
   of one of the sides of the triangle.

step 1

2. **Draw segments representing the remaining two sides of the triangle**.
   Measure and adjust the length of each line to match the lengths given.

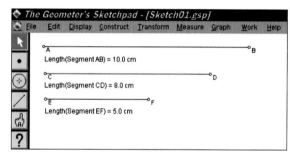

step 2

3. **In steps 3 and 4, draw the remaining two sides.**

   (a) Use one of the line segments as the base of the triangle. Usually, the longest segment is a good choice. Position the base of the triangle on the screen so that there is room to attach the other two sides.

   (b) You cannot position the other two sides exactly, since you do not know what angles are required. However, you can use small circles to show where you would place the end point of each side.

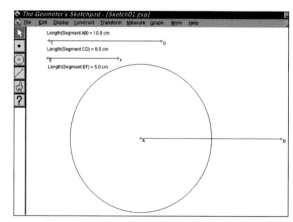

step 3(b)

(c) Select one end point of the base to be the centre of a circle. Select one of the other segments to be the radius.
To draw the circle, choose **Circle By Center And Radius** from the **Construct** menu.

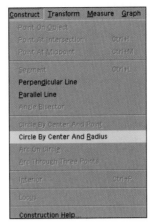

step 3 (c)

4. Draw another circle, using the other end point of the base as the centre of the circle and the other side length segment as the radius.

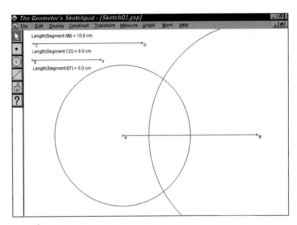

step 4

5. **Construct the remaining sides of the triangle.**

The points where the circles intersect are the possible locations for the third vertex. Select one of the intersection points and the end points of the base segment. Choose **Segment** from the **Construct** menu.

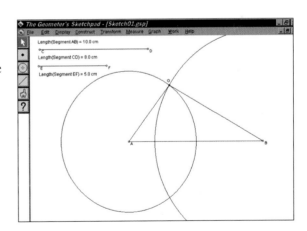

step 5

TECHNOLOGY

Sketch 2: A Triangle, Given Two Angles and the Contained Side

Use *The Geometer's Sketchpad* to construct a triangle with a side of 8 cm and angles of 30° and 50° at the end points of this side.

1. **Open a new sketch. Draw the base of the triangle.**

   Draw a line segment on *The Geometer's Sketchpad* screen. Select it and measure its length. Adjust the length to the desired length for the base of the triangle.

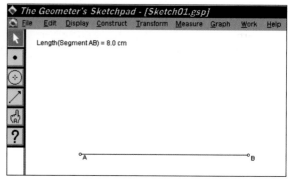

step 1

2. **Draw a ray that meets the base at one of the required angles.**

   (a) Change the line-drawing tool so that it will draw a ray.

step 2(a)

   (b) Draw a ray from one end of the base segment.

   (c) Measure and adjust the ray to produce the desired angle.

   Using the **Selection** arrow tool

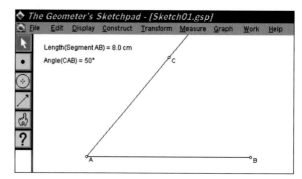

step 2(b)

   , and holding down the shift key, select points in this order: a point on the ray, the vertex of the angle, and the other end point of the base. Choose **Angle** from the **Measure** menu. Adjust the ray position until you get one of the required angle measures. It is easier to adjust the angle if you first move the point on the ray away from the vertex.

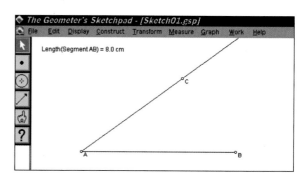

step 2(c)

3. **Draw, measure, and adjust a ray for the required angle at the other end point of the base.**

   Repeat step 2 for the other end point of the base to make another ray and the other required angle. The point where the two rays intersect is the third vertex of the triangle.

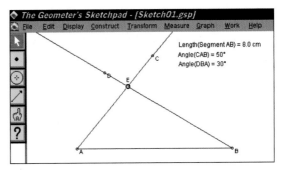

step 3

Sketch 3: A Triangle, Given Two Sides and the Contained Angle

Use *The Geometer's Sketchpad* to construct a triangle with two sides equal to 5 cm and 8 cm, and an angle of 40° between the sides.

1. **Open a new sketch. Draw the base of the triangle and a ray that meets the base at the required angle.**

   Repeat steps 1–3 of Sketch 2.

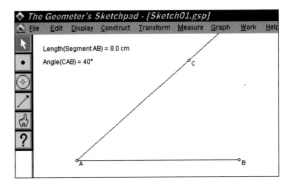

step 1

2. **Draw a line segment with a length equal to the second required side.**

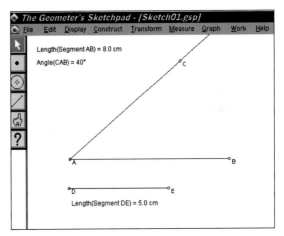

step 2

3. **Determine the position of the third vertex of the triangle.**

Select the vertex of the angle and the length of the new segment to **Construct** a **Circle By Center And Radius**. The point where the circle intersects the ray is the third vertex of the required triangle. Select the end points of the missing side and choose **Segment** from the **Construct** menu to complete the triangle.

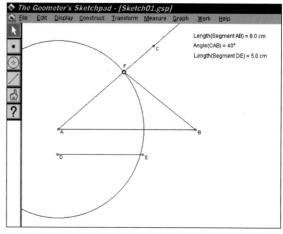

step 3

Practise 5.1

1. Draw $\triangle ABC$ as described. Determine the measure of any angle or side that is not given.
   (a) $AB = 2$ cm, $BC = 5$ cm, $AC = 6$ cm
   (b) $AB = 4$ cm, $BC = 6$ cm, $\angle ABC = 35°$
   (c) $\angle ABC = 50°$, $AB = 4$ cm, $\angle CAB = 20°$

2. (a) Draw $\triangle PQR$ with $PQ = 5$ cm, $QR = 12$ cm, and $PR = 13$ cm. Verify that it is a right triangle with the 90° angle at Q.
   (b) Draw $\triangle STU$ in which $\angle STU = 45°$, $ST = 6$ cm, and $\angle TSU = 45°$. Verify that it is an isosceles right triangle.
   (c) Draw $\triangle VWX$ with $VW = 5$ cm, $\angle VWX = 60°$, and $WX = 5$ cm. Verify that it is an equilateral triangle.

Did You Know?

Are Bees Mathematicians?

Completely cover a plane surface with tiles. You can use tiles in the shape of squares, equilateral triangles, circles, or any other shape. For which shape will the total perimeter of all the tiles be the least?

Long ago, people thought bees built their honeycombs in the shape of hexagons simply because they were pretty. But in 4th century Greece, a mathematician named Pappus suggested a more practical reason. He said that bees used hexagons because they used less wax than any other shape. Think about it: why is this an answer to the question above?

It wasn't until 1999 that Thomas Hales proved that Pappus was right. Do some research on the Internet on bees, monkeys, and other animals that could be said to "use" mathematics. Do a report on what you find.

Investigating and Comparing Triangles

How much do you need to know about two triangles to be able to say that they are identical? Or that they have the same shape?

Investigate the shapes of triangles using dynamic geometry software. If a computer is not available, this activity can be done using a ruler, a compass, and a protractor.

Part 1: Are Three Sides Enough?

Can you determine whether or not two triangles are identical, if you know the lengths of all three sides of both triangles?

Think, Do, Discuss

1. Draw $\triangle ABC$ with $AB = 3$ cm, $BC = 6$ cm, and $AC = 5$ cm.

2. Draw $\triangle XYZ$ with $XY = 3$ cm and $YZ = 6$ cm.
   (a) Explain why the length of side XZ has many possible values.
   (b) What length of XZ would make $\triangle XYZ$ identical to $\triangle ABC$?
   (c) How could you demonstrate that the length for XZ that you gave in (b) would produce a triangle identical to $\triangle ABC$?
   (d) If you placed the identical triangles on top of one another, what pairs of vertices would match up?

3. Draw $\triangle DEF$ with $DE = 6$ cm, $EF = 12$ cm, and $FD = 10$ cm.
   (a) Explain why $\triangle DEF$ is not identical to $\triangle ABC$.
   (b) What properties does $\triangle DEF$ share with $\triangle ABC$?
   (c) Why would it be accurate to say the triangles have the same shape?
   (d) Picture the smaller triangle inside the larger one, with the matching sides parallel. What pairs of vertices match up between the small and large triangles?
   (e) How do the lengths of the sides of the two triangles compare?

Part 2: Are Two Sides Enough? ———————————

If you know the lengths of two sides of two triangles, can you determine whether or not they are identical?

Think, Do, Discuss

1. Draw $\triangle ABC$ with $AB = 7$ cm and $AC = 5$ cm. Explain why it is possible to draw many different shapes of $\triangle ABC$ with the given side lengths.

2. Now, in $\triangle ABC$ from question 1, assume that $\angle A = 40°$.
   (a) How many different shapes of $\triangle ABC$ fit the new requirements?
   (b) Explain how this one additional piece of information reduces the number of possible triangles.

3. Draw $\triangle DEF$ with $DE = 7$ cm, $DF = 5$ cm, and $\angle E = 40°$.
   (a) What two different triangles meet these requirements?
   (b) Discuss whether either of these triangles is identical to $\triangle ABC$.
   (c) Discuss whether either of these triangles has the same shape as $\triangle ABC$.

4. Draw $\triangle GHI$ with $GH = 7$ cm, $GI = 9.8$ cm, and $\angle G = 40°$.
   (a) Explain why $\triangle GHI$ is not identical to $\triangle ABC$.
   (b) Explain why $\triangle GHI$ does have the same shape as $\triangle ABC$.
   (c) How do the lengths of the sides of the two triangles compare?

Part 3: Are Two Angles Enough? ———————————

If you know the measures of two angles of two triangles, can you determine whether or not they are identical?

Think, Do, Discuss

1. Draw $\triangle ABC$ with $\angle B = 50°$ and $\angle C = 60°$.
   (a) Why is it possible to draw many triangles that fit this description?
   (b) Explain whether you need to know the size of the third angle to draw $\triangle ABC$.

2. Now, draw $\triangle ABC$ from question 1, assuming $BC = 4$ cm.
   (a) How many triangles fit the new requirements?
   (b) Explain how this additional piece of information reduces the number of possible triangles to just one.
   (c) How do the sides of this triangle compare to the triangle you drew in question 1?

3. Draw $\triangle PQR$ with $\angle Q = 50°$, $\angle R = 60°$, and $PQ = 4$ cm.
   (a) Explain why $\triangle PQR$ is not identical to $\triangle ABC$ in question 2.
   (b) Explain why $\triangle PQR$ has the same shape as $\triangle ABC$. How do the sides of $\triangle PQR$ compare to the sides of $\triangle ABC$?

Focus 5.2

Key Ideas

- Two triangles may be congruent, similar, or neither. The order of the letters naming the vertices of congruent or similar triangles indicates the order in which the vertices, sides, and angles of one triangle correspond to the vertices, sides, and angles of the other.

Congruent	Similar

- **Congruent triangles** are identical in every way. They have exactly the same shape and size.
  The expression $\triangle ABC \cong \triangle XYZ$ means that $\triangle ABC$ is **congruent** to $\triangle XYZ$.

- **Similar triangles** have the same shape, but are different sizes. One triangle is an enlargement or a reduction of the other. The expression $\triangle ABC \sim \triangle XYZ$ means that $\triangle ABC$ is **similar** to $\triangle XYZ$.

- If $\triangle ABC \cong \triangle XYZ$, then
  $$\left.\begin{array}{l} AB = XY \\ BC = YZ \\ AC = XZ \end{array}\right\} \text{Corresponding sides are equal.}$$
  $$\left.\begin{array}{l} \angle A = \angle X \\ \angle B = \angle Y \\ \angle C = \angle Z \end{array}\right\} \text{Corresponding angles are equal.}$$

- If $\triangle ABC \sim \triangle XYZ$, then
  $$\frac{AB}{XY} = \frac{BC}{YZ} = \frac{AC}{XZ} \quad \begin{array}{l}\text{Corresponding sides} \\ \text{are proportional.}\end{array}$$
  $$\left.\begin{array}{l} \angle A = \angle X \\ \angle B = \angle Y \\ \angle C = \angle Z \end{array}\right\} \begin{array}{l}\text{Corresponding} \\ \text{angles are equal.}\end{array}$$
  The sides of $\triangle ABC$ are **proportional** to the sides of $\triangle XYZ$.

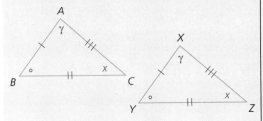

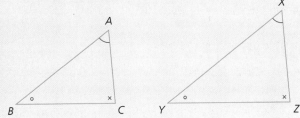

Conditions for Congruence

- $\triangle ABC \cong \triangle XYZ$ if three pairs of corresponding sides are equal, that is, $AB = XY$, $BC = YZ$, and $AC = XZ$.
  (Side-side-side congruence or **SSS**$\cong$)

Conditions for Similarity

- $\triangle ABC \sim \triangle XYZ$ if three pairs of corresponding sides are proportional, that is, $\frac{AB}{XY} = \frac{BC}{YZ} = \frac{AC}{XZ}$.
  (Side-side-side similarity or **SSS**$\sim$)

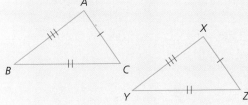

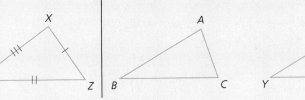

- $\triangle ABC \cong \triangle XYZ$ if two pairs of corresponding sides and the contained angles are equal, for example, $AB = XY$, $\angle B = \angle Y$, and $BC = YZ$. (Side-angle-side congruence or **SAS**$\cong$)

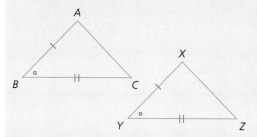

- $\triangle ABC \sim \triangle XYZ$ if two pairs of corresponding sides are proportional and the contained angles are equal, for example, $\frac{AB}{XY} = \frac{BC}{YZ}$ and $\angle B = \angle Y$. (**SAS**$\sim$)

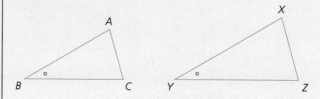

- $\triangle ABC \cong \triangle XYZ$ if two pairs of corresponding angles and the contained sides are equal, for example, $\angle B = \angle Y$, $BC = YZ$, and $\angle C = \angle Z$. (**ASA**$\cong$)

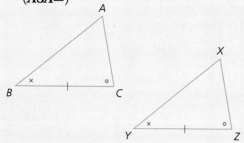

- $\triangle ABC \sim \triangle XYZ$ if two pairs of corresponding angles are equal, for example, $\angle B = \angle Y$ and $\angle C = \angle Z$. (**AA**$\sim$)

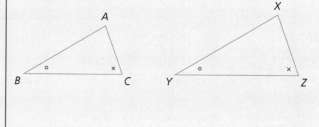

Example 1

Determine which of these triangles is similar to $\triangle PQR$.

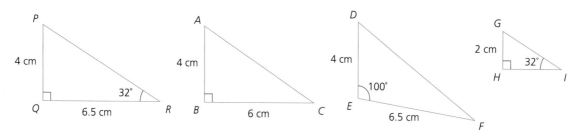

Solution

$\triangle ABC \not\sim \triangle PQR$
$\angle B = \angle Q = 90º$, but
the adjacent sides are
not proportional.

$\dfrac{AB}{PQ} \neq \dfrac{BC}{QR}$ since $\dfrac{4}{4} \neq \dfrac{6}{6.5}$

$\triangle DEF \not\sim \triangle PQR$
$\triangle PQR$ is a right triangle.
Since $\angle E$ in $\triangle DEF$ is 100°,
neither $\angle D$ nor
$\angle F$ can equal 90°.

$\triangle GHI \sim \triangle PQR$ (using $AA\sim$)
$\angle H = \angle Q = 90°$ and
$\angle I = \angle R = 32°$
If $\triangle GHI$ is enlarged by a
factor of 2, the result is
identical to $\triangle PQR$. The sides
are all proportional with a
common ratio of 1 : 2.

Example 2

$\triangle ABC$ has sides $AB = 9$ cm, $BC = 12$ cm, and $AC = 15$ cm. $\triangle YXZ$ has $YX = 6$ cm,
$XZ = 8$ cm, and $\angle X = 90°$. Show that $\triangle ABC$ and $\triangle YXZ$ are similar.

Solution

Sketch the two triangles.

The Pythagorean property in right
triangle YXZ shows that $YZ = 10$ cm.

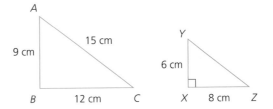

$$6^2 + 8^2 = YZ^2$$
$$36 + 64 = YZ^2$$
$$100 = YZ^2$$
$$\sqrt{100} = \sqrt{YZ^2}$$
$$10 = YZ$$

When you compare the ratios of the corresponding sides of the two triangles, you
find that they are proportional:

$$\dfrac{AB}{YX} = \dfrac{9}{6} = \dfrac{3}{2} \qquad \dfrac{BC}{XZ} = \dfrac{12}{8} = \dfrac{3}{2} \qquad \dfrac{AC}{YZ} = \dfrac{15}{10} = \dfrac{3}{2}$$

Therefore, using $SSS\sim$, $\triangle YXZ \sim \triangle ABC$.

Example 3

Determine the unknown measures.

(a)

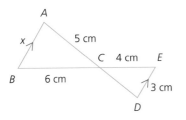

(b)

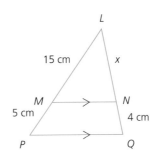

Solution

(a)

$\angle ABC = \angle DEC$ and $\angle BAC = \angle CDE$
(alternate angles between parallel lines AB and ED)

$\therefore \triangle ABC \sim \triangle DEC \; (AA\sim)$

$$\frac{AB}{DE} = \frac{BC}{EC}$$

$$\frac{x}{3} = \frac{6}{4} \qquad \text{Multiply by the lowest common denominator of 12.}$$

$$\overset{4}{\cancel{12}}\left(\frac{x}{\cancel{3}_1}\right) = \frac{6}{\cancel{4}_1}(\overset{3}{\cancel{12}}) \qquad \text{Simplify.}$$

$$4x = (6)(3) \qquad \text{Solve for } x.$$

$$\frac{4x}{4} = \frac{18}{4}$$

$$x = \frac{18}{4}$$

$$x = 4.5 \text{ cm}$$

(b)

$\angle LMN = \angle LPQ$ and $\angle LNM = \angle LQP$
(corresponding angles between parallel lines MN and PQ)

$\triangle LMN \sim \triangle LPQ \; (AA\sim)$

$$\left.\begin{array}{l}\dfrac{LM}{LP} = \dfrac{LN}{LQ} \\[4pt] \dfrac{15}{20} = \dfrac{x}{x+4}\end{array}\right\} \begin{array}{l}\text{Multiply by the lowest} \\ \text{common denominator} \\ \text{of } 20(x+4).\end{array}$$

$$\overset{1}{\cancel{20}}(x+4)\frac{15}{\cancel{20}_1} = \frac{x}{\cancel{x+4}_1}(20)(\cancel{x+4})^1 \quad \text{Simplify.}$$

$$15(x+4) = 20x \qquad \text{Expand.}$$

$$15x + 60 = 20x \qquad \text{Solve for } x.$$

$$60 = 20x - 15x$$

$$\frac{60}{5} = \frac{5x}{5}$$

$$x = 12 \text{ cm}$$

Practise, Apply, Solve 5.2

1. For each pair of triangles,
  i. explain what makes them similar
  ii. determine the scale factor that relates lengths in the larger triangle to lengths in the smaller triangle
  iii. compute any unknown lengths, if possible

(a)

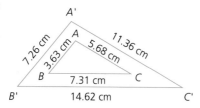

(b)

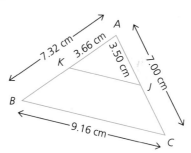

2. For each pair of triangles,
  i. explain why they are congruent
  ii. write the congruence statement using symbols and the proper order for naming the triangles

(a)

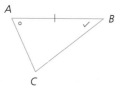
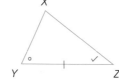

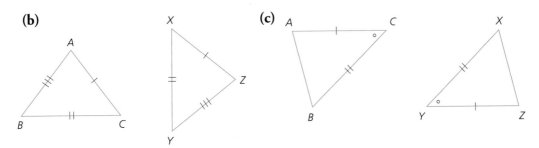

(b)

(c)

3. **(a)** Which triangles are congruent to △*ABC*?
   (b) Which triangles are similar to, but not congruent to, △*ABC*?

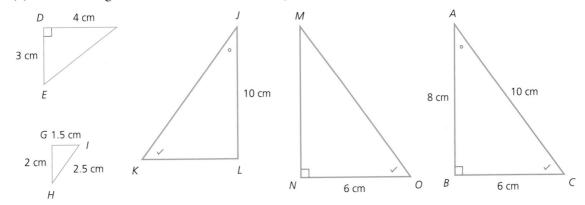

B

4. **Knowledge and Understanding**
   i. For each pair of right triangles, tell whether they are congruent, similar, or neither.
   ii. If the triangles are congruent, identify the pairs of equal corresponding angles and sides.
   iii. If the triangles are similar, identify the pairs of equal corresponding angles and the equal ratios of corresponding sides.

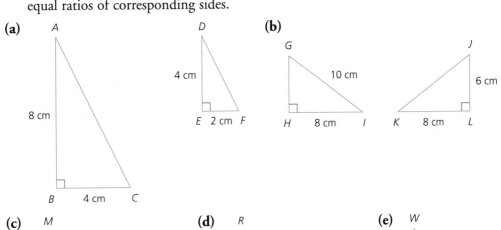

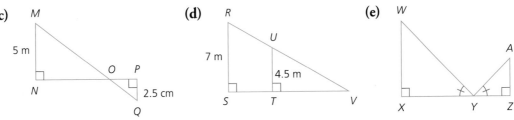

5. In each diagram,

    i. explain what makes $\triangle ABC$ and $\triangle EDC$ congruent

    ii. identify the pairs of equal corresponding sides and angles

(a)

(b)

(c)

(d)

6. Application: Find the value of each indicated quantity. If a value cannot be determined, explain why.

(a)

(b)

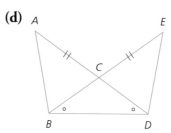

(c)

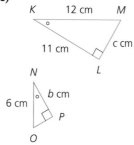

(d)

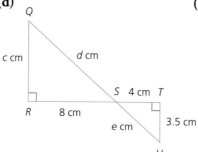

(e)

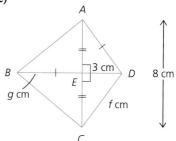

7. Use what you know about congruent and similar triangles to find the unknown values in each diagram.

(a)

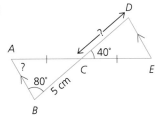

(b)

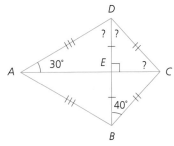

(c)

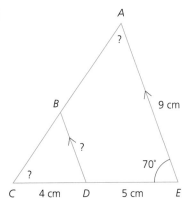

(d)

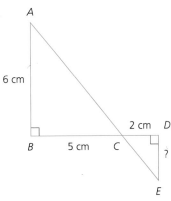

(e)

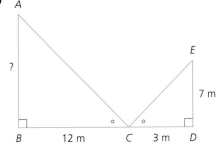

(f)

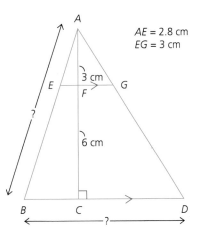

AE = 2.8 cm
EG = 3 cm

8. If $\triangle ABC \sim \triangle XYZ$ and a, c, x, and z are the lengths of BC, AB, YZ, and XY respectively, use algebra to show that if $\frac{a}{c} = \frac{x}{z}$, then $\frac{a}{x} = \frac{c}{z}$.

9. **Communication:** A is the centre of a circle and B and C are points on the circle. Explain why the perpendicular AD bisects the chord BC.

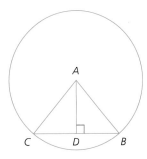

10. Suppose $\triangle PQR \sim \triangle LMN$ and $\angle P = 90°$.
  (a) What angle in $\triangle LMN$ equals 90°? How do you know?
  (b) If $MN = 13$ cm, $LN = 12$ cm, $LM = 5$ cm, and $PQ = 15$ cm, how long are PR and QR?

11. Check Your Understanding: List the properties that two triangles must share for them to be similar. Use the triangles in this photograph of the Ottawa City Hall as a guide.

C

12. **Thinking, Inquiry, Problem Solving:** Use similar triangles to prove the Pythagorean theorem. **Hint:** Show that the two smaller triangles are similar to the larger triangle and then examine the ratios of corresponding sides.

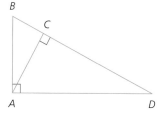

The Chapter Problem—Mechanical Engineering

In this section, you worked with triangles to find out what information you need to determine whether two triangles are identical or not. Apply what you learned to answer these questions on the chapter problem on page 446.

Sketch the bicycle frame, showing the two sprocket wheels. Draw the chain, showing how it contacts each sprocket wheel.
(a) Draw the radius to the point where the chain first meets each sprocket wheel. Measure the angle between the radius and the chain at that point.
(b) Draw a line segment joining the centres of the sprocket wheels. Measure the length of this line segment.
(c) Form a triangle with the following sides:
  • a radius of the larger sprocket wheel
  • the chain segment from the end of that radius to the smaller sprocket wheel
  • a segment parallel to the line joining the centres of the sprocket wheels
  What kind of triangle is this? How does this triangle compare to the triangle formed the same way using the other chain segment?
(d) Find the lengths of the sides of these two triangles. What information does this give you about how long the bicycle chain should be? What still needs to be found?

Enlarging or Reducing a Triangle 5.3 with *The Geometer's Sketchpad*

When a shape is **dilated**, it is stretched or shrunk by a dilation factor, the way the pupil in your eye expands or contracts to changes in the light. The transformation treats the page on which the shape is drawn as if it were made of rubber. If the page is stretched outward from a central point in all directions, the shape is enlarged. If the page is shrunk in all directions toward the central point, the shape is reduced. In both cases, the central point is called the **centre of the dilation.**

The **Dilate** command on the **Transform** menu of *The Geometer's Sketchpad* lets you magnify or reduce any shape on the screen.

Use *The Geometer's Sketchpad* to construct a triangle with side lengths of 6 cm, 12 cm, and 15 cm. Then create a version of the triangle that is reduced by a factor of $\frac{1}{3}$.

Reducing a Triangle by a Factor of $\frac{1}{3}$

1. **Open a new sketch. Draw the triangle described above.**

   Use the method described in section 5.1.

   Select the circles that were used to construct the triangle and choose **Hide** on the **Display** menu to get rid of them.

   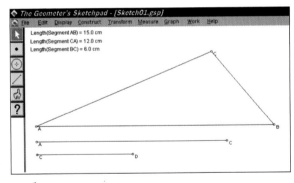

   step 1

2. **Locate the point that will be used as the centre for the dilation.**

   Place another point anywhere on the work sheet. Select that point and choose **Mark Center** from the **Transform** menu to make that point the centre of the dilation.

   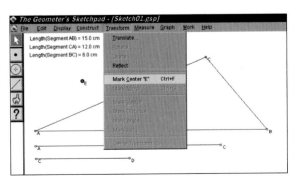

   step 2

TECHNOLOGY

3. Dilate (reduce) the triangle.

(a) Select the vertices of the triangle and choose **Dilate** from the **Transform** menu. The dialogue box may be a bit different in your version of *The Geometer's Sketchpad*.

Enter "1" beside (**New**) and "3" beside (**Old**) for a reduction by a factor of $\frac{1}{3}$. (One unit in the new shape equals three units in the old shape.) Click **OK**.

The dilation produces three new points, which are the three transformed vertices. For example, the image of point A is the new point A'.

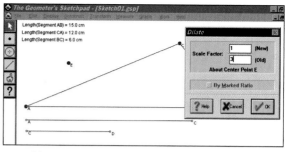

step 3(a)

(b) **Draw the sides of the dilated triangle.**

Select the new vertices and construct a triangle. Choose **Segment** from the **Construct** menu.

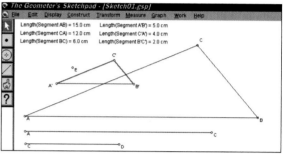

step 3(b)

Change the line weight and colour to distinguish it from the original triangle. Select all three sides of the new triangle and choose the desired line style from the **Display** menu, as well as the new colour. Measure the new sides to verify the reduction by a factor of $\frac{1}{3}$.

4. Compare the area and perimeter of the two triangles.

Select the three vertices of the larger triangle and choose **Polygon Interior** from the **Construct** menu. Choose **Area** from the **Measure** menu, then **Perimeter** from the **Measure** menu. Repeat this for the smaller triangle. Does the reduction factor effect perimeter? area?

Practise 5.3

1. Draw $\triangle XYZ$ with $XY = 5$ cm, $\angle Y = 45°$, and $YZ = 7$ cm.
   Use the **Dilate** command to construct these reduced or enlarged versions.
   Verify each construction by measuring the sides of the new triangles.

   (a) a triangle that is $\frac{1}{2}$ the size of $\triangle XYZ$

   (b) a triangle that is 2 times the size of $\triangle XYZ$

   (c) an enlarged version of $\triangle XYZ$, in which the ratio of the enlarged sides to the original sides is $\frac{6}{5}$

   (d) a reduced version of $\triangle XYZ$, in which the ratio of the reduced sides to the original sides is $\frac{3}{4}$

Modelling with Similar Triangles 5.4

Part 1: Investigating Scale Drawings of Triangles

Planners, engineers, and architects often use scale models and drawings of buildings in their work. The models and drawings help them place the building on its site, design landscaping, and locate roads, sidewalks, and other services. You could do this activity using dynamic geometry software. If it is not available, you could use a ruler, pair of compasses, and protractor.

Think, Do, Discuss

1. (a) Draw $\triangle ABC$ with $AB = 4$ cm, $\angle B = 90°$, and $BC = 3$ cm.
   (b) Draw triangle $\triangle A'B'C'$ so that it is an enlargement of $\triangle ABC$ by a factor of 2.
   (c) Verify that $A'B' = 2AB$.
   (d) Measure the angles in each triangle. How do they compare?
   (e) Compare the perimeter of $\triangle ABC$ to the perimeter of $\triangle A'B'C'$.
   (f) Compare the area of $\triangle ABC$ and $\triangle A'B'C'$.
   (g) In each triangle, draw the altitude from the vertex of the 90° angle to the hypotenuse. Measure the altitudes. How do the lengths compare?

2. (a) Draw $\triangle PQR$ with $PQ = 12$ cm, $\angle Q = 90°$, and $QR = 10$ cm.
   (b) Draw triangle $\triangle P'Q'R'$ so that it is a reduction of $\triangle PQR$ by a factor of $\frac{1}{2}$.
   (c) Verify that $P'Q' = \frac{1}{2}PQ$.
   (d) Measure the angles in each triangle. How do they compare?
   (e) Compare the perimeter of $\triangle PQR$ to the perimeter of $\triangle P'Q'R'$.
   (f) Compare the area of $\triangle PQR$ and $\triangle P'Q'R'$.
   (g) In each triangle, draw the altitude from the vertex of the 90° angle to the hypotenuse. Measure the altitudes. How do the lengths compare?

3. (a) Draw any right triangle and label it $\triangle XYZ$.
   (b) Draw $\triangle X'Y'Z'$ so that it is an enlargement of $\triangle XYZ$ by a scale factor of $\frac{3}{2}$.
   (c) Compare the perimeter of $\triangle XYZ$ to the perimeter of $\triangle X'Y'Z'$.
   (d) Compare the area of $\triangle XYZ$ and $\triangle X'Y'Z'$.
   (e) In each triangle, draw the altitude from the vertex of the 90° angle to the hypotenuse. Measure the altitudes.

4. What effect does the scale factor have on
   (a) the length of the sides, altitude, and base of the reduced or enlarged triangle?
   (b) the perimeter of the reduced or enlarged triangle?
   (c) the area of the reduced or enlarged triangle?

Part 2: Surveying the Width of the Classroom with a Drinking-Straw Transit ———

It isn't practical to measure large distances on a building site with a measuring tape. Surveyors use a *transit* to measure these distances indirectly. Then they use these measurements to create scale drawings. These drawings are used for planning.

You can use a simple device, made from a drinking straw and a piece of graph paper, to simulate how a surveyor uses a transit to determine a distance.

surveyor using a transit

Think, Do, Discuss

1. (a) Place a piece of graph paper on a desk so that the long side of the paper is parallel to the front wall of the room.
   (b) Stand behind the desk, facing the front of the room. Label the midpoint of the side of the graph paper closest to you with the letter *A*. Make sure that you can see each front corner of the room from *A*. If you can't, move the paper.
   (c) Measure the perpendicular distance from *A* to the front of the classroom (*AP* on the diagram).
   (d) Lay one end of a drinking straw on point *A*. Kneel down and look through the straw. Rotate the straw while you look through it until you sight the right front corner of the room (*R*). Label the point where the line of sight through the straw crosses the edge of the paper with the letter *B*. In the illustration, *B* is on the right edge of the paper, but on your paper it might be on the edge opposite *A*.
   (e) Repeat step (d), but this time sight the left front corner of the room (*L* in the diagram). Label with the letter *C* the point where your line of sight crosses the edge of the graph paper—the left edge in the illustration, but possibly the front edge on your paper.

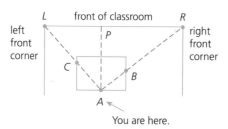

2. Compare △*ABC* and △*ARL*.

    (a) Explain why △*ABC* is not a scale drawing of △*ARL*.

    (b) In the diagram of △*ABC*, *C* is farther from the bottom edge than *B*. Your diagram may not show the same relationship. Explain why the positions of *B* and *C* will be different for different desk positions.

    (c) In the diagram, *BD* has been drawn parallel to the long edge of the graph paper. Explain why △*ABD* is a scale drawing of △*ARL*. (In your diagram, the new line, parallel to the long edge of the paper, may have to be drawn through *C* rather than *B*, depending on which point is closer to *A*.)

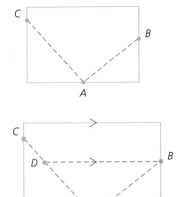

3. **(a)** What required information is missing to find the width of the classroom?

    (b) Carry out the measurement needed to allow you to determine the ratio that relates lengths in the drawing of △*ABD* to △*ARL*. Write the scale factor that corresponds to this ratio.

    (c) Each side in △*ABD* is a reduced version of a side in △*ARL*. Explain why the sides match up as follows: *AB* to *AR*, *AD* to *AL*, *BD* to *RL*.

    (d) Measure the sides of △*ABD* and use the scale factor from (b) to make a table like this in your notebook.

Measured Length vs. Calculated Length

△*ABD* Measured (cm)	△*ARL* Calculated (cm)
AB = ■	*AR* = ■
AD = ■	*AL* = ■
BD = ■	*RL* = ■
?? = ■	*AP* = ■

    (e) Accurately measure the width of the front of the room. Compare the measured width to the calculated value. Describe any sources of error that could affect the accuracy of the calculation.

4. Explain why saying that one triangle is a scale model of the other is the same as saying they are similar.

Part 3: Measuring the Height of a Tree with a Drinking-Straw Hypsometer

Darquise used a simple device called a *hypsometer* to indirectly measure the height of a tree. The hypsometer was constructed with a drinking straw, graph paper glued to a rigid piece of cardboard, a length of string, and a washer to weight the string, as shown.

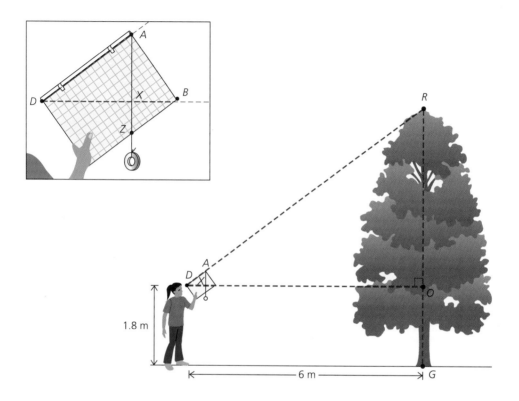

Darquise is 1.8 m tall. She stood 6 m from the base of the tree. She sighted the top of the tree through the straw of the hypsometer and had a partner mark the point X where the weighted string crossed a horizontal line from Darquise's eye.

Think, Do, Discuss

1. Explain why $\triangle AXD$ on the drinking-straw hypsometer is a scale drawing of triangle $\triangle ROD$ formed by Darquise and the tree.

2. By measuring with a ruler, Darquise found $DX = 10$ cm and $AX = 7$ cm.
   (a) What is the scale factor that relates the sides of $\triangle AXD$ to the sides of $\triangle ROD$?
   (b) Use the scale factor to compute the height of the tree. What do you need to consider in addition to the length of RO?
   (c) What sources of error could affect the accuracy of Darquise's estimate of the height of the tree?

3. Examine $\triangle ZBA$.

    (a) Discuss why $\triangle ZBA$ also is a scale drawing of $\triangle ROD$.

    (b) Which angles of $\triangle ZBA$ correspond to the angles of $\triangle ROD$?

    (c) Which sides of $\triangle ZBA$ correspond to the sides of $\triangle ROD$?

    (d) If Darquise wanted to use $\triangle ZBA$ to find the height of the tree, which side of the triangle would correspond to DX in $\triangle AXD$? Why?

    (e) Discuss whether $\triangle ZBA$ and $\triangle AXD$ have to be identical (congruent) for them to both be scale drawings of $\triangle ROD$.

4. **(a)** Which triangles in this problem are similar?

    (b) Explain how Darquise used the relationships between the sides of similar triangles to find the height of the tree.

Focus 5.4

Key Ideas

- If $\triangle ABC$ is a **scale drawing** of $\triangle XYZ$, the two triangles are **similar**. One triangle is an enlargement or reduction of the other.
  In symbols, $\triangle ABC \sim \triangle XYZ$ means that $\triangle ABC$ is similar to $\triangle XYZ$.

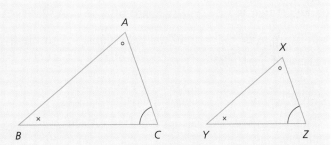

- The **scale factor** or **scale ratio** is a measure of the amount of enlargement or reduction that relates one similar triangle to the other. If $\triangle ABC \sim \triangle XYZ$, then the scale factor is the ratio of the lengths of any pair of corresponding sides in the two triangles. In this diagram. $\triangle GHI$ is a reduction of $\triangle DEF$ and $\triangle JKL$ is an enlargement of $\triangle DEF$. So

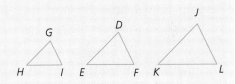

$$\frac{DE}{GH} = \frac{EF}{HI} = \frac{FD}{IG} \quad \text{and} \quad \frac{DE}{JK} = \frac{EF}{KL} = \frac{FD}{LJ}.$$

- If $\triangle ABC \sim \triangle XYZ$ and the scale factor is $n = \frac{AB}{XY}$, then

  ◆ the length of any side or altitude of $\triangle ABC$
  $= n(\text{length of corresponding side or altitude of } \triangle XYZ)$

  ◆ the perimeter of $\triangle ABC = n(\text{perimeter of } \triangle XYZ)$

  ◆ the area of $\triangle ABC = n^2(\text{area of } \triangle XYZ)$

- Similar triangles can be used to find lengths that cannot be measured directly. This method is called **indirect measurement**.

- In the case of area, multiplying the known area by the square of the scale factor gives the corresponding area of the reduced or enlarged triangle.

Example 1

In $\triangle ABC$, $AB = 4$ cm, $BC = 3$ cm, and $\angle B = 90°$. In $\triangle XYZ$, $XY = 8$ cm, $YZ = 6$ cm, and one of the angles is 90°. Show that there are two ways to draw $\triangle XYZ$. Explain why one is similar to $\triangle ABC$ and the other is not.

Solution

The diagram for $\triangle ABC$ is shown. By the Pythagorean theorem, the hypotenuse (AC) is 5 cm.

In $\triangle XYZ$, XY can be one of the perpendicular sides (diagram **A**) or the hypotenuse (diagram **B**).

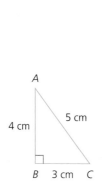
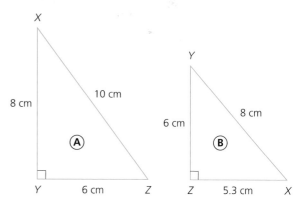

In diagram **A**, $\triangle XYZ$ is a right triangle that is a 2$\times$ enlargement of $\triangle ABC$. $\triangle XYZ \sim \triangle ABC$ and the scale factor is 2.

In diagram **B**, the ratio of the hypotenuse XY to the hypotenuse AC indicates a scale factor of $\frac{8}{5} = 1.6$.

$\dfrac{XY}{AC} = \dfrac{8}{5}, \dfrac{YZ}{AB} = \dfrac{6}{4} \neq \dfrac{8}{5}, \dfrac{ZX}{BC} = \dfrac{5.3}{3} \neq \dfrac{8}{5}$

This version of $\triangle XYZ$ is *not* similar to $\triangle ABC$.

Example 2

Mayson estimates the distance across a wide river as follows. He marks point B near the riverbank, directly across from a large rock on the opposite side A. Then he walks 10 paces along the riverbank, perpendicular to the line joining A and B, and marks the point C. He continues one more pace in the same direction and marks the point D. Mayson now moves away from the river, parallel to the line joining A and B, until his position E lines up with mark C and the rock. He reasons that the width of the river is 10 times the distance between points D and E. Is he correct? Explain.

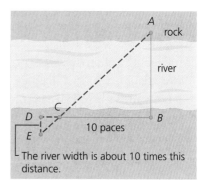

The river width is about 10 times this distance.

Solution

The two triangles both have right angles at B and D.
Also, because they are opposite angles at a vertex, $\angle ACB = \angle ECD$.
Therefore, $\triangle ABC \sim \triangle EDC$ because of AA$\sim$.
Because the triangles are similar, $\dfrac{DC}{BC} = \dfrac{ED}{AB}$.
Since BC is 10 paces and DC is 1 pace, the scale ratio is $\frac{1}{10}$ and Mayson is correct.

Example 3

Beth is an engineer. She is designing a system of pipes needed to keep the ice cold on an outdoor rink. The rink will be in a triangular park. First, Beth draws a scale diagram of the triangular rink, using a scale factor of 1 cm = 6.25 m. The dimensions of the lot on the diagram are 5 cm, 12 cm, and 13 cm. Also one of the angles of the lot is 90°.

(a) Draw the scale diagram.
(b) Use the diagram to measure the other angles.
(c) What is the perimeter of the actual lot?
(d) What is the area of the actual lot?

Solution

(a) The triangle must be a right triangle, since it has a 90° angle. The largest side is 13 cm—this side must be the hypotenuse and must be opposite the right angle.

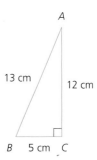

(b) Use a protactor to measure.

$$\angle B \doteq 67°$$
$$\angle A \doteq 23°$$

(c) To convert the scale factor of 1 cm = 6.25 m, make all the units the same. In this case, they will be changed to centimetres. The scale ratio is

$$\frac{1 \text{ cm}}{6.25 \text{ m}} = \frac{1 \text{ cm}}{625 \text{ cm}}$$
$$= \frac{1}{625}$$

Call the actual measures of the lot a, b, and c. Then,

$$\frac{5}{a} = \frac{1}{625} \qquad\qquad \frac{12}{b} = \frac{1}{625} \qquad\qquad \frac{13}{c} = \frac{1}{625}$$

Solve each ratio.

$$a = 5 \times 625 \qquad\qquad b = 12 \times 625 \qquad\qquad c = 13 \times 625$$
$$a = 3125 \text{ cm} \qquad\qquad b = 7500 \text{ cm} \qquad\qquad c = 8125 \text{ cm}$$
$$a = 31.25 \text{ m} \qquad\qquad b = 75.0 \text{ m} \qquad\qquad c = 81.25 \text{ m}$$

The perimeter is

$$P = a + b + c$$
$$= 31.25 + 75.0 + 81.25$$
$$= 187.5 \text{ m}$$

(d) The three sides form the sides of a right triangle with base a and altitude b. The area of the lot is

$$A = \frac{ab}{2}$$
$$A = \frac{(31.25)(75.0)}{2}$$
$$A = 1171.875 \text{ m}^2$$
$$A \doteq 1171.9 \text{ m}^2$$

Practise, Apply, Solve 5.4

Ⓐ

1. Miki is standing in a parking lot on a sunny day. He is 1.6 m tall and casts a shadow that is 4.8 m long. Draw a scale diagram of the situation that can be used to measure the angle at which the sun's rays hit the ground.

2. David held a 30 cm ruler far enough in front of his eye so that a cabinet on a far wall appeared to be 30 cm tall. The ruler was 45 cm in front of David's eye, and he was standing 3 m from the cabinet. Use a scale drawing to estimate the height of the cabinet.

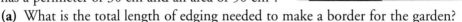

3. Marta made a 1 : 20 scale drawing of her triangular garden. In the drawing, the garden has a perimeter of 30 cm and an area of 50 cm².
   (a) What is the total length of edging needed to make a border for the garden?
   (b) What is the total area of the garden?

4. A telephone pole is supported by a guy wire anchored in the ground 3 m from the base of the pole. The wire makes a 75° angle with the ground and joins the pole 5 m from the top. Use a scale diagram to estimate the height of the pole.

5. Ruben is a graphic artist. He designed a mural for a restaurant and prepared a small-scale version to show to the restaurant owner. Once the owner approved it, Ruben enlarged the design to put on the restaurant wall. The original design and the enlargement are shown.
   (a) Measure the dimensions of the small version and the enlargement. State the scale of the enlargement as a ratio.
   (b) Ruben used 0.45 L of paint for the sample mural. How much paint is needed for the enlarged wall mural?

6. Shirin is standing beside a lighthouse on a sunny day.
  (a) Shirin's height and her shadow form the perpendicular sides of a right triangle. What does the hypotenuse represent? Why is it reasonable to assume the triangle has a right angle?
  (b) The tower and its shadow also form two sides of a right triangle. What does the hypotenuse of that triangle represent?
  (c) Explain why the two triangles are similar.
  (d) Find the scale factor that relates the two triangles.
  (e) Use the scale factor to estimate the height of the tower.

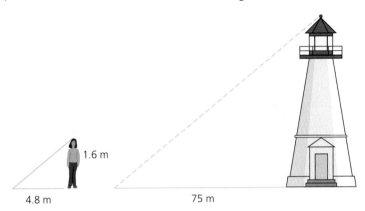

1.6 m

4.8 m   75 m

7. A 3.6 m ladder is leaning against a wall with its base 2 m from the wall.
  (a) Use the Pythagorean theorem to determine how high up the wall the ladder reaches.
  (b) Suppose a 2.4 m ladder is placed against the wall parallel to the longer ladder. How far will it reach up the wall and how far will its base be from the wall?
  (c) Communication: Explain why the triangles formed by the ground, the wall, and the two ladders are similar.
  (d) Knowledge and Understanding: Suppose that an even longer ladder is placed parallel to the first two ladders, with its base 5 m from the wall. How long is this ladder?

3.6 m

2.4 m

8. On June 30, 1859, Jean Francois Gravelet crossed the Niagara Gorge on a tightrope. Since it was not possible to measure the distance across the gorge directly, he used indirect measurement, as shown.

(a) Explain why $\triangle DEC$ is similar to $\triangle ABC$.

(b) What ratio determines the scale factor for the two triangles?

(c) Compute the distance across the gorge.

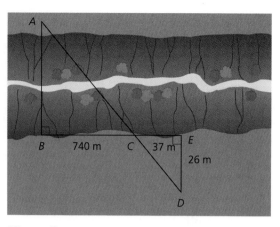

Niagara Gorge

9. How wide is the river?

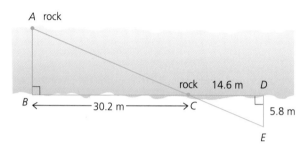

10. How far is Dock A from Dock B?

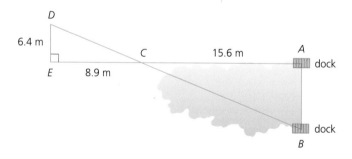

11. How wide is the bay?

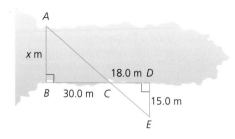

12. Application: Maria, at point F, used a 3 m surveyor's pole to sight from the ground to the top of a 100 m radio tower. Based on her diagram, how far was she from the tower?

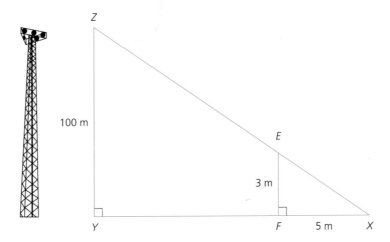

13. Romeo uses a mirror to determine the height of Juliet's window. He knows that when light is reflected from a mirror, it makes the same angle on both sides of the point where it strikes the mirror. (The angle of incidence equals the angle of reflection.) How high is the window from the ground?

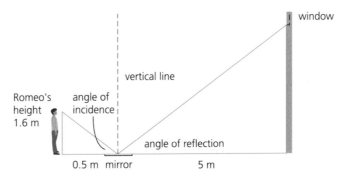

14. Check Your Understanding: Suppose you want to model a situation where a building and a person nearby both cast shadows.
   (a) Sketch two triangles to represent this situation, one for the person and one for the building.
   (b) Why can you assume the triangles are similar?
   (c) If you know that the building's shadow extends 12 m from its base, what additional information do you need to find the height of the building?

C

15. A triangular roof is supported at its peak by a vertical post, as shown. Compute the length of the post and the span of the roof. (The **span** is the width of the space covered by the roof. In this diagram it is BC.)

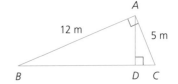

16. Thinking, Inquiry, Problem Solving: More than 2200 years ago, the Greek mathematician Eratosthenes used similar triangles to estimate the circumference of Earth. He got the idea when he observed that at noon on the day of the summer solstice, the sun shone straight down to the bottom of a well in the town of Syene (which is called Aswan, Egypt, today).

(a) Find out how Eratosthenes solved the problem and explain why his solution was a valid way to estimate the size of Earth.

(b) List some limitations of his method.

The Chapter Problem—Mechanical Engineering

In this section, you modelled problems with similar triangles. Apply what you learned to answer these questions about the chapter problem on page 446.

1. Draw a scale diagram to accurately represent the dimensions and positions of the sprocket wheels of the bicycle.

   (a) Find the length of the curved sections of the bicycle chain on your diagram as accurately as you can using a piece of string.

   (b) Use these measured values to estimate the total length of the chain.

2. Measure the angles that correspond to the arcs covered by the bicycle chain on the two wheels.

   (a) How does the angle in the smaller circle compare to the angle in the larger circle?

   (b) What fraction of the entire 360° circle angle does each arc represent?

   (c) What fraction of the circumference of each circle does each arc represent?

   (d) Use these fractions and the circumference of each circle to compute the length of each arc.

3. Compare the answers you got for the curved sections of chain in questions 1 and 2. Discuss which answer is more accurate.

Did You Know?

Tangram

The tangram is an ancient Chinese puzzle that has seven geometric shapes called tans (two large triangles, one medium triangle, two small triangles, a square, and a parallelogram.) The seven pieces form a square. The object of the game is to arrange the pieces to form other shapes or outlines of animals, objects, or people.

Obtain one of the commercial versions that are available or make your own set. Rearrange the pieces to see what figures you can create.

Slopes and Angles of Ramps

Shawn's Restaurant is going to install a ramp to provide access for people in wheelchairs.

The building code for the city says that in commercial buildings wheelchair access ramps must meet the following requirements:

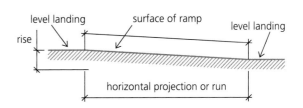

> When a ramp is added to provide an accessible entrance, the slope of the ramp should be as shallow as possible but not more than 1 : 12. It is also important to provide handrails whenever the slope is more than 1 : 20 and the vertical rise is greater than 15 cm.

Think, Do, Discuss

1. Draw a scale diagram to find the angle of rise for a ramp with a slope of 1 : 12.

2. Handrails must be installed if the rise is more than 15 cm and the slope is more than 1 : 20.
   (a) Draw a scale diagram to find the rise angle for a ramp with a slope of 1 : 20.
   (b) What is the maximum run the ramp could have without rising more than 15 cm?

3. In some cities the building code has more restrictions on the slope of a ramp. A short ramp with a small vertical rise can have a relatively steep slope, but it is not safe to install a long ramp with a steep slope. Tables like this one are used to specify limits on the slope of short ramps.

Maximum Slope for Short Ramps

Vertical Rise (mm)	Maximum Slope	Maximum Angle	Minimum Run
0 to 15	1 : 2		
15.1 to 50	1 : 5		
50.1 to 200	1 : 10		
over 200	1 : 12		

Copy this table into your notebook. Draw a scale diagram to determine the maximum angle of rise and the minimum run for each vertical rise category in the table.

5.6 Investigating the Connection Between Slope and Angle

In the real world, the concept of slope is expressed in various ways.

- Architects often express the slope of a ramp as the ratio $\frac{rise}{run}$. If a ramp has a slope of 1 : 12, it means that the ramp rises 1 cm for every 12 cm of run.

- Carpenters refer to the **pitch** of a roof.

- Engineers often express the grade of a hill as a percentage. For example, a road going up a hillside might have a grade of 10%, which means the road rises 10 m for every 100 m of run.

No matter how it is expressed, the slope is related to the angle that a line, ramp, road, or roof makes with a horizontal line. This angle is called the **slope angle**. In this section, you will investigate the connection between slope and slope angle.

Slopes of Lines—Ratios and Angles

A linear relationship plotted on the Cartesian plane produces a line with a definite slope. The slope is equal to the ratio $\frac{\Delta y}{\Delta x} = \frac{rise}{run}$.

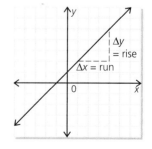

Think, Do, Discuss

1. **(a)** Plot a line through the origin that slopes upward at an angle of 40° to the x-axis.
   (b) Select a point on the line and verify that the slope is approximately 0.84.
   (c) Select two more points on the line and use them to calculate the slope.
   (d) Does the value of the slope depend on which points are used in the calculation?
   (e) Draw a line through (0, 5), parallel to the first line. Why does it make sense to say that this line also slopes upward with an angle of 40°?

2. **(a)** Repeat step 1 for a line through the origin that slopes downward at an angle of 40° to the x-axis.
   (b) How does the slope of this line compare to the slope of the line in step 1?
   (c) If this line were perpendicular to the line in step 1, what angle would it make with the x-axis? What would its slope be?
   (d) Draw a line, parallel to the line in (a), that passes through (−1, −3). Why does it make sense to say that this line also slopes downward at an angle of 40°?

3. **(a)** Draw two lines through the origin that slope up, one at an angle of 20° and the other at an angle of 80°. Compare the slopes to the slope of the line in step 1.
   (b) Does doubling the slope angle double the slope? Explain.
   (c) Does reducing the slope angle by half reduce the slope by half? Explain.

4. Suppose two lines have the same slope angle, but one slopes upward and the other slopes downward.
   (a) What do you think the relationship is between the slopes of the two lines?
   (b) Try several different slopes to confirm your hypothesis.
   (c) Why does it make sense to say that an upward slope angle is positive while a downward slope angle is negative?

5. Draw a graph and complete this table of values in your notebook. Find the slopes, to one decimal place, from the coordinates of points on the lines you have drawn. Measure as accurately as you can.

Slope vs. Angle

Slope Angle	Slope	Slope Angle	Slope
10°		−10°	
20°		−20°	
30°		−30°	
40°	0.8	−40°	
50°		−50°	
60°		−60°	
70°		−70°	
80°		−80°	

6. Think about how you computed the slope for each angle in the table in step 5. In each case, you selected two points A and B on the line and computed $\frac{\Delta y}{\Delta x} = \frac{rise}{run}$ using a right triangle like the one shown. Of course, you could have used two different points P and Q.

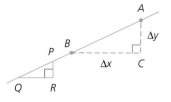

(a) Explain why $\triangle ABC \sim \triangle PQR$.

(b) Explain how the fact that the triangles are similar proves that
$$\frac{\Delta y}{\Delta x} = \frac{AC}{BC} = \frac{PR}{QR}.$$

7. (a) Why does it make sense for a line with slope angle of 45° to have slope of 1?

(b) A 45° angle is half way between 40° and 50°. Is that also true for the slopes of the corresponding lines? That is, is the slope of a line with a 45° angle halfway between the slopes of lines with angles of 40° and 50°?

(c) Based on the pattern in the table in step 5, what would you expect the slope to be for an angle of 0°? For an angle of 90°?

8. The slope angles used so far have ranged from $-90°$ to 90°. However, the full range of angles in a Cartesian coordinate system is 360°.

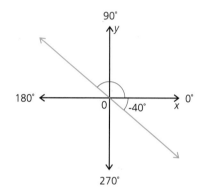

(a) Refer to the diagram and explain how a slope angle of $-40°$ can also be treated as an angle of $+140°$.

(b) Describe why a negative slope angle can be treated as a positive angle greater than 90°.

(c) If a line has a positive slope, what are the possible values, between 0° and 360°, of its corresponding slope angle? Have you included all possible slope angles?

(d) If a line has a negative slope, what are the possible values, between 0° and 360°, of its corresponding slope angle?

Did You Know?

In 1885, the Canadian Pacific Railway was constructed through the Rogers Pass. Grades of up to 4% or 2.3° were encountered over this route, making operations difficult and not very economical when traffic began to increase. In 1989, the CPR opened the longest railway tunnel in North America, 14.7 km, built through Mt. Macdonald to reduce the grade for westbound trains. If the tunnel through Mt. Macdonald has a 2.4% grade, how much vertical distance does the track rise through this tunnel?

Focus 5.6

Key Ideas

- The **slope** of a line is given by the ratio $\frac{\Delta y}{\Delta x} = \frac{rise}{run}$. The slope is related to the angle the line makes with the *x*-axis, which is called the **slope angle**.

  - ◆ When the line rises above the horizontal, the angle formed is called the **angle of inclination,** or **angle of elevation** of the line.

  - ◆ When the line falls below the horizontal, the angle formed is called the **angle of declination,** or **angle of depression** of the line.

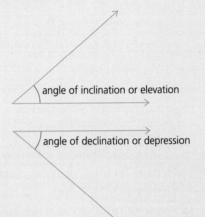

- Parallel lines have equal slopes and equal slope angles.

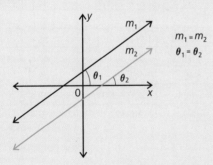

$m_1 = m_2$
$\theta_1 = \theta_2$

- Lines with a positive slope have slope angles between 0° and 90°.

- Lines with a negative slope have slope angles between −90° and 0°. If a slope angle is negative, it can be expressed as an equivalent angle between 90° and 180° using the expression (*slope angle*) + 180°.

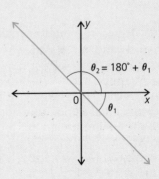

$\theta_2 = 180° + \theta_1$

- If the slope of a line is equal to −1 times the slope of another line, then the slope angle of the first line is equal to −1 times the slope angle of the second line.

- The table below shows the slope of lines with slope angles between 0° and 90°.

Slope vs. Angle

Angle (°)	Slope	Angle (°)	Slope	Angle (°)	Slope	Angle (°)	Slope
0	0	23	0.42447482	45	1.000 000 00	68	2.475 086 85
1	0.017 455 06	24	0.44522869	46	1.035 530 31	69	2.605 089 06
2	0.034 920 77	25	0.46630766	47	1.072 368 71	70	2.747 477 42
3	0.052 407 78	26	0.48773259	48	1.110 612 51	71	2.904 210 88
4	0.069 926 81	27	0.50952545	49	1.150 368 41	72	3.077 683 54
5	0.087 488 66	28	0.531 709 43	50	1.191 753 59	73	3.270 852 62
6	0.105 104 24	29	0.554 309 05	51	1.234 897 16	74	3.487 414 44
7	0.122 784 56	30	0.577 350 27	52	1.279 941 63	75	3.732 050 81
8	0.140 540 83	31	0.600 860 62	53	1.327 044 82	76	4.010 780 93
9	0.158 384 44	32	0.624 869 35	54	1.376 381 92	77	4.331 475 87
10	0.176 326 98	33	0.649 407 59	55	1.428 148 01	78	4.704 630 11
11	0.194 380 31	34	0.674 508 52	56	1.482 560 97	79	5.144 554 02
12	0.212 556 56	35	0.700 207 54	57	1.539 864 96	80	5.671 281 82
13	0.230 868 19	36	0.726 542 53	58	1.600 334 53	81	6.313 751 51
14	0.249 328 00	37	0.753 554 05	59	1.664 279 48	82	7.115 369 72
15	0.267 949 19	38	0.781 285 63	60	1.732 050 81	83	8.144 346 43
16	0.286 745 39	39	0.809 784 03	61	1.804 047 76	84	9.514 364 45
17	0.305 730 68	40	0.839 099 63	62	1.880 726 47	85	11.430 052 3
18	0.324 919 70	41	0.869 286 74	63	1.962 610 51	86	14.300 666 3
19	0.344 327 61	42	0.900 404 04	64	2.050 303 84	87	19.081 136 7
20	0.363 97 023	43	0.932 515 09	65	2.144 506 92	88	28.636 253 3
21	0.383 864 04	44	0.965 688 77	66	2.246 036 77	89	57.289 961 6
22	0.404 026 23			67	2.355 852 37	90	—

Example 1

Find, to the nearest degree, the angle of inclination of a ramp with a slope of 1 : 12.

Solution

The slope is $\frac{1}{12} \doteq 0.083$.

From the table of angles and slopes, this slope corresponds to an angle of inclination of about 5°.

Example 2

Find the slope angle for the line with equation $y = 2x + 5$.

Solution

The equation is in the form $y = mx + b$. In this case, $m = 2$, so the slope of the line is 2. Look in the table to find a slope that is 2 or close to 2. The closest slope is 1.962 610 51, and the angle for this slope is 63°. This slope corresponds to an angle of about 63°.

Example 3

Esther is using a topographical map to plan a mountain hike. The map shows that she will start from a point 600 m above sea level and finish at another point, 5 km away, that is 750 m above sea level. Assuming she follows a straight path, what will be the average slope angle of her route?

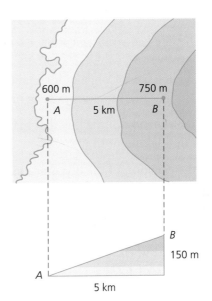

Solution

Esther's path has a rise of $(750 - 600) = 150$ m and a run of 5 km = 5000 m.

The slope of this path is $\frac{150}{5000} = 0.03$. From the table, the slope angle is a little less than 2°.

Practise, Apply, Solve 5.6 ——————

A

1. Find the slope of the line
   (a) $y = -3x - 2$
   (b) that passes through $P(2, -1)$ and $Q(-2, 1)$
   (c) that makes an angle of 45° with the x-axis
   (d) that makes an angle of $-70°$ with the x-axis

2. Find the angle of inclination or declination each line makes with the x-axis.
   (a) The equation of the line is $y = 3x + 1$.
   (b) The slope of the line is $\frac{1}{4}$ and the y-intercept is -2.
   (c) $A(2, 5)$ and $B(-2, 3)$ are points on the line.
   (d) The x-intercept of the line is 4 and the y-intercept is -1.
   (e) $C(-2, 5)$ and $D(2, 3)$ are points on the line.
   (f) The x-intercept of the line is -4 and the y-intercept is -2.

3. A line has a *y*-intercept of 5 and makes an angle of inclination of 55° with the *x*-axis.
  (a) Find the slope of the line.
  (b) Find the equation of the line.
  (c) Find the *x*-intercept of the line.

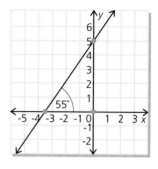

4. Sketch each line. Then find its equation and its *x*-intercept.
  (a) The line has a *y*-intercept of −2 and an angle of inclination of 60° with the *x*-axis.
  (b) The line has an angle of inclination of 45° and passes through point (2, −7). Also find the *y*-intercept of the line.

5. Find the equation of the line that makes an angle of −20° with the *x*-axis and passes through point (3, 3).

6. Find the equation of the line that makes an angle of −60° with the *x*-axis and has an *x*-intercept of −5.

7. In this diagram, $AC \perp CD$, using points $A(0, 0)$, $C(5, 6)$, and $D(a, 0)$. Determine
  (a) the slope of AC
  (b) the slope of CD
  (c) the value of a
  (d) the measure of $\angle CAD$
  (e) the measure of $\angle CDA$

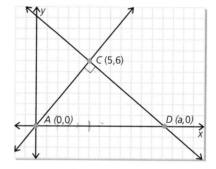

8. (a) A line through the origin makes an angle of 30° with the *x*-axis. Find the equation of a parallel line with a *y*-intercept of −4.
  (b) A line with positive slope makes an angle of 40° with the *y*-axis and passes through point (2, 2). Find the equation of the line.

9. The graphs of $y = 2x$ and $y = -3x$ intersect at the origin.
  (a) Find the angle each line makes with the *x*-axis.
  (b) Find the angle at which the two lines intersect.

10. Knowledge and Understanding
  (a) Find the coordinates of the point where $y = -3x + 10$ and $y = 4x + 2$ intersect.
  (b) Find the angle each line makes with the *x*-axis.
  (c) Find the angle between the lines at the point of intersection.

11. A circle is centred at $A(0, 0)$ and has a radius of 5 units. $D(-5, 0)$, $E(3, 4)$, and $C(5, 0)$ are points on the circle.

(a) Calculate the slopes of DE and EC.

(b) From the slope of the line, what is the measure of $\angle EDA$?

(c) From the slope of the line, what is the measure of $\angle ECA$?

(d) What is the measure of $\angle DEC$?

(e) Explain how the values of the slopes confirms the measure of $\angle DEC$ found in (d).

(f) Select several other locations for point E on the circumference of the circle. Is the result regarding the measure of $\angle DEC$ true for all the points selected?

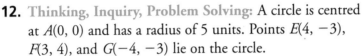

12. **Thinking, Inquiry, Problem Solving:** A circle is centred at $A(0, 0)$ and has a radius of 5 units. Points $E(4, -3)$, $F(3, 4)$, and $G(-4, -3)$ lie on the circle.

(a) Use slopes to determine the measure of $\angle GFE$.

(b) Use slopes to determine the measure of $\angle GAE$.

(c) Repeat these calculations for different locations of E, F, and G on the circle. State your hypothesis about the relationship between the angle at the centre ($\angle GAE$) and the angle on the circumference ($\angle GFE$).

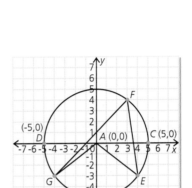

13. A teacher set up an activity to see if students could use a sonic ranging device accurately. A flat, reflective piece of metal was placed 3 m above the ground on a classroom wall. The metal was tilted so that it would reflect the signal from a ranging device directly back to the receiver of the unit. The device, which includes a transmitter and receiver in one unit, was placed on the floor, directly in front of the reflector, 5 m from the base of the wall.

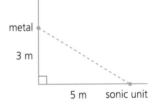

(a) At what angle from the floor would the students have to point the device so that the signal would be reflected directly back to the receiver?

(b) The reflector was tilted at an angle to the wall so that the signal would reflect directly back to the device. Find the angle from the vertical at which it was hung.

(c) How far from the base of the wall would the unit have to be placed if the required angle of inclination was 45°?

14. Application: A surveyor made these measurements to determine the width of a river. Starting at a point directly across from a hydro tower on the far shore, the surveyor moved exactly 50 m along the bank. From that point, he used a transit to sight two lines: one to the tower and the other parallel to the river. The angle between the lines was 70°.

   (a) The surveyor knew that the tower was 30 m from the bank of the river. How wide was the river?

   (b) From his original position, the surveyor used the transit to sight the top of the tower. The angle of inclination to the top was 28°. If the transit was mounted on a tripod that was 1.2 m high, how tall was the tower?

15. Communication: A builder's plan indicated that the access road to a hockey rink should have a 5% grade—a rise of 5 m for a run of 100 m. Any grade between 4.5% and 5.5% was acceptable, according to the designer. Using a transit, a surveyor found that the actual inclination angle of the ramp was 4°. Was the grade of the ramp within the designer's limits?

16. A film director has called for a "follow-shot," in which the camera moves along a set of tracks to follow the action. An actor will run on a path that is at a 30° angle to the tracks, and the camera, moving along the tracks, will keep pace with the actor. The actor will move away from the camera as the scene progresses. The camera operator has to adjust the lens so that the actor is in focus throughout the scene.

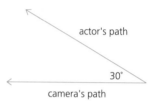

actor's path

30°

camera's path

Suppose the actor and the camera start off side by side. How far from the camera will the actor be at the end of the scene, if the camera has moved 30 m along the tracks?

17. Check Your Understanding

   (a) Explain how the slope and the slope angle of a line are related.

   (b) Explain how to find the angle of inclination of a line if you know the slope of the line.

C

18. A carpenter is installing a new roof. The pitch of the roof is
35°. The distance from the centre of the attic to the wall of the
house is 12 m.
   (a) Find the vertical distance from the floor of the attic to the
   roof.
   (b) Find the angle at which the rafters need to be cut to be
   flush with the wall supports.

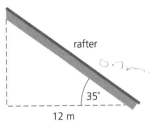

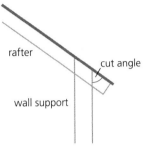

19. Nalini and Jodi are both looking at the top of the same flagpole. They are
standing in a line on the same side of the flagpole, 50 m apart. The angle to the
top of the pole from Jodi's position is 11°. From Nalini's position, it is 7°. Nalini
and Jodi are both 173 cm tall.
   (a) How tall is the flagpole?
   (b) How far is each girl from the base of the flagpole?
   (c) Suppose the two girls are standing in a line on *opposite* sides of the pole. In
   this situation, how tall is the flagpole and how far is each girl from it?

The Chapter Problem—Mechanical Engineering

In this section, you saw the connection between the slope and angle of a line.
Apply what you learned to answer these questions about the chapter problem
on page 446.

1. Accurately draw a scale diagram of the sprocket wheels and bicycle chain
   on a piece of graph paper. Put the centres of the wheels on the *x*-axis.
2. Examine the right triangles formed by the radius of the larger wheel, the
   straight segment of chain, and a line parallel to the *x*-axis. What side
   lengths can be determined without measurement?
3. What is the slope angle of the straight chain segment?
4. Use the slope angle of the chain segment to find the angle formed by the
   radius of the larger wheel and the line joining the centre of the wheel.
5. Use this angle to find the fraction of the circumference of both the large
   and small sprocket wheels that the chain must cover.

5.7 The Primary Trigonometric Ratios

In this section, you will learn about three important trigonometric ratios, the sine ratio, the cosine ratio, and the tangent ratio.

Part 1: Investigating Ratios in Similar Right Triangles

Similar right triangles share some interesting relationships. Their corresponding angles are equal and the ratios of corresponding sides are also equal. Each triangle is an enlarged or a reduced version of the other.

This diagram shows some similar triangles with a common 40° angle at A. Copy this diagram into your notebook.

Think, Do, Discuss

1. Copy this diagram using dynamic geometry software. If it is not available, use the copy you made in your notebook. Measure the lengths of the sides of each triangle. Use the values to complete a table like this in your notebook. Compute each ratio to at most three decimal places.

Triangle	Side Opposite to ∠A	Side Adjacent to ∠A	Hypotenuse	Trigonometric Ratios		
				$\frac{\text{opposite}}{\text{hypotenuse}}$	$\frac{\text{adjacent}}{\text{hypotenuse}}$	$\frac{\text{opposite}}{\text{adjacent}}$
$\triangle ABC$	$BC = \blacksquare$	$BA = \blacksquare$	$AC = \blacksquare$	$\frac{BC}{AC} = \blacksquare$	$\frac{AB}{AC} = \blacksquare$	$\frac{BC}{BA} = \blacksquare$
$\triangle ADE$						
$\triangle AFG$						
$\triangle AHI$						

2. (a) Explain why $\triangle ABC$, $\triangle ADE$, $\triangle AFG$, and $\triangle AHI$ are all similar.
   (b) How does this explain the pattern of values for the ratios in the last three columns of the table?

3. (a) Describe what would happen to the values in the table if $\angle A$ were 20°, 30°, 60°, and 80°.
   (b) Which ratios would increase as the angle increases? Which would decrease as the angle increases?

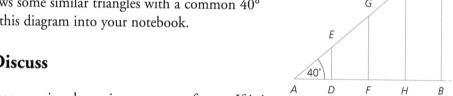

4. (a) Assume AB is horizontal. Explain how you could use the slope table in the previous section to find the lengths of AD and DE.

   (b) Why does AB have to be horizontal for this strategy to work?

Part 2: Historical Trigonometry

As early as 140 B.C.E., the Greek mathematician Hipparchus had begun to work with the ideas of trigonometry in his study of chords in circles. Hipparchus was trying to solve problems in astrology, astronomy, and navigation.

For a given angle A in a right triangle, there are three important ratios. These are called the **primary trigonometric ratios**.

sine of A

$$\sin A = \frac{\text{opposite}}{\text{hypotenuse}}$$

cosine of A

$$\cos A = \frac{\text{adjacent}}{\text{hypotenuse}}$$

tangent of A

$$\tan A = \frac{\text{opposite}}{\text{adjacent}}$$

Hipparchus lived about 2200 years ago. He is the first Greek astronomer known to history. He was also the first person known to chart the positions of the stars.

Think, Do, Discuss

1. This diagram shows how ancient Greek mathematicians named certain line segments in a circle.

   (a) Draw this diagram as accurately as you can using dynamic geometry software. If it is not available, use a ruler and protractor. Measure the lengths of the sine, cosine, and tangent segments.

   (b) Compare the lengths you found in (a) to the ratios in the table in part 1.

   (c) Explain why the length of the sine segment has the same value as $\sin A$.

   (d) Explain why the length of the cosine segment has the same value as $\cos A$.

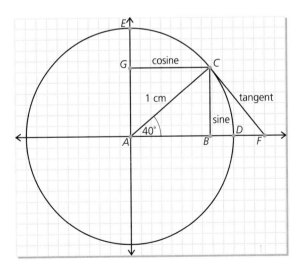

2. **(a)** Show that $\triangle ABC \sim \triangle CBF$.

(b) Show that the result of (a) suggests that tangent $= \dfrac{\text{sine}}{\text{cosine}}$ for this circle.

(c) Why does this mean that the length of the tangent segment is tan A for this circle?

(d) What information does tan A give about the line that passes through A and C?

3. Redraw the diagram, but this time increase the radius of the circle to 2 cm.

(a) Explain what happens to the lengths of the sine, cosine, and tangent segments.

(b) How will these new lengths compare to the ratios sin A, cos A, and tan A?

(c) Describe what would happen if the radius were 3 cm, 5 cm, or 0.5 cm.

Part 3: Trigonometric Ratios on a Scientific Calculator

In the days before calculators, people had to look in books of tables to find the values for the three trigonometric ratios. This process was tedious and inconvenient. Today, scientific calculators can give these values at the push of a button.

Think, Do, Discuss

1. Make sure your calculator is set to work in *degree mode* for angle calculations.

2. **(a)** Use the $\boxed{\text{SIN}}$, $\boxed{\text{COS}}$, and $\boxed{\text{TAN}}$ keys to compute sin 40°, cos 40°, and tan 40°.

(b) Compare the values in (a) to those in the table on page 484.

(c) Use the calculator to verify the slopes and slope angle pairs you created in section 5.6.

3. You can also use scientific calculators to find an angle, given the value of its trigonometric ratio. This is usually done using the $\boxed{\text{SIN}^{-1}}$, $\boxed{\text{COS}^{-1}}$, and $\boxed{\text{TAN}^{-1}}$ keys. On most calculators, these are accessed by first pressing the $\boxed{\text{2nd}}$ or $\boxed{\text{INV}}$ key, followed by the appropriate trigonometric key.

(a) Use your calculator to find the angle that corresponds to a slope of 1 : 2.

(b) Find the angle with a cosine value of 0.5.

(c) Find the angle with a sine value of 0.5.

Focus 5.7

Key Ideas

- For a right angle triangle, the three **primary trigonometric ratios** are:

$$\sin A = \frac{\text{opposite}}{\text{hypotenuse}} \qquad \cos A = \frac{\text{adjacent}}{\text{hypotenuse}} \qquad \tan A = \frac{\text{opposite}}{\text{adjacent}}$$

- The values of the trigonometric ratios depend on the angle to which the opposite side, adjacent side, and hypotenuse correspond.

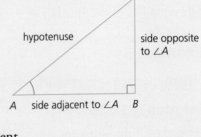

- The slope of a line is the tangent of the slope angle that the line makes with the *x*-axis.

- The values of the three primary trigonometric ratios can be found either in a book of trigonometric tables or with a scientific calculator. The calculator is more convenient.

- If the value of a trigonometric ratio is known, its corresponding angle can be found on a scientific calculator using the inverse of that ratio. On the TI-83 Plus calculator, use 2nd SIN for $\sin^{-1}$, use 2nd COS for $\cos^{-1}$, or use 2nd TAN for $\tan^{-1}$.

Example 1

Find, to the nearest degree, the angle of inclination of a ramp with a slope of 1 : 12.

Solution

The slope ratio is $\frac{1}{12} \doteq 0.083$.

Use the keystrokes

2nd TAN . 0 8 3) ENTER.

The result is shown at right.

To the nearest degree, the angle is 5°. Note that this is the same result as for example 1 on page 484.

Example 2

Find the equation, in the form $y = mx + b$, of the line that makes an angle of 35° with the *x*-axis and has a *y*-intercept of -2.

Solution

For this line, $b = -2$. We need to find m, the slope of the line.

The slope of the line is tan 35°.

Use the keystrokes TAN 3 5) ENTER.

The result is shown at right.

The slope of this line is $m = 0.7$ to one decimal place.

The equation of the line is $y = 0.7x - 2$.

Example 3

Determine the angle at which $y = 2x - 1$ and $y = 0.5x + 2$ intersect.

Solution

First, sketch the situation.

The slope of $y = 2x - 1$ is 2.

Therefore, the slope angle is $\tan^{-1}(2)$ or 63.43°.

Therefore, $\angle ACB = 180° - 63.43°$
$= 116.47°$

The slope of $y = 0.5x + 2$ is 0.5.

Therefore, the slope angle is $\tan^{-1}(0.5)$ or 26.57°.

So, $\angle BAC = 180° - (\angle ABC + \angle ACB)$
$\angle BAC = 180° - (26.57° + 116.47°)$
$\angle BAC = 36.96°$
$\angle BAC \doteq 37°$

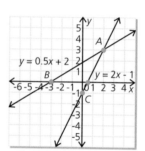

The lines intersect at an angle of about 37°.

Example 4

Determine the value of x to the nearest centimetre.

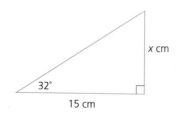

Solution

Name the sides of the triangle in terms of the given angle. Set up a ratio that can be solved.

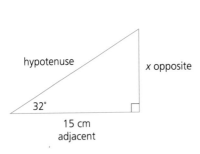

hypotenuse

x opposite

32°

15 cm
adjacent

$$\frac{x}{15} = \frac{\text{opposite}}{\text{adjacent}} \quad \text{This is the tangent of } 32°.$$

$$\tan 32° = \frac{x}{15}$$

$$15 \tan 32° = \left(\frac{x}{\cancel{15}}\right)\cancel{15}$$

$$15(0.6249) = x$$

$$x = 9.3735$$

$$x \doteq 9 \text{ cm}$$

Example 5

Calculate the measure of $\angle A$ to the nearest degree.

A

12 cm

B   5 cm   C

Solution

Name the sides of the triangle in terms of $\angle A$.

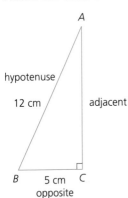

A

hypotenuse

12 cm

adjacent

B   5 cm   C
opposite

$$\frac{5}{12} = \frac{\text{opposite}}{\text{hypotenuse}} \quad \text{This is the sine of } \angle A.$$

$$\sin A = \frac{5}{12}$$

$$\sin A = 0.4167$$

$$\angle A = \sin^{-1}(0.4167)$$

$$\angle A = 24.6°$$

$$\angle A \doteq 25°$$

Career: Civil Engineer

Civil engineers design and supervise the construction of roads, airports, tunnels, bridges, and dams. They often use trigonometry in their work. For example, a civil engineer would use trigonometry to determine the height of an exit ramp that can be used at a maximum speed and still be safe under normal conditions.

Practise, Apply, Solve 5.7

1. △*XYZ* is a right triangle with ∠*X* = 90°.
    (a) Sketch △*XYZ*.
    (b) Write the ratios that correspond to sin *Y*, cos *Y*, and tan *Y*.

2. Determine the value of each ratio to four decimal places.
    (a) sin 35°   **(b)** cos 60°   **(c)** tan 45°   **(d)** cos 75°
    (e) sin 18°   **(f)** tan 38°   **(g)** cos 88°   **(h)** sin 7°

3. Determine the size of ∠*A* to the nearest degree.
    (a) sin *A* = 0.5299   **(b)** cos *A* = 0.4226
    (c) tan *A* = 4.3315   **(d)** cos *A* = 0.5
    (e) sin *A* = 0.2419   **(f)** tan *A* = 0.0875
    (g) cos *A* = 0.7071   **(h)** sin *A* = 0.8829
    (i) tan *A* = 1.6003

4. Solve for *x* to one decimal place.
    (a) $\sin 35° = \frac{x}{8}$ **(b)** $\cos 70° = \frac{x}{15}$ **(c)** $\tan 20° = \frac{x}{19}$
    (d) $\tan 55° = \frac{8}{x}$ **(e)** $\sin 10° = \frac{12}{x}$ **(f)** $\sin 75° = \frac{5}{x}$

5. Solve for *B* to the nearest degree.
    (a) $\cos B = \frac{3}{8}$ **(b)** $\sin B = \frac{7}{8}$ **(c)** $\tan B = \frac{15}{9}$
    (d) $\cos B = \frac{16.8}{21.5}$ **(e)** $\tan B = \frac{25}{12}$ **(f)** $\sin B = \frac{1}{2}$

6. Find sin *B*, cos *B*, and tan *B* for each triangle. Express each answer as a ratio in lowest terms.

(a)
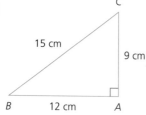

(b)
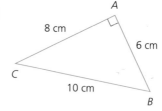

(c)
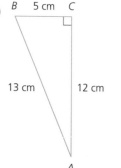

(d)
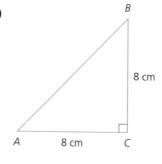

7. Find the measure of $\angle B$ in each triangle in question 6.

B

8. In $\triangle XYZ$, $\angle Y = 90°$. Find
  (a) sin Z if $XZ = 10$ cm and $XY = 5$ cm
  (b) cos X if $XZ = 10$ cm and $YZ = 5$ cm
  (c) sin X if $XY = 8$ cm and $YZ = 6$ cm
  (d) cos X if $XY = 8$ cm and $YZ = 6$ cm
  (e) $\angle X$ if sin $\angle X = 0.8$
  (f) $\angle X$ if cos $\angle X = \dfrac{5}{24}$

9. For each triangle,
  i. state two trigonometric ratios you could use to find x
  ii. find x to one decimal place

(a)

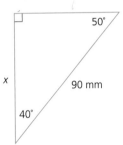

(b)

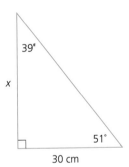

10. Find the length of the hypotenuse to one decimal place.

(a)

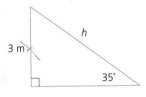

(b)

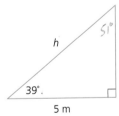

11. Use two different methods to find the measure of the unknown side in each triangle. Round your answer to one decimal place.

(a)

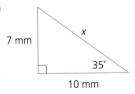

(b)

12. Communication: Discuss which of the methods you used in question 11 is easier to use or is more accurate.

13. Correct the following solution.

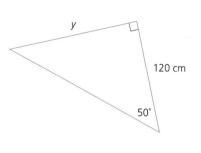

$$\tan 50° = \frac{120}{y}$$

$$y \times \tan 50° = 120$$

$$y = \frac{120}{\tan 50°}$$

$$y = \frac{120}{1.1918}$$

$$y = 100.68 \text{ cm}$$

14. A monument casts a shadow 13 m long. The sun's rays form an angle of 63° with the ground. Calculate the height of the monument to one decimal place.

15. A ladder leans against a wall forming a 25° angle with the wall. If the ladder reaches 2.8 m up the wall, how long is the ladder?

16. For each pair of side lengths, calculate the measure of angle *x* to the nearest degree.

(a) *a* = 10 and *c* = 10

(b) *b* = 12 and *c* = 6

(c) *a* = 9 and *b* = 15

17. Find the length of side *d*. Round to one decimal place.

(a)

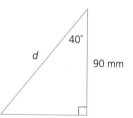

(b)

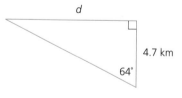

(c)

(d)

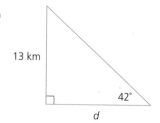

18. For each pair of side lengths, calculate the measures of angles x and y.

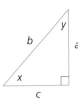

(a) $a = 10$ and $c = 10$

(b) $b = 12$ and $c = 6$

(c) $a = 9$ and $b = 15$

19. Correct the following solution to this problem: A ski run reaches a height of 250 m along a hill 1600 m long. What interior angle is formed where the bottom of the hill meets the horizontal?

$$\sin A = \frac{250}{1600}$$
$$\angle A = \sin^{-1}\left(\frac{250}{1600}\right)$$
$$\angle A = \sin^{-1}(0.0156)$$
$$\angle A = 89°$$

20. Nathan made these observations about $\triangle ABC$. Correct any errors.

(a) $\sin A = \dfrac{12}{25.5}$

(b) $\cos C = \dfrac{22.5}{25.5}$

(c) $\cos A = 4.706$

(d) $\sin C = \dfrac{24}{51}$

(e) $\angle A = 65°$

(f) $\angle C = 28°$

21. Calculate each angle to the nearest degree.

(a) $\sin A = \dfrac{9}{26}$

(b) $\cos B = 0.1841$

(c) $\sin D = 0.738$

(d) $\cos F = \dfrac{11}{30}$

22. Calculate the measures of $\angle A$ and $\angle B$ to the nearest degree.

(a)

(b)

23. **Thinking, Inquiry, Problem Solving:** A ladder leaning against a wall at certain angles can be unstable. Some repair manuals recommend that the angle the ladder makes with the ground should be no more than 75° and no less than 60°. If the base of an 8 m ladder is placed 1.5 m from the wall, is the ladder safe? Explain. Determine the minimum and maximum distances the base of the ladder can be placed from the wall safely.

24. In $\triangle ABC$, $\angle B = 90°$ and $AC = 10$ cm. Find

(a) BC if $\angle C = 35°$

(b) AB if $\angle C = 60°$

(c) $\angle A$ if $BC = 7$ cm

(d) $\angle C$ if $BC = 5$ cm

25. Find, to one decimal place, the slope angle of the line

  (a) $y = 3x + 1$

  (b) with a slope of $\frac{1}{4}$ and a y-intercept of -2

  (c) that passes through $A(2, 5)$ and $B(-2, 3)$

  (d) with an x-intercept of 4 and a y-intercept of -1

  (e) that passes through $C(-2, 5)$ and $D(2, 3)$

  (f) with an x-intercept of -4 and a y-intercept of -2

26. Solve each triangle by finding all the unknown values.

(a)

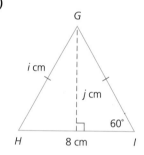

(b)

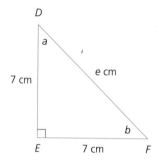

(c)

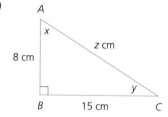

(d)

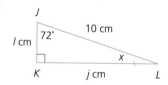

(e)

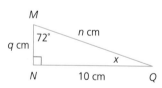

(f)

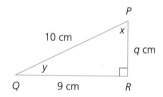

(g)

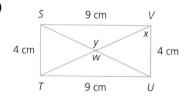

(h)

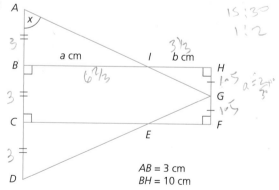

$AB = 3$ cm
$BH = 10$ cm

27. Jasmine is planning to climb up a cliff face. She will be attached to a rope that is anchored to the top of the cliff. To find out how much rope she will need, she uses a clinometer to check the height of the cliff. She stands 500 m from the base of the cliff and measures a 73° angle to the top. How high is the cliff?

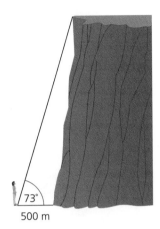

28. Suppose the maximum angle at which a wheelchair ramp can be inclined is 6°. Could a ramp with a slope of 1 : 9 be used for wheelchairs? a ramp with a slope of 1 : 7.5?

29. A carpenter leans a 4 m ladder against a wall. It reaches 3.5 m up the wall. Find the angle the ladder makes with the wall.

30. A rocket is launched at an angle of 80° to the ground and travels in a straight line. What is the rocket's altitude when it has travelled for 15 km?

31. Knowledge and Understanding:
   (a) Line AB passes through the origin and makes an angle of 37° with the x-axis. Find the equation of the line that is parallel to AB and has a y-intercept of -4.
   (b) Line CD has a positive slope and makes an angle of 48° with the y-axis. This line also passes through (2, 2). Find the equation of CD.

32. The graphs of $y = 2x$ and $y = -3x$ intersect at the origin.
   (a) Find the angle each line makes with the x-axis.
   (b) Find the angle at which the lines intersect.

33. Application
   (a) Find the coordinates of the point where $y = -3x + 10$ and $y = 4x + 2$ intersect.
   (b) Find the angle each line makes with the x-axis.
   (c) Find the angle between the lines at the point of intersection.

34. Suppose you can determine the value of sin A for a right triangle, $\triangle MAT$, in which $\angle M = 90°$. Describe the procedure for finding the size of $\angle A$.

35. Check Your Understanding: Suppose $\triangle ABC$ has a right angle at B and $\angle A = 55°$. Why do the lengths of the sides of the triangle have no effect on the values of sin A, cos A, and tan A?

Part 1: Flight Path

You are in charge of an airport radar system. The radio dish is on top of a 100 m tower, with the vertex of the radio dish 9 m above the top of the tower. The radar shows that an approaching airplane is 50 km away, along a 20° **angle of elevation**. Find the airplane's altitude and ground distance from the tower.

Think, Do, Discuss

1. Verify that this sketch represents all the information in the description.

2. **(a)** Copy the sketch. Label the ground distance from the airplane's position to the tower.

    (b) Write the trigonometric ratio of the 20° angle using the 50 km distance and the ground distance.

    (c) Write an equation that equates the ratio to the value of the trigonometric ratio found in (b) using a scientific calculator.

    (d) Solve the equation for the ground distance.

    (e) Check that the answer in (d) makes sense. Does it seem reasonable?

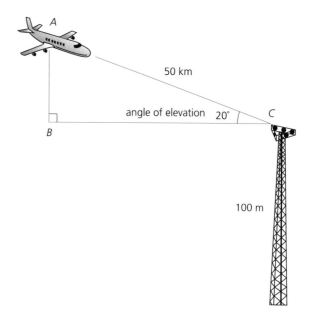

3. **(a)** Now find the altitude of the airplane. Use a process like the one in step 2.

    (b) Why will the side length you compute using the appropriate trigonometric ratio not solve the problem completely? What else do you need to consider?

Part 2: Compass Bearings

Sometimes map directions are given in compass bearings, such as north by northwest or south by southeast. At other times, the position of an object is given in terms of a coordinate system. For instance, a road map might say that Colborne and Adelaide streets meet at coordinates B2.

You have found a map that shows where a pirate buried his treasure. His instructions are to walk 50 paces east from the dead tree and then 23 paces north. Show how to find a compass bearing that will take you directly to the treasure. If you followed this bearing, how many paces would you actually need to walk?

Think, Do, Discuss

1. Sketch the situation. Mark all the information you need.
   (a) If you use an *x-y* coordinate system, what location should the origin represent?
   (b) What directions does the *x*-axis represent? the *y*-axis?
   (c) What kind of geometric figure is outlined in the diagram?

2. (a) Describe how to find the distance from the dead tree to the treasure.
   (b) Compute the distance.
   (c) Discuss whether or not the answer makes sense.

3. (a) Show how to find the bearing angle without using the distance you found in step 2.
   (b) Show two different ways to find the bearing angle using the distance you found in step 2.
   (c) Which of the three computations in (a) and (b) is the most accurate? Why?

Part 3: Width of a Searchlight Beam

A searchlight is mounted at the front of a search-and-rescue helicopter. The pilot is flying the helicopter 150 m above the ground and the beam is angled at 70° from the horizontal. The beam spreads out at an angle of 5°.

How wide an area does the beam illuminate?

Think, Do, Discuss

In mathematics, and other subjects, it is often helpful to use a problem-solving model. Here is one possible model. Use it to solve the problem about the light beam.

1. **Understand the problem.**
   (a) Draw a rough sketch.
   (b) List all the information you are given. Is any of the information unnecessary?
   (c) Write down what you need to know to be able to find the width of the beam.
   (d) List the mathematical concepts that might be useful for solving this problem. Tell how you could use them.
   (e) List the steps that you think would lead to the solution.

2. **Create a mathematical model of the problem.**
   (a) Draw an accurate diagram. Use standard geometric shapes to represent the situation.
   (b) Label your diagram, so you can refer to lengths and angles by name.
   (c) On your diagram, mark all the information that you need.
   (d) Write the formulas or equations you need to find the width of the beam.
   (e) Using trigonometric ratios requires right triangles. Identify the right triangles in your diagram.
   (f) Use the information in your diagram to identify a relationship that you can use to find the unknown information.

3. **Plan a solution.**
   (a) Describe the problem you must first solve to find the beam's width.
   (b) Explain how you can use the relationships you identified in step 2 to find the base length of each triangle in the diagram.
   (c) Explain how you will use the two base lengths to find the width of the beam.

4. **Execute the plan.**
   Compute the width of the beam to the nearest metre.

5. **Interpret and evaluate the solution.**
   (a) Describe how you can check whether your answer is reasonable.
   (b) To what degree of accuracy should you calculate the answer?
   (c) Is it reasonable to compute the width to the nearest metre? Justify your opinion.

6. **Generalize your results.**
   Can you always use the method in steps 1 to 5 to find the length of a side of a non-right triangle? Are there triangles for which the method won't work?
   (a) See if you can find an example for which this method does not work. Try various acute and obtuse triangles.
   (b) Describe how to use the method above to find the base of △*ABC*.

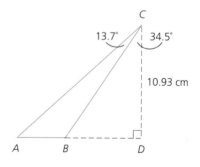

Part 4: Area of a Triangle

Erise has just bought a new house with a triangular lawn. She makes this diagram of the lawn. She wants to cover the lawn with sod rather than plant grass seed. How much would it cost to put new sod on the land if sod costs $1.50/m²?

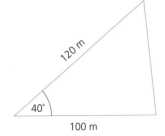

Think, Do, Discuss

1. **Understand the problem.**
   (a) Draw a rough sketch.
   (b) List all the information you are given. Is any of the information unnecessary?
   (c) Write down what you need to know to be able to find the cost of the sod.
   (d) List the mathematical concepts that might be useful for solving this problem. Explain how you could use them.
   (e) List the steps that you think would lead to the solution.

2. **Create a mathematical model of the problem.**
   (a) Draw an accurate diagram. Use standard geometric shapes to represent the situation.
   (b) Label your diagram, so you can refer to lengths and angles by name.
   (c) On your diagram, mark all the information that you need.
   (d) Write the formulas or equations you need to find the area of the lawn.
   (e) What information is missing from the diagram that you need to find the area of the lawn?
   (f) Identify the relationship that will allow you to use the information in the diagram to find the missing information.

3. **Plan a solution.**
   (a) Describe the problem you must first solve to find the area.
   (b) Explain how you can use the relationships you identified in step 2 to find the area.
   (c) Explain how you will use the area to compute the cost of the sod.

4. **Execute the plan.**
   Compute the cost of the sod to the nearest cent.

5. **Interpret and evaluate the solution.**
   (a) Describe how you can check whether your answer is reasonable.
   (b) To what degree of accuracy should you calculate the answer?
   (c) Is it reasonable to compute the cost to the nearest cent? Justify your opinion.

6. Generalize your results.

Can you always use the method in steps 1 to 5 to find the area of a non-right triangle? Are there triangles for which the method will not work?

(a) See if you can find an example for which this method does not work. Try various acute and obtuse triangles.

(b) Describe how to use the method above to find the area of △*ABC*. Assume that the lengths of *AB* and *BC*, and the size of ∠*ABC* are known, but the length of the altitude *AD* is not known.

(c) Write an equation or a formula that corresponds to your result in (b).

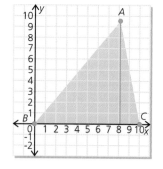

Focus 5.8

Key Ideas

- If a problem involving the computation of a length or an angle can be represented with a right triangle, then it can be solved using trigonometric ratios.

Example 1

To evacuate some refugees, a bridge needs to be built across a river. The first step is to find out how wide the river is. A surveyor is on one side of the river, with a transit mounted on a tripod 1.2 m above the ground. An assistant stands on the other side of the river, holding a 3 m pole vertically. The angle of elevation from the transit to the top of the pole is 8.5°. How wide is the river?

Solution

Sketch the situation.

The pole is 3 m tall, but the transit is 1.2 m above the ground. So, the actual height of the pole in the diagram is 3.0 m − 1.2 m or 1.8 m.

The triangle formed by the pole, the width of the river, and the line of sight from the transit to the top of the pole is right angled. So, the tangent ratio can be used.

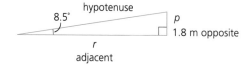

Let r represent the width of the river. Let p represent the height of the pole.

$$\tan 8.5° = \frac{\text{opposite}}{\text{adjacent}} \qquad \text{Set up the ratio.}$$

$$\tan 8.5° = \frac{p}{r}$$

$$\tan 8.5° = \frac{1.8}{r}$$

$$r \tan 8.5° = \left(\frac{1.8}{\cancel{r_1}}\right)\cancel{r}^1$$

$$r = \frac{1.8}{\tan 8.5°}$$

$$r = \frac{1.8}{0.149\ 451}$$

$$r = 12.044$$

$$r \doteq 12$$

The river is about 12 m wide.

Example 2

A video camera is mounted on the top of a 120 m tall building. When the camera tilts down 36° with the horizontal, it views the bottom of another building. If it tilts up 47° with the horizontal, it can view the top of the same building.

(a) How far apart are the two buildings?
(b) How tall is the building viewed by the camera?

Solution

Sketch the situation.

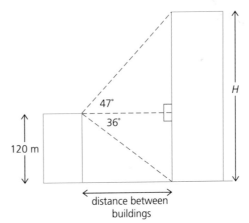

(a) Let x represent the distance between the buildings.
Then, in the right triangle shown,

$$\tan 36° = \frac{120}{x}$$

$$x \tan 36° = \left(\frac{120}{\cancel{x_1}}\right)\cancel{x}^1$$

$$x = \frac{120}{\tan 36°}$$

$$x = \frac{120}{0.726\ 542\ 25}$$

$$x = 165.165\ 83\ldots$$

$$x \doteq 165$$

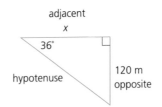

The buildings are about 165 m apart.

(b) Apply the value of x to the second triangle. Let h represent the difference in height between the two buildings. Let H represent the height of the taller building.

$$\tan 47° = \frac{h}{165} \qquad \text{Set up the ratio and substitute the known values.}$$

$$h = 165 \tan 47° \qquad \text{Solve for } h.$$

$$h \doteq 177$$

$$H = 120 + 177 \qquad \text{Add the two heights.}$$

$$H = 297$$

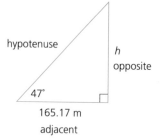

The second building is about 297 m high.

Example 3

A communications antenna is attached to the roof of a school and held in place with two 16 m guy wires. The antenna is 12.5 m tall.

(a) What angle do the wires make with the roof?

(b) At what distance from the base of the tower should the wires be secured to the roof?

Solution

(a) Draw a diagram. Name the sides of the triangle relative to $\angle B$ or $\angle C$. In this case, $\angle B$ is used in $\triangle ABD$.

Find the measure of $\angle B$.

$$\frac{12.5}{16} = \frac{\text{opposite}}{\text{hypotenuse}} \qquad \text{This is the sine of } \angle B.$$

$$\sin B = \frac{12.5}{16}$$

$$\sin B = 0.781\ 25$$

$$\angle B = \sin^{-1}(0.781\ 25)$$

$$\angle B \doteq 51°$$

The wires make an angle of 51° with the roof.

(b) The distance to be determined corresponds to BD in the diagram.

$$\frac{BD}{16} = \frac{\text{adjacent}}{\text{hypotenuse}} \qquad \text{This is the cosine of } \angle B.$$

$$\cos B = \frac{BD}{16} \qquad \angle B = 51°$$

$$\cos 51° = \frac{BD}{16}$$

$$16(\cos 51°) = \cancel{16}\left(\frac{BD}{\cancel{16}}\right)$$

$$16(0.6293) = BD$$

$$10 \text{ m} \doteq BD$$

The wires should be attached around 10 m from the base of the antenna.

Practise, Apply, Solve 5.8

A

1. A tree that is 8.5 m tall casts a shadow 6 m long. At what angle are the sun's rays hitting the ground?

2. **Communication:** Jasmine is planning to do some rock climbing. Before she scales the cliff, she paces off 100 m from the base of the cliff and sights the top with a clinometer. The angle of elevation to the top is 80°. How high is the cliff? Show all your steps.

3. A ramp rises 2.5 m for every 5.5 m of run. What is the slope angle of the ramp?

4. A local building code states that the maximum slope for a set of stairs in a home is a 72 cm rise for every 100 cm of run. To one decimal place, what is the maximum angle at which a set of stairs can rise?

5. In Mexico, one of the Maya pyramids at Chichen Itza has stairs that rise about 64 cm for every 71 cm of run. Find the angle of rise of these stairs.

6. A communications tower 62 m tall has to be supported with cables running from the top of the tower to anchors in the ground on both sides of the tower. The cables must form an angle of 50°. How far from the base of the tower should the anchors be placed?

7. An airplane takes off from a runway near some mountains. The peak of the mountain is on the flight path 2.5 km from the end of the runway. The mountain is 2000 m high. What angle of ascent is needed to clear the mountain top?

B

8. To avoid slipping, a ladder should not be placed against a wall at an angle less than 45° with the ground. What is the minimum height up a wall that the top of a 10 m ladder should reach?

9. Laurier places at 10 m ladder against a wall at an angle of 70° with the ground. How high is the top of the ladder?

10. **Knowledge and Understanding:** A captain knows that his ship is due south of a lighthouse. His destination is 20 km due west of the lighthouse, on a course setting of 40° west of the lighthouse. How far south of the lighthouse is the ship?

11. The owner of an auto shop is designing a ramp that lets her mechanics work underneath a car parked on a platform. None of the mechanics are more than 2 m tall. The ramp is to meet the ground at an angle of 20°. How long should the ramp be?

12. Lee is standing at the top of a hill that is 200 m high. Using a clinometer, she sights the base of the hill at an angle of depression of 40° from the horizontal. If the slope of the hill is constant, how far will her walk be from the top of the hill to the base?

13. **Application:** A geologist has determined that an oil deposit lies under a lake. The lake is 150 m deep and the oil deposit is 1500 m below the bottom of the lake. Owing to environmental concerns, oil wells are not allowed in the lake itself and must be built on shore. The well is to be 1000 m from the point directly above the edge of the oil deposit.
   (a) To minimize the cost of drilling, the drill has to be angled so that it pierces the deposit at the closest point. What angle should be used?
   (b) The drill bit is extended using 10 m sections that are added on as the drill cuts through the earth. How many sections will be needed to reach the deposit?

14. Building codes often include tables like this one. These tables identify the allowable slope for ramps. Compute the maximum angle of incline for each vertical rise category in the table to one decimal place.

	Changes in Vertical Rise (mm)	Slope cannot be steeper than
(a)	0 to 15	1 : 2
(b)	15.1 to 50	1 : 5
(c)	50.1 to 200	1 : 10
(d)	More than 200	1 : 12

15. The pilot of an airplane is flying at 350 km/h. After one hour, she notices that owing to strong winds, she is 48 km west of her intended flight path. At what angle to her intended flight path has she been flying?

16. **Check Your Understanding:** Think of a real-life problem that can be modelled using a right triangle, in which the hypotenuse and an angle are known. Sketch the situation and explain how you could use trigonometry to find the unknown sides and angle.

C

17. Angle measurements were taken from two points on directly opposite sides of a tree as shown. How high is the tree?

18. A regular hexagon has perimeter of 50 cm.
   (a) Find the area of the hexagon.
   (b) The hexagon is the base of a prism 100 cm tall. Find the volume and surface area of the prism.

19. *Thinking, Inquiry, Problem Solving:* A tunnel is being dug through a hill. Ventilation shafts must be placed every 70 m from the entrance to the tunnel. On one side, the hill climbs steadily upward at an angle of 30°. The hill is steeper on the other side, which has a slope of 40°. The top of the hill is 300 m high.
   (a) How many shafts must be drilled?
   (b) Special corrugated metal pipes are used to line the shaft. These pipes come in 5 m sections. How many sections should the builder order?

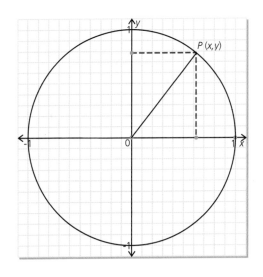

20. Consider a circle centred at the origin, with a radius of 1 cm. Suppose $P(x, y)$ is a point in the first quadrant.
   (a) Express the three trigonometric ratios for $\angle PAB$ in terms of the coordinates (x, y) of P.
   (b) Suppose point P was moving counter clockwise around the circle at a speed of 1°/s (one degree per second). If P started at $(1, 0)$, find the coordinates for P every 10 s until it returns to its starting position.
   (c) Graph the x- and y-coordinates of P against time.
   (d) Find the coordinates of P after 27 s.
   (e) How would the graphs in (c) change if the radius of the circle had been 5 cm? 0.25 cm?
   (f) How would the graphs in (c) change if the speed had been 2°/s? 0.5°/s?

The Chapter Problem—Mechanical Engineering

Consider the right triangle formed by the straight chain segment from the smaller wheel to the larger wheel, the radius of the larger wheel, and a line segment parallel to the segment joining the centres of the two wheels.

(a) Use this triangle to form all the possible trigonometric ratios that will give you information about the angle formed at the centre of the larger wheel by the radii to the chain's contact points on the wheel. Which ratio is most useful? Why? Use the trigonometric ratio to determine the angle.
(b) Use this angle to compute the length of chain that curves around the larger wheel.
(c) Repeat (b) for the smaller wheel.
(d) Compute the total chain length needed.

Introduction to Trigonometry
Check Your Understanding

1. Explain how the magnitude of the slope of a line segment is related to the angle the segment makes with the x-axis. How is the sign of the slope related to the angle?

2. Explain why the position or length of a line segment has no effect on its slope.

3. If a ramp has a slope of 1 : 15, describe how to find the angle of inclination of the ramp. If the same ramp is 20 m long, explain how to find the height.

4. What does it mean when two geometric shapes are similar? What does it mean when they are congruent?

5. What conditions must be satisfied for two right triangles to be similar? What conditions must be satisfied for two right triangles to be congruent?

6. What is the minimum amount of information needed to find the measure of all sides and angles in a right triangle?

7. Explain how the three trigonometric ratios are related to the slope triangle of a line segment.

8. Draw a right triangle. For one of the angles, show how each of the three trigonometric ratios for that angle can be computed in terms of the lengths of the sides of the triangle.

9. Explain how to use a scientific calculator to find an angle in a right triangle if you know one of the trigonometric ratios of that angle.

10. Explain how the perimeters and areas of two similar triangles are related.

11. Describe two procedures for finding the height of a hydro transmission tower without directly measuring it. One procedure should use similar triangles and the other should use trigonometry.

5.1–5.2 Investigating and Comparing Triangles—

- Two triangles may be congruent, similar, or neither. The order of the letters naming the vertices of congruent or similar triangles indicates the order in which the vertices, sides, and angles of one triangle correspond to the vertices, sides, and angles of the other.

Congruent	Similar
Congruent triangles are identical in every way. They have exactly the same shape and size. The expression $\triangle ABC \cong \triangle XYZ$ means that $\triangle ABC$ is **congruent** to $\triangle XYZ$.	**Similar triangles** have the same shape, but are different sizes. One triangle is an enlargement or a reduction of the other. The expression $\triangle ABC \sim \triangle XYZ$ means that $\triangle ABC$ is **similar** to $\triangle XYZ$.

- If $\triangle ABC \cong \triangle XYZ$, then

$$\left.\begin{array}{l} AB = XY \\ BC = YZ \\ AC = XZ \end{array}\right\} \text{Corresponding sides are equal.}$$

$$\left.\begin{array}{l} \angle A = \angle X \\ \angle B = \angle Y \\ \angle C = \angle Z \end{array}\right\} \text{Corresponding angles are equal.}$$

- If $\triangle ABC \sim \triangle XYZ$, then

$$\frac{AB}{XY} = \frac{BC}{YZ} = \frac{AC}{XZ} \quad \text{Corresponding sides are proportional.}$$

$$\left.\begin{array}{l} \angle A = \angle X \\ \angle B = \angle Y \\ \angle C = \angle Z \end{array}\right\} \text{Corresponding angles are equal.}$$

The sides of $\triangle ABC$ are **proportional** to the sides of $\triangle XYZ$.

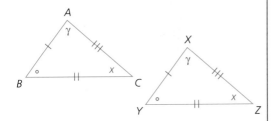

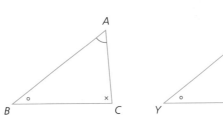

Conditions for Congruence

- $\triangle ABC \cong \triangle XYZ$ if three pairs of corresponding sides are equal, that is, $AB = XY$, $BC = YZ$, and $AC = XZ$. (Side-side-side congruence or **SSS**$\cong$)

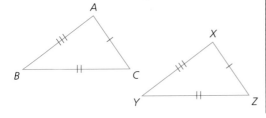

Conditions for Similarity

- $\triangle ABC \sim \triangle XYZ$ if three pairs of corresponding sides are proportional, that is, $\frac{AB}{XY} = \frac{BC}{YZ} = \frac{AC}{XZ}$. (Side-side-side similarity or **SSS**$\sim$)

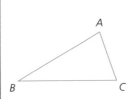

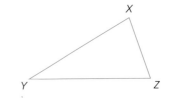

- $\triangle ABC \cong \triangle XYZ$ if two pairs of corresponding sides and the contained angles are equal, for example, $AB = XY$, $\angle B = \angle Y$, and $BC = YZ$. (Side-angle-side congruence or **SAS**$\cong$)

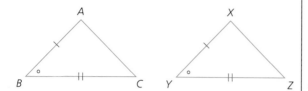

- $\triangle ABC \sim \triangle XYZ$ if two pairs of corresponding sides are proportional and the contained angles are equal, for example, $\frac{AB}{XY} = \frac{BC}{YZ}$ and $\angle B = \angle Y$. (**SAS**$\sim$)

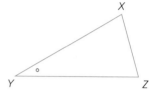

- $\triangle ABC \cong \triangle XYZ$ if two pairs of corresponding angles and the contained sides are equal, for example, $\angle B = \angle Y$, $BC = YZ$, and $\angle C = \angle Z$. (**ASA**$\cong$)

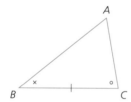

- $\triangle ABC \sim \triangle XYZ$ if two pairs of corresponding angles are equal, for example, $\angle B = \angle Y$ and $\angle C = \angle Z$. (**AA**$\sim$)

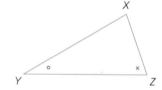

Example

Find the unknown measures in each diagram.

(a)

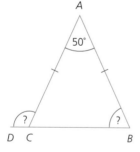

(b)

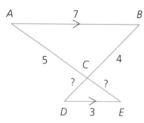

Solution

(a) Draw a median from A that meets BC at its midpoint E.

In $\triangle AEC$ and $\triangle AEB$,

$AC = AB$, $CE = BE$, and $AE = AE$.

Therefore, $\triangle AEC \cong \triangle ABE$ (SSS $\cong$)

So, $\angle ABE = \angle ACE$ and

$\angle ABE + \angle ACE = 130°$

$\angle ABE$ and $\angle ACE$ must both be $\dfrac{135°}{2}$ or $65°$.

Therefore, $\begin{aligned} \angle ACD &= \angle DCE - \angle ACB \\ &= 180° - 65° \\ &= 115° \end{aligned}$

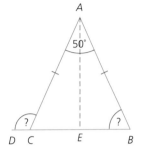

(b) $AB \parallel DE$, therefore, $\angle ABC = \angle CDE$ and $\angle BAC = \angle DEC$ (alternate angles)

Since $\triangle ABC$ and $\triangle EDC$ have two angles in common, they are similar.

Therefore, the sides of $\triangle ABC$ are proportional to the corresponding sides of $\triangle EDC$.

$$\frac{BC}{CD} = \frac{AB}{ED}$$

$$\frac{4}{CD} = \frac{7}{3} \qquad \text{Solve for } CD.$$

$$3\,\overset{1}{\cancel{CD}}\left(\frac{4}{\cancel{CD}_1}\right) = \overset{1}{\cancel{3}}CD\left(\frac{7}{\cancel{3}_1}\right)$$

$$\frac{12}{7} = \frac{7CD}{7}$$

$$\frac{12}{7} = CD$$

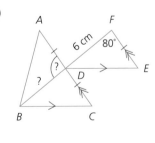

Similarly, $CE = \dfrac{15}{7}$

Extra Practice

1. State which triangles are congruent and find the unknown measures.

(a)

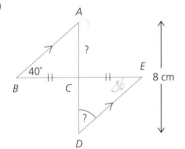

8 cm

(b)

6 cm   80°

2. State which triangles are similar and find the unknown measures.

(a)

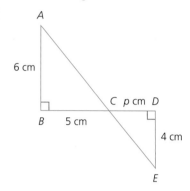

(b)

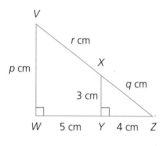

(c)

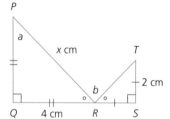

(d)

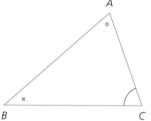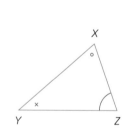

5.3–5.4 Modelling with Similar Triangles ───

- If $\triangle ABC$ is a **scale drawing** of $\triangle XYZ$, the two triangles are **similar**. One triangle is an enlargement or reduction of the other. In symbols, $\triangle \boldsymbol{ABC} \sim \triangle \boldsymbol{XYZ}$ means that $\triangle ABC$ is similar to $\triangle XYZ$.

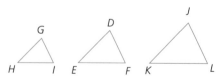

- The **scale factor** or **scale ratio** is a measure of the amount of enlargement or reduction that relates one similar triangle to the other. If $\triangle ABC \sim \triangle XYZ$, then the scale factor is the ratio of the lengths of any pair of corresponding sides in the two triangles. In this diagram, $\triangle GHI$ is a reduction of $\triangle DEF$ and $\triangle JKL$ is an enlargement of $\triangle DEF$. So

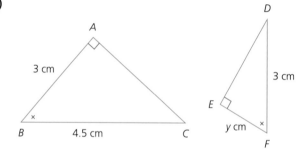

$$\frac{DE}{GH} = \frac{EF}{HI} = \frac{FD}{IG} \quad \text{and} \quad \frac{DE}{JK} = \frac{EF}{KL} = \frac{FD}{LJ}.$$

- If $\triangle ABC \sim \triangle XYZ$ and the scale factor is $n = \frac{AB}{XY}$, then

  ◆ the length of any side or altitude of
    $\triangle ABC = n$(length of corresponding side or altitude of $\triangle XYZ$)

  ◆ the perimeter of $\triangle ABC = n$(perimeter of $\triangle XYZ$)

  ◆ the area of $\triangle ABC = n^2$(area of $\triangle XYZ$)

- Similar triangles can be used to find lengths that cannot be measured directly.
  This method is called **indirect measurement**.

Example

Lakshmi is a lighting technician for a skating show. At one performance, she noticed
that a spotlight shining down on the ice reflected off the ice onto a nearby wall. She
estimated the light hit the ice about 10 m from the wall and the reflection appeared
about 3 m up the wall. The spotlight was mounted on a wall about 30 m from the wall
on which the reflection appeared. About how high was the spotlight above the ice?

Solution

First, sketch the information.

Based on this sketch, you want to find the
length of SX. Look for two similar triangles.

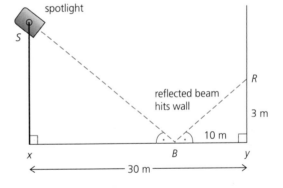

The **angle of incidence** of the beam from the
spotlight equals its **angle of reflection**.
Therefore, $\angle SBX = \angle RBY$.

Also, we can assume the walls are vertical. So,

$$\angle SXB = \angle RYB$$
$$= 90°$$

Therefore, $\triangle SBX \sim \triangle RBY \, (AA\sim)$

From the diagram, $XB = XY - BY$
$$= 30 - 10$$
$$= 20$$

$\dfrac{SX}{RY} = \dfrac{XB}{YB}$ The triangles are similar, so the ratios of the corresponding sides are equal.

$\dfrac{SX}{3} = \dfrac{20}{10}$ Substitute known values and solve for SX.

$SX = \dfrac{3 \times 20}{10} = 6$

The spotlight is about 6 m above the ice.

Extra Practice

3. (a) i. Why is $\triangle JKL \sim \triangle XYZ$?

ii. Find the unknown measures.

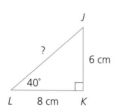 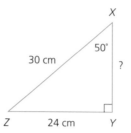

(b) i. Why is $\triangle ABD \sim ECD$?

ii. Find the length of BD.

iii. Find the length of BC.

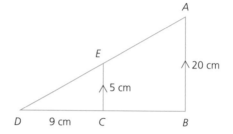

(c) i. Why is $\triangle MNO \sim \triangle PQO$?

ii. Find the unknown side measures.

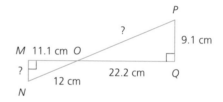

4. A surveyor is working with an engineer to build a tunnel through a hill. They used a map of the area and some known distances to make this sketch. How long should the tunnel be?

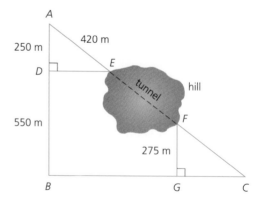

5. Bill placed a mirror on the ground 5 m from the base of a flagpole. He stepped back until he could see the top of the flagpole reflected in the mirror. Bill is 1.5 m tall and saw the reflection when he was 1.25 m from the mirror. How high is the flagpole?

6. Janelle is an artist, and she plans to draw a picture of a client's house. She sets up her easel about 17 m from the house. To get a sense of perspective, she holds her arm horizontally in front of her eye and puts her thumb up vertically. She sees that her thumb appears to completely cover the back door of the house.
If Janelle's arm is 65 cm long and her thumb is 8 cm long, about how high is the door?

5.5–5.6 Investigating the Connection Between Slope and Angle

- The **slope** of a line is given by the ratio $\frac{\Delta y}{\Delta x} = \frac{rise}{run}$, and it is related to the angle the line makes with the *x*-axis, which is called the **slope angle**.

  * When the line rises above the horizontal, the angle formed is called the **angle of inclination**, or **angle of elevation**, of the line.

    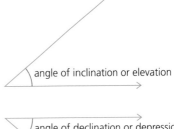

    angle of inclination or elevation

  * When the line falls below the horizontal, the angle formed is called the **angle of declination**, or **angle of depression**, of the line.

    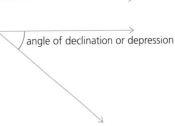

    angle of declination or depression

- Parallel lines have equal slopes and equal slope angles.

- Lines with positive slope have slope angles between 0° and 90°.

- Lines with negative slope have slope angles between −90° and 0°. If a slope angle is negative, it can be expressed as an equivalent angle between 90° and 180° using the expression (*slope angle*) + 180°.

- If the slope of a line is equal to −1 times the slope of another line, then the slope angle of the first line is equal to −1 times the slope angle of the second line.

- The table of values in section 5.6 gives the slopes that correspond to positive slope angles.

Example

Mario is planning to load cars onto a transport truck. To do this, he has to drive the cars up a ramp onto the truck bed. The truck bed is 1.5 m high and the maximum slope angle of the ramp is 35°.

(a) How far is it from the rear of the truck to the point where the ramp touches the ground?

(b) How long, to one decimal place, should the ramp be?

Solution

First, draw a sketch. Show all the information.

Let d represent the distance from the truck to the point where the ramp touches the ground.

Let r represent the length of the ramp.

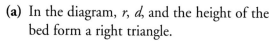

(a) In the diagram, r, d, and the height of the bed form a right triangle.

The table in section 5.6 shows the slope for an angle of 35° is 0.700 207 54. Therefore,

$$0.700\ 207\ 54 = \frac{1.5}{d} \qquad \text{Solve for } d.$$

$$d(0.700\ 207\ 54) = \left(\frac{1.5}{d}\right)d^1$$

$$d = \frac{1.5}{0.700\ 207\ 54}$$

$$d = 2.142\ 222\ 01\ldots$$

$$d \doteq 2.14$$

The ramp will touch the ground about 2.14 m from the rear of the truck.

(b) Use the Pythagorean theorem to find r.

$$r^2 = 1.52^2 + d^2$$

$$r^2 = 2.25 + 4.589\ 115\ 14$$

$$r^2 = 6.839\ 115\ 14$$

$$r = \sqrt{6.839\ 115\ 14}$$

$$r = 2.615\ 170\ 193\ldots$$

$$r \doteq 2.6$$

The ramp will be about 2.6 m long.

Extra Practice

7. Find the angle that each line makes with the x-axis.

   (a) $y = 3x - 4$

   (b) $y = \frac{1}{3}x + 2$

   (c) $y = -\frac{3}{5}x - 6$

   (d) $3x - 2y - 4 = 0$

8. Find the equation of the line that makes an angle of $50°$ with the x-axis and passes through $(-2, -3)$.

9. A ski hill has an angle of descent of $50°$ from the horizontal. According to a map, the horizontal distance from the top of the hill to the bottom is 1.3 km.
   (a) How high is the hill?
   (b) How long is the ski run?

10. Determine the measure of the four angles at the point where $y = 3x + 1$ and $y = -2x - 4$ intersect.

5.7 The Primary Trigonometric Ratios

- For a right triangle, the three **primary trigonometric ratios** are:

$$\sin A = \frac{\text{opposite}}{\text{hypotenuse}}$$

$$\cos A = \frac{\text{adjacent}}{\text{hypotenuse}}$$

$$\tan A = \frac{\text{opposite}}{\text{adjacent}}$$

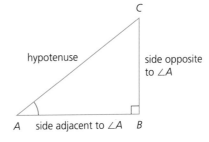

- The values of the trigonometric ratios depend only on the angle to which the opposite side, adjacent side, and hypotenuse correspond.

- The slope of a line is the tangent of the slope angle that the line makes with the x-axis.

- The values of the three primary trigonometric ratios can be found either in a book of tables or with a scientific calculator. The calculator is far more convenient to use.

- If the value of a trigonometric ratio is known, its corresponding angle can be found on a scientific calculator using the inverse of that ratio. On the TI-83 Plus calculator, use 2nd SIN for $\sin^{-1}$, use 2nd COS for $\cos^{-1}$, or use 2nd TAN for $\tan^{-1}$.

Example

Solve the triangle by finding the unknown measures.

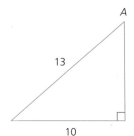

Solution

(a) To find $\angle D$,

$$\tan D = \frac{AC}{CD}$$

$$\tan D = \frac{9}{8} \qquad \text{Substitute known measures.}$$

$$\tan D = 1.125$$

$$\tan^{-1}(1.125) = 48.366\ 461\ldots \qquad \text{Use a scientific calculator.}$$

$$\angle D \doteq 48.4°$$

(b) To find AB,

$$\sin B = \frac{9}{AB}$$

$$\sin 70° = \frac{9}{AB}$$

$$AB \sin 70° = \left(\frac{9}{\cancel{AB}}\right)\overset{1}{\cancel{AB}}$$

$$AB = \frac{9}{\sin 70°}$$

$$AB = \frac{9}{0.939\ 692\ 6\ldots}$$

$$AB \doteq 9.6 \text{ cm}$$

Extra Practice

11. For each triangle, find,
  i. the value of the three primary trigonometric ratios for $\angle A$
  ii. the measure of $\angle A$

(a)

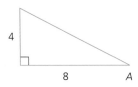

(b)

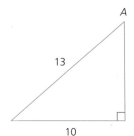

12. For each triangle, find the length of the unknown sides.

(a)

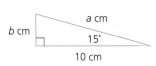

(b)

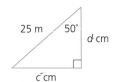

13. Solve each triangle by finding all the unknown sides and angles.

(a)

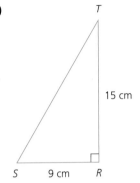

(b)

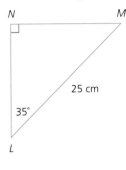

14. A tow truck raises the front end of a car 0.85 m above the ground. The car is 3.85 m long. What angle does the car make with the ground?

5.8 Solving Problems Using Right Triangle Models and Trigonometry ————————

- If a problem involving the computation of a length or an angle can be represented with a right triangle, then it can be solved with trigonometric ratios.

Example

A surveyor and her assistant use a laser transit and marking pole to sight two corners on one side of a lot. The surveyor sights a reference point perpendicular to the lot line. One corner is 100 m away, at an angle of 20° east of the reference point. The other corner is 200 m away, at an angle of 60° west of the reference point. To the nearest metre, how long is that side of the lot?

Solution

1. **Understand the problem.**

   Read the problem carefully. Identify all the key pieces of information and how they are related to one another.

2. **Create a mathematical model of the problem.**

   Sketch the situation. Show all the information.

3. **Plan a solution.**

   Segment *AB* is composed of segments *AP* and *PB*.
   Use trigonometric ratios to find the lengths of *AP* and *PB*.
   Then add these lengths to find the length of *AB*.

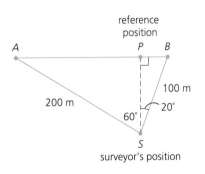

4. Execute the plan.

$\triangle BPS$ is right angled.

Therefore, $\dfrac{BP}{SB} = \sin 20°$ Solve for BP.

$$BP = SB(\sin 20°)$$
$$BP = 100(0.342\ 020\ 143...)$$
$$BP \doteq 34.20$$

$\triangle APS$ is right angled.

Therefore, $\dfrac{AP}{AS} = \sin 60°$ Solve for AP.

$$AP = AS(\sin 60°)$$
$$AP = 200(0.866\ 025\ 403...)$$
$$AP \doteq 173.21$$

5. Interpret and evaluate the solution.

$$
\begin{aligned}
AB &= AP + PB \\
&= 34.20 + 173.21 \\
&= 207.41 \\
&\doteq 207
\end{aligned}
$$

The side is about 207 m.

Extra Practice

15. An airplane is approaching a runway at an angle of descent of 30°. What is the altitude of the airplane when it is 15 km along its flight path from the runway?

16. Lucien wants to photograph the first stage separation of the space shuttle rocket. With his camera on a tripod with a clinometer, he first aims his lens at the launch pad. Then he sets his clinometer for the angle that should aim his camera at the point in the sky where the first stage should separate. Lucien is 1500 m from the launch pad and the first stage should separate at 20 000 m. At what angle should Lucien set his clinometer?

17. From a helicopter flying at a height of 1625 m, the angle of depression to the landing pad is 36°. How far is the pad from the helicopter?

18. The angle of elevation from the top of a 16 m building to the top of the second building is 48°. The buildings are 30 m apart. How high is the taller building?

Chapter 5 Summary

In this chapter, you found that the slope of a line is equal to the tangent of the angle that the line makes with the x-axis. The tangent ratio is one of three primary trigonometric ratios associated with right triangles.

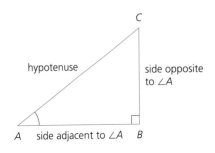

For a given angle A, these ratios are always the same, regardless of the right triangle used. This is a result of the fact that right triangles with one common angle are similar and, in similar triangles, the ratios of pairs of corresponding sides are equal.

The primary trigonometric ratios are

$$\sin A = \frac{\text{opposite}}{\text{hypotenuse}} \qquad \cos A = \frac{\text{adjacent}}{\text{hypotenuse}} \qquad \tan A = \frac{\text{opposite}}{\text{adjacent}}$$

A scientific calculator can be used to find the value of any of these ratios for a given angle. It can also be used to find the angle, given the ratio.

The primary trigonometric ratios can be used to find the measures of unknown sides and angles in right triangles. A problem that can be modelled using right triangles can be solved using the three basic trigonometric ratios if you have enough information.

Introduction to Trigonometry

1. Find the length of the unknown sides or angles in each diagram.

(a)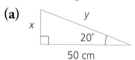
x, y, 20°, 50 cm

(b)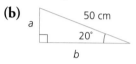
a, 50 cm, 20°, b

(c)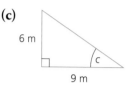
6 m, c, 9 m

(d)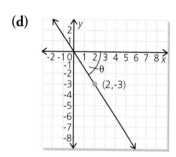
θ, (2,-3)

(e)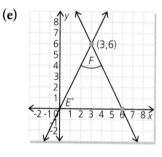
(3,6), F, $E°$

(f)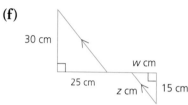
30 cm, w cm, 25 cm, z cm, 15 cm

2. Triangle ABC is an equilateral triangle with sides of length 2 cm.
   (a) How long is the altitude of $\triangle ABC$?
   (b) Use $\triangle ABC$ to find exact values for sin 60°, cos 60°, and tan 60°.

3. The navigator of a search-and-rescue airplane notes that the angle of depression to a disabled freighter is 12°. The airplane is flying at an altitude of 1200 m. How much farther does the aircraft have to fly to be over top of the ship?

4. A mountain road rises with a constant 17° incline. Calculate the increase in altitude of a cyclist who rides 4 km up the road.

5. Solve each triangle by finding the unknown angles and sides.
   (a) In $\triangle XYZ$, $\angle X = 90°$, $\angle Y = 15°$, and $YZ = 73.6$ cm
   (b) In $\triangle ABC$, $\angle B = 90°$, $AC = 40.3$ cm, and $BC = 29.0$ cm

6. Find the area of $\triangle ABC$ if $\angle A = 46°$, $AC = 4.5$ cm, and $AB = 6.8$ cm

7. Two fire towers are 575 m apart. The first tower is 14 m high; the second is 30 m high.
   (a) What is the angle of depression from the top of the second tower to the top of the first tower?
   (b) The patrollers in each tower spot a fire at the same time. The angle of depression of the fire from the lower tower is 1.6° and from the higher tower the angle is 3.4°. Which tower is closer to the fire?

For connections to this chapter, visit **www.math.nelson.com**.

Chapter 6

Investigating Non-Right Triangles as Models for Problems

Earlier you explored the relationships between the angle measures and sides of right triangles. You developed ratios of the lengths of the sides of similar triangles and called these trigonometric ratios **sine**, **cosine**, and **tangent**. Of course, not all real-world situations can be modelled with right triangles. Other methods must be found to solve problems that involve general, non-right triangles.

For example, an air traffic controller may have to determine a new flight path for an airliner that has drifted off course. The controller might visualize a triangle with the origin, the destination, and the current location as vertices.

The trigonometry of non-right triangles is also used to calculate distances that cannot be easily measured—for instance, distances between the planets and stars. Similar techniques are used by navigators, map-makers, surveyors, and graphics software designers to calculate the lengths of line segments and the sizes of angles without actually measuring them.

In this chapter you will

- discover which properties of right triangles also work for non-right triangles

- use similar triangles to solve problems

- discover new relationships between side lengths and angles that can be used to solve problems that do not involve right angles

- use non-right triangles and trigonometric ratios to make models and calculate distances that cannot be found by direct measurement

- determine which methods work best for various problems

527

The Chapter Problem

Modelling the Solar System

Your class has been chosen to paint a space mural outside the science classrooms. The mural will show Earth, the sun, and the moon, and the other planets of the solar system. It must fit on a wall 30 m long and 3.5 m high.

- It is 1.08×10^8 km from Venus to the sun, and the diameter of Venus is 12 100 km.

- Jupiter has a diameter that is 11 times that of Earth. It is approximately five times farther from the sun than Earth is.

- Pluto is 5.9×10^9 km from the sun and it has a diameter of about 2300 km.

- Uranus's diameter is almost four times that of Earth. It is so far away that it looks like a faint star. Even so, it is about half as far from the sun as Pluto is.

- Neptune is about 1.4×10^9 km closer to the sun than Pluto and has a diameter that is 200 km greater than four times the diameter of Venus.

Your group also found this photo and this illustration in a science book:

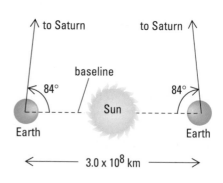

It is possible to use the diameter of Earth's orbit as a baseline to estimate the radius of Saturn's orbit. As shown in the illustration, the angles to Saturn, taken six months apart, are both 84°. Also, Saturn's diameter is about 1.21×10^5 km. Use this information to find the distance from Saturn to the sun.

Design a scale drawing of the mural so that the distances between the planets, sun, and moon are proportional to their actual distances. Also be sure that the sizes of the planets are correctly scaled, relative to each other. You will have to use different scales for the sizes of the planets and for the distances from the sun. The distances are so large that the planets would not be visible if you used the same scale.

For help with this problem, see pages 544, 557, and 570.

Challenge 1

You are the pilot of a helicopter that monitors traffic flow. A gas station is at the corner where two roads intersect at a 42° angle. Two cars leave the gas station at exactly the same time and each takes a different road. One car travels at 90 km/h and the other at 120 km/h. After two minutes, your helicopter, which is at an altitude of 600 m on a line between the two cars, sights the angle of depression to the faster car to be 22°. How far—in horizontal distance—is the helicopter from the faster car? How far is the helicopter from the gas station?

Challenge 2

Think about the neighbourhood around your school. Imagine that you are a map-maker. How would you begin to create a map of this community? Consider these points:

- Which distances are easy to measure and which are difficult?

- How can you tell the angles at street corners or decide if a park is really rectangular?

- What scale will you use to draw your map?

- How can you minimize the number of measurements that you need to take?

Create a map of your school neighbourhood. Make sure that it is to scale and that distances and angle measures are accurate. You may want to divide the class into groups and give each group a section of the community to map. Then you will have to put it all together. Once the map is ready, create questions to solve that require the use of your map and a knowledge of trigonometry. For instance, "If Ravi cut across the park rather than following the sidewalk, what distance would he save?"

To complete these Challenges, you may need to discuss a research plan with your teacher or fellow students. You may also need to research outside the classroom.

In this chapter, you will have to use your algebraic skills. You will also investigate

- the Pythagorean theorem
- non-right triangles
- ratios and proportions
- the trigonometric ratios from chapter 5

These exercises will help you prepare for the work in this chapter.

1. Calculate the length of the unknown side, correct to one decimal place.

(a)   (b)

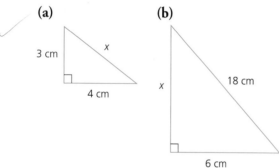

2. Calculate the length of the diagonal of a rectangle with a length of 8 m and a width of 5 m.

3. Calculate the measure of the unknown angle.

(a)   (b)

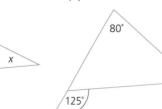

4. Find the value of the variables, correct to one decimal place.

(a) $\dfrac{3}{5} = \dfrac{6}{x}$ (b) $\dfrac{5}{x} = \dfrac{6}{5}$

(c) $4 : x : 10 = y : 6 : 15$

(d) $a : 1.5 = 3 : 5$

5. Expand and simplify:

(a) $(x + 2)^2$ (b) $(3x + 2)^2$

(c) $(a - y)^2$ (d) $(x - 2y)^2$

6. Find the value to three decimal places.

(a) $\sin 28°$ (b) $\cos 77°$

(c) $\sin 38°$ (d) $\sin 82°$

(e) $\tan 48°$ (f) $\tan 36°$

7. Evaluate correct to three decimal places.

(a) $54 \sin 50°$ (b) $106 \sin 47°$

(c) $46 \cos 65°$ (d) $2560 \cos 58°$

8. Solve for a.

(a) $25 = 15 - 15a$ (b) $a^2 = 61 - 60 \cos 71°$

9. Find the value of A to the nearest tenth of a degree.

(a) $\sin A = 0.829$ (b) $\cos A = 0.906$

(c) $\sin A = 0$ (d) $\cos A = 0.122$

(e) $\tan A = 0.726$ (f) $\tan A = 14.3$

10. Find the value of B to the nearest degree.

(a) $\angle B = \cos^{-1}\left(\dfrac{0.3271}{0.5483}\right)$ (b) $\angle B = \sin^{-1}\left(\dfrac{0.4219}{0.8526}\right)$

(c) $\angle B = \tan^{-1}\left(\dfrac{8.2514}{3.6819}\right)$

11. Determine if the two triangles are similar.

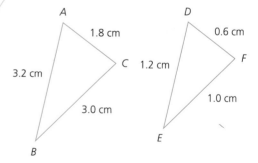

12. $\triangle CAT \sim \triangle DOG$

(a) Which angles are equal?

(b) Write the equations for the proportional sides.

13. In this diagram, *AB* is parallel to *CD*.

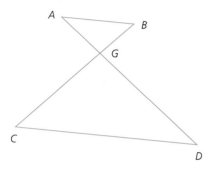

(a) Name the similar triangles and tell why they are similar.

(b) Write the corresponding equivalent ratios for the sides of the two triangles.

14. In each triangle, find the indicated unknown measure correct to the nearest tenth.

(a) $\triangle ABC \sim \triangle XYZ$

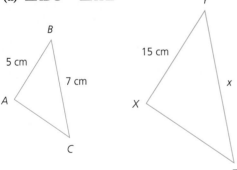

(b) $\triangle DEF \sim \triangle JKL$

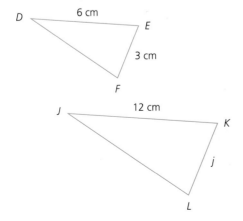

15. In this diagram, $\angle ABC = \angle E = 90°$.

(a) Name two similar triangles.

(b) If *AC* = 5, *BC* = 2, and *DE* = 3, find the length of *AE* correct to the nearest tenth.

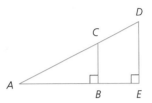

16. Determine the length of each unknown side and the measure of each unknown angle.

(a)

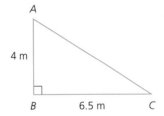

(b)

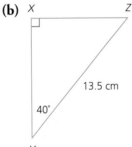

(c)

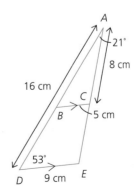

6.1 Fractals: Exploring Self-Similarity

Fractals are complex designs made up of smaller parts that are similar to the whole. The pattern can repeat to many levels. Fractal patterns are everywhere: in a fern leaf, a snowflake, the growth patterns of organisms, and human lungs.

a fractal pattern on a leaf

Some fractal patterns studied by mathematicians include the Cantor set, the Koch snowflake, and the Mandelbrot and Julia sets. In this section, you will use what you know about similar triangles to explore the fractal called the Sierpinski triangle.

the Mandelbrot Fractal

Think, Do, Discuss

1. Start with an equilateral triangle. Connect the midpoints of each side. Imagine that the small triangle in the centre is removed, and you have the first image of the Sierpinski triangle. Repeat the process with three outside triangles, and again and again with the remaining triangles.

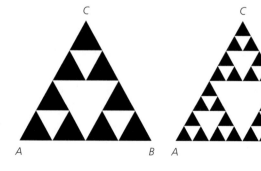

2. The Sierpinski triangle is an example of **self-similarity**. What do you think self-similarity means?

3. In step 1, you created three smaller triangles inside the original triangle. Circle one of the smaller triangles.
   (a) What is the ratio of the sides of that triangle to the larger triangle?
   (b) What is the ratio of the area of the small triangle to the larger triangle?

4. Now choose the next smaller triangle inside the one you already circled.
   (a) What is the ratio of the sides of this smaller triangle to the one you circled?
   (b) How does this triangle compare in side length and area to the original triangle?

5. What is the pattern of self-similarity in these fractals?

6. If you have access to *The Geometer's Sketchpad*, explore the fractal scripts that come with it.

Did You Know?

Although fractals seem to appear in nature almost everywhere, it is only relatively recently that mathematicians in Europe and North America began to study them. However, according to Ron Eglash, fractal patterns have been known and widely used in African countries for many years, perhaps centuries.

This idea occurred to Eglash as he studied aerial photographs of a Tanzanian village. He noticed that the buildings were constructed and arranged in a fractal pattern. For example, circular buildings were arranged in circles and rectangular buildings were arranged in rectangles. Curious, he looked at aerial photographs of other villages from around the world to see if these villages also showed fractal patterns. But only the African villages showed these patterns. Doing more research, he found that fractal patterns occur in many African cultures, including in such examples as blankets and the corn-row hairstyles of some African women. According to Eglash, this awareness of fractals may well mean that traditional African mathematics is more sophisticated, and complicated, than Europeans have sometimes assumed.

For information on this topic, you might enjoy reading *African Fractals: Modern Computing and Indigenous Design,* by Ron Eglash.

You can also research fractals in the library or on the Internet. Some web sites allow you to create your own fractal.

6.2 Similar-Triangle Models

Earlier, you learned how to measure distances indirectly using right-triangle models. It is not always possible to use a right triangle to build a model, but many problems can be solved using similar, non-right triangles. Similar triangles are often used to determine distances that are difficult to measure directly.

Part 1: Can You Measure Something You Can't Reach?

While Emily and Karen are out hiking, they come to a wide canyon. Emily estimates the canyon is 20 m across. Karen says it is about 100 m. They decide to measure the distance across the canyon to see who is right. They climb to a spot directly opposite a tall pine tree on the far side of the canyon. Sighting to the tree, they place stakes at *A*, *B*, *C*, and *D*, in straight lines and measure the distances between the stakes, as shown. They use a compass to make sure that *AB* is parallel to *TD*.

Think, Do, Discuss

1. Why are the two triangles in the diagram similar?

2. Write the similarity statement. Be sure to match the vertices properly.

3. If Karen and Emily measure *AB* = 12 m, *DC* = 52 m, *BC* = 25 m, and *AC* = 18 m, calculate the distance *TD* across the canyon.

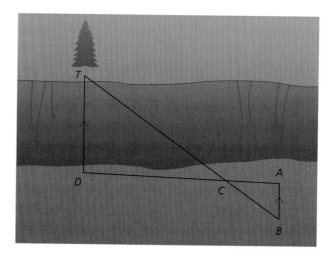

Part 2: Drawing Your Diagram

Making a good diagram is essential for this kind
of modelling and problem solving.
Mathematicians often use a simple shorthand
method to label and refer to the sides and angles
in a triangle: If A is a vertex, then the measure
of the side opposite A is labelled a. The interior
angle at A is referred to as $\angle A$. Sometimes, for clarity,
an angle is referred to in terms of three points, such as $\angle CAB$.

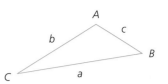

Think, Do, Discuss

1. How would you draw a triangle with two sides of 5 cm and 6 cm and two angles
   of 52° and 71°. Where should you place the angles with respect to the sides of
   5 cm and 6 cm? To help you answer this question, draw the following triangles
   using the measurements and labels shown. Which combinations of
   measurements are possible for the triangle shown?

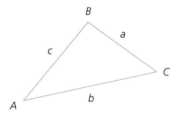

   (a) $c = 5$ cm, $a = 6$ cm, $\angle B = 71°$, $\angle A = 52°$
   (b) $b = 6$ cm, $c = 5$ cm, $\angle A = 71°$, $\angle B = 52°$
   (c) $a = 5$ cm, $b = 6$ cm, $\angle A = 52°$, $\angle B = 71°$

2. **(a)** What is the measure of the third angle in the triangle?
   (b) Which is the largest side of the triangle?
   (c) Which is the largest angle?
   (d) What is the relationship between the largest side and the largest angle?

3. **(a)** Which is the smallest side in the triangle?
   (b) Which is the smallest angle?
   (c) How are the smallest angle and the smallest side related?

4. Summarize your findings. What instructions would you give to someone to help
   them label the sides and angles of triangles?

Focus 6.2

Key Ideas

- In $\triangle ABC$, the side opposite vertex A is commonly referred to as a, the side opposite vertex B is b, and the side opposite vertex C is c.

- When you label and refer to similar triangles, be sure corresponding vertices are in the same order.

- In any triangle, the largest side is opposite the largest angle, and the smallest side is opposite the smallest angle. For example, in this diagram

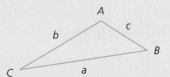

  - ♦ $\angle C$ is the smallest angle and c is the smallest side

  - ♦ $\angle A$ is the largest angle and a is the largest side

- To solve for an unknown side in a pair of similar triangles, set up a proportion statement that includes the known sides of the triangles and the unknown side. Then solve for the unknown.

Example 1

Given $AB \parallel DE$, $AB = 8$ cm, $EC = 5$ cm, $AC = 6$ cm, and $ED = 6$ cm, find the unknown lengths.

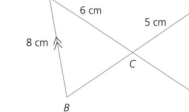

Solution

Since $AB \parallel DE$, $\angle CAB = \angle CDE$ and $\angle CBA = \angle CED$. (Or equivalently, $\angle A = \angle D$ and $\angle B = \angle E$.)

$\angle ACB = \angle DCE$ (AA~) or vertically opposite angles

Therefore, $\triangle ACB \sim \triangle DCE$, and since the triangles are similar, $\dfrac{AC}{DC} = \dfrac{BC}{EC} = \dfrac{AB}{DE}$.

To find DC,

$$\frac{AC}{DC} = \frac{AB}{DE}$$

$$\frac{6}{DC} = \frac{8}{6} \qquad \text{Substitute.}$$

$$36 = 8(DC)$$

$$DC = \frac{36}{8}$$

$$DC = 4.5$$

To find BC,

$$\frac{BC}{EC} = \frac{AB}{DE}$$

$$\frac{BC}{5} = \frac{8}{6} \qquad \text{Substitute.}$$

$$6(BC) = 40$$

$$BC = \frac{40}{6} \doteq 6.7$$

Example 2

Mark is making a kite from a 2 : 25 scale drawing. If the area of the scale drawing is 0.0025 m², how much fabric will Mark need to cover his kite?

Solution

The ratio of the areas is the square of the ratio of the side lengths.
Since the ratio of the sides is 2 : 25, then the ratio of the areas is

$$area_{drawing} : area_{kite} = 2^2 : 25^2$$
$$= 4 : 625$$

Let x represent the amount of fabric needed for the kite.

$$\frac{4}{625} = \frac{0.0025}{x}$$
$$4x = (0.0025)(625)$$
$$4x = 1.5625$$
$$x = 0.390\,625$$
$$x \doteq 0.4$$

Mark will need about 0.4 m² of fabric.

Example 3

This scale diagram shows the locations of ancient tombs that have been found in Egypt's Valley of the Kings. Even today, more tombs are still being found there.

On this scale map, it is 3.5 cm from the tomb of King Tut (location 62) to the tomb of Hatshepsut (location 20). The actual distance is 262.5 m. On the map, it is 5.0 cm from the tomb of Hatshepsut to the tomb of Rameses VII (location 1). What is the actual distance?

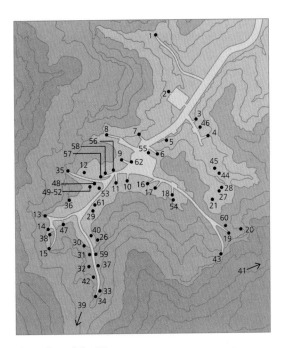

the Valley of the Kings

Solution

First, draw a diagram showing the similar triangles that will be used to solve the problem.

scale diagram

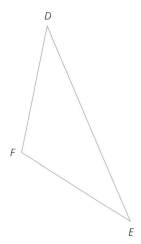

actual distances

Since $\triangle ABC$ is a scale model of $\triangle DEF$, the triangles are similar. So,

$$\frac{CB}{FE} = \frac{AB}{DE}$$

$$\frac{3.5 \text{ cm}}{262.5 \text{ m}} = \frac{5.0 \text{ cm}}{x \text{ m}} \qquad \text{Substitute known measures.}$$

$$\frac{0.035 \text{ m}}{262.5 \text{ m}} = \frac{0.05 \text{ m}}{x \text{ m}} \qquad \text{Convert centimetres to metres.}$$

$$x = \frac{0.05 \times 262.5}{0.035}$$

$$= 375.0$$

It is 375.0 m from the tomb of Hatshepsut to the tomb of Rameses VII.

Practise, Apply, Solve 6.2

A

1. Find the length of the indicated side.

(a) $\triangle ABC \sim \triangle DEF$

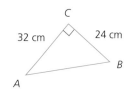

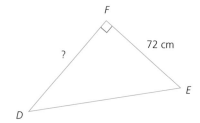

(b) $\triangle STV \sim \triangle MNP$

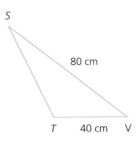

2. In the diagram, $ST \parallel QR$, $PQ = 8$ cm, $PS = 7$ cm, and $PT = 4$ cm. Find TR.

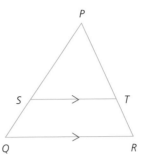

B

3. **(a)** Find a.

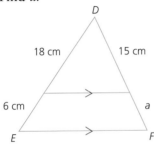

(b) Find n and m.

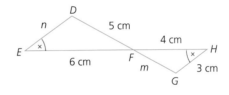

(c) Find c and d.

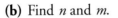
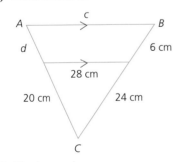

(d) Find x and y.

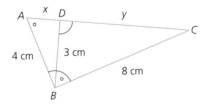

(e) Find p and q.

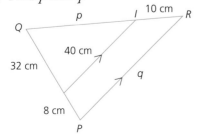

4. In a camera, a similar-triangle relationship exists between an actual object and its image on the film, as shown. Use the information in the diagram (which is not to scale) to calculate the height of the tree.

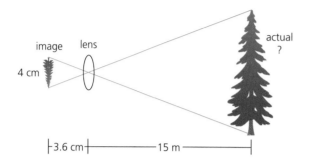

5. When you see a film in a movie theatre, the projection booth is at the back of the theatre. In the projector, light shines through the image on the film and onto the movie screen. In a theatre with a screen that is 10 m high, the projection booth is placed 32 m from the screen. If a new 15 m screen is installed, where should the projection booth to be placed?

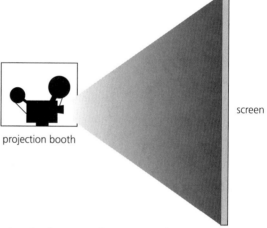

6. Two years ago, Fabio made a skateboard ramp that had a rise of 30 cm and a run of 1 m. Now he plans to build another ramp with the same slope, but with a 2 m long board for the ramp. What will be the rise and run of his new ramp?

7. **Knowledge and Understanding:**
A wildlife organization plans to build a boardwalk through a marshland in their community. To measure the distance across the marshland, they set up pegs and ropes as shown and took these measurements:

$DE = 1.2$ m $DC = 1.5$ m
$BC = 68$ m

If AB is parallel to DE, find the distance across the marsh, AB, to the nearest metre.

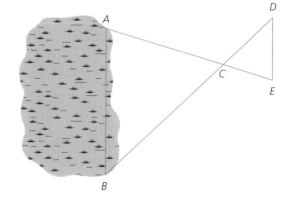

8. Communication: Mr. March, the science teacher, often uses the overhead projector. Sometimes students complain that the writing on the screen is too small to read. Should Mr. March move the overhead projector closer to the screen or farther away to enlarge the words? Explain your answer and include a diagram that involves similar triangles.

9. In the diagram, $BC \parallel DE$, $BC = 13$, $DE = 17$, $AB = 10$, and $AE = 15$.

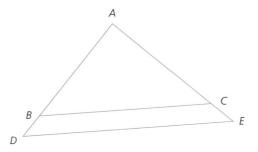

    (a) Calculate the length of AC to the nearest tenth.

    (b) Calculate the length of BD to the nearest tenth.

10. In the diagram, $AB \parallel DE$, $CE = DE = 32$, $AB = 8$, and $CD = 30$. Find the length of AC.

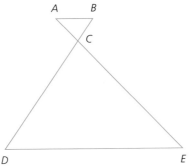

11. Jason is building a model of a cottage that he designed for his technology class. His roof plan is drawn to scale and looks like this:

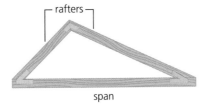

Measure the span of the roof and the length of the rafters in the drawing. If the span of the model roof is 22 cm, how long, to the nearest centimetre, should the rafters be?

12. Application: Aerial photography revolutionized map-making. To use an aerial photograph, a map-maker must know the scale of the image. There are several ways to determine the scale. The diagram shows how an aerial photo is taken.

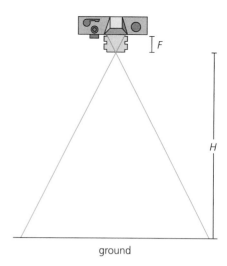

ground

You can find the scale from the focal length of the camera, F, and its height, H, when the picture was taken. The scale is represented by the ratio of $F : H$. (F and H must be in the same units.)

(a) Explain why the ratio of $F : H$ gives the scale of the photograph.

(b) In taking an aerial photograph, an airplane flew at an altitude of 2500 m and a camera with a focal length of 15 cm was used. What would be the scale of the photograph?

(c) If two buildings were 4.5 cm apart in the photograph, what would be the actual distance between them?

13. This is a scale diagram of the main street of a small town. If the street is actually 12 m wide, how far is it

(a) from the library to the convenience store?

(b) from the department store to the library and then to the arcade?

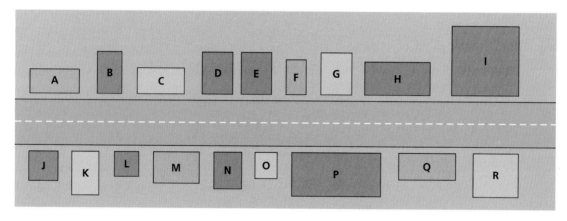

A - Hardware Store
B - Convenience Store
C - Pet Shop
D - Gift Shop
E - Hair Salon
F - Donut Shop

G - Police Station
H - Library
I - Arena
J - Arcade
K - General Store
L - Florist

M - Kitchen Shop
N - Video Store
O - Bakery
P - Department Store
Q - Grocery Store
R - Seniors' Centre

14. Harold works in a photography studio. One of his customers wants a 3" by 5" photograph enlarged to 5" by 7". Is it possible? Use similar figures to make your explanation.

15. A spotlight shines straight down on an outdoor skating rink from a height of 5 m. It illuminates a circle on the ice that is 2.8 m across. If the light was 2 m higher, how large would the circle of light be? Include a diagram with your solution.

16. Check Your Understanding

(a) How do you determine if two triangles are similar?

(b) List the steps to solve problems modelled by similar triangles.

(c) Explain what you need to think about when you make a diagram of any situation involving similar triangles.

(d) Create a question that uses similar triangles to determine a distance that cannot be measured directly. Be sure to include all necessary information. Ask a classmate to check and solve your problem.

 C

17. Kool Kones sells regular ice cream cones for $1.75 and kiddie cones for $1.10. Kiddie cones are the same shape as regular cones, but $\frac{3}{4}$ the height. Which is the better buy? Justify your answer.

18. Given that $\angle CAD = \angle CBA = 90°$, show that $y^2 = xz$. **Note:** y is called the **mean proportional** of x and z.

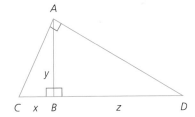

19. Thinking, Inquiry, Problem Solving: Idris has a flower garden in the back corner of his fenced yard as shown.

He wants to move the low garden fence to double the area of the flower garden. If he keeps the fence parallel to its old position, what will be the new dimensions of the two sides of the garden along the edge of his property? Draw a diagram that shows both the old and new gardens.

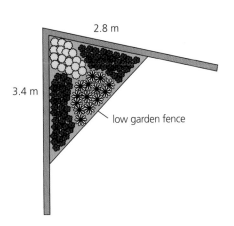

20. The small triangles $\triangle DEF$ and $\triangle GHI$ in this diagram were drawn by joining the midpoints of the sides of the next larger triangles. If AC is 160 cm, AB is 180 cm, and BC is 200 cm, what is the perimeter of the smallest triangle?

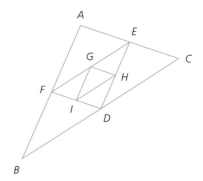

Chapter Problem—Modelling the Solar System

In this section, you solved problems involving similar triangles. Apply what you learned to answer these questions about the chapter problem on page 528.

A total eclipse of the sun occurs when the ratio of the diameter of the moon to its distance from Earth is about the same as the ratio of the sun's diameter to its distance from Earth.

1. Draw a diagram of triangles to model the situation.
2. Label the vertices of the triangles.
3. Determine which triangles are similar.
4. Write out the proportions represented in your diagram.
5. The sun's diameter is about 1.392×10^6 km. It is about 1.5×10^8 km from Earth to the sun, and about 3.84×10^5 km from Earth to the moon. What is the moon's diameter?

Career: City Planner

City or town planners check for proposed new development to ensure that buildings meet community standards. In addition to safety and health requirements, plans are checked for shadow impact. For example, a city plan may stipulate that in some neighbourhoods the sidewalk and buildings of the north side of the street are entitled to five hours of sunlight during peak hours of use. The same standard might apply to a park or school playground.

When a plan is submitted for aproval, planners use a CAD (Computer-Aided Design) program to generate two-dimensional diagrams modelling the shadows cast. Seasonal sun angles, times of the day, and geographic location are programmed in relation to the height and size of the building. If the planned building would shadow a street or park, changes to the design of the building will be requested such as lowering the height or changing the design of the roof to minimize the shadow.

Investigating the Sine Law 6.3

Part 1: How Can You Determine the Dimensions of a Triangle?

An architect designed a new building that is to be 12 m wide. The roof consists of rafters of two different lengths that meet at the top at an 80° angle. The long rafters make a 135° angle with the exterior wall. How long should the carpenter cut the short rafters? The long rafters?

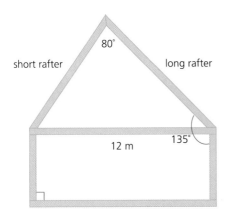

Think, Do, Discuss

1. What angle does the long rafter make with the horizontal?

2. What angle does the short rafter make with the horizontal?

3. Explain why you cannot use the primary trigonometric ratios to solve this problem.

Part 2: Trigonometric Relationships in Acute Triangles—The Sine Law

Are there properties of the sine, cosine, and tangent ratios that are true for all triangles? Can any of these be used to solve problems like the one above? Dynamic geometry software can be used in this activity.

Think, Do, Discuss

1. Construct an acute triangle, $\triangle ABC$, and measure all sides and angles.

2. Compute the ratio $\dfrac{\sin \text{ (angle)}}{\text{length of opposite side}}$ for each vertex angle of the triangle.

   (a) What do you notice about the value of this ratio for each angle?

   (b) Calculate the ratios $\dfrac{a}{b}$, $\dfrac{b}{c}$, and $\dfrac{a}{c}$. Now calculate $\dfrac{\sin A}{\sin B}$, $\dfrac{\sin B}{\sin C}$, and $\dfrac{\sin A}{\sin C}$. What do you notice about the values of these ratios?

   (c) Explain how the results in (b) are related to (a).

3. Investigate whether replacing the sine with the cosine or tangent gives the same results.

4. Repeat the steps above for a triangle with different vertex angles. Compare the values of the new ratios with the ratios for your original triangle.

5. (a) The relationship between the ratios of the sines of the angles of a triangle and the lengths of the opposite sides is called the **sine law**. Write an equation that expresses the sine law relationship that is true for any triangle.

   (b) Discuss whether or not a similar equation could be written for a "cosine law" or a "tangent law" that would be true for all triangles.

6. One standard way to write the sine law is

$$\frac{a}{\sin A} = \frac{b}{\sin B} = \frac{c}{\sin C}$$

   How does this compare with the equations that you have been using?

Part 3: Applying the Sine Law to Solve a Problem

You now have a simple way to solve the roof design problem. First, prepare a simplified diagram of the roof. You have enough information to determine the measure of all the angles in the triangle.

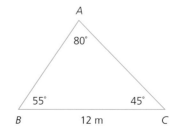

Think, Do, Discuss

1. Write the general form of the sine law as an algebraic expression.

2. Examine the triangle that models the roof. Rewrite the sine law as it applies to this triangle. Substitute all the known information about the triangle into the equation.

3. (a) Write equations that can be used to find each of the unknown lengths.

   (b) Solve the equations to find the unknown lengths.

   (c) Compare this method with the use of a scale diagram to solve the problem. State the advantages and disadvantages of each method.

Focus 6.3

Key Ideas

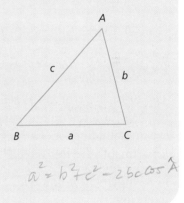

- For a triangle labelled as shown, the **sine law** can be written as $\dfrac{a}{\sin A} = \dfrac{b}{\sin B} = \dfrac{c}{\sin C}$

- To solve a problem using the sine law, start by finding the ratio of the sine of a known angle to the known length of the opposite side.
  Then set up an equation that equates this ratio to the ratio for another angle and its corresponding side, where either the angle or the side is unknown. From the equation, you can determine the value of the unknown quantity.

$$a^2 = b^2 + c^2 - 2bc \cos A$$

Example 1

Dylan, Ed, and Faye are standing at the corners of a triangular plot of land. Ed is 54 m from Faye. Using a simple transit he sights both Faye and Dylan, and finds the angle between the two sight lines is 50°. Dylan does the same and finds that the angle between his sight lines to Ed and Faye is 34°. How far is Dylan from Faye?

Solution

First, draw a diagram. Then use the sine law to write the equation of ratios and substitute the known measurements:

$$\frac{e}{\sin E} = \frac{d}{\sin D}$$

$$\frac{e}{\sin 50°} = \frac{54}{\sin 34°}$$

$$e = \frac{54 \sin 50°}{\sin 34°}$$

$$e = \frac{54(0.766\ 044\ 4\ \ldots)}{0.559\ 192\ \ldots}$$

$$e \doteq 74$$

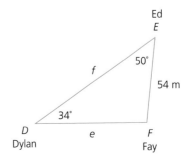

Dylan and Faye are about 74 m apart.

Example 2

Given $\triangle DST$ with $\angle D = 47°$, $d = 78$ cm, and $s = 106$ cm, find the measure of $\angle S$.

Solution

First, draw a diagram as shown, placing the known measurements in it.

To find $\angle S$, use the sine law.

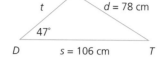

$$\frac{s}{\sin S} = \frac{d}{\sin D}$$

$$\frac{106}{\sin S} = \frac{78}{\sin 47°} \qquad \text{Substitute.}$$

$$\sin S = \frac{106 \sin 47°}{78} \qquad \text{Solve for } \angle S.$$

$$\sin S = 0.993\ 890\ldots$$

$\angle S \doteq \sin^{-1}(0.993\ 890)$ Use the $\sin^{-1}$ function of a calculator.

$$\angle S \doteq 83.663\ 541\ldots$$

$$\angle S \doteq 84°$$

Example 3

The town surveyor has to stake the lot markers for a new public park beside an existing building lot. The engineering department gave this sketch.

How much chain-link fence will be needed to enclose the entire park?

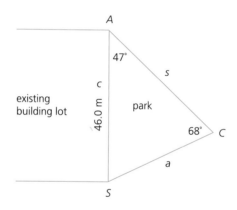

Solution

First, calculate the measure of side a.

$$\frac{a}{\sin A} = \frac{c}{\sin C} \qquad \text{Substitute.}$$

$$\frac{a}{\sin 47°} = \frac{46}{\sin 68°} \qquad \text{Solve for } a.$$

$$a \sin 68° = 46 \sin 47°$$

$$a = \frac{46 \sin 47°}{\sin 68°}$$

$$a = 36.284\ 357\ 31$$

$$a \doteq 36.3$$

To calculate side s, you first find the measure of $\angle S$.

$$\angle S + 47° + 68° = 180°$$

$$\angle S = 180° - 47° - 68°$$

$$\angle S = 65°$$

$$\frac{s}{\sin S} = \frac{c}{\sin C}$$

$$\frac{s}{\sin 65°} = \frac{46}{\sin 68°}$$

$$s = \frac{46 \sin 65°}{\sin 68°}$$

$$s = 44.964\ 284\ 05$$

$$s \doteq 45.0$$

Total fencing $= 46 + 36.3 + 45.0$

$\qquad\qquad\quad = 127.3$

In all, 127.3 m of fencing are needed.

Practise, Apply, Solve 6.3 ——————

A

1. Find the length of the indicated side, to one decimal place.

(a)

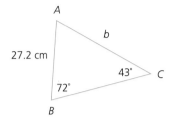

(b)

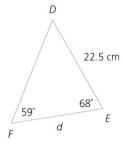

2. Find the measure of angle θ.

(a)

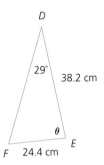

(b)

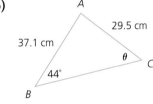

3. Find the measure of sides *a* and *b*.

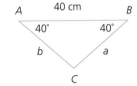

4. Find *y*.

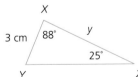

5. Communication: In $\triangle PQR$, $\angle Q = 90°$, $r = 6$, and $p = 8$.

(a) Find the measure of $\angle P$.

(b) Explain another way to find this answer, without using the sine law. Does this give you the same answer?

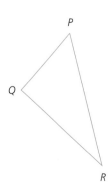

B

Include labelled diagrams with your answers.

6. **Knowledge and Understanding:** In △*SUN*, find the measure of side *u*, given that *n* = 58 cm, ∠*N* = 38°, and ∠*U* = 72°.

7. In △*PQR*, find the value of *q*, if ∠*R* = 73°, ∠*Q* = 32°, and *r* = 23 cm.

8. In △*TIM*, *t* = 8 cm, *m* = 5 cm, and ∠*T* = 40°. Find the measure of ∠*M*.

9. In △*TRH*, *T* is the tomb of Tuthmosis III, *R* is the tomb of Rameses IV, and *H* is Hatshepsut's tomb. In △*TRH*, *r* = 338 m, ∠*T* = 43°, and ∠*H* = 78°. Find the measures of *t*, *h*, and ∠*R*.

10. In △*CAT*, ∠*C* = 32°, ∠*T* = 81°, and *c* = 24.1 m. Solve the triangle. That is, find all of the unknown sides and angles.

11. **Thinking, Inquiry, Problem Solving:** Does the sine law apply to right triangles? Explain your answer.

12. **Knowledge and Understanding:** Louise is a naturalist studying the effect of acid rain on fish populations in different lakes. As part of her research, she needs to know the length of Lake Labarge. Louise makes the measurements shown. How long is the lake?

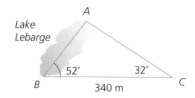

13. A parallelogram has one side that is 12.0 cm and one angle that is 65°. The shorter diagonal is 25.0 cm. To the nearest tenth of a centimetre, how long is the other side of the parallelogram?

14. An architect designs a house that is 12 m wide. The rafters holding up the roof are equal in length and meet at an angle of 70°. The rafters extend 0.3 m beyond the supporting wall. How long are the rafters?

15. A radio tower is supported by two wires on opposites sides, as shown. The wires form an angle of 60° at the top of the post. On the ground, the ends of the wire are 15.0 m apart, and one wire is at a 45° angle to the ground. How long will the wires be?

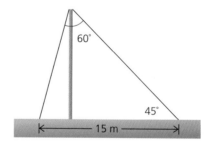

16. **Application:** To reduce the loading from snow on the roof, a ski chalet design calls for the roof slope to be 36° from vertical. If the width of the base of the chalet is 14.0 m, what is the slant height of the roof?

17. Check Your Understanding
  (a) State the equation relating the ratios of sides and the sines of angles for any $\triangle LMN$.
  (b) In $\triangle PQR$, you know the measures of p, $\angle P$, and $\angle Q$. How would you find the measure of r?
  (c) To use the sine law, what information do you need to have and what information could you be asked to find?

C

18. In $\triangle PQR$, $PQ = 45$, $\angle P = 70°$, and $\angle R = 49°$. Find the altitude from R to PQ.

19. In $\triangle ABC$, $\angle A = 58°$, $\angle C = 74°$, and $b = 6$.
  (a) Find a to one decimal place.
  (b) Find the area of $\triangle ABC$ to one decimal place.

20. An isosceles triangle has legs that are 8 cm long and base angles of 50°. Find the length of the angle bisector of one of the base angles.

21. Given $\triangle ABC$, use the sine law to state one ratio that is equivalent to each expression.
  (a) $\dfrac{a}{\sin A}$ (b) $\dfrac{\sin A}{\sin B}$ (c) $\dfrac{a}{c}$ (d) $\dfrac{a \sin C}{c \sin A}$

Did You Know?

Origami, the art of paper folding, began in China during the first or second century. By the sixth century, origami was also being practised in Japan. Origami links the precision of mathematics with the beauty of art and produces many intricate composite figures. Unit origami differs from traditional origami in that several symmetrical geometric shapes are constructed and interlocked through folding techniques to create complex geometrical figures.

6.4 Proving and Using the Sine Law

Part 1: Proving the Sine Law

In section 6.3, you discovered a relationship between the ratios of the sines of angles in a triangle and the measures of their opposite sides.

$$\frac{a}{\sin A} = \frac{b}{\sin B} = \frac{c}{\sin C}$$

Although you verified the relationship for many different cases, you did not actually prove that it is true for all possible triangles.

In mathematics, a **proof** shows that something is true for every possible case. In this activity, you will prove the sine law.

Think, Do, Discuss

1. Construct $\triangle ABC$ to be a non-right triangle in which AB is the base and also the longest side.

2. Construct a perpendicular from C to meet AB at E. Explain how this allows you to use the trigonometric ratios developed for right triangles in a triangle that does not contain a right angle.

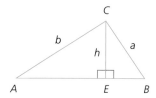

3. Use your diagram to write the equations for $\sin A$ and $\sin B$.
   (a) What quantity do the two equations have in common?
   (b) Solve each equation for the common quantity.
   (c) Since you have isolated the common quantity in two equations, what expressions must be equal to each other?
   (d) Explain how this equality relates to the sine law.

4. After step 3, you are still missing the third ratio in the sine law. Explain how you could show that $\frac{\sin A}{a} = \frac{\sin B}{b} = \frac{\sin C}{c}$.

5. Explain why you could also write the sine law as $\frac{a}{\sin A} = \frac{b}{\sin B} = \frac{c}{\sin C}$.

Part 2: Using the Sine Law

An engineer wants to build a bridge over a river. She marks two points, X on the left bank and Y on the right bank, to be the ends of the bridge. Then she marks a third point, Z, on the left bank, 18 m from X. She uses a transit and measures $\angle YZX = 72°$ and $\angle YXZ = 89°$.

Think, Do, Discuss

1. Draw a diagram showing a view of the situation from above. Label all parts of the diagram.

2. Write the sine law in terms of X, Y, and Z.

3. Which two parts of the sine law equation are needed in this problem?

4. Substitute the given values and solve for the unknown.

Part 3: When Can You Use the Sine Law?

The sine law has helped you to solve several problems. Can you use it to solve any problem that involves an acute triangle?

Think, Do, Discuss

1. Review the examples and problems that you did in this section and the previous section. What type of information do you need to solve a problem using the sine law?

2. If you are given the measures of two sides and any angle in a triangle, can you apply the sine law? Why or why not?

Focus 6.4

Key Ideas

- To use the sine law to solve a triangle you must know either
  - ◆ two sides and one angle *across from a known side*, or
  - ◆ two angles and any side
- The sine law can be written in several ways, including

$$\frac{\sin A}{a} = \frac{\sin B}{b} = \frac{\sin C}{c}, \text{ or } \frac{a}{\sin A} = \frac{b}{\sin B} = \frac{c}{\sin C}$$

Example 1

A chandelier is suspended from the ceiling by two chains. One chain is 46 cm long and forms an angle of 60° with the ceiling. The other chain is 64 cm long. What angle does the longer chain make with the ceiling?

Solution

Start with a diagram.

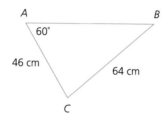

Using the sine law,

$$\frac{a}{\sin A} = \frac{b}{\sin B}$$

$$\frac{64}{\sin 60°} = \frac{46}{\sin B}$$

$$64 \sin B = 46 \sin 60°$$

$$\sin B = \frac{46 \sin 60°}{64}$$

$$\angle B \doteq 38.5°$$

Example 2

Two tracking stations, 20 km apart, measure the angles of elevation of a rocket that was launched with a weather satellite. From station A, the angle of elevation is 41°; from station B, it is 75°, as shown. What is the altitude of the rocket, to the nearest tenth of a kilometre?

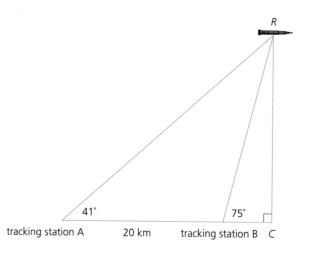

Solution

In $\triangle ARB$, $\angle RAB = 41°$.

First, find $\angle ABR$.

$\angle ABR = 180° - 75°$ (supplementary angles)

$\angle ABR = 105°$

Find $\angle ARB$.

$\angle ARB + \angle ABR + \angle RAB = 180°$

$\angle ARB = 180° - 105° - 41°$

$\angle ARB = 34°$

Use the sine law to set up a proportion.

$$\frac{AR}{\sin ABR} = \frac{AB}{\sin ARB}$$

$$\frac{AR}{\sin 105°} = \frac{20}{\sin 34°} \qquad \text{Substitute.}$$

$$AR = \frac{20 \sin 105°}{\sin 34°} \qquad \text{Solve for } AR.$$

$$\doteq 34.5$$

AR is 34.5 km.

The larger triangle, $\triangle ARC$, is a right triangle. The altitude of the rocket is RC.

$$\sin 41° = \frac{RC}{AC}$$

$$\sin 41° = \frac{RC}{34.5}$$

$$RC = 34.5 \sin 41°$$

$$RC \doteq 22.6$$

The altitude of the rocket is 22.6 km.

Practise, Apply, Solve 6.4

1. A cottage under construction is to be 12.6 m wide. The two sides of the roof are to be supported by rafters that meet at a 50° angle. How long should the rafters be?

2. Communication: A new ferry boat will run between two towns on the opposite sides of a lake. To know how long each trip will take, the width of the lake needs to be found. These measurements were made. Write an explanation, telling how to find the width of the lake.

3. A nest of falcons sits atop a high city building, *S*. Across the street, in building *T*, a camera is filming the falcons for an Internet site. The producer of the site needs to know how far apart the buildings are. A survey crew sets up a transit at points *S* and an arbitrary point *A*, 30 m from *S* on the same side of the street, as shown. In Δ*SAT*, they measure the angle at *A* to be 42° and the angle at *S* to be 75°. How far apart are the two buildings?

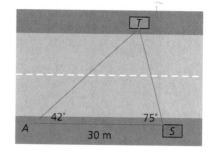

4. In a new home with solar heating panels, the roof must be built to certain specifications. The rafters supporting the roof must be inclined at angles of 24° and 62° to the horizontal. The house is 15.3 m wide. How long are the rafters?

B

5. Application: Two helicopters, flying at the same altitude, spot a boat in distress on the water below and between them. The helicopters are 1.2 km apart and the angles of depression to the boat are 53° and 42°. The Coast Guard is trying to determine which helicopter to send to respond to the distress call. Which helicopter should fly to the boat to rescue its passengers? Explain your choice.

6. Two points *B* and *G* are separated by a swamp. To find the distance between the points, Shari walked 100 m from point *B* to another point *O*. Then she estimated that ∠*OBG* = 38° and ∠*BOG* = 72°. Find the distance from *B* to *G*, correct to the nearest metre.

7. Knowledge and Understanding: How long is the base of an isosceles triangle if the equal sides are 20 cm long and the base angles measure 52°?

8. A regular pentagon is inscribed in a circle with a radius of 15 cm. How long is each side of the pentagon?

9. Two angles of a triangle are 30° and 65° and the longest side is 34 cm. How long is the shortest side? Explain how you know how to label your triangle.

10. Omid and Ritu are determining the height of a cliff they plan to climb. They are 18 m apart on the same side of the cliff. Sighting along the same line, Omid views the top of the cliff at an angle of elevation of 23°, and Ritu views the top at an angle of elevation of 29°. How high is the cliff?

11. Check Your Understanding

    (a) Describe the steps you should take to solve a word problem using the sine law.

    (b) What questions should you ask yourself to determine if the sine law can be used to solve a problem?

    (c) Describe a situation involving triangles where the sine law cannot be applied. Include a diagram.

C

12. **Thinking, Inquiry, Problem Solving**
Sara is riding in a hot air balloon, directly over John, who is standing on the ground. Sara spots Pat on the ground at an angle of depression of 28°. The balloon rises 34 m. Now the angle of depression to Pat is 35°. How far is Pat from John?

Chapter Problem—Modelling the Solar System

In this section, you used the sine law. Apply what you learned to answer this question about the chapter problem on page 528.

Earth and Mercury form a triangle with the sun as shown.

The distance from Mercury to the sun is 5.89×10^7 km. The distance from Earth to the sun is 1.5×10^8 km. The angle between the lines of sight from Earth to the sun and from Earth to Mercury is 22°. At this position, how far is it from Earth to Mercury?

For future reference, the diameter of Mercury is 4.8×10^3 km.

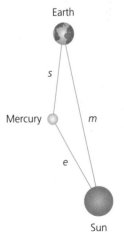

Earth

s

Mercury m

e

Sun

6.5 Using Compass Directions and Bearings to Navigate

Part 1: Compass Directions

A ship is sailing due east at night. The ship's navigator spots a lighthouse on a direction of N40°E. According to the map, the water within 400 m of the lighthouse is too shallow for the ship. After the ship continues to sail east for 800 m, the new direction of the lighthouse is N48°W.

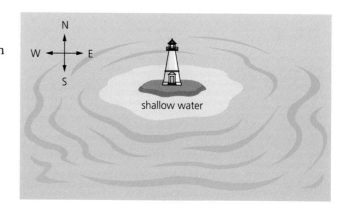

shallow water

(a) How far away is the lighthouse now?

(b) How close did the boat come to the lighthouse?

(c) Was the ship ever within the 400 m range of shallow water?

Think, Do, Discuss

1. N40°E means 40° east of N. Draw a diagram to illustrate this direction.

2. What is meant by N48°W? Draw a diagram to illustrate this direction.

3. Draw a diagram for this problem.

4. Solve the problem.

Part 2: Bearings

Another way to give direction is to express it as a bearing. Bearings are always measured from the north, moving in a clockwise direction. Thus, E20°S is a bearing of 110°.

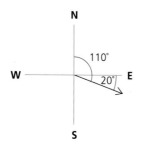

Think, Do, Discuss

1. How would E20°N be expressed as a bearing? S25°W?

2. Express a bearing of 80° in terms of compass directions.

3. On a map of the province of Quebec, Quebec City is 245 km from Montreal, on a bearing of 41°. Draw a diagram to show their relative positions.

4. The bearing of Ottawa from Toronto is 55°. To get from Toronto to Ottawa, a plane flew on a bearing of 15° for 300 km before strong winds made it necessary to change course. The plane then turned and flew 238 km to reach Ottawa. What was the bearing of the second leg of the journey? How far is it from Toronto to Ottawa as the crow flies?

Part 3: Programming a Robot Using Bearings —

A remote control robot called a turtle is programmed using bearings to follow a certain path.

Think, Do, Discuss

1. Use a protractor and graph paper to map out the following path for the turtle. Be sure to use a scale for any distances.

   • 5 m at a bearing of 110°, then

   • 8 m at a bearing of 210°, then

   • 9 m at a bearing of 260°

2. How far is the turtle from its starting point?

3. What bearing will return the turtle to its starting position?

François Viète (1540-1603)

Considered the greatest French mathematician of the 16th century, François Viète (Vee-et) is best known for the development of symbolic algebra.

In his book *In artem* he introduced the practice of using vowels to represent unknown quantities, and the consonants for known ones. He used the same letter for powers of the same base, rather than different letters as other mathematicians did. Viète also rewrote the coefficients of polynomial equations so that the equations were in terms of a particular variable.

6.6 Adjusting the Pythagorean Theorem: The Cosine Law

Part 1: The Pythagorean Theorem ─────────

When working with right triangles, you know that you can use the Pythagorean theorem to solve problems.

For $\triangle ABC$, $c^2 = a^2 + b^2$, where a, b, and c are as shown.

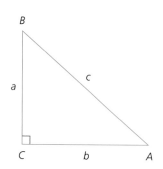

In this section, we are going to explore whether this relationship holds true for other triangles. Dynamic geometry software can be used in this activity.

Think, Do, Discuss

1. Do you think the Pythagorean theorem would hold true for non-right triangles? That is, given that a, b, and c are the sides of a non-right triangle do you think that $c^2 = a^2 + b^2$? Explain how changing the 90° angle might affect the relationship between the lengths of the sides.

2. Create a non-right triangle. Label the vertices A, B, and C, and the sides a, b, and c. Find the measure of each side. For example,

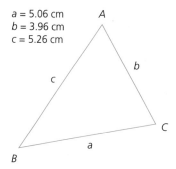

a = 5.06 cm
b = 3.96 cm
c = 5.26 cm

In this case, $\angle A = 65°$, $\angle B = 45°$, and $\angle C = 70°$.

3. Calculate the square of each side of the triangle. Does the sum of the squares of any two sides equal the square of the third side? Consider all possibilities. What can you conclude?

4. If the square of one side does not equal the sum of the squares of the other two sides, is it greater or less than this sum? Apply this to all sides and record your results in a table like this.

Triangle	Angle Measure	Square of Opposite Side	=, <, or >	Sum of Squares of Other Two Sides
$\triangle ABC$	$\angle C = 70°$	$c^2 = 27.67$	<	$a^2 + b^2 = 41.29$
$\triangle ABC$	$\angle B = 45°$			
$\triangle ABC$	$\angle A = 65°$			

5. Create four other non-right triangles. If you use paper and pencil, compare your results with those of other students. If you are using *The Geometer's Sketchpad*, you can drag one of the points in the diagram you already made. Check the sums of the squares of all three pairs of sides with the square of the remaining side. In each case, check if the two quantities are equal or which is greater. Enter your values in the table.

6. Did any of your triangles satisfy the Pythagorean relationship? If so, what were its angle measures? Do you notice anything about the triangle?

7. For what angle measures are the values in column 5 greater than those in column 3? For what angle measures are the values in column 3 greater than those in column 5?

8. For which angles do you think that $a^2 + b^2 = c^2$? $a^2 + b^2 < c^2$? $a^2 + b^2 > c^2$?

Did You Know?

Pythagoras (550 B.C.E.) was a Greek philosopher and the leader of a religious community known as the Pythagorean brotherhood. This group influenced the development of mathematics, science, and philosophy.

When Pythagoras created the Pythagorean theorem, a crisis followed. This was because the theorem showed that if the two legs of a right triangle are 1, the hypotenuse will be $\sqrt{2}$. This was the first time the Greek mathematicians had confronted a number that could not be expressed as a fraction. They did not believe it could exist.

Pythagoras

Part 2: Developing the Cosine Law

You probably noticed in part 1 that $a^2 + b^2 = c^2$ only when $\angle C$ is a right angle. However, there is a value that can be subtracted from $a^2 + b^2$ to establish a relationship between the sides and the angle opposite side c. The **cosine law** shows this relationship.

Start with $\triangle ABC$.

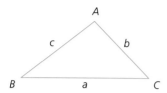

Draw h to be perpendicular to side a and meet at BC at D. Let x represent the length of BD and let y represent the length of DC.

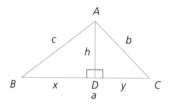

Since $AD \perp BC$, then $\triangle ABD$ is a right triangle. Express the Pythagorean relationship for $\triangle ABD$. Then,

$$c^2 = h^2 + x^2 \qquad \text{Express } x \text{ in terms of } a \text{ and } y.$$
$$c^2 = h^2 + (a - y)^2 \qquad \text{Expand.}$$
$$c^2 = h^2 + a^2 - 2ay + y^2 \qquad \text{Rearrange the terms.}$$
$$c^2 = h^2 + y^2 + a^2 - 2ay \qquad \text{Call this equation ①.}$$

In $\triangle ADC$,

$$h^2 + y^2 = b^2. \qquad ②$$

Also in $\triangle ADC$, $\cos C = \dfrac{y}{b}$, so

$$y = b \cos C \qquad ③$$

Substitute equations ② and ③ into ① to get a formula that refers to the letters from $\triangle ABC$.

Then,

$$c^2 = b^2 + a^2 - 2ay$$

$$c^2 = b^2 + a^2 - 2ab \cos C$$

This is the cosine law for any triangle $\triangle ABC$.

$$c^2 = b^2 + a^2 - 2ab \cos C$$

Think, Do, Discuss

1. Test the cosine law on the triangle you drew in part 1. Does the cosine law agree with your results?

2. When $\angle C = 90°$, what is cos C?

3. Look at your table from part 1. Notice that sometimes $c^2 > a^2 + b^2$. How can you subtract from the right side and have the entire right side get larger? Test the cosine law for a few of these situations and explain why it works here.

4. You developed one form of the cosine law for $\triangle ABC$. It can also be expressed in two other forms:

   $a^2 = b^2 + c^2 - 2bc \cos A$ and $b^2 = a^2 + c^2 - 2ac \cos B$

   Explain how to get these two other forms of the cosine law starting with $\triangle ABC$ in part 2. What would the three forms of the cosine law look like for $\triangle XYZ$?

5. Use the cosine law to find the value of c, given $a = 5$ cm, $b = 4$ cm, and $\angle C = 55°$.

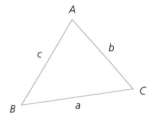

6. (a) For $\triangle ABC$ in step 5, could you have found the value of c given the length of a, the length of b, and the measure of $\angle B$? Explain.
   (b) What information do you need to use the cosine law?

7. If three sides of a triangle are known, how could the cosine law be used to find the angle between two sides?

8. Is there a situation where the cosine law can be used to solve a problem and the sine law cannot? Give an example of such a situation.

Career: Structural Engineer

Structural engineers are responsible for making sure that our buildings and bridges are built to last in the prevailing environmental conditions. Designing and building bridges is an important aspect of the job.

the Quebec Bridge

Right triangles are a key to good supporting structures because the triangles are rigid and strong. The Quebec bridge is a fine example of a cantilever bridge, the longest in the world, which uses right triangle supports. Most cantilever bridges have two supporting spans on each side connected to a suspended span in the middle.

Focus 6.6

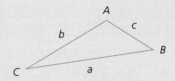

Key Ideas

- The **cosine law** says that for any $\triangle ABC$,

$$c^2 = a^2 + b^2 - 2ab \cos C$$

$$a^2 = b^2 + c^2 - 2bc \cos A$$

$$b^2 = a^2 + c^2 - 2ac \cos B$$

- The cosine law is used to find the third side of a triangle when two sides and a contained angle are known or to find an angle measure when the length of three sides are known.

- The contained angle in a triangle is the angle between the two given sides of the triangle. For example, in $\triangle ABC$, B is the contained angle between AB and BC.

Example 1

In $\triangle ABC$, for which set(s) of data could you use the cosine law to solve for c?

(a) $a = 5$ cm, $\angle A = 52°$, $\angle C = 43°$

(b) $a = 6$ cm, $\angle A = 52°$, $b = 7$ cm

(c) $a = 5$ cm, $b = 7$ cm, $\angle C = 43°$

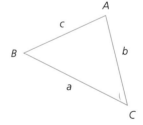

Solution

(a) To use the cosine law, you need to know at least two sides of a triangle, and this set of data only gives one side. This set of data could not be used.

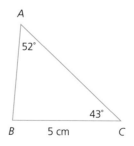

(b) This set of data could be used, but you would have to solve for *c* indirectly. That is, first you would have to find ∠B. Then you could find the measure of ∠C and solve for *c* using either the sine law or cosine law.

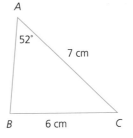

(c) This set of data is the best one for which to use the cosine law, because it gives two sides and the contained angle.

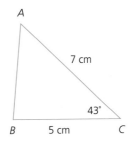

Example 2

A triangular lot sits at the corner of two streets that intersect at an angle of 58°. One street side of the lot is 32 m and the other is 40 m. How long is the back of the lot (the third side), to the nearest metre?

Solution

First, draw a diagram of the situation.

No combination of side length and opposite angle measure is given. Therefore, the sine law cannot be used. Use the cosine law to solve for *a*.

$$a^2 = b^2 + c^2 - 2bc \cos A$$
$$a^2 = (32)^2 + (40)^2 - 2(32)(40)\cos 58°$$
$$a^2 = 1024 + 1600 - 2560 \cos 58°$$
$$a^2 = 2624 - 2560 \cos 58°$$
$$a^2 = 2624 - (2560)(0.5299…)$$
$$a^2 = 2624 - 1356.5933…$$
$$a^2 = 1267.4067…$$
$$a = \sqrt{1267.4067…}$$
$$a = 35.6005…$$
$$a \doteq 36$$

The back of the lot is about 36 m.

Example 3

A bicycle race follows a triangular course. The
three legs of the race are, in order, 2.3 km,
5.9 km, and 6.2 km. Find the angle between
the starting leg and the finishing leg to the
nearest degree.

Solution

Draw a diagram.

You need to find $\angle P$. No combination of side length and
opposite angle measure are given, so the sine law cannot be
used. Use the cosine law instead.

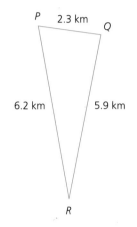

$$p^2 = q^2 + r^2 - 2qr \cos P$$
$$(5.9)^2 = (6.2)^2 + (2.3)^2 - 2(6.2)(2.3)\cos P$$
$$34.81 = 38.44 + 5.29 - 28.52 \cos P$$
$$34.81 = 43.73 - 28.52 \cos P$$
$$34.81 - 43.73 = -28.52 \cos P$$
$$-8.92 = -28.52 \cos P$$
$$\cos P = \frac{8.92}{28.52}$$
$$\angle P = \cos^{-1}\left(\frac{8.92}{28.52}\right) \qquad \text{Use the inverse cosine feature on a calculator.}$$
$$\angle P = 71.7741\ldots°$$
$$\angle P \doteq 72°$$

The angle is 72° to the nearest degree.

Practise, Apply, Solve 6.6 ———————————

Ⓐ

1. Which of these triples could represent the sides of a right triangle? Give reasons.

    (a) 2, 3, 4   **(b)** 5, 3, 7   **(c)** 4, 5, 3

    (d) 3, 8, 4   **(e)** 5, 7, 12   **(f)** 5, 12, 13

2. Find the measure of x.

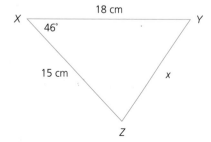

3. Solve each triangle.

    (a) $\triangle CAT$, with $c = 5$ cm, $a = 6$ cm, and $\angle T = 63°$

    (b) $\triangle XYZ$, with $x = 3.2$ cm, $y = 4.5$ cm, and $\angle Z = 87°$

    (c) $\triangle PIE$, with $e = 18$ m, $p = 21$ m, and $\angle I = 72°$

4. Calculate $\angle A$ for $\triangle ABC$ if $a = 5$ cm, $b = 6$ cm, and $c = 7$ cm.

B

5. Knowledge and Understanding: Two sides of a triangle measure 18.0 cm and 23.0 cm, and the angle between them is 60°. How long is the third side?

6. An ice-cream company is designing cones to serve frozen yogurt. The design has a bottom angle of 38° and the sides of the cone should be 12 cm long. What must be the radius of the top of the cone?

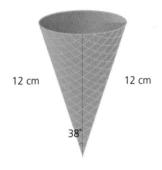

12 cm   12 cm

38°

7. Find the perimeter of $\triangle SAT$, if $\angle S = 56°$, $a = 14$ cm, and $t = 25$ cm.

8. Two roads diverge at a 52° angle. Two bike riders take separate routes at 17 km/h and 24 km/h. How far apart are they after 2 h? Include a diagram.

9. The posts of a hockey goal are 2.0 m apart. A player tries to score a goal by shooting the puck along the ice from a point 4.8 m from one post and 6.7 m from the other. Within what angle must the player shoot the puck? Include a diagram.

10. Find the measure, to the nearest degree, of the smallest angle in a triangle with sides of 4 m, 7 m, and 8 m.

11. Communication: Draw a diagram to solve this problem: Beaverton is 10 km due east of Deerfield. Crowden is 8 km NW of Beaverton. How far is it from Crowden to Deerfield? Explain whether you have enough information to solve the problem.

12. A three-pointed star is made up of an equilateral triangle and three isosceles triangles.

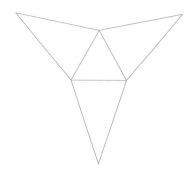

This pysanki, a giant Ukranian decorated egg in Vegreville, Alberta, has 2208 equilateral triangles, and 524 three-pointed stars on it.

(a) Find the dimensions of the equilateral triangle if each isosceles triangle has a vertical angle of 20° and equal side lengths of 12 cm.

(b) Find the angle at each point of a star made up of isosceles triangles with a base of 10 cm and equal sides of 15 cm.

13. A clock has a 30 cm minute hand and a 21 cm hour hand. How far apart are the tips of the hands at

(a) 2 o'clock?   (b) 3 o'clock?   (c) 4 o'clock?   (d) 6 o'clock?

14. Application: The bases on a baseball diamond are 30 m apart. A player picks up a fair ground ball 3 m from third base, along the line from second to third base. How far must he throw it to first base?

15. The radar screen of an airport control tower shows that two planes are at the same altitude. According to the range finder, one plane is 100 km away, in the direction N60°E. The other is 160 km away, at a direction of S50°E. How far apart are the planes?

16. A boat leaves Kingston and heads due east for 25 km. At the same time, a second boat travels in a direction 30° south of east from Kingston for 15 km. How far apart are the boats at this moment when they reach their destinations?

17. A golfer hits a tee shot on a 350 m long straight golf hole. The ball is sliced (hit at an angle) 21° to the right. The ball lands 210 m away from the tee. How far is the ball from the hole to the nearest metre?

18. A satellite is positioned so that it makes an angle of 6.8° with the ground at Toronto, Ontario, and an angle of 16.9° with the ground at Houston, Texas. If it is 2100 km from Toronto to Houston
(a) how far is the satellite from Toronto?
(b) how high is the satellite?

Note: Neglect the curvature of Earth in this problem.

19. The Nautilus is sailing due east toward a buoy, while the Porpoise approaches the buoy heading N40°E. If the Nautilus is 5.4 km from the buoy and the Porpoise is 5.4 km from the Nautilus, how far is the Porpoise from the buoy?

20. Gale takes a slap shot that is tipped by Stephane, who is 8 m from Gale. If the puck travels 10.3 m in all and ends up 5° off from its original path, how much did the puck's direction change as a result of the tip? Answer to the nearest degree.

21. Given the points $O(0, 0)$, $A(3, 1)$, and $B(1, 4)$, what is the measure of $\angle AOB$?

22. Check Your Understanding
   (a) Express the cosine law for $\angle PQR$. What helps you remember which letters go where?
   (b) Give an example where the cosine law will not solve a triangle but the sine law will.
   (c) Give an example of a problem in which you would need to use both the sine law and cosine law.

C

23. A water molecule is made up of one atom of oxygen and two atoms of hydrogen. The bonds between the oxygen and hydrogen atoms form an angle that makes the molecule triangular. As water freezes, the shape of the triangle changes, as shown.

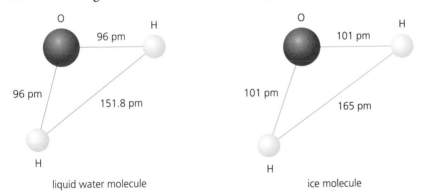

liquid water molecule   ice molecule

Note: All measurements are given in picometres (pm) where 1 pm $= 10^{-12}$ m.
   (a) Find the angles formed by the two bonds in water.
   (b) Find the angles formed by the two bonds in ice.
   (c) As water freezes, the volume expands. How do your findings support this?

24. Two search and rescue ships are out at sea looking for a downed aircraft. The two ships, SR1 and SR2, are 108 km apart. SR1 picks up a signal from the downed aircraft and estimates that it is 95 km away. SR1 calculates that the angle between the line of sight from SR1 to SR2 and the line from SR1 to the downed aircraft is 36°. Determine who is closer to the downed aircraft, SR1 or SR2.

25. A clock with a radius of 15 cm has an 11 cm minute hand and a 7 cm hour hand. How far apart are the tips of the hands at
   (a) 3:30?   **(b)** 3:38?

26. Thinking, Inquiring, Problem Solving: Find the perimeter and area of this regular pentagon.

1.5 cm

27. An airplane is flying from Montreal to Vancouver. The wind is blowing from the west at 60 km/h. The plane flies at 750 km/h relative to the air. If the pilot wishes to fly at a heading of N65°W

(a) what heading should he take to compensate for the wind?

(b) what is the speed of the plane relative to the ground?

Did You Know?

Braille is a system of writing and printing for people who are visually impaired. Braille symbols representing letters, numerals, or words, are imprinted as arrangements of raised dots on a page, and are read by touching the dots with the fingertips.

Several instruments are available to help teach visually impaired students. For example, Braille writing machines and typewriters make it possible to translate any text into Braille. Mathematical diagrams are reproduced with wax-coated string, or using special heat-sensitive paper. When this paper is heated, the image drawn on it becomes raised from the page, and is thus made readable to the fingertips.

Chapter Problem—Modelling the Solar System

In this section you developed the cosine law. Apply what you learned to answer this question about the chapter problem on page 528.

1. One astronomical unit (1 A.U.) is the average distance from Earth to the sun. On one occasion, Earth, Mars, and the sun form a triangle in which the angle between the lines of sight from Earth to the sun and from Earth to Mars is about 80°; and the angle between the lines of sight from Mars to the sun and from Mars to Earth is about 39°.

Also, the diameter of Mars is 415 km more than one-half the diameter of Earth, which is 1.2760×10^4 km.

To two decimal places, how many astronomical units is it from Mars to the sun? How many kilometres is this?

Solving Measurement Problems Modelled by Triangles

Trigonometry is used in many different areas, including navigation, surveying, construction, engineering, map-making, photography, astronomy, graphic design, and architecture. And, you have used different strategies to solve problems that involve trigonometry.

In this section, you will investigate how to decide which strategy is best for a given problem.

You will also develop an approach to solving triangles.

Think, Do, Discuss

1. When solving any type of trigonometry problem, what will always help you to visualize the problem?

2. For which kinds of triangles can you use the primary trigonometric ratios that you explored in chapter 5?

3. What information do you need to have to use the sine law to solve a problem?

4. How do you use the sine law to solve for a side? an angle?

5. Under what conditions can you **not** use the sine law to find the length of a side or measure of an angle in a triangle?

6. What information do you need to have to use the cosine law to solve a problem?

7. How do you use the cosine law to solve for a side? an angle?

8. Give examples of situations in which you can use either the sine law or the cosine law to solve a problem. In these situations, which should you use? Why?

9. **Solving a triangle** means to find the lengths of all three sides and the measures of all three angles. What are some strategies that you can use to solve a typical triangle?

Focus 6.7

Key Ideas

- **Solving a triangle** means to find the lengths of all three sides and the measures of all three angles of the triangle.

- Drawing a clearly labelled diagram can help you to solve problems.

- Right triangles can be solved with the primary trigonometric ratios.

- Use the sine law to solve a triangle when two sides and one opposite angle are known, or when two angles and one opposite side are known.

- Use the cosine law to solve a triangle if all three sides are known, or two sides and the angle between them are known.

- If both the sine law and the cosine law can be used to solve a triangle, use the sine law, since it is the easier method.

Example 1

In $\triangle ABC$, $a = 6$ cm, $b = 5.3$ cm, and $c = 7.2$ cm. Find the measure of $\angle A$ to the nearest degree.

Solution

First, draw a diagram.

Three sides are given, so use the cosine law. Use the form of this law that refers to $\angle A$.

$$a^2 = b^2 + c^2 - 2bc \cos A$$
$$(6)^2 = (5.3)^2 + (7.2)^2 - 2(5.3)(7.2)\cos A \quad \text{Substitute known measures.}$$
$$36 = 28.09 + 51.84 - 76.32 \cos A \quad \text{Simplify.}$$
$$36 - 28.09 - 51.84 = -76.32 \cos A$$
$$-43.93 = -76.32 \cos A$$
$$\cos A = \frac{43.93}{76.32} \quad \text{Solve for } \cos A.$$
$$\angle A = \cos^{-1}\left(\frac{43.93}{76.32}\right) \quad \text{Use the inverse cosine feature on a calculator}$$
$$\doteq 55° \quad \text{to solve for } \angle A.$$

The measure of $\angle A$ is 55°.

Example 2

Rashid is building a house and he needs to know information about the roof's design. The base of the roof is 12.8 m wide and the rafters form angles of 48° and 44° to the horizontal. How long, to the nearest tenth of a metre, is each rafter?

Solution

Draw a diagram.
(Since ∠A is opposite to a known side, the sine law can be used provided ∠A is known.)

Two angles are given, so ∠A can be calculated.

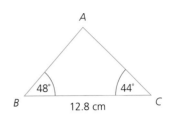

$$\angle A = 180° - (48° + 44°)$$
$$= 180° - 92°$$
$$= 88°$$

To find AC,

$$\frac{b}{\sin B} = \frac{a}{\sin A}$$ Substitute known values.

$$\frac{b}{\sin 48°} = \frac{12.8}{\sin 88°}$$ Solve for b.

$$b = \frac{12.8 \sin 48°}{\sin 88°}$$

$$b = \frac{12.8 \times 0.7431...}{0.9993...}$$

$$b = 9.5180...$$

$$b \doteq 9.5$$

Similarly, to find AB,

$$\frac{c}{\sin C} = \frac{a}{\sin A}$$ Substitute known values.

$$\frac{c}{\sin 44°} = \frac{12.8}{\sin 88°}$$ Solve for c.

$$c = \frac{12.8 \sin 44°}{\sin 88°}$$

$$c = \frac{12.8 \times 0.6946...}{0.9993...}$$

$$c = 8.8970...$$

$$c \doteq 8.9$$

The rafters should be 9.5 m and 8.9 m long.

Example 3

Tyson is doing a project on the seasonal change in the size and flow of a river near his house for his environmental studies class. Among the statistics he must compile is the width of the river at different times during the school year. There is a 130 m building on one bank of the river. Tyson stands on the opposite bank and measures that the angle of elevation to the top of the building is 42°. How wide is the river to the nearest metre?

Solution

Start with a diagram.

Notice that $\angle Y = 90°$. This means we do not need to use the sine law or cosine law. We can use the trigonometry of right triangles to find the width of the river, YZ.

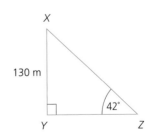

$$\tan 42° = \frac{130}{YZ} \quad \text{Set up an equation and solve for } YZ.$$

$$YZ \tan 42° = 130$$

$$YZ = \frac{130}{\tan 42°}$$

$$YZ = 144.3796\ldots$$

$$YZ \doteq 144$$

The river is 144 m wide.

Practise, Apply, Solve 6.7

A

1. Kashiro delivers milk to grocery stores in three towns in a remote area. The roads connecting the towns form a triangular route. The first section of the route is 32.8 km. The third section is 28.2 km. The angle between the first section and the third section is 46°. How long is

   (a) the second section of the route?

   (b) the route in total?

2. The angle between two equal sides of an isosceles triangle is 52° and the equal sides are each 18 cm long.

   (a) Find the measures of the two equal angles of the triangle.

   (b) How long is the third side?

3. A representative from the Ministry of the Environment is measuring the distance across a small lake as part of the data for her study to find growth and decay patterns in the local water system. She takes the measurements shown. Find the distance, *d*, across the lake.

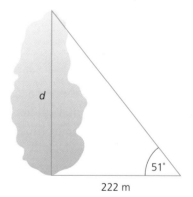

4. Anika is drawing a map of a rural district in Ontario for her geography class. Three towns, Chatsworth, Durham, and Flesherton form a triangle. It is 32 km from Chatsworth to Durham, 35 km from Chatsworth to Flesherton, and 25 km from Durham to Flesherton. If there are straight, direct roads between the towns, what is the angle between the roads leading from Flesherton to Chatsworth and from Chatsworth to Durham?

5. The angle of depression of a ship from the top of a 22.5 m lighthouse is 16°. How far is the boat from the base of the lighthouse?

6. A radar operator on a ship discovers a large sunken vessel lying flat on the ocean floor 200 m directly beneath the ship. The operator measures the angles of depression of the front and back of the sunken ship to be 56° and 62°. How long is the sunken ship?

7. *Thinking, Inquiry, Problem Solving:* The Queen Charlotte Islands in British Columbia form a fairly triangular region in the Pacific Ocean. Two sides of this triangular region are about 256 km and 288 km and form an angle of 19°. What is

(a) the length of the third side?

(b) the approximate area bounded by the Queen Charlotte Islands?

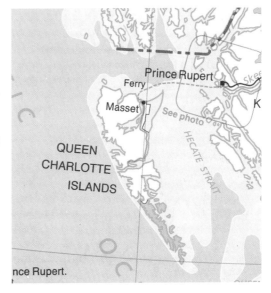

8. A boat in a race starts at point *A*, sails 18.3 km to a red buoy, and then 29 km to a blue buoy. The angle formed by the line of sight from the red buoy to the starting point and the red buoy to the blue buoy is 62°. How far is it from the blue buoy to the starting point?

9. A flagpole stands on top of a 27 m building. From a point on the ground some distance away, the angle of elevation of the top of the flagpole is 43°. The angle of elevation of the bottom of the flagpole is 32°.

(a) How far is it from the point on the ground to the bottom of the building?

(b) How high is the flagpole?

10. A group of mountain climbers are using trigonometry to find the height of a mountain. From point *A*, which is due west of the mountain, the angle of elevation to the top is 29°. From point *B*, which is due west of the mountain, the angle of elevation to the top is 35°. Points *A* and *B* are 8.2 km apart. How high is the mountain?

11. **Knowledge and Understanding:** Two scuba divers are 50 m below the surface of the water. They see their boat above at an angle of elevation of 40°. How far are they from the boat?

12. A regular hexagon has a perimeter of 72 cm. What is
    (a) the length of its apothem?
    (b) its area?

13. Two ships, the Albacore and the Bonito, are 50 km apart. The Albacore sights a distress flare at S5° E. The Bonito sights the same flare at S13° W. The Albacore is N45° W of the Bonito. How far is each ship from the distress flare?

14. In a parallelogram, two adjacent sides measure 10 cm and 12 cm. The diagonal that joins these sides is 15 cm. Find, to the nearest degree, the size of all four angles of the parallelogram.

15. The building code for a roof says that the slope of the roof must not make an angle of more than 30° with the horizontal. Jeroen wants to build a house with a roof with an isosceles triangle profile. The house is going to be 9 m wide. What is the maximum length that the rafters can be?

16. **Application:** Part of the roof of a warehouse has a slope of $\frac{1}{3}$, and the other part of the roof has a slope of $\frac{1}{2}$.
    (a) Find the measure of the angle at the peak of the roof.
    (b) Find h.

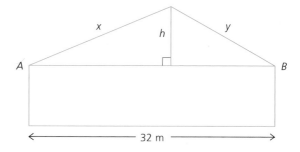

17. **Communication:** Which formula would you use to solve for the unknown side in each triangle? Explain your choice.

(a)

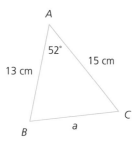

(b)

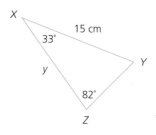

18. Frida and Agnetha are 626 m apart. Bjorn flies overhead in a plane between them. At the same time, they measure the angle of elevation of the plane. Frida measures the angle of elevation to be 63°. Agnetha measures it to be 36°. What is the altitude of the plane?

19. Check Your Understanding

(a) State the sine law and cosine law for $\triangle AEF$. Draw $\triangle AEF$ with three known measures and one specified unknown measure that would need the sine law to solve. Draw another $\triangle AEF$ for the cosine law.

(b) Create a table, flowchart, or decision tree to show how the type of information you have about a triangle determines the best method to use to solve it.

20. A window in a building is 18 m above the ground. From this window, the angle of elevation to the top of the building across the street is 40° and the angle of depression to the bottom of the building across the street is 42°. How tall is the building across the street?

21. From the top of a lighthouse, 30 m above the sea, the angle of depression of a tanker is 31° and the angle of depression of a sailboat is 20°. From the base of the lighthouse (sea level) the angle between the lines of sight to the tanker and sailboat is 54°. How far apart are the tanker and sailboat? 66.7 m

22. A 20 m wheelchair ramp forms an angle of 5° with the ground. To meet the province's new accessibility guidelines, the ramp must be changed to form an angle of 2.9° with the ground.

(a) How long will the new ramp be?

(b) How much farther along the ground will the new ramp extend?

(c) How could the ramp be designed so that it didn't appear to be so long?

Did You Know?

There are many whole number solutions to the equation $a^2 + b^2 = c^2$. For instance, $a = 3$, $b = 4$, and $c = 5$, is just one solution. Do you think that there are any whole number solutions to the equation $a^n + b^n = c^n$, for $n > 2$?

In about 1637, Pierre de Fermat said he could prove that there were no solutions to such an equation—but there wasn't enough room in the margin of his book to write out the proof. Thus was born perhaps the most famous problem in the entire history of mathematics, Fermat's Last Theorem.

For over 350 years, the greatest mathematicians tried to prove that Fermat was right, but all their efforts failed. Many thought that the problem would never be solved. But in 1995 Andrew Wiles did prove that Fermat was right. It was a stunning achievement. You might enjoy reading more about Fermat's Last Theorem and Andrew Wiles in the book *Fermat's Enigma* by Simon Singh.

Pierre de Fermat

Investigating Non-Right Triangles as Models for Problems
Check Your Understanding

1. How can you tell whether two triangles are similar?

2. List all of the things you know about similar triangles.

3. Express all forms of the sine law and cosine law for $\triangle CAT$.

4. What is meant by a *contained* angle?

5. Copy this table and fill it in to remind yourself when to use which law.

Number of Known Sides	Number of Known Angles	Method of Solution
1	2	
2	1 (uncontained)	
2	1 (contained)	
3	0	

6. In each case, would you first try the sine law or the cosine law to solve the triangle?
   (a) $\triangle ABC$, with $a = 5$ cm, $b = 6$ cm, and $\angle C = 80°$
   (b) $\triangle DEF$, with $d = 5$ m, $e = 6$ m, $f = 7$ m
   (c) $\triangle NET$, with $n = 6$ cm, $e = 10$ cm, and $\angle N = 30°$
   (d) $\triangle MAC$, with $\angle A = 88°$, $m = 5$ m, and $c = 6$ m
   (e) $\triangle XYZ$, with $\angle X = 24°$, $\angle Y = 62°$, and $x = 10$ cm

7. If you know the measures of all three sides of a triangle, how would you find the measures of the angles?

6.1–6.2 Similar-Triangle Models

- In $\triangle ABC$, the side opposite vertex A is commonly referred to as a, the side opposite vertex B is b, and the side opposite vertex C is c.

- When you label and refer to similar triangles, be sure to state corresponding vertices in the same order.

- In any triangle, the largest side is opposite the largest angle, and the smallest side is opposite the smallest angle. For example, in this diagram

  - ♦ $\angle C$ is the smallest angle and
    c is the smallest side

  - ♦ $\angle A$ is the largest angle and
    a is the largest side

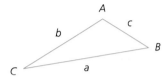

- To solve for an unknown side in a pair of similar triangles, set up a proportion statement that includes the known sides of the triangles and the unknown side. Then solve for the unknown.

Example

A convoy is delivering food and medical supplies to earthquake survivors. An emergency bridge needs to be built over a river. To calculate the distance across the river, these measurements were taken.

How wide is the river to the nearest metre?

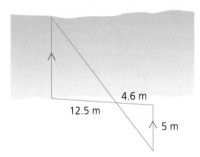

Solution

First, label the diagram.

The problem is to calculate the length of AB.

The corresponding angles are equal, so $\triangle ABC \sim \triangle EDC$. So,

$$\frac{AB}{ED} = \frac{BC}{DC}$$ Substitute known measures.

$$\frac{AB}{5} = \frac{12.5}{4.6}$$ Solve for AB.

$$AB = \frac{12.5 \times 5}{4.6}$$

$$AB \doteq 13.6$$

The river is 13.6 m wide.

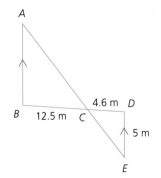

Extra Practice

1. An artisan is designing a vase as shown. The radius of the base of the vase is 4 cm, the slant height of the bottom cone is 6 cm, and the slant height of the upper cone is 12 cm. What is the radius of the top of the vase?

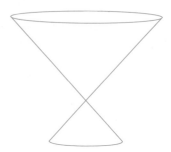

2. Calculate the unknown measures, given $AB = 12$ cm, $DE = 15$ cm, $BC = 8$ cm, and $CD = 10$ cm.

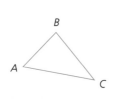

3. $\triangle ABC \sim \triangle DEF$. Also, $AB = 5$ cm, $AC = 8$ cm, $DF = 12$ cm, and $EF = 10.5$ cm.
   (a) How long is DE?
   (b) How long is BC?
   (c) What is the ratio of the perimeters of $\triangle ABC$ and $\triangle DEF$?
   (d) What is the ratio of the areas of $\triangle ABC$ and $\triangle DEF$?

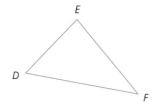

6.3 Investigating the Sine Law ———————

- For a triangle labelled as shown, the **sine law** can be written as $\dfrac{a}{\sin A} = \dfrac{b}{\sin B} = \dfrac{c}{\sin C}$.

- To solve a problem using the sine law, start by finding the ratio of the sine of a known angle to the known length of the opposite side. Then set up an equation that equates this ratio to the ratio for another angle and side, where either the angle or the side is unknown. From the equation, you can determine the value of the unknown quantity.

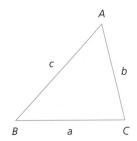

Example

Two points A and B are on either side of a small lake. To find how far apart they are, Alex walks 500 m from point A to another point C. He measures that $\angle A = 52°$ and $\angle C = 72°$. To the nearest metre, how far apart are A and B?

Solution

First, draw a diagram.

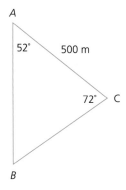

The only side that is given is side b. First, find the measure of $\angle B$. Use the fact that the sum of the angles in a triangle is 180°.

$$\angle A + \angle B + \angle C = 180°$$
$$\angle B = 180° - \angle A - \angle C$$
$$\angle B = 180° - 52° - 72°$$
$$\angle B = 56°$$

To find the distance from A to B (side c), set up this proportion.

$$\frac{c}{\sin C} = \frac{b}{\sin B}$$
$$\frac{c}{\sin 72°} = \frac{500}{\sin 56°} \qquad \text{Substitute.}$$
$$c = \frac{500 \sin 72°}{\sin 56°} \qquad \text{Solve for } c.$$
$$c \doteq 574$$

It is 574 m from A to B.

4. In $\triangle ABC$, $a = 4$ cm, $\angle A = 49°$, and $\angle B = 73°$. How long is b?

5. In $\triangle PWR$, $w = 5.4$ cm, $r = 6.2$ cm, and $\angle W = 56°$. Find the measure of $\angle R$.

6.4 Proving and Using the Sine Law

- To use the sine law, you must know either

  ♦ two sides and one angle *across from a known side,* or

  ♦ two angles and any side

- The sine law can be written in several ways, including

  ♦ $\dfrac{\sin A}{a} = \dfrac{\sin B}{b} = \dfrac{\sin C}{c}$, and

  ♦ $\dfrac{a}{\sin A} = \dfrac{b}{\sin B} = \dfrac{c}{\sin C}$

Extra Practice

6. Allison is flying a kite and has let out the entire 150 m ball of kite string. She notices that the string forms a 70° angle with the ground. Marc is on the other side of the kite and sights the kite at an angle of elevation of 30°. How far is Marc from Allison?

6.5–6.6 Adjusting the Pythagorean Theorem: The Cosine Law

- The **cosine law** says that for any $\triangle ABC$,

  $$c^2 = a^2 + b^2 - 2ab \cos C$$

  $$a^2 = b^2 + c^2 - 2bc \cos A$$

  $$b^2 = a^2 + c^2 - 2ac \cos B$$

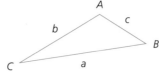

- The cosine law is used to find the third side of a triangle when two sides and a contained angle are known or to find an angle measure when the length of three sides are known.

- The contained angle in a triangle is the angle between the two given sides of the triangle. For example, in $\triangle ABC$, B is the contained angle between AB and BC.

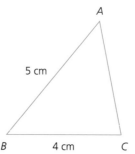

Example

In $\triangle PQR$, how long is side p to one decimal place?

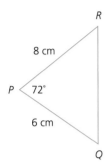

R

8 cm

P 72°

6 cm

Q

Solution

Use the cosine law.

$$p^2 = q^2 + r^2 - 2qr \cos P \qquad \text{Substitute known measures.}$$
$$p^2 = 8^2 + 6^2 - 2(8)(6) \cos 72° \qquad \text{Solve for } p.$$
$$p^2 = 64 + 36 - 96 \cos 72°$$
$$p^2 = 100 - (96)(0.3090...)$$
$$p^2 = 100 - 29.6656...$$
$$p^2 = 70.3343...$$
$$p = \sqrt{70.3343...}$$
$$p \doteq 8.4$$

Side p is 8.4 cm long.

Extra Practice

7. In $\triangle CAT$, $c = 6.4$ m, $a = 4.0$ m, and $\angle T = 65°$. How long is side t?

8. An isosceles triangle has sides of 8 cm, 12 cm, and 12 cm. Find the measures of the base angles.

9. Two airplanes leave an airport at the same time. One travels at 355 km/h and the other at 450 km/h. Two hours later they are 800 km apart. Find the angle between their courses.

6.7 Solving Measurement Problems Modelled by Triangles

- **Solving a triangle** means to find the lengths of all three sides and the measures of all three angles of the triangle.

- Draw a clearly labelled diagram to help you solve problems.

- Right triangles can be solved with the primary trigonometric ratios.

- Use the sine law to solve a triangle when two sides and one opposite angle are known, or when two angles and one opposite side are known.

- Use the cosine law to solve a triangle if all three sides are known, or two sides and the angle between them are known.

- If both the cosine law and the sine law can be used to solve a triangle, use the sine law, since it is the easier method.

Example

Solve $\triangle ABC$, given $\angle A = 48°$, $c = 15$ m, and $b = 12$ m.

Solution

To solve a triangle means to find all of its unknown measures. First draw the triangle.

The three measures that need to be found are
(a) the length of side a, **(b)** $\angle B$, and **(c)** $\angle C$.

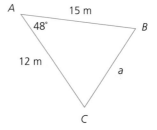

(a) To find a, use the cosine law, since two sides and the contained angle are known.

$a^2 = b^2 + c^2 - 2bc \cos A$ Substitute known measures.

$a^2 = (12)^2 + (15)^2 - 2(12)(15)\cos 48°$ Solve for a.

$a^2 = 144 + 225 - 360 \cos 48°$

$a^2 = 369 - (360)(0.6691...)$

$a^2 = 369 - 240.8870...$

$a^2 = 128.1129...$

$a = \sqrt{128.1129...}$

$a \doteq 11.3$

Side a is 11.3 m long.

(b) To find $\angle B$, use the sine law.

$$\frac{a}{\sin A} = \frac{b}{\sin B}$$

$$\frac{11.3}{\sin 48°} = \frac{12}{\sin B} \qquad \text{Substitute.}$$

$$\sin B = \frac{12 \sin 48°}{11.3} \qquad \text{Solve for } \angle B.$$

$$\angle B = \sin^{-1}\left(\frac{12 \sin 48°}{11.3}\right)$$

$$\angle B = 52.1089...°$$

$$\angle B \doteq 52°$$

The measure of $\angle B$ is 52°.

(c) To find $\angle C$, use the fact that the sum of the angles in a triangle is 180°.

$$\angle C = 180° - \angle A - \angle B$$

$$\angle C = 180° - 48° - 52°$$

$$\angle C = 80°$$

The measure of $\angle C$ is 80°.

Extra Practice

10. Solve $\triangle MAT$, given that $m = 6.8$ cm, $t = 4.2$ cm, and $\angle A = 68°$.

11. From the top of an 8 m house, the angle of elevation to the top of the school's flagpole across the street is 9°. The angle of depression is 42° to the bottom of the pole. How tall is the flagpole?

12. A baseball diamond is a square that is about 30 m on a side. The pitcher's mound is about 20 m from home plate on the diagonal from home to second base. How far does the pitcher have to throw the ball to first base?

Chapter 6 Summary ——————————————

In this chapter, you saw that similar acute triangles have the same properties as the similar right triangles you explored in chapter 5. You also used similar triangles to solve a wide variety of problems.

As well, you used two trigonometric relationships that help you to solve problems with non-right triangles.

The **sine law** says that for any $\triangle ABC$,

$$\frac{a}{\sin A} = \frac{b}{\sin B} = \frac{c}{\sin C}$$

The **cosine law** says that for any $\triangle ABC$,

$$c^2 = a^2 + b^2 - 2ab \cos C$$
$$a^2 = b^2 + c^2 - 2bc \cos A$$
$$b^2 = a^2 + c^2 - 2ac \cos B$$

One of these laws can be used to solve any triangle, as long as three measures of the triangle are known. Many problems can be modelled using triangles and solved with these trigonometric relationships.

Investigating Non-Right Triangles as Models for Problems

1. Find the lengths, to the nearest tenth, for CE and BC, given that $DE = 18$ m, $AB = 14$ m, $BD = 1$, and $AC = 12$ m. Also, $BC \parallel DE$.

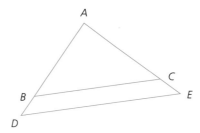

2. Nilani and Sonia are using an overhead projector to enlarge a design that they are tracing on a wall to draw a mural. When they place the projector 2 m from the wall, the image is 0.75 m high. They want the image to be 2 m high. Where should they place the projector?

3. Find $\angle C$ in $\triangle ABC$, if $\angle B = 27°$, $b = 15$ cm, and $c = 8$ cm.

4. In $\triangle MNP$, $\angle M = 67°$, $\angle N = 32°$, and $n = 15$ cm. Find m.

5. In $\triangle DEF$, $\angle D = 68°$, $e = 6.2$ cm, and $f = 3.2$ cm. Solve $\triangle DEF$.

6. In $\triangle PQR$, $\angle P = 83°$, $\angle Q = 45°$, and $r = 18$ cm. Solve $\triangle PQR$.

7. Which of these does not state the cosine law for $\triangle ABC$?
   (a) $a^2 = b^2 + c^2 - 2bc \cos B$
   (b) $c^2 = a^2 + b^2 - 2ab \cos C$
   (c) $b^2 = a^2 + c^2 - 2ac \cos B$

8. A sail is in the shape of a triangle with sides of 10 m, 7 m, and 13 m. Find the largest angle of the sail.

9. Myrna and Ravinder went out in two separate boats to place markers for a boat race. Their paths formed an angle of 85°. Myrna rowed 85 m and Ravinder rowed 102 m to place their markers. How far apart are the markers?

10. Two support wires are fastened to the top of a TV satellite dish tower from two points on the ground, A and B on either side of the tower. One wire is 18 m long and the other is 12 m long. The angle of elevation of the longer wire is 28°.
    (a) How far apart are A and B?
    (b) How tall is the satellite dish tower?

Trigonometry

1. i. State, with an explanation, whether the indicated pairs of triangles are congruent, similar but not congruent, or neither similar nor congruent.

   ii. Find the indicated measures in each case if possible.

   (a) Given Information:
   $AB \parallel DE$, $AC = CE$, $\angle CBF = 110°$
   Triangle Pair to Consider: $\triangle ABC$ and $\triangle CDE$
   Measure(s) to Determine: $\angle CDE$

   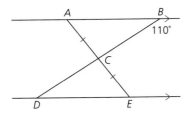

   (b) Given Information:
   $AB \parallel DE$, $AC = 3$ cm, $BC = 2$ cm, $CE = 6$ cm
   Triangle Pair to Consider: $\triangle ABC$ and $\triangle CDE$
   Measure(s) to Determine: DC

   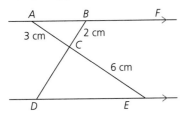

   (c) Given Information:
   $\angle ABC = 90°$, $\angle ADB = 90°$, $AB = 8$ cm, $BC = 6$ cm
   Triangle Pairs to Consider:
   $\triangle ABC$ and $\triangle ABD$, $\triangle ABC$ and $\triangle BDC$
   Measure(s) to Determine: BD, AD, and DC

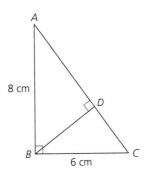

2. A triangle is formed by the x-axis, the graph of $y = 3x$, and the graph of $y = -2x + 4$. Determine the measures of the three vertex angles in the triangle.

3. i. State the values of the three primary trigonometric ratios for $\angle X$.

   ii. Determine the measure of $\angle X$ to the nearest degree.

   (a)

   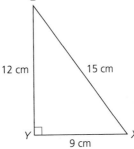

   (b)

   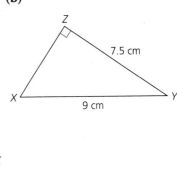

4. Determine the measures of all unknown sides to one decimal place and of all unknown angles to the nearest degree.

   (a)

   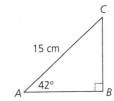

(b)

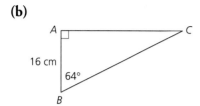

(c)

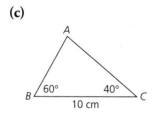

(d)

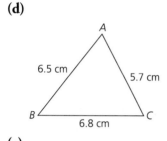

(e)

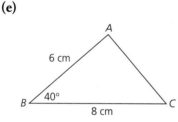

5. Fiona is repairing the wiring on a radio broadcast tower. She is in the basket of the repair truck 40 m from the tower. If she looks up at an angle of 42° she can see the top of the tower. She can see the base of the tower if she looks down at an angle of 32°. How high is the tower to the nearest tenth of a metre?

6. On a sunny day, a tower casts a shadow 35.2 m long. At the same time, a 1.3 m parking meter casts a shadow 4.8 m long. How high is the tower to the nearest tenth of a metre?

7. The police are trying to catch the operator of a pirate radio station. They park two vehicles with directional antennas on the side of a straight section of road 2000 m apart. They then aim the antennas to find the pirate station's signal, which is coming from a location somewhere between them. From Constable Abel's vehicle, the angle is 70° and from Constable Baker's vehicle it is 30°. Which police officer is closer to the pirate radio station and how far away, to the nearest metre, is it from that officer?

8. Two helicopters flying at an altitude of 250 m are 2000 m apart when they spot a life raft below. The raft is directly between the two helicopters. The angle of depression from one helicopter to the raft is 37°. The angle of depression from the other helicopter is 49°. Both helicopters are flying at 170 km/h. How long, to the nearest second, will it take the closer aircraft to reach the raft?

9. A concrete border is to be built around a triangular flower garden that has sides of 10 m, 7 m, and 8 m. The border is to be a straight walking path 1 m wide on all sides of the garden. Before the concrete can be poured, wooden forms need to be placed on the inside perimeter and on the outside perimeter of the border. Determine the total length of wood needed to build the forms.

Performance Tasks for Chapters 5 and 6

Trigonometry

THE FOLLOWING ACTIVITIES SHOULD EACH TAKE LESS THAN A PERIOD TO COMPLETE

1. Octagonal Artwork

A glass crystal sculpture is made in the shape of a regular octagonal prism with 10 cm sides. Each of the lateral faces is a square.

To avoid breakage in shipment, the piece is padded with plastic foam beads when it is packed in its square-based rectangular box. The layer of beads must be at least 1 cm thick on all sides of the glass, including the top and bottom.

(a) What is the minimum volume of beads required to protect the piece?

(b) If the object was packed in a cylindrical container instead of a rectangular box, how would the minimum volume of beads change?

2. Cloud Ceiling

For safety when taking off and landing, airplane pilots need to know the height of the base of the clouds above an airport. One way to determine the *ceiling*, or cloud height, involves shining a searchlight beam at a known angle onto the clouds. An observer a known distance from the searchlight measures the angle of elevation to the reflected light.

Compute the ceiling represented in this diagram.

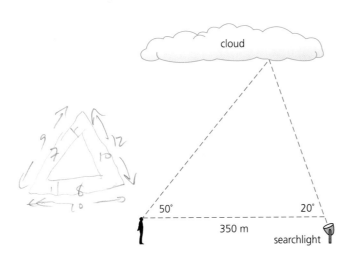

3. Where Is the Fire?

Forest rangers watch for fires from tall observation towers. The towers are located throughout a forested region and are tall enough to provide a view over the treetops. Suppose that smoke is spotted at a compass bearing of N14°E from tower *A* and at a bearing of N34°W from tower *B*. Tower *A* is 20 km west of tower *B*. How far is the fire from the closest tower?

Note: N14°E is standard surveyor's notation for a bearing or direction that is 14° east of north. That is, start facing north, then turn 14° toward east. In this notation, the first letter is always N or S (north or south), the angle is always between 0° and 90°, and the last letter is always E or W (east or west).

4. Another Coordinate System

Radar systems report the position of an object in terms of the compass bearing and distance of the object from the radar antenna. Most maps, on the other hand, report position in terms of a Cartesian *x-y* coordinate system.

Suppose that a radar antenna is positioned at (0, 0) on a Cartesian coordinate grid. A ship is located at (−8, 10) on the grid.

(a) What is the bearing of the ship from the radar antenna?

(b) What is the distance to the ship from the radar antenna?

Research Extension (Extra Time)

(c) The system of angle and distance coordinates described in this activity is called a *polar coordinate* system. The position of an object in polar coordinates is expressed as a distance-angle ordered pair (r, θ), where *r* is the distance from the origin and θ is the angle measured counter-clockwise from due east. Find the formulas that relate the polar coordinates of a point to the *x-y* Cartesian coordinates of the same point, assuming that the origin is the same for both systems.

5. Tower on a Hill

An electrical transmission tower has been built on the side of a hill that rises steadily at an angle of 8° to the horizontal. The vertical tower is 50 m tall and is supported by two guy wires attached to the top of the tower. One of the guy wires is anchored 50 m downhill from the centre of the base of the tower. The other guy wire is anchored 50 m uphill.

(a) What is the length of each guy wire?

(b) What angle does each guy wire make with the surface of the hill?

6. A Shorter Route?

During a portage, the leader of a scout troop decided to save time by hiking around a wooded area between the base camp and a lake. The troop reached the lake by walking for 30 minutes on a bearing of N60°E, then for 45 minutes on a bearing of N80°W. The leader figured that they walked at an average speed of 3 km/h.

If they could have walked straight through the forested area at 1 km/h, did the troop save any time by going around? If so, how much?

THE FOLLOWING ACTIVITIES SHOULD EACH TAKE MORE THAN ONE PERIOD TO COMPLETE

7. Cloud Ceiling (Extension)

Small airports without specialized radar equipment can measure the cloud ceiling with a device called an *alidade*. The alidade is positioned a known distance from the searchlight. The observer sights the illuminated spot on the cloud base with a movable sighting bar. The scale on the alidade indicates the ceiling height directly.

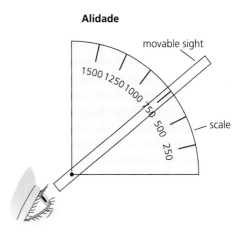

Alidade

You have been asked to construct an alidade that will be located 350 m from the searchlight. The searchlight is permanently aimed up at an angle of 70° to the horizontal, in the same plane as the sighting bar and scale.

(a) Find the angles needed to construct a scale for the alidade that shows the ceiling in increments of 250 m.

(b) Build the alidade and write a description of how it works.

8. Another Coordinate System (Extension)

Objects in 3-dimensional space can be located using an ordered triple (x, y, z) of Cartesian coordinates. The diagram at right shows how the point with coordinates (a, b, c) is located.

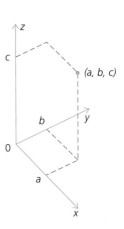

An alternative system called *spherical coordinates* can also be used to represent the position of an object in 3-dimensional space. The spherical coordinate system uses two angles and the distance from the origin to locate a point. An ordered triple (r, θ, ϕ) describes a point's position in space, as shown in the diagram at right.

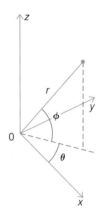

(a) Find the spherical coordinates of a point in space that has Cartesian coordinates (3, 4, 12).

(b) Find the formulas that relate a point's spherical coordinates to its Cartesian coordinates.

Research Extension (Extra Time)

(c) Research the use of longitude and latitude as coordinates for points on the surface of the earth. How do distances computed using a flat map—for example, a Mercator projection—get distorted by the curvature of the earth?

9. Mounting a Projector on the Ceiling

Ben has purchased a projection television for his home theatre system. He plans to mount the projector on the ceiling so that he can watch the screen from anywhere in the room. The unit comes with mounting brackets already installed for a ceiling installation.

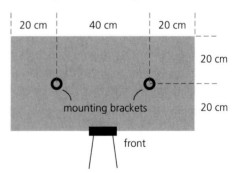

Top view of TV Projector

Unfortunately, the recreation room is not a rectangle and the corner where he wants to mount the unit has a 120° angle. Ben wants the projector to be as close to the corner as possible, with the beam from the projector bisecting the corner angle. Fire regulations require that no part of the projector can be closer than 30 cm to any wall.

Where should the drill holes for the mounting brackets be located with respect to the corner of the room and the nearest wall?

Answers

Glossary

Index

Technology Index

Photo Credits

Answers

Review of Essential Skills—Part I

Operations with Integers, page 16

1. (a) 3   (b) -23 (c) -3
   (d) 25   (e) -24 (f) -10
   (g) -29 (h) -6 (i) 6
2. (a) <   (b) >   (c) >
   (d) =   (e) >
3. (a) second, first   (b) first and second, third
   (c) first, third   (d) all equal
   (e) first and third, second
4. (a) 55   (b) -42 (c) 60
   (d) 672   (e) -7 (f) 8
   (g) 11   (h) 16   (i) $\frac{45}{21}$
   (j) $\frac{1}{49}$
5. (a) 1   (b) 5   (c) 20
   (d) -9 (e) 76   (f) -12
   (g) -1 (h) 6
6. (a) 3   (b) -1 (c) -2
   (d) 1   (e) -3 (f) -40
   (g) -16 (h) 8
7. (a) -18 (b) 59   (c) -23

Operations With Rational Numbers, page 18

1. (a) $\frac{-1}{2}$ (b) $\frac{7}{6}$ (c) $\frac{-1}{2}$
   (d) $\frac{-27}{20}$ (e) $\frac{-19}{12}$ (f) $\frac{-103}{12}$
   (g) $\frac{-5}{2}$ (h) $\frac{-19}{6}$ (i) $\frac{-41}{20}$
   (j) $\frac{4}{3}$
2. (a) $\frac{-16}{25}$ (b) $\frac{-9}{5}$ (c) $\frac{2}{15}$
   (d) $\frac{3}{2}$ (e) $\frac{1}{5}$ (f) 2
   (g) 10   (h) $\frac{1}{2}$ (i) $\frac{-17}{5}$
   (j) $\frac{775}{24}$
3. (a) 2   (b) $\frac{-19}{4}$ (c) $\frac{16}{9}$
   (d) $\frac{-9}{2}$ (e) $\frac{15}{2}$ (f) $\frac{2}{3}$
   (g) 5   (h) $\frac{-5}{9}$ (i) $\frac{13}{11}$
   (j) $\frac{-1}{8}$
4. (a) $\frac{1}{5}$ (b) $\frac{-9}{5}$ (c) $\frac{3}{10}$
   (d) $\frac{1}{15}$ (e) $\frac{165}{128}$ (f) 3
   (g) $\frac{-1}{18}$ (h) $\frac{1}{4}$
5. (a) $\frac{-9}{4}$ (b) $\frac{36}{5}$ (c) -12
   (d) $\frac{-1}{8}$ (e) $\frac{1}{18}$ (f) $\frac{-217}{240}$

6. (a) $-\frac{3}{8}$ (b) $\frac{-42}{115}$ (c) $-\frac{1}{26}$
7. (a) $-2\frac{1}{12}$ (b) $\frac{9}{25}$ (c) $\frac{159}{56}$ (d) $-2\frac{1}{20}$

Evaluating Algebraic Expressions and Formulas, page 19

1. (a) -3 (b) 28   (c) 95
   (d) -17 (e) -59 (f) 104
   (g) 99   (h) 1   (i) -3311
   (j) $\frac{9}{20}$
2. (a) $\frac{1}{6}$ (b) $\frac{-7}{6}$ (c) $\frac{5}{6}$
   (d) $\frac{-17}{6}$ (e) $\frac{-7}{12}$
3. (a) $\frac{1}{24}$ (b) $\frac{-35}{24}$
   (c) $\frac{-5}{48}$ (d) $\frac{8}{9}$
4. (a) 52   (b) $\frac{1}{12}$
   (c) $\frac{1}{12}$ (d) $\frac{-22}{9}$
5. (a) 14.7   (b) 36.6   (c) 12.96
   (d) -1.5625 (e) -105.516
6. (a) 82.35 cm^2 (b) 58.1 m^2
   (c) $V = 23\ 520$ mm^3 (d) $c = 10$ m
   (e) $V = 4849.0$ cm^3 (f) $h = 4.8$ m
   (g) $S = 12\ 686.1$ km/h

Simplifying Algebraic Expressions, page 21

1. (a) $v = x, c = 5$ (b) $v = a, c = -13$
   (c) $v = c, c = 7$ (d) $v = m, c = -1.35$
   (e) $v = y, c = \frac{4}{7}$ (f) $v = x, c = \frac{5}{8}$
2. (a) $a, -3a, 12a;\ 5x, -9x$
   (b) $c^2, 13c^2;\ 6c, -c, 1.25c$
   (c) $5x^2y, 9x^2y, 12x^2y;\ 3xy, -3xy$
   (d) $x^2, -x^2;\ y^2, -y^2;\ 2xy, -4xy$
3. (a) binomial   (b) monomial   (c) trinomial
   (d) monomial   (e) binomial   (f) trinomial
4. (a) $3x$ (b) $8a$ (c) $-4c$
   (d) x^2 (e) $21xy$ (f) $-3a + 3b$
   (g) $8c - 2m$ (h) $-2x^2 - x$ (i) $11x^2 - 5x^3$
   (j) $13x - 4$ (k) $-15x - 2y + 7$ (l) xy
   (m) $5x^3 - 3x^2 + 4x$ (n) $-5x^2y^2 + 11x^2y - 8xy^2$
   (o) $13x - 21y - 6z + 7$ (p) $3x^3 - 3x^2 + 7x^{-2}$
5. (a) $6x - 10y + 4$ (b) $6x^2 - 12x - 15$
   (c) $24a - 40c + 48b$ (d) $12g - 8h + 28$
   (e) $10r^2 + 20t - 5v$ (f) $5x + 5y - 5z$
   (g) $-7x^3 - 7x^2 + 14y^2$ (h) $36a + 24b - 72c + 24$
6. (a) $3x - 3y + 3$ (b) $x + 21y$
   (c) $-9a - 7ab - b$ (d) $-2x^2 - 3x - 7y$
   (e) $7x^2 + 2x - 21y$

7. **(a)** $10x + 8$ **(b)** $-2x + 15y$

(c) $12a - 16ab + 3b$ **(d)** $-23x - 28$

(e) $-40x + 18y$ **(f)** $-26x + 44xy + 38y$

(g) $-13x^2 + 18x + 4y$ **(h)** $-5d^3 - 11d^2 + 30$

(i) $2a - 34ab - 54b$ **(j)** $-17x^2 - 37x - 108y$

(k) $27d^3 + 70d^2 - 56$ **(l)** $-4x - 12xy - 44y$

Solving Equations, page 23

1. **(a)** $y = 2$ **(b)** $x = -2$ **(c)** $c = 5$

(d) $x = -9$ **(e)** $p = 2$ **(f)** $m = 5.2$

(g) $a = 2.4$ **(h)** $m = 2$ **(i)** $y = 2.1$

(j) $m = 4.2$

2. **(a)** $n = 6$ **(b)** $x = 4$ **(c)** $x = \frac{5}{2}$

(d) $c = 11$ **(e)** $m = 6$ **(f)** $r = \frac{1}{2}$

(g) $m = 2$ **(h)** $x = 14$ **(i)** $x = 3$

3. **(a)** $x = 8$ **(b)** $x = -15$ **(c)** $m = 24$

(d) $x = -21$ **(e)** $x = 4$ **(f)** $x = 28$

(g) $x = 10$ **(h)** $x = 9$ **(i)** $y = 6$

(j) $b = 12$ **(k)** $x = 10$ **(l)** $x = -8$

4. **(a)** $y = \frac{1}{12}$ **(b)** $x = 2$ **(c)** $n = 20$

(d) $m = -12$ **(e)** $y = 15$ **(f)** $x = -75$

(g) $x = \frac{59}{5}$ **(h)** $x = 12$ **(i)** $x = 8$

5. **(a)** $x = 2$ **(b)** $y = 3$ **(c)** $x = 10$

(d) $y = -6$ **(e)** $x = -5$ **(f)** $x = 3$

(g) $x = \frac{-17}{2}$ **(h)** $y = 22$ **(i)** $y = 5$

6. **(a)** 116   **(b)** 24   **(c)** 16

(d) 32   **(e)** 25   **(f)** 64

7. 147 student tickets, 62 adult tickets

8. $l = 15$ cm, $w = 12$ cm

Graphing Linear Relationships, page 26

1. **(a)** $y = 2x + 3$ **(b)** $y = \frac{1}{2}x - 2$

(c) $y = \frac{-1}{2}x + 2$ **(d)** $y = 5x + 9$

(e) $y = \frac{2}{5}x - 4$ **(f)** $y = 4x - 6$

(g) $y = -x + 1$ **(h)** $\frac{-5}{3}x + \frac{10}{3}$

2. **(a)**

x	y
−2	−7
−1	−4
0	−1
1	2
2	5

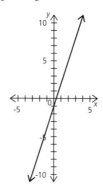

(b)

x	y
−2	−8
−1	−3
0	2
1	7
2	12

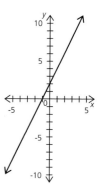

(c)

x	y
−2	3
−1	3.5
0	4
1	4.5
2	5

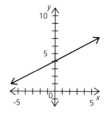

(d)

x	y
−2	0
−1	1
0	2
1	3
2	4

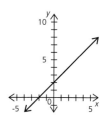

(e)

x	y
−2	0
−1	2
0	4
1	6
2	8

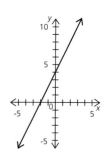

(f)

x	y
−2	$\frac{10}{3}$
−1	$\frac{8}{3}$
0	2
1	$\frac{4}{3}$
2	$\frac{2}{3}$

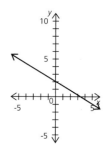

(g)

x	y
−2	4
−1	4
0	4
1	4
2	4

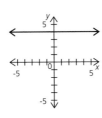

(h)

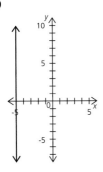

x is always −5, no matter what y is.

3. (a) (10, 0), (0, 10) **(b)** (8, 0), (0, 4)
(c) (7, 0), (0, −5) **(d)** (6, 0), (0, 9)
(e) (−9, 0), (0, 4) **(f)** (5, 0), (0, 50)
(g) (2, 0), (0, 4) **(h)** (10, 0), (0, −20)
4. (a) (4, 0), (0, 4)

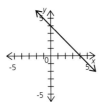

(b) (3, 0), (0, −3)

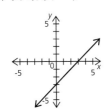

(c) (3, 0), (0, 6)

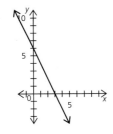

(d) (−8, 0), (0, 2)

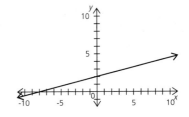

(e) (5, 0), (0, 2)

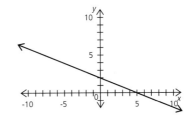

(f) (4, 0), (0, −3)

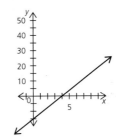

(g) (−4, 0), (0, 2)

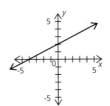

(h) (−3, 0), (0, −7)

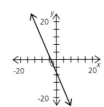

5. (a) m = 2, (0, 3)

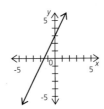

(b) $m = -1$, $(0, -5)$

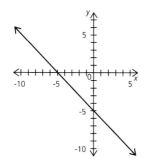

(c) $m = \frac{2}{3}$, $(0, 1)$

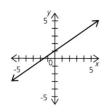

(d) $m = \frac{-3}{4}$, $(0, -2)$

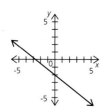

(e) $m = \frac{1}{2}$, $(0, 3)$

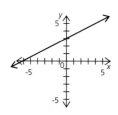

(f) $m = \frac{-2}{3}$, $(0, -2)$

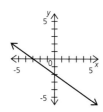

(g) $m = \frac{-1}{4}$, $(0, 2)$

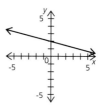

(h) $m = -1$, $(0, -1)$

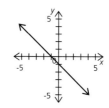

6. (a)   **(b)**

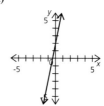 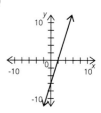

(c)   **(d)**

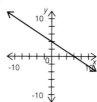 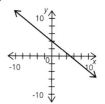

Slope and the Equation of the Tangent Line, page 28

1. (a) -1 (b) -1
   (c) 2 (d) $\frac{3}{4}$

2. (a) $y = 2x + 8$ (b) $y = \frac{3}{4}x - 6$
   (c) $y = 6x - 1$ (d) $y = \frac{5}{6}x + 13$

3. (a) $3x + y - 10 = 0$ (b) $x + y + 4 = 0$
   (c) $2x + y - 4 = 0$ (d) $2x - 3y = 0$
   (e) $30x - 9y \ 4 = 0$

4. (a) i. $(0, 7)$

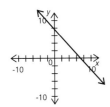

ii. $y = -x + 7$
iii. $x + y - 7 = 0$
(b) i. $(0, -7)$

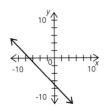

ii. $y = -x - 7$
iii. $x + y + 7 = 0$
(c) i. $(0, 1)$

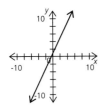

ii. $y = 2x + 1$
iii. $2x - y + 1 = 0$
(d) i. $(0, 3)$

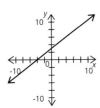

ii. $y = \frac{3}{4}x + 3$
iii. $3x - 4y + 12 = 0$

5. (a) neither   **(b)** perpendicular
  (c) parallel   **(d)** neither
  (e) perpendicular

6. (a) $x = -4$ **(b)** $y = 5$
  (c) $y = -3$ **(d)** $x = 1$
  (e) $y = -2x - 3$ **(f)** $y = \frac{-2}{3}x - 2$
  (g) $y = \frac{-1}{3}x - 6$

Creating Scatter Plots and The Line of Best Fit, page 30

1) a)

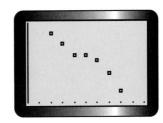

negative

b)

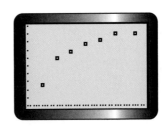

positive

c)

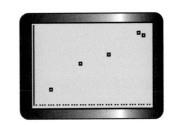

positive

d)

negative

The Pythagorean Theorem, page 31

1. (a) $6^2 + 8^2 = x^2$ **(b)** $13^2 + 6^2 = c^2$
  (c) $5^2 + y^2 = 9^2$ **(d)** $3.2^2 + a^2 = 8.5^2$
2. (a) $x = 10$ **(b)** $c = 14.3$
  (c) $y = 7.5$ **(d)** $a = 7.9$
3. (a) $a = \pm 13$ **(b)** $f = \pm 17.5$
  (c) $m = \pm 6$ **(d)** $b = \pm 23.07$
  (e) $c = \pm 5.23$ **(f)** $d = \pm 1.88$

4. (a) 11.2   **(b)** 6.7
    (c) 7.4   **(d)** 4.9
5. 10.6 cm
6. 69.4 m
7. 631.5 m

Properties of Triangles, page 34

1. (a) $x = 120°$ **(b)** $x = 82.5°$
   (c) $x = 75°$ **(d)** $x = 31°$
   (e) $x = 40°$ **(f)** $x = 42.5°$
   (g) $x = 12°$ **(h)** $x = 20°$
   (i) $x = 62.5°$
2. (a) i.   **(b)** ii.
   (c) iii.   **(d)** iv.
3. (a) 4.2 cm   **(b)** 7.2 cm
   (c) 35°   **(d)** 60°
4. $BE = 8$ cm, $DE = 4$ cm
5. (e) D, I, and C are collinear.
6. (e) These points are in the same location.
7. (e) no
8. (e) The orthocentre and circumcentre are outside the triangle.

Properties of Quadrilaterals, page 37

1. (a) ii.   **(b)** i.
   (c) iii.   **(d)** v.
   (e) iv.
3. (a) F   **(b)** T
   (c) T   **(d)** F
   (e) F
4. (a) $x = 25°$, $y = 25°$, $z = 65°$
   (b) $x = 60°$, $y = 60°$, $z = 30°$
   (c) $x = 90°$, $y = 35°$, $z = 55°$
   (d) $x = 90°$, $y = 40°$, $z = 65°$
5. (a) square, rectangle, parallelogram, rhombus
   (b) square, rhombus, kite
   (c) square, rectangle
   (d) square, rhombus
6. parallelogram
7. (a) $x = 81.25$ **(b)** $x = 30$
   (c) $x = 50$

Area and Perimeter, page 39

1. (a) 13 cm²   **(b)** 36 cm²
   (c) 6.25 m²   **(d)** 105.7 mm²
   (e) 8.64 cm²   **(f)** 1072 mm²
   (g) 7543.0 cm²   **(h)** 23.1 cm²
2. (a) 104 cm   **(b)** 9.8 m
   (c) 34 cm   **(d)** 13 cm
3. (a) 30.16 mm   **(b)** 94.25 m
   (c) 25.71 cm   **(d)** 14.28 m
4. (a) $P = 32$ cm, $A = 70.4$ cm²
   (b) $P = 32.5$ m, $A = 81.25$ m²
   (c) $P = 66.4$ cm, $A = 332$ cm²
   (d) $P = 106.8$ m, $A = 822.36$ m²

(e) $P = 52.5$ mm, $A = 204.75$ mm²
(f) $P = 163.8$ cm, $A = 2047.5$ cm²
5. (a) 12 cm   **(b)** 6 m
   (c) 5.6 cm   **(d)** 5.6 m
   (e) 9.5 cm   **(f)** 56 mm
   (g) 7.2 m   **(h)** 12.4 cm
6. (a) $A = 224.4$ cm²   **(b)** $A = 63$ cm²
   (c) $A = 221.1$ m²   **(d)** $A = 660.1$ cm²
   (e) $A = 82.5$ m²   **(f)** $A = 88$ cm²
   (g) $A = 203$ cm²   **(h)** $A = 19.1$ cm²

Chapter 1

Getting Ready, page 44

1. (a) -15 **(b)** 4
   (c) 14   **(d)** -10.5
2. (a) $-\dfrac{1}{2}$ **(b)** $\dfrac{15}{32}$
   (c) $-\dfrac{9}{64}$ **(d)** $\dfrac{9}{256}$
3. (a) -24 **(b)** -4
   (c) -2 **(d)** $-\dfrac{20}{3}$
4. (a) 2   **(b)** -2
   (c) 4   **(d)** 7
   (e) $\dfrac{7}{5}$ **(f)** -3
   (g) 9   **(h)** 3
   (i) 20   **(j)** 10
   (k) -19 **(l)** $-\dfrac{1}{2}$
5. (a) $y = -6x + 12$ **(b)** $y = \dfrac{2}{3}x - 4$
   (c) $y = -\dfrac{7}{2}x + 7$ **(d)** $y = \dfrac{6}{5}x - \dfrac{11}{5}$
6. (a)

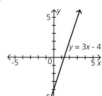

(b)

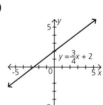

(c)

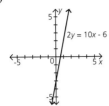

$2y = 10x - 6$

(d)

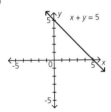

$2x - 3y = 6$

7. (a)

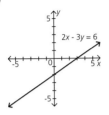

$x + y = 5$

(b)

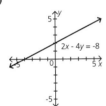

$2x - 4y = -8$

(c)

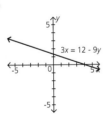

$3x = 12 - 9y$

(d)

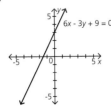

$6x - 3y + 9 = 0$

8. (a)

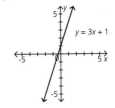

$y = 3x + 1$

(b)

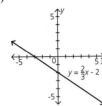

$y = \frac{2}{3}x - 2$

(c)

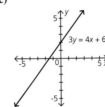

$3y = 4x + 6$

(d)

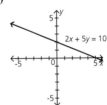

$2x + 5y = 10$

9. (a) $5x + y + 6$ **(b)** $-8x + 6y - 2$
   (c) $-2x + 4y - 1$ **(d)** $9x - 15y - 7$
10. (a) $5x + 8y$ **(b)** $4x - 5y$
   (c) $3x + 7y$ **(d)** $x + 2y$
11. (a) $x + y = 12$ **(b)** $y = 1.15x$
   (c) $25x + 0.15y = 135$ **(d)** $x + y = 1254$
   (e) $0.08x + 0.1y = 235$
   (f) $12.35x + 12.65y = 12\ 500$
   (g) $0.1x + 0.25y = 5.75$

12. (a)

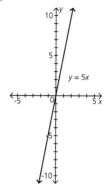

$y = 5x$

(b)

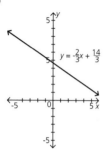

$y = -\frac{2}{3}x + \frac{14}{3}$

(c)

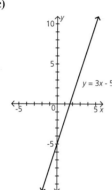

$y = 3x - 5$

(d)

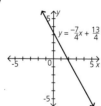

$y = -\frac{7}{4}x + \frac{13}{4}$

13. (a) $\frac{4}{3}$ **(b)** 1   **(c)** 3   **(d)** $\frac{58}{57}$

14. (a)

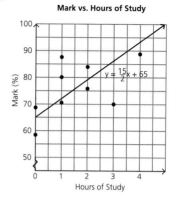

ii. $y = 4x + 65$

iii. weak positive correlation

(b)

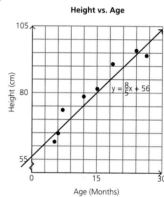

ii. $y = \frac{8}{5}x + 56$

iii. strong positive correlation

(c)

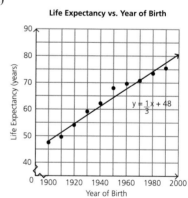

ii. $y = \frac{1}{3}x + 48$

iii. strong positive correlation

(d)

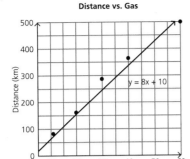

Distance vs. Gas

ii. $y = 8.5x + 1$

iii. strong positive correlation

15. (a) no   **(b)** yes   **(c)** yes   **(d)** no

16. (a)

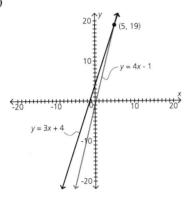

(b)

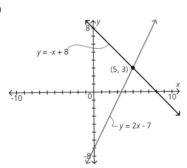

(c)

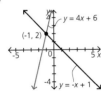

(d)

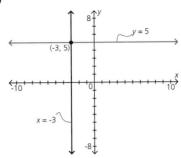

Practise, Apply, Solve 1.1, page 50

1. (a) $(1, 9), (20, -10), (5\frac{1}{4}, 4\frac{3}{4})$

 (b) $(4, 4), (-2, -8), (12, 20)$

 (c) $(12, 0), (18, 1), (0, -2)$

 (d) $(3, 1), (12, 10), (1, -1)$

2. (a) $(6, 2)$ **(b)** $(3, 2)$

 (c) $(-2, -6)$ **(d)** $(0, 0)$

3. (a) $(10, 2)$ **(b)** $(5, 3)$

 (c) $(1, 2)$ **(d)** $(7, 3)$

4. (a) $x + y = 12$

 (b) $x + y = 36$

 (c) $0.05x + 0.1y = 0.75$

 (d) $5x - 3y = 10$

 (e) $0.05x + 0.08y = 150$

 (f) $y = 5x + 50$

 (g) $y = x + 2$

 (h) $5x + 10y = 135$

5. Yes, it is composed of linear equations with two unknowns.

6. It does not satisfy $y = 3x - 4$.

7. $x + y = 72, x - y = 48$

8. $y = 4x, 6x + \frac{1}{2}y = 212$

9. $x + y = 38, x + 2y = 55$

10. $y = 0.12x + 50, y = 0.2x + 40$

11. $x + y = 40, 2x + 5y = 155$

12. $x + y = 36, x + 4 = y$

13. $x + y = 76, 0.1x + 0.25y = 13$

14. $y = 1.5x + 4, y = x + 5$

15. $x + y = 8000, 0.1x + 0.12y = 900$

16. $12x + y = 117, 10x + y = 110$

17. $x + y = 20, 2.25x + 1.75y = 41$

18. $x + y = 8, 50x + 80y = 550$

19. $x + y = 5, 40x + 600y = 1320$

20. $x + y = 20, 30x + 50y = 700$

21. $x + y = 2000, 0.09x + 0.1y = 191$

22. $2x + \frac{1}{2}y = 48, 3x - \frac{1}{2}y = 27$

23. $x + y = 200, 2.3x + 3.2y = 600$

24. $x + y = 12, 100x + 80y = 1050$

25. $y = 4x + 455, y = 25x$

26. $x + y = 23, 9x + 12y = 231$

27. $(6, 2)$

28. $x + y = 10, 4x - 12y = 0$

29. Possible answer: identify the variables, choose appropriate variable names, write the equation

30. Answers may vary.

31. true

32. $x = 3y, y + 5 = x - 45$

33. $x + y = 1000, 8.5x + 6y = 7950$

Practice, Apply, Solve 1.3, page 60

1. (a) $y = 2x - 4$ (b) $y = 5x - 10$

(c) $y = -\frac{3}{4}x + 2$ (d) $y = \frac{3}{5}x + 3$

(e) $y = -\frac{8}{3}x + 4$ (f) $y = \frac{4}{7}x - \frac{10}{7}$

2. (a) x-intercept 3, y-intercept -9

(b) x-intercept 6, y-intercept 6

(c) x-intercept 2, y-intercept -6

(d) x-intercept 3, y-intercept 2

(e) x-intercept 3, y-intercept -4

(f) x-intercept -6, y-intercept 6

3. (a) $m = 5, y = -6$ (b) $m = 1, y = -3$

(c) $m = -\frac{1}{2}, y = 3$ (d) $m = \frac{3}{5}, y = -\frac{8}{5}$

(e) $m = -\frac{1}{3}, y = \frac{2}{3}$ (f) $m = 2, y = -5$

4. (a) $(-4, -2)$ (b) $(6, 5)$ (c) $(5, -4)$

5. (a) yes (b) no (c) yes

(d) no (e) yes (f) yes

6. (a) $(1, 2)$

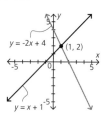

(b) $(2, 3)$

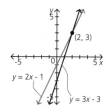

(c) $(6, -2)$

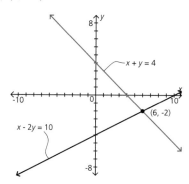

7. (a) $(2, 2)$

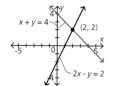

(b) $(0, 3)$

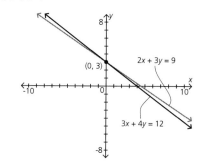

(c) $(2, -4)$

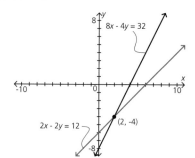

8. (a) $(-2, -1)$

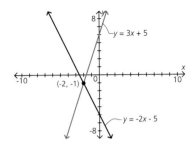

$y = 3x + 5$

$(-2, -1)$

$y = -2x - 5$

(b) $(0, -4)$

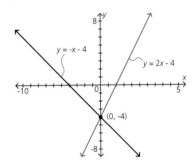

$y = -x - 4$

$y = 2x - 4$

$(0, -4)$

(c) $(-2, 2)$

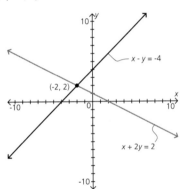

$x - y = -4$

$(-2, 2)$

$x + 2y = 2$

9. (a) $(1, 4)$

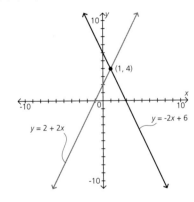

$(1, 4)$

$y = 2 + 2x$

$y = -2x + 6$

(b) $(-3, 2)$

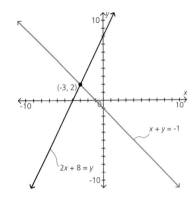

$(-3, 2)$

$x + y = -1$

$2x + 8 = y$

(c) $(8, 6)$

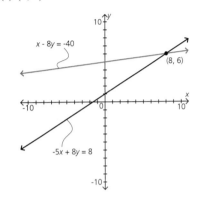

$x - 8y = -40$

$(8, 6)$

$-5x + 8y = 8$

(d) $(-1, 1)$

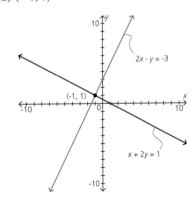

$2x - y = -3$

$(-1, 1)$

$x + 2y = 1$

(e) $(0, 3)$

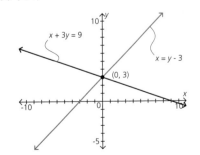

$x + 3y = 9$

$x = y - 3$

$(0, 3)$

(f) $(\frac{11}{7}, \frac{6}{7})$

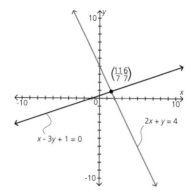

10. Draw a bigger graph or use an alternate method of solving.

11. **(a)** $y = 8x + 20$ **(b)** $y = 10x + 12$
   (c) $(4, 52)$

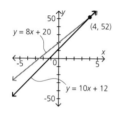

(d) The number of hours at which the costs will be the same

(e) Tools-R-Us is cheaper.

(f) buy her own

12. **(a)** $3x + 5y = 22$, $6x + 2y = 28$
   (b) ($4, $2)

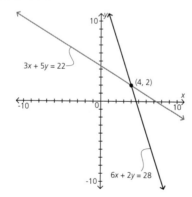

(c) $42

13. 50 lawns

14. **(a)** $y = 0.08x + 55$, $y = 0.16x + 45$

(b) (125km, $65)

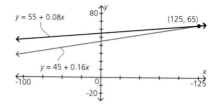

(c) The distance at which cost is equal.
(d) Ottoz

15. **(a)** $x + y = 835$, $2x + 4y = 2114$
   (b) $(222, 613)$

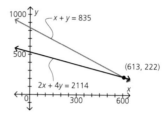

16. **(a)** $y = 125x + 15\,000$, $y = 500x$
   (b) 40   **(c)** sell > 40

17. substitute in and show LHS = RHS

18. 5

19. **(a)** $(1, 2)$, $(4, 2)$, $(2, 6)$

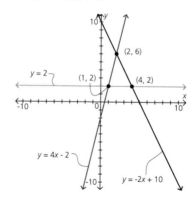

(b) 6 units^2

20. **(a)** $(5, 0)$

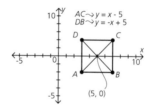

(b) AC: $y = x - 5$, DB: $y = -x + 5$
(c) substitute in and show LHS = RHS

21. **b)** isosceles   **(c)** $(0, -\frac{4}{3})$

22. iii, iv, i, ii, v

23. (a) 36 months
(b) The population will increase at the same rate as the carrying capacity of the pond.
24. $(-1, 9)$
25. (a) $(\frac{1}{4}, -1)$ **(b)** $(0, 0)$, $(4, 2)$
(c) $(3, 9)$, $(-1, 1)$

Practise 1.4, page 65

(a) x-intercept $-\frac{6}{5}$, y-intercept 6
(b) x-intercept 5, y-intercept 10
(c) x-intercept 5, y-intercept 3
(d) x-intercept $= \frac{25}{11}$, y-intercept $-\frac{25}{17}$
(e) x-intercept $-\frac{12}{5}$, y-intercept 600
(f) x-intercept $-\frac{113}{250}$, y-intercept 226

Practise, Apply, Solve 1.5, page 69

1. (a) 1   **(b)** 1   **(c)** 0   **(d)** infinite
2. (a)

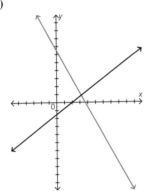

(b)

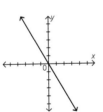

(c)

3. (a) $x + 2y = 20$ **(b)** $x + 2y = -4$
(c) $x + y = 1$
4. (a) $x + y = 1$, $x - y = 1$
(b) $x + y = 1$, $2x + 2y = 2$
(c) $x + y = 1$, $x + y = 2$

5. (a) 1   **(b)** 0   **(c)** infinite
(d) 0   **(e)** infinite   **(f)** 1
(g) 1   **(h)** 0   **(i)** 1
6. Look at the slope and y-intercept.
7. (a) $y = 4$, $y = \frac{4}{3}x$
(b) $y = \frac{1}{2}x - 2$, $y = -\frac{3}{4}x + 3$
(c) $y = 2x + 4$, $y = 2x - 4$
(d) $y = \frac{5}{4}x + \frac{25}{4}$, $y = -4x + 1$
(e) $y = -\frac{2}{3}x - 2$, $x = 4$
(f) $y = -\frac{2}{5}x + 6$, $y = \frac{2}{5}x + 2$
8. no
9. about 17 m of silk and 8 m of gingham
10. never
11. (a) $100   **(b)** $10.25
(c) Shannon   **(d)** Never, since they earn at the same rate.
12. infinitely many
13. (a) $c = 15d$ **(b)** 4
(c) True North Outfitters
14. (a − b)

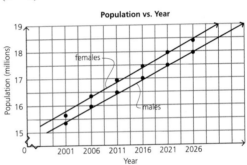

(c) females: $y = \frac{13}{125}x - 192.4$;
males: $y = \frac{1}{10}x - 184.7$
(d) No, the female population is increasing faster than male population (lines are not parallel).
15. (a)

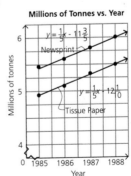

(b) increasing at same rate
(c) $y = 0.2x - 392.1$
$y = 0.2x - 391.6$

16. (a) same slope and y-intercept
(b) $(0, 3)$, $(1, 1)$, $(2, -1)$, and so on
17. $y = x + 5$
18. (a) $F = 2C + 30$ **(b)** yes
(c) $(10, 50)$

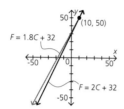

(d) $-15 < C < 35$
19. no
20.

Number of Solutions	How Slopes Related	How y-intercepts Related
no solutions	same	different
one solution	different	same or different
many solutions	same	same

21. $a = \frac{12}{5}, b = 4$
22. $a = 8, b \neq -14$ (or there would be an infinite number of solutions)
23. $a = 4, b = 7$
24. 1

Practise 1.6, page 75

(a) $(3, 7)$ **(b)** $(-2, -1)$ **(c)** $(-3, -0.5)$
(d) $(18, 21)$ **(e)** $(2, \frac{3}{2})$ **(f)** $(-\frac{160}{9}, \frac{290}{9})$

Practise, Apply, Solve 1.7, page 82

1. (a) $(5, 19)$ **(b)** $(5, 3)$ **(c)** no solution
(d) $(5, 21)$ **(e)** $(0, 0)$ **(f)** $(-1, 2)$
(g) $(3, -1)$ **(h)** $\left(\frac{8}{3}, \frac{34}{3}\right)$
2. (a) $(18, 1)$ **(b)** $\left(\frac{5}{2}, -\frac{7}{3}\right)$ **(c)** $(2, 3)$
(d) $(3, -4)$ **(e)** $(-2, 1)$ **(f)** $(4, 2)$
3. (a) no solution   **(b)** $(3, -2)$
(c) $x \in R, y = -\frac{2}{3}x - \frac{4}{3}$ **(d)** $(12, 10)$
(e) $\left(\frac{3677}{2235}, \frac{-139}{2235}\right)$ **(f)** $\left(\frac{1}{2}, 2\right)$
4. Graphing by technology is more accurate than graphing by hand.
5. (a) $y = 5x, y = 4.5x + 10$

(b) $(20, 100)$

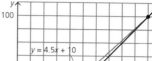

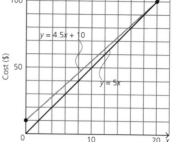

(c) The number of videos rented to make costs equal
(d) > 20 videos rented, Videorenters; < 20, Movies To Go
6. (a) $y = x + 5, y = 1.25x + 3.5$
(b)

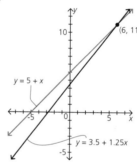

(c) mass at which costs are equal
(d) less when > 6kg, more when < 6 kg
7. \$675
8. (a) $y = 0.1x + 120$ **(b)** $y = 0.5x$
(c)

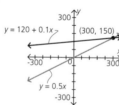

(d) the break-even point
(e) i. loss, **ii.** equal, **iii.** profit
9. (a) Yes, he just has to sell more cookies.
(b) The intersection will be farther from origin.
(c) \$0.55
10. (a) > 175 km   **(b)** < 175 km
11. Graph both lines then select calculate intersection.
12. (a) Budget: if $m \geq 30$, $C = 0.5(m - 30) + 20$; if $m < 30$, $C = 20$; Pro: $C = 0.25m + 50$
(b) $m > 180$ **(c)** $m < 180$

13. 7. $(60, 12)$; **8.** $(\frac{53}{2}, 106)$; **9.** $(21, 17)$; **10.** 125 km,
Rent a Heap; < 125km, Kurt's; **11.** 15 \$2, 25 \$5

14. 800 km

15. 42 units^2

16. (a) scalene **(b)** $(-6, 0)$, $(2, 4)$, $(6, -2)$

17. deny

18. (a) Walton, Norwich **(b)** Everett, Mactier, Marysville
(c) Barrie **(d)** Delhi, Vernon

19. (a)

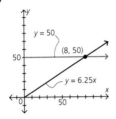

(b) 8

20. Possible solution using TI-83 Plus:
Enter Y1 = 5X − 6; enter Y2 = −3X + 9;
ZOOM 0 ; 2nd TRACE and follow instructions.

21. (a) $(0, \frac{-1}{3})$ **(b)** $(\frac{1}{4}, \frac{-1}{5})$

22. (a) $(0, 1)$, $(\frac{-3}{2}, \frac{11}{2})$ **(b)** $(\frac{1}{2}, 2)$, $(\frac{-1}{2}, -2)$
(c) $(0, 0)$, $(1, 1)$ **(d)** $(\sqrt{3}, 0)$, $(-\sqrt{3}, 0)$

Practise, Apply, Solve 1.8, page 92

1. (a) $y = -3x + 12$ **(b)** $y = 4x + 15$
(c) $y = 12x - 3$ **(d)** $y = 8x - 6$
(e) $y = x + 9$ **(f)** $y = \frac{13}{12}x - \frac{7}{6}$

2. (a) $x = -3y + 5$ **(b)** $x = 2y + 18$
(c) $x = 8y - 5$ **(d)** $x = -3y + 8$
(e) $x = \frac{1}{5}y - \frac{1}{5}$ **(f)** $x = 7y + 6$

3. (a) $b = -8a + 4$ **(b)** $n = 4m - 3$
(c) $r = -\frac{1}{2}s + \frac{3}{2}$ **(d)** $e = \frac{4}{5}d - \frac{12}{5}$
(e) $p = -\frac{1}{2}q + 2$ **(f)** $v = -\frac{3}{7}u + 3$

4. (a) $y = -1$ **(b)** $x = 3$ **(c)** $y = 0$
(d) $s = \frac{15}{2}$ **(e)** $m = -\frac{13}{2}$ **(f)** $b = 3$

5. (a) $x = -4y - 10$; $(2, -3)$
(b) $y = -2x + 1$; $(2, -3)$
(c) It does not matter which way one solves the problem.

6. Substitution is more accurate but graphing by technology is easier when a non-exact solution is required.

7. (a) $(2, 1)$ **(b)** $(-1, 2)$ **(c)** $(1, 0)$
(d) $(1, 0)$ **(e)** $(-1, -1)$ **(f)** $(0, 1)$

8. (a) $(\frac{7}{4}, \frac{-11}{4})$ **(b)** $(6, 2)$ **(c)** $(x, 4 - x)$
(d) $(-1, 1)$ **(e)** $(1, 2)$ **(f)** $(2, 1)$
(g) $(-12, -13)$ **(h)** $(1, -1)$ **(i)** $(4, -3)$

9. (a) no solution
(b) Both variables cancel out and an untrue statement results. Therefore, the lines are parallel and distinct.
(c)

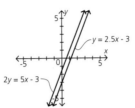

10. (a) $x \in R$, $y = -\frac{5}{3}x + 10$
(b) Everything cancels out since the lines are identical.
(c)

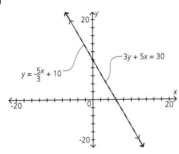

11. (a) \$5000
(b) if they thought they could not sell more than \$5000/month

12. (a) $(-5, -3)$ **(b)** $(9, 6)$ **(c)** $(\frac{-33}{7}, \frac{-17}{7})$
(d) $(6, -6)$ **(e)** $(-15, -5)$ **(f)** $(-4, -6)$
(g) $(2, 4)$ **(h)** $(1, -3)$ **(i)** $(2, 1)$

13. $(31, 58)$

14. plane: 250 km/h, wind: 50 km/h

15. Substitute the value of one of the variables into the other equation.

16. 9 m × 11 m

17. 810

18. 63

19. 12. John is 16, Margie is 20; **13.** 40 dimes, 36 quarters; **14.** < 2 kg; **15.** \$3000 at 10%, \$5000 at 12%; **16.** \$3.50

20. \$5.10

21. (a) $x = 60, y = 30$ **(b)** $x = 104, y = 28$
(c) $x = 50, y = 70$ **(d)** $x = 100, y = 50$
(e) $x = 40, y = 30$ **(f)** $x = 40, y = 50$

22. > 8 cheques, Ontario Trust; < 8 cheques, Maple Leaf Savings

23. -10 should be $+10$; $2x - (4x - 10) = 4$;
$-2x + 10 = 4$; $-2x = -6$; $x = 3$

24. $(-2, -5)$

25. meat submarines \$2900, veggie submarines \$1300

26. (a) $(4, 2)$ **(b)** $(3, 12)$

27. (a) $(10a, -2a)$ **(b)** $(a, 2b)$

Practise, Apply, Solve 1.9, page 101

1. **(a)** (8, 7)   **(b)** (8, 7)   **(c)** yes; yes
2. **(a)** x by subtraction   **(b)** x by subtraction
   (c) y by subtraction   **(d)** y by addition
   (e) y by subtraction   **(f)** x by subtraction or y by addition
3. **(a)** (3, 1)   **(b)** (2, −1)   **(c)** (−1, 3)
   (d) (1, 0)   **(e)** (0, −2)   **(f)** (3, 1)
4. **(a)** multiply $x - 2y = -7$ by 3, and subtract
   (b) multiply $3x + y = 9$ by 2, and add
   (c) $\left(\frac{11}{7}, \frac{30}{7}\right)$
5. plane 336 km/h, wind 48 km/h
6. **(a)** (1, 1)   **(b)** (−3, −1)   **(c)** (2, −3)
   (d) $\left(\frac{40}{3}, 25\right)$ **(e)** (4, 0)   **(f)** (−2, 3)
   (g) (8, −1)   **(h)** (5, 4)   **(i)** (2, −2)
   (j) (5, −6)   **(k)** (2, 7)   **(l)** (1, −3)
7. Elimination is easier when an LCM can be found easily between either the x- or y-coefficients. Otherwise, use substitution.
8. **(a)** simplify $3(x - 1) - 2(y + 2) = 7$
   (b) (6, 2)
9. Multiply $3x + 2y = 22$ by 5 and $5x - 4y = 22$ by 3.
10. **(a)** (−1, −1)   **(b)** (0, −1)   **(c)** (0, −2)
    (d) (0, 3)   **(e)** (−1, 4)   **(f)** (3, 12)
11. **(a)** $y = x$, $y = x + 1$
    (b) All variables are eliminated and an untrue statement results.
12. **(a)** $y = x$, $2y = 2x$
    (b) All variables are eliminated and a true statement results.
13. Answers may vary.
14. 72 chicken, 228 beef
15. $600 in savings, $150 in chequing
16. 90 g of 40%, 60 g of 50%
17. 6 h 40 min
18. 2000 bass, 8000 perch
19. **17.** 12 kg raisins, 8 kg peanuts; **18.** 400 km; **19.** 2 h; **20.** 15 practice, 5 game; **21.** $900 at 9%, $1100 at 10%; **22.** Sarah is 15, her mother is 36
20. signs same: subtract; signs different: add
21. $\left(\frac{53}{20}, \frac{3}{20}\right)$
22. $p = -\frac{9}{5}$, $q = \frac{113}{5}$
23. 5 h
24. 45
25. $x = \frac{(de - bf)}{(ad - bc)}$, $y = \frac{(ce - af)}{(bc - ad)}$; $bc \neq ad$

Practise 1.10, page 107

(a) $y = ax + b$, $a = 3.690\ 909\ 091$, $b = 6.090\ 909\ 091$, $r^2 = 0.984\ 095\ 522\ 4$, $r = 0.992\ 015\ 888\ 2$
(b) $y = ax + b$, $a = 1.380\ 090\ 498$, $b = -2.067\ 873\ 303$, $r^2 = 0.937\ 477\ 955$, $r = 0.968\ 234\ 452\ 5$
(c) $y = ax + b$, $a = 2.6$, $b = 0$, $r^2 = 1$, $r = 1$

(d) $y = ax + b$, $a = -0.270\ 454\ 545\ 5$, $b = 591.881\ 818\ 2$, $r^2 = 0.869\ 092\ 917\ 6$, $r = -0.932\ 251\ 531\ 3$
(e) $y = ax + b$, $a = 158.5$, $b = -18.714\ 285\ 71$, $r^2 = 0.927\ 739\ 906\ 7$, $r = 0.963\ 192\ 559\ 5$
(f) $y = ax + b$, $a = 0.595$, $b = -9.471\ 111\ 111$, $r^2 = 0.865\ 508\ 420\ 9$, $r = 0.930\ 327\ 050\ 5$

Practise, Apply, Solve 1.11, page 112

1. **(a − b)**

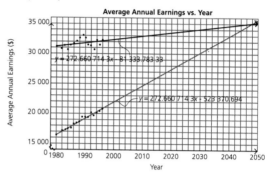

(c) (2048, $35 097)
(e) linear regression
(f) Linear regression is more accurate than a hand-drawn scatter plot.

2. **(a)** not very confident
   (b) unconfident
   (c) reasonably confident
   (d) unconfident
3. **(a)** (0.05, 5.29)   **(b)** (−1.12, −0.53)
   (c) A: not very confident, B: somewhat confident
4. 1863
5. never
6. **(a)** 1908
   (b) urban 21 575 000, rural 6 835 000
7. Answers will vary.
8. 1993
9. **(a)** yes
   (b) commercial increasing, passenger decreasing
   (c) 1999
10. 2082
11. **(a)** males decreasing spending, females increasing spending
    (b) no, according to data
12. Never, since Vancouver prices increasing faster − already occurred in 1981.
13. Answers may vary.
14. The crime rate is decreasing in Toronto and increasing in Calgary.
15. The claim is not valid.
16. The predictions will not always come true because most data is not perfectly represented by a linear model.

17. x and y are variables: x is the independent variable, y the dependent variable, a is slope, b is y-intercept, r^2 is coefficient of determination, r is correlation coefficient

Chapter 1 Review, page 119

1. yes
2. **(a)** $x + y = 50$, $x + 4y = 92$
  (b) $y = 0.1x + 55$, $y = 0.25x + 40$
  (c) $y = x + 190$, $y = \frac{5}{3}x$
  (d) $x + y = 1200$, $0.42x + 0.33y = 457.02$
3. **(a)** $(2, 0)$ **(b)** $(2, 3)$ **(c)** $(-6, -8)$
4. **(a)** $(-1, 2)$ **(b)** $(10, -2)$
5. **(a)** $y = 20x + 300$, $y = 35x + 175$
  (b) $\left(\frac{25}{3}, \frac{1400}{3}\right)$
  (c) The number of weeks after which they have saved the same amount.
6. **(a)** 0 **(b)** 1 **(c)** infinite
7. **(a)** $y = 5.5x - 35$, $y = 5.5x - 25$
  (b) The two payments cannot be the same, since the lines are parallel.
8. **(a)** $4x = 2y + 8$ (Answers may vary.)
  (b) $(0, -4)$, $(1, -2)$, $(2, 0)$ (Answers may vary.)
9. $x + y = 6$, $2x - 3y = -13$ (Answers may vary.)
10. **(a)**

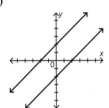

  (b)

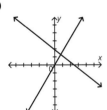

  (c)

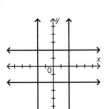

11. **(a)** $(1, 0)$ **(b)** $(2, 1)$ **(c)** $(3020, 76)$
12. Venus 68, Extreme 7
13. 18 cm by 72 cm
14. **(a)** 4 h **(b)** Fraser's

15. $\left(\frac{1}{2}, 3\right)$
16. **(a)** $(-2, 4)$ **(b)** $(1, 2)$ **(c)** $(8, 1)$
17. **(a)** $\left(\frac{34}{11}, \frac{37}{11}\right)$ **(b)** $(4, -8)$
18. Louise is 16 and Todd is 18.
19. $2300 in mutual funds, $2500 in GICs
20. **(a)** 170 km **(b)** 15 km
21. **(a)** $(3, -4)$ **(b)** $(-2, 1)$ **(c)** $(3, 3)$
22. **(a)** $\left(x, -\frac{3}{2}x + \frac{5}{2}\right)$ **(b)** $(50, -40)$
  (c) $\left(\frac{7}{12}, \frac{-1}{3}\right)$
23. $(23, 17)$
24. $\frac{500}{9}$ h
25. $\frac{3}{4}$ L of 5%, $\frac{9}{4}$ L of 9%
26. **(a)**

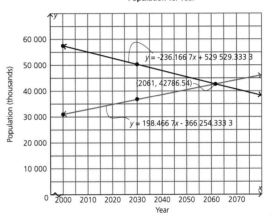

  (b) 198 470 per year **(c)** 236 170 per year
  (d) 2061 **(e)** not very sure
27. 1994

Chapter 1 Review Test, page 137

1. **(a)** $(2, 2)$ **(b)** $(2, 2)$
2. **(a)** $(3, -4)$ **(b)** $(-2, 3)$ **(c)** $\left(\frac{7}{3}, \frac{-2}{9}\right)$
3. **(a)** $(18, 1)$ **(b)** $(2, 3)$ **(c)** $(-2, 1)$
4. confirm
5. 36 $5s, 40 $10s
6. helicopter 210 km/h, wind 30 km/h
7. **(a)** 20 h **(b)** Netaxes
8. 600 L of premium, 400 L of regular
9.

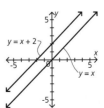

10. **(a)** $\left(3, \frac{-1}{2}\right)$ **(b)** $(5, 3)$

11. (a)

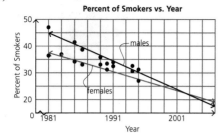

Percent of Smokers vs. Year

(b) both are decreasing

(c) 1998   **(d)** women

Chapter 2

Getting Ready, page 142

1. (a) $\frac{-3}{2}$ **(b)** $\frac{-3}{56}$

   (c) $\frac{35}{3}x$ **(d)** $\frac{3}{8}y$

   (e) $\frac{23}{20}$ **(f)** -1.4375

2. (a) 52   **(b)** $\frac{41}{100}$ **(c)** 0.25

   (d) 17   **(e)** 25

3. (a) $x = -2$ **(b)** $x = -1$

   (c) $x = 8$ **(d)** $x = 6$ or $x = -6$

   (e) $x = 3$ or $x = -3$ **(f)** $x = 8$ or $x = -8$

4. (a) $(1, 7)$ **(b)** $\left(1, \frac{3}{2}\right)$ **(c)** $\left(\frac{6}{5}, -\frac{1}{2}\right)$

5. (a) $x = 13$ m   **(b)** $x = 192.29$ m

6. (a) 6   **(b)** $\frac{1}{4}$

   (c) 0.7

7. (a) $m = \frac{1}{2}$ **(b)** $m = 2$

   (c) $m = -3$ **(d)** $m = -\frac{3}{2}$

8. (a) $y = \frac{1}{3}x + \frac{14}{3}$ **(b)** $y = -\frac{3}{4}x - 7$

   (c) $y = 1$ **(d)** $y = -4x - 6$

9. See glossary.

10. (a) 11.865 m^2 **(b)** 1002.24 cm^2

11. (a) 36.19 cm^2 **(b)** 56.97 cm^2, 41.75 cm

12. (a) $x = 15°$, $2x = 30°$, $4x = 60°$

   (b) $x = 35°$, $y = 75°$, $z = 70°$

   (c) $x = 10°$, $(5x + 20) = 70°$, $(7x + 40) = 110°$

   (d) $42.5°$, $(2x - 10) = 75°$, $3x = 127.5°$

   (e) $x = 105°$

   (f) $x = 63°$, $y = 63°$

13. $x = 80°$, $y = 60°$, $z = 40°$

Practise, Apply, Solve 2.3, page 151

1. (a) Answers will vary.

   (b) 300 km, 100 km, 400 km

2. (a) 13   **(b)** 9.5

   (c) 1.4   **(d)** 26

3. Y is the shortest distance.

4. Answers may vary.

5. use Pythagorean theorem; 12.8

6. A

7. (a) the town at (26, 77)

   (b) possible answer: wind currents

8. (a)

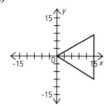

   (b) 51.49   **(c)** isosceles

9. 10.78

10. Beast

11. (c) about 11.3   **(d)** about 5.7

12. about 9.5

13. Possible answer points: specific location coordinates allow quick response and distance computation; locate accident scene and nearby hospitals, then compute or measure the distance.

14. (a) Construct 2 circles of radius 5 with centres at (0, 0) and (3, −4). Any point on either circle will make an isosceles triangle. Also any intersection of 2 circles of identical size with centres at (0, 0) and (3, −4) will also be a solution. e.g.. (3, 4), (3, 1).

   (b) The answer is any intersection of 2 circles of radius 5 with centres at (0, 0) and (3, −4), which are (0.598, 4.964) and (−4.598, 1.964).

15. 4.85

16. The relationship between the origins will correspond to the relationships between all other points.

17. It can graze in a 10 m circle; both location of post and shape of field will affect the available grazing area.

18. Answers may vary.

Practise, Apply, Solve 2.4, page 155

1. (a) $x^2 + y^2 = 9$ **(b)** $x^2 + y^2 = 2500$

   (c) $x^2 + y^2 = \frac{59}{4}$ **(d)** $x^2 + y^2 = 160\ 000$

   (e) $x^2 + y^2 = 0.0625$

2. (a) (0, 0), 6, x-intercepts 6, −6; y-intercepts 6, −6

   (b) (0, 0), 7, x-intercepts 7, −7; y-intercepts 7, −7

   (c) (0, 0), 0.2, x-intercepts 0.2, −0.2; y-intercepts 0.2, −0.2

   (d) (0, 0), 13, x-intercepts 13, −13; y-intercepts 13, −13

3. (a) $x^2 + y^2 = 361\ 000\ 000$

   (b) $x^2 + y^2 = 1225$ **(c)** $x^2 + y^2 = 32\ 400$

   (d) $x^2 + y^2 = 14.0625$ **(e)** $x^2 + y^2 = 1190.25$

4. (a) 5   **(b)** 5

   (c) 3   **(d)** 17

5. **(a) i.** $x^2 + y^2 = 25$, **ii.** $x^2 + y^2 = 25$,
   iii. $x^2 + y^2 = 9$, **iv.** $x^2 + y^2 = 289$
   (b) i. (3, 4), (4, 3); **ii.** (−5, 0), (0, −5)
   iii. (3, 0), (−3, 0) **iv.** (0, 17), (0, −17)
6. Answers may vary.
7. does not say how much the shock waves move for every 5 s
8. 1256 km
9. **(a)** on **(b)** outside
   (c) inside **(d)** outside
10. 37.268 s
11. $a = 10$, $b = 6.6$
12. $r = 20\ 345.8$; outside; the second has a larger radius
13. **(a)** $x^2 + y^2 = r^2$
   (b) coordinate (a, b): use Pythagorean theorem to find $r = \sqrt{a^2 + b^2}$ then use (a)
14. 0.0133 m
15. 11.3 by 11.3
16. no

Practise, Apply, Solve 2.5, page 162

1. **(a)** 3 **(b)** 6.08
   (c) 6.32 **(d)** 8.24
   (e) 6.08 **(f)** 8
   (g) 8.06 **(h)** 4
   (i) 10.43
2. **(a)** 5, $\frac{-4}{3}$ **(b)** 6.32, $\frac{-1}{3}$
   (c) 4.12, undefined **(d)** 10.05, 10
   (e) 8.06, $\frac{-1}{8}$ **(f)** 16, 0
   (g) 181, $\frac{180}{19}$ **(h)** 111.13, $\frac{-75}{82}$
3. *D*
4. **(a)** *c*; *x*-values are the same; subtract the *y*-values
   (b) *f*; *y*-values are the same; subtract the *x*-values
5. scalene: no equal sides or angles; isosceles: 2 equal sides and 2 equal angles; equilateral; all sides and angles equal
   (a) isosceles **(b)** scalene
   (c) scalene **(d)** isosceles
6. **i.** yes; the square of the hypoteneuse is equal to the sum of the squares of the other two sides
   ii. (a) yes **(b)** no **(c)** yes
7. **(a)** W*X*: 5.39 m, slope $\frac{2}{5}$; *XY*: 6.4 m, slope $\frac{-5}{4}$;
   YZ: 5.39 m, slope $\frac{2}{5}$; *ZW*: 6.4 m, slope $\frac{-5}{4}$
   (b) parallelogram (opposite side lengths and slopes are equal)
   (c) 2.416
8. **(a)** (8, 2)
   (b) apply transformation of *Q* to *R* to *P*
   (c) *PR* = 12.04, *QS* = 12.04 (same length)
9. 96.5928 m
10. **(a)** 90 km **(b)** 120 km **(c)** 270 km
11. 245.89 m
12. 101.8 units; likely need more to go around obstacles
13. **(a)** no **(b)** (9.5, 6.5)

14. All four sides are the same length, $\sqrt{29}$ units; slope of *PQ* and *QR* = $\frac{5}{2}$, slope of *RS* and *SP* = $\frac{2}{5}$; *PQRS* is a square.
15. **(a)** Possible solutions: compute the distance between first and third and between second and third points using $d = \sqrt{(\Delta x)^2 + (\Delta y)^2}$.
   (b) See if lengths obey $h^2 = a^2 + b^2$ or see if two sides are negative reciprocals
16. **(c)** 143 m
17. **(i)** $A(−3, 0)$, $B(0, 6)$, $C(4, 2)$
   (ii) $\triangle ABC$ is congruent to $\triangle GHI$.
18. distance between two points =
   $\sqrt{(x_2 − x_1)^2 + (y_2 − y_1)^2}$, distance between of point (x, y) from origin = $\sqrt{x^2 + y^2}$;
   $(x_2 − x_1)^2 + (y_2 − y_1)^2 = r^2$
19. (7, 3), (2, 8), (−3, 3), (2, −2),
   $(x_1 − 2)^2 + (y_1 − 3)^2 = 25$

Practise 2.6, page 167

(a) (5, 1) **(b)** (5, 3.3) **(c)** (−0.5, −5)
(d) (−4, 0) **(e)** (1, 1) **(f)** (0.5, 1)

Practise, Apply, Solve 2.7, page 173

1. *AB* (0, 3), *CD* (1, 5), *EF* (2.5, −0.5), *GH* (0.5, −3), *JK* (7, 2)
2. **(a)** (2, 5) **(b)** (2, −2)
   (c) (05, 3.5) **(d)** (−0.5, 0.5)
   (e) (1, −1) **(f)** (2.5, −2)
   (g) (4, −8.5) **(h)** (−1, −1)
   (i) (0.25, 0.75)
3. (7.45, 25.75)
4. **(a)** (−0.25, −1) **(b)** 2.136
5. (5, 3)
6. (6, 9)
7. midpoint *O* (−4, 4), midpoint *R* (5, 1)
8. $\dfrac{\text{*x*-coordinate of known end point + *x*-coordinate of unknown end point}}{2}$ = *x*-coordinate of midpoint,

   $\dfrac{\text{*y*-coordinate of known end point + *y*-coordinate of unknown end point}}{2}$ = *y*-coordinate of midpoint;

   example: if midpoint is (1, 1) and one end point is (−3, −1), then $\frac{−3 + x}{2} = 1$, and $\frac{−1 + y}{2} = 1$, so $x = 5$ and $y = 3$, midpoint is (5, 3)
9. *PR* (4.5, 1.5), *QS* (4.5, 1.5), rhombus
10. Use midpoint and other end of the line.
11. (611236.816, 4857045.89) 4.8 W, 6.4
12. **(a)** (2, 2) **(b)** (6, 0)
13. *A* to midpoint of *BC* = $\sqrt{20}$, *B* to midpoint of *CA* = $\sqrt{50}$, *C* to midpoint of *AB* = $\sqrt{50}$
14. $y = \frac{7}{5}x − \frac{11}{5}$, $y = 8x − 11$, $y = −\frac{1}{4}x$
15. $3x − 2y − 7 = 0$

16. (a) passes through one point and opposite midpoint
    (b) passes through midpoint and has negative reciprocal slope
17. (a) PQ (2, 1), QR (1, −4), RP(6, 2)
    (b) slope of PQ and QR = 5, slope of QR and $RP = \frac{6}{5}$, slope of PQ and $RP = \frac{1}{4}$
    (c) slope of $PQ = \frac{6}{5}$, slope of $QR = \frac{1}{4}$, slope of $RP = 5$
    (d) The midsegment of two midpoints is parallel to the other side of the triangle.
18. (a) PQ and QR = 5.1, QR and RP = 7.8, PQ and RP = 4.1
    (b) PQ = 15.6, QR = 8.2, RP = 10.2
    (c) The midsegment of two midpoints is exactly half the length of the other side of the triangle.
19. (a) Add x-values of each end point and divide by 2 for the x-value. Do the same for the y-values.
    (b) i. Find coordinates of midpoint of a side. Use these and the coordinates of the opposite vertex to find the equation.
    ii. Use coordinates of midpoint. Slope will be negative reciprical of slope of side.
21. (4, 6) For every increase of 3 in the x-coordinate, the y-coordinate decreases by 1.
22. (a) (0, 2)   (b) (0, 2), (0, 2)
    (c) This point is the centroid.
    (d) Yes, the centroid is the point in a triangle where the medians intersect.

Practise, Apply, Solve 2.8, page 182

1. (a) parallel   (b) perpendicular
   (c) neither   (d) perpendicular
   (e) parallel   (f) neither
2. (a) slopes are the same, $\frac{1}{4}$
   (b) slopes are negative reciprocals, $\frac{-1}{2}$ and 2
3. parallelogram or rhombus, side length
4. square or rhombus, slope of sides
5. slope of $PQ = -3$ and slope of $RP = \frac{1}{3}$, so they are perpendicular; so $\triangle PQR$ is right.
   another way: $PQ^2 + RP^2 = QR^2$
6. $KL = LM = \sqrt{25}$, $KM = \sqrt{50}$; two sides are equal, so triangle is isosceles
7. $RS = TU$, $m = \frac{1}{5}$; $ST = UR$, $m = \frac{4}{3}$
8. $AB = CD = 5$, $m = \frac{5}{6}$ or undefined; $BC = DA = 5$, $m = \frac{3}{4}$
9. (a) $EF = FG = GH = HE = \sqrt{20}$, slope of EF and $GH = \frac{-1}{2}$ and perpendicular to FG and HE (slope of 2)
   (b) slope of $EG = -3$, slope of $FH = \frac{1}{3}$; slopes are negative reciprocals so they are perpendicular
10. slope of $PQ = -\frac{7}{9}$, slope of $QR = \frac{3}{2}$, slope of $RS = -\frac{2}{3}$, slope of $SP = \frac{7}{4}$; opposite sides are not parallel, so $PQRS$ is not a rectangle

11. (a) isosceles, 2 equal sides
    (b) scalene, no equal sides
    (c) right, $FD^2 = EF^2 + DE^2$
    (d) isosceles, 2 equal sides
    (e) isosceles, 2 equal sides
    (f) isosceles and right, 2 equal sides whose squares equal the square of the third side
12. rectangle: all lengths are equal, rhombus: adjacent sides are perpendicular
13. (a) rhombus, all sides equal, adjacent sides not perpendicular
    (b) rectangle, opposite sides are parallel and equal
    (c) parallelogram, opposite sides are equal and parallel, but adjacent sides are not perpendicular
    (d) rectangle, opposite sides are parallel and equal
    (e) parallelogram, opposite sides are equal and parallel, but adjacent sides are not perpendicular
14. square, all sides = $\sqrt{106}$, adjacent sides are perpendicular (slopes = $\frac{5}{9}$ and $\frac{-9}{5}$)
15. (a) square   (b) rectangle
    (c) parallelogram
16. trapezoid. Find the length and slope of each side. If the slopes of two sides are the same, the sides are parallel; if negative reciprocals, they are perpendicular; if neither, the sides are neither perpendicular nor parallel. In a parallelogram, opposite sides are equal and parallel. In a rectangle opposite sides are equal and parallel, and adjacent sides are perpendicular. A rhombus has all the characteristics of a parallelogram, plus all 4 sides are equally long. In a square all sides equal, opposite sides are parallel, and adjacent sides are perpendicular.
17. (a) (7.5, 9)   (b) (3.61, −4.22), (0.39, 2.22)
18. Change (−10, 140) to (−10, 150).
19. find lengths and slopes of slides and compare opposite sides
20. (b) no
21. (b) no

Practise 2.9, page 185

(a) (3, 1)   (b) (0.86, −0.43)   (c) (4, 0)
(d) (3, 2)   (e) (−2.5, 2.5)   (f) (4, 1)

Practise, Apply, Solve 2.10, page 194

1. (a) median   (b) (2, 0)
2. (a) altitude   (b) 5
3. (a) perpendicular bisector
   (b) (0, −0.5)   (c) −2

4. (a)

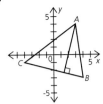

(c) $\frac{-1}{4}$

(d) 4   **(e)** $y = 4x - 8$

(f) 6.55 units   **(g)** 27 units^2

5. (a)–(b)

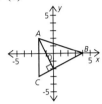

(c) $\frac{1}{2}$

(d) -2 **(e)** $y = -2x - 2$

(f) 4.47 units   **(g)** 15 units^2

6. (a)–(b)

(c) $x = 2$ **(d)** $y = -\frac{5}{6}x + 7$

(e) (2, 5.33)   **(f)** orthocentre

7. (a)–(b)

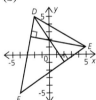

(c) $y = -\frac{3}{2}x + 2$ **(d)** $y = -\frac{1}{5}x + 2$

(e) (0, 2)

8. (a)–(b)

(c) $y = -\frac{9}{10}x - \frac{24}{5}$

(d) $y = 0$ **(e)** $(-5.33, 0)$

9. (a)–(b)

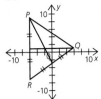

(c) $y = -2x - 3$ **(d)** $y = 1$

(e) $(-2, 1)$

10. (a)–(b)

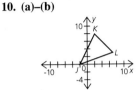

(c) JK: $y = -\frac{1}{2}x + 4$, LJ: $y = -3x + 9$

(d) (2, 3)

(e) circumcentre is point equidistant from each vertex

11. (a)–(b)

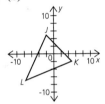

(c) JK: $y = x$, LJ: $-\frac{1}{2}x + \frac{3}{2}$

(d) (1, 1)

12. (11, 12)

13. (1.25, 2)

14. (1, 4)

15. (b) 7.07 units from the iceberg

16. (a) (5, 5)

(b) $y = \frac{4}{3}x - \frac{5}{3}$, $y = \frac{1}{7}x + \frac{30}{7}$

(c) They intersect at (5, 5).

(d) slope of $PR = \frac{1}{7}$, slope of $QR = -7$, so PR and QR are perpendicular, and $\triangle PQR$ must be a right triangle

17. (a) $y = -\frac{5}{3}x - 3$ **(b)** $y = -\frac{5}{3}x - 3$

(c) $y = -\frac{5}{3}x - 3$

(d) They are the same; triangle is symmetric.

(e) isosceles

18. (7.33, 8)

19. Answers will vary.

20. centre (7.07, 16.07)

21. (a) find intersection of 2 medians

(b) find intersection of 2 perpendicular bisectors

(c) find intersection of 2 altitudes

22. (a) A 37.2, B 26.8, C -34.8, 98.8 m

(b) (12.58, -2.26)

23. Use technique from question 22.

24. $(\frac{-10}{3}, 8)$

25. $(\frac{36}{23}, \frac{-15}{23})$

26. $(1, 3)$

Practise, Apply, Solve 2.11, page 203

1. $AC = 22.8 = BD$

2. $PQ = 5 = QR$, so isosceles

3. The diagonals intersect at $(-1, -3)$, the midpoint of JL and KM.

4. The midpoint of EF is $(0, 3)$; this satisfies the equation of the altitude, $y = -\frac{1}{5}x + 3$.

5. K satisfies the equation of the right bisector of LM, $y = 5x - 13$.

6. Let A, B, C, and D be midpoints. Then $AB = 2.12 = CD$, AB and CD have slopes of -1, $BC = 3.54 = AD$, BC and AD have slopes of 1; so $ABCD$ is a rectangle.

7. Let W, X, Y, and Z be midpoints. Then $WX = YZ = XY = WZ = 8.9$, WX and YZ have slopes of -2, and XY and WZ have slopes of $\frac{1}{2}$.

8. It is valuable to know that these properties work all the time. Analytic geometry is used to prove these properties.

9. All are represented by the equation $y = 3x - 12$.

10. The length from each point to the centre is $\sqrt{41}$.

11. Let X, Y, and Z be the midpoints. Then, XZ and QR have slopes of $\frac{4}{5}$, $XZ = 3.2$, $QR = 6.4$, $XZ = \frac{1}{2}QR$.

12. The slope of RT is -1, and its midpoint is $(-3.5, 0.5)$; the slope of SU is 1 and its midpoint is also $(-3.5, 0.5)$. The equation of RT is $y = -x - 3$ and the equation of SU is $y = x + 4$. Their slopes are negative reciprocals so they intersect at right angles.

13. so the property can be used later; diagram, state what is known and what is to be proved, proof, conclusion

14. Let X, Y, and Z be the midpoints; area of large $\Delta = \frac{1}{2}(7)(4)$ or 14; area of small $\Delta = \frac{1}{2}(2)(3.5)$ or 3.5; $\frac{14}{3.5} = 4$, so area of large $\Delta = \frac{1}{4}$ area of small Δ

15. It is parallel to the parallel sides.

16. (a) (a, b)

(b) $\sqrt{(a - 0)^2 + (b - 0)^2} = \sqrt{(0 - a)^2 + (b - 0)^2}$; $\sqrt{a^2 + b^2} = a^2 + b^2$

17. (a) $(\frac{b}{2}, \frac{c}{2})$, $(\frac{a}{2}, 0)$

(b) The slope of BC is $\frac{-c}{a - b}$, and the slope of the midsegment of AB and AC is $\frac{-c}{a - b}$, so they are parallel. $BC = \sqrt{c^2 + a^2 - 2ab + b^2}$ and length of midsegment $= \frac{1}{2}\sqrt{c^2 + a^2 - 2ab + b^2}$ or $\frac{1}{2}BC$.

18. The four vertices are $(0, 0)$, $(a, 0)$, (b, c), and (d, c). The midpoint of (d, c) is $(\frac{d}{2}, \frac{c}{2})$. The midpoint of (b, c) and $(a, 0)$ is $(\frac{a + b}{2}, \frac{c}{2})$. Since $d = a + b$, the midpoints are the same; that is, the diagonals bisect each other.

19. (a) $P(\frac{a + c}{2}, \frac{b + d}{2})$, $Q(\frac{c + e}{2}, \frac{d + f}{2})$, $R(\frac{e + g}{2}, \frac{f + h}{2})$, $S(\frac{a + g}{2}, \frac{b + h}{2})$

(b) PS and QR have the same slope, $\frac{h - d}{g - c}$; PQ and SR have the same slope, $\frac{f - b}{e - a}$; since both pairs of opposite sides have the same slope, $PQRS$ is a parallelogram.

Chapter 2 Review, page 206

1. B

2. P

3. isosceles, $MN = MO = 25$, $NO = 30$

4. (a) $(0, 0)$, 13, 26, $(13, 0)$, $(-13, 0)$, $(0, 13)$, $(0, -13)$

(b) $(0, 0)$, 1.7, 3.4, $(1.7, 0)$, $(-1.7, 0)$, $(0, 1.7)$, $(0, -1.7)$

(c) $(0, 0)$, 9.9, 19.8, $(9.9, 0)$, $(-9.9, 0)$, $(0, 9.9)$, $(0, -9.9)$

5. (a) $x^2 + y^2 = 25$ (b) $x^2 + y^2 = 49$

(c) $x^2 + y^2 = 73$ (d) $x^2 + y^2 = 97$

6. $x^2 + y^2 = 900$

7. (a) 5.39 (b) 12.08 (c) 3.16

8. $AB = 3.6$, $BC = 5.1$, $CA = 3.6$, isosceles, since $AB = BC$

9. 90.94

10. (a) $(-4, 4)$ (b) $(3, 2)$

(c) $(1.5, 4)$ (d) $(6.5, -5.5)$

(e) $(6, -2)$ (f) $(0.5, 4)$

11. $(6, -3)$, 3.16

12. (a) midpoint of PQ $(3, 3)$, midpoint of QR $(-5, 0)$, midpoint of RP $(4, 1)$

(b) 10.05

(c) $y = -9x + 30$

13. length and slope of each side

14. $AB = 4.12$, $BC = 4.12$, $CA = 7.07$, $AB = BC$ so isosceles

15. parallelogram: opposites sides parallel (and equal), slope of opposite sides; rectangle: opposite sides parallel (and equal) and adjacent sides perpendicular; slope of opposite sides, length of sides; square: all properties of rectangle and all sides equal, length and slope of sides; rhombus: parallelogram with all sides equal, length and slope of sides

16. $JK = 5$, $KL = 5$, $LM = 5$, $MJ = 5$, $JK \parallel LM$ (slope $\frac{3}{4}$), $KL \parallel MJ$ (slope 0)

17. (a) parallelogram: $AB = \sqrt{26}$, $CD = \sqrt{26}$, $AB \parallel CD$ (slope -5); $BC = \sqrt{122}$, $DA = \sqrt{122}$, $BC \parallel DA$ (slope $\frac{1}{11}$)

(b) square: $EF \parallel GH$ (slope -4) and $FG \parallel HE$ (slope $\frac{1}{4}$), adjacent sides are parallel and all sides $= \sqrt{68}$

18. (19.9, 89.3)

19. $\left(\frac{-19}{3}, \frac{-58}{3}\right)$

20. 4.34

21. Let WX and YZ be midsegments. $WX \parallel YZ$ (slope $\frac{-1}{5}$) and $XY \parallel ZW$ (slope $\frac{3}{2}$)

22. Each point is 13 units from the centre, so they are all on the circle.

23. (a) PQ (slope $\frac{5}{2}$) is perpendicular to QR (slope $\frac{-2}{5}$), so ΔPQR is right triangle
(b) The midpoint of the hypotenuse is (2, 2.5). This point satisfies both equations of the other two perpendicular bisectors, $y = -\frac{2}{5}x + \frac{33}{10}$ and $y = \frac{5}{2}x - \frac{5}{2}$, so the midpoint is the circumcentre.

Chapter 2 Review Test, page 218

1. (a) 40 m   **(b)** (4, 5.5)
2. (a) $x^2 + y^2 = 1296$ **(b)** 5 s
3. $AB = 5$, $BC = 5$, $CA = 7.07$, $CA^2 = 50$, $AB^2 = 25$, $BC^2 = 25$, $AB^2 + BC^2 = CA^2$; 2 sides are equal and the sides conform to Pythagorean theorem, so ΔABC is an isosceles right triangle.
4. (a) PQ and RS have same slope ($\frac{4}{3}$) and length (65), and QR and SP have same slope ($\frac{-3}{4}$) and length (130), so $PQRS$ is a rectangle.
(b) 382 m
5. rhombus, all sides have length 5, JK and LM have same slope ($\frac{-3}{4}$) as do KL and MJ ($\frac{3}{4}$)
6. (a) $(-4.6, -51.6)$ **(b)** circumcentre
(c) 2683 units^2
7. $(\frac{8}{3}, 3)$, centre of mass
8. Let A, B, C, and D be midpoints. Then AB and CD have same slope ($\frac{-4}{3}$) and length (5); BC and DA also have same slope ($\frac{2}{3}$) and length ($\sqrt{13}$); so $STUV$ is a parallelogram.

Cumulative Review Test 1, page 219

1. $(2, -4)$
2. $(1, 1)$
3. (a) $y = 42 + 0.12x$, $y = 30 + 0.15x$
(b) (400, 90)
(c) number of kilometres at which costs are the same
(d) \$1.20 (440 km in total)
4. 40 kg of hard candy, 20 kg of soft candy
5. \$640 at 4.5%, \$560 at 2%

6. (a) The window for this graph is $X_{min} = 1994$, $X_{max} = 2000$, $Y_{min} = 4.8$, $Y_{max} = 6.1$.

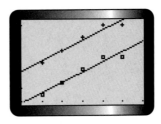

(b) Never - both are increasing at about the same rate.
(c) Furniture - it always sells more.
7. (a) scalene   **(b)** $6x - 7y - 1 = 0$
8. (a) midpoint of $AC =$ midpoint of BD
11. (a)

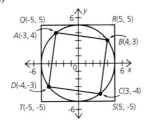

(c) $(5, 5)$, $(5, -5)$, $(-5, 5)$, $(-5, -5)$
(d) area of $ABCD = 50$ units^2, area of $QRST = 100$ units^2

Review of Essential Skills—Part II

Exponent Laws, page 228

1. (a) x^6 **(b)** c^{10} **(c)** y^{-2}
(d) g^{-8} **(e)** x^5
2. (a) c^2 **(b)** d^8 **(c)** x^{-4}
(d) b^{-11} **(e)** x^{13}
3. (a) f^6 **(b)** k^{-8} **(c)** m^{12}
(d) n^{-5} **(e)** x^{24}
4. (a) 64   **(b)** 1   **(c)** $\frac{1}{25}$
(d) -9 **(e)** 9   **(f)** -1
(g) $\frac{1}{8}$ **(h)** $\frac{1}{16}$ **(i)** $\frac{9}{4}$
(j) 0.166375   **(k)** 1   **(l)** -1
(m) $\frac{-1}{64}$ **(n)** -32 **(o)** -4
5. (a) x^5 **(b)** a^7 **(c)** x^8
(d) a^3 **(e)** m^5n^5 **(f)** $\frac{x^3}{y^3}$
(g) b^{10} **(h)** d^{-9} **(i)** g^6
(j) a^6b^{-10} **(k)** x^{-11} **(l)** $\frac{a^6}{b^9}$
6. (a) 5   **(b)** $\frac{1}{9}$ **(c)** 1
(d) $\frac{-5}{6}$ **(e)** $\frac{7}{8}$ **(f)** 9

7. (a) 2 **(b)** $\frac{7}{12}$ **(c)** $\frac{7}{2}$

(d) $\frac{4}{3}$ **(e)** 16 **(f)** 3

(g) 1 **(h)** 4 **(i)** $\frac{-3}{4}$

(j) -8

8. (a) $\frac{3}{8}$ **(b)** 5

(c) 5 **(d)** $\frac{11}{18}$

9. (a) $\frac{1}{18}$ **(b)** $\frac{1}{256}$

(c) $\frac{1}{25}$ **(d)** $\frac{1}{17}$

Simplifying Algebraic Expressions, page 230

1. (a) $12xy$ **(b)** $6x^2$ **(c)** $20ab$
(d) $3x^3$ **(e)** $36a^3$ **(f)** $-12x^3y^2$
(g) $-18xyz$ **(h)** $-21a^2b^2c$ **(i)** $90xyz$
(j) $-x^3y^4$
2. (a) $-3x^3 + 3x^2 - 3xy$ **(b)** $-2xy^2 - 2yz$
(c) $-7ab + 14b^2 - 21bc$
(d) $8p^2 - 20pq$ **(e)** $-20a^2 + 12a^3 + 4a^4$
3. (a) $-3x^2 + 6xy$ **(b)** $-2m^2 - 2mn$
(c) $4x^3 - 12x^3y$ **(d)** $18x^2y - 12y^3$
(e) $10x^2y - 15xy^2 + 20x^2y^2$
4. (a) $23x^2 - 2x$ **(b)** $-26y^2 + 26y$
(c) $-7x + 7y$ **(d)** $5y + 2$
(e) $-3x^2 + 3x$ **(f)** $-8y^2 + 2y$
5. (a) $n = 2$ **(b)** $n = 2x$
(c) $n = (1 - 2y)$ **(d)** $n = (y^2 + 2y - 4)$
(e) $n = (-3x + 2y - 5xy)$
(f) $n = (-3am + 2m + 6a)$
6. (a) $6(1 - 2x)$ **(b)** $x(5x - 3)$
(c) $3(3y - 4x)$ **(d)** $xy(5 - 3y)$
(e) $2x(x - 3)$ **(f)** $a(a - 2)$
(g) $b(4a - b)$ **(h)** $4(y + 2)(y - 2)$
(i) $14a(2a - b)$ **(j)** $mn(36 - 25mn)$
(k) $3(2x^2 - 4x + 5)$ **(l)** $5(m^3 - 5m^2 + 3)$
(m) $25(a + b)(2a + b)$ **(n)** $10xy(x^2y^2 + 2xy - 1)$
(o) $xy(x - xy - y)$ **(p)** $2q(p^2 - 2p + 4q)$
(q) $3k(k - 3 + 4k^3)$ **(r)** $3m^2n^3(1 - 9mn)$
7. (a) -8 **(b)** -153

Transformations of Two-Dimensional Shapes, page 233

1. (a) different position **(b)** reflected
(c) rotated
2. (a) reflection **(b)** translation **(c)** rotation
3. (a) rotation **(b)** translation **(c)** rotation
(d) reflection **(e)** reflection **(f)** rotation
4. (a) $(x + 1, y - 5)$ **(b)** $(x + 6, y - 2)$
(c) $(x + 7, y + 1)$
5. (a) $J'(-2, 0), K'(-2, -3), L'(1, -3)$
(b) $J'(4, 5), K'(4, 2), L'(1, 2)$
(c) $J'(-4, -5), K'(-4, -2), L'(-1, -2)$
(d) $J'(5, 4), K'(2, 4), L'(2, 1)$
6. (a) across x-axis **(b)** across y-axis

7. (a) 90° CCW or 270° CW Centre at (0, 0)
(b) 90° CW or 270° CCW Centre at (0, 0)
(c) 180° CW or 180° CCW Centre at (0, 0)

Finite Differences and Rate of Change, page 236

1. (a) First Differences 9.8, 9.8, 9.8, 9.8, 9.8, 9.8, 9.8, 9.8; linear;

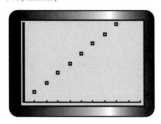

(b) First Differences 3.142, 5.236, 7.33, 9.425, 11.519, 13.614, 15.708; nonlinear;

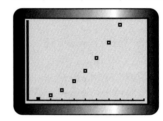

(c) First Differences 1.5, 1.5, 1.5, 1.5, 1.5, 1.5, 1.5, 1.5; linear;

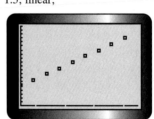

(d) First Differences -950, -950, -950, -950, -950, -950, -950; linear;

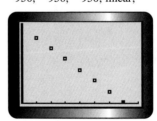

(e) First Differences 156, 172, 189, 208, 229, 251, 277; nonlinear;

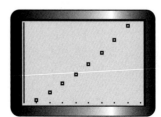

(f) First Differences 33.1, 23.3, 13.5, 3.7, −6.1, −15.9; nonlinear;

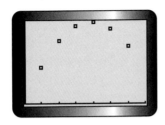

2. (a) 9.8 m/s²   **(c)** 1.5 $/km
    (d) −950 $/year

Interpolating and Extrapolating, page 239

1. (a) 53 m and 54 m   **(b)** 73 m and 77 m

2. (a)

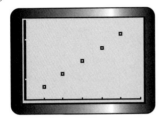

   (b) 24.5 m/s, 34.3 m/s, 46.55 m/s
   (c) 58.8 m/s, 88.2 m/s, 98 m/s

3. Extrapolation is a prediction based on the data while interpolation is taken directly from the data.

4. Find the equation for the line of best fit, then substitute in your y−value.

5. (a) Mass of Object (kg): 0, 1, 2, 3, 4, 6, **10**, 12
    Kinetic Energy (J): 0, 48.02, 96.04, **144.06, 192.08,** 288.12, 480.2, **576.24**

   (b)

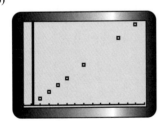

   (c) 240.1 J
   (d) 11.45 kg

6. (a)

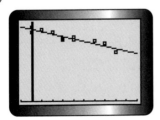

   (b) The average for 0 absences is 90%. For every time absent, the average mark drops by about 3%.

(c) 72%
(d) 13 days missed

Chapter 3

Getting Ready, page 244

1. (a) x-intercept $\frac{5}{3}$, y-intercept 5
   (b) x-intercept 2, y-intercept −5
   (c) x-intercept −2, y-intercept 4
   (d) x-intercept 4, y-intercept −5

2. (a) yes   **(b)** yes   **(c)** yes

3. (a) 250   **(b)** 12   **(c)** −28
   (d) 414   **(e)** 275   **(f)** 92.5
   (g) 2   **(h)** −0.9   **(i)** −5
   (j) $\frac{-3}{8}$ **(k)** −25   **(l)** 2
   (m) $\frac{-1}{12}$

4. (a) $-3x + 5y$ **(b)** $-7ab - 3bc$ **(c)** $-2x^2 + 7$
   (d) $5m - 21$ **(e)** $-5y + 12$ **(f)** $-2w^2 + 16w$
   (g) $2x^5 - 5x^2$ **(h)** $10x^6 - 15x^5$ **(i)** $-16x^6 - 8x^5$

5. (a) linear, $x = 0.5$

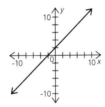

   (b) linear, $x = \frac{7}{6}$

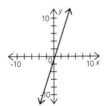

   (c) nonlinear, $x = \pm 2.1$

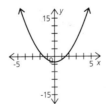

   (d) nonlinear, $x = 20.25$

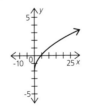

6. (a) 432 **(b)** 755
(c) 40.5 **(d)** 55.97
(e) 84 **(f)** 0

7. (a) $x = \frac{7}{2}, x = \frac{5}{2}, x = 11, x = -\frac{19}{3}$

(b) $a = 1, a = -\frac{1}{3}$, no solution, $a = 0.8$

8. (a) $a = 3$ **(b)** $b = -\frac{25}{2}$
(c) $c = -3$ **(d)** $d = 1$
(e) $e = \frac{6}{5}$ **(f)** $f = 11$

9. (a) $2w\,(8 - w)$ **(b)** $4\,(x + 5)\,(x - 2)$
(c) $2x^2\,(x^2 + 2x + 4)$ **(d)** $5xy(xy - 3 + 4x^2y)$

10. (a) Let x be length in centimetres. Let y be width in centimetres. $2x + 2y = 100$.
(b) Let x be side length in metres. $4x = 36$
(c) Let x, y, z be the lengths of the sides in centimetres. $x + y + z = 13$
(d) Let x be the width in centimetres. Let y be the length in centimetres. $xy = 40$
(e) Let x be the side length in centimetres. $x^2 = 81$
(f) Let x be the length of the base. $\frac{1}{2}x^2 = 14$
(g) Let x and y be the lengths of the sides of the large rectangle in centimetres. Let A be the area. $xy - 100 = A$
(h) Let x and y be the dimensions of the floor in centimetres. Let N be the number of tiles needed. $\frac{xy}{100} = N$
(i) Let x be the volume of gas in the storage tank in litres. Let y be the number of cans filled. $\frac{x}{5} = y$
(j) Let x be the distance driven in km. Let y be the cost in dollars. $0.059\,31x = y$

Practise, Apply, Solve 3.1, page 254

1. (a) 9, 9 **(b)** −3, 93
(c) 4, −74 **(d)** 21, 15
(e) −1, −25 **(f)** 15, 0
2. (a) linear **(b)** nonlinear
(c) nonlinear, quadratic **(d)** nonlinear
(e) nonlinear **(f)** nonlinear
3. (a) 2
4. (a) 7, 4, 1, −5, −8
(b) 8, 5, 5, 8; −3, −1, 3
(c) −15, −2, 3, 7, 10; 7, 5, 4
5. (a) 1 **(b)** 2 **(c)** 1
(d) 2 **(e)** 2 **(f)** 3
(g) 2 **(h)** 2 **(i)** 5
(j) 3 **(k)** 1 **(l)** 2
6. b, d, e, g, h, l

7. (a)

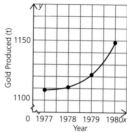

(b)

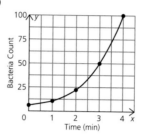

(c)

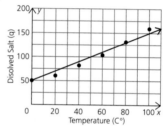

(d)

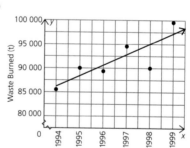

8. (a) (b)

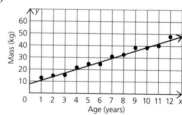

(c) linear - close to a line with some variations
(d) The model is reasonably accurate.

9. (a)–(b)

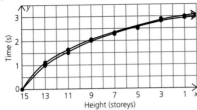

(c) very good fit   (d) nonlinear

10. (a)

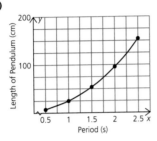

(b) 1.35 s   (c) 120 cm

(d) quadratic (second differences equal)

11. (a)

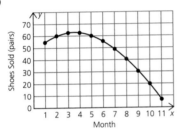

(b) months 3-4

(c) There were less shoes sold - new types of shoes to buy

(d) months 1-2: +4, months 4-5, −2; sales increasing in months 1-2 and decreasing in months 4-5

(e) months 1-2: +4, months 2-3, +2; sales increasing faster in months 1-2 than in months 2-3

(f) months 4-5: −2, months 5-6: −4; sales decreasing faster in months 5-6 than in months 4-5

(g) The second differences are equal.

12. (a) (c)

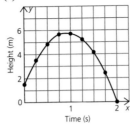

(b) quadratic

(d) 0.9 s, 5.8 m   (e) 2 s

13.(a)

Shape	Width(cm)	Length(cm)	Area(cm²)
	1	2	2
	2	4	8
	3	6	18
	4	8	32
	5	10	50
	6	12	72

(b) nonlinear (first differences are not equal)

(c) yes, the relation is quadratic

(d) Area $= 2(\text{width})^2$; degree $= 2$

14. (a) 8 by 8, 10 by 10

(b) 64, 100

(c) nonlinear

(d) quadratic (second difference is constant)

(e)

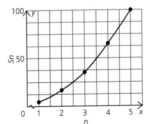

(f) $S_n = 4n^2$; degree $= 2$

15. (b)

Number of points	Number of connecting line segments
2	1
3	3
4	6
5	10

(c)

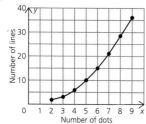

Number of dots (x-axis), Number of lines (y-axis)

(d) nonlinear - first differences are not identical

(e) number of lines $= \frac{n(n-1)}{2}$ where n is the number of dots

(f) 21

(g) substitute 21 into equation in **(e)**

16. (a) quadratic (parabola)

(b)

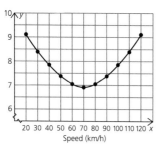

Speed (km/h)

(c) 70 km/h

(d) more strain on engine - more gas used

(e) \$6; 2.57 h longer

17. linear - first differences close to equal, quadratic - second differences close to equal, other, large fluctuations with some pattern

18. 59 900

19. (a)

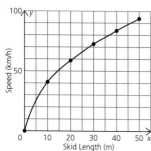

Skid Length (m), Speed (km/h)

(b) 94.1 m

(c) 36 m

(d) maximum skid length would be 32.4 m

(e) 69 m

(f) different material would have a different frictional coefficient while moisture conditions would increase the skid length

Practise, Apply, Solve 3.2, page 266

1. (a) no   **(b)** yes   **(c)** no
   (d) no   **(e)** yes   **(f)** no
   (g) yes   **(h)** no

2. (a) down   **(b)** up   **(c)** down
   (d) up

3. (a) $(3, 2)$ **(b)** 2
   (c) $x = 3$ **(d)** $x = 0, x = 6$
   (e) negative

4. (a) $(2, -3)$ **(b)** -3 (minimum)
   (c) $x = 2$ **(d)** $x = 0$ or $x = 4$
   (e) positive (slope is strictly increasing)

5. (a) minimum   **(b)** 2.5
   (c) negative (is a minimum and the graph has 2 intersections with the x-axis)

6. (a) maximum   **(b)** 7.5   **(c)** positive

7. (a) $x = 0$ or $x = 20$ **(b)** $x = 0$ or $x = 12$
   (c) $x = 0$ or $x = 2$ **(d)** $x = 0$ or $x = 18$
   (e) $x = 0$ or $x = -\frac{6}{5}$ **(f)** $x = 0$ or $x = \frac{16}{3}$

8.

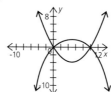

9. (a) $w(15 - w)$; $x = 0$ or $x = 15$; $x = 7.5$
   (b) $L(24 - L)$; $x = 0$ or $x = 24$; $x = 12$
   (c) $2x(x - 5)$; $x = 0$ or $x = 5$; $x = 2.5$
   (d) $x(15 - 2x)$; $x = 0$ or $x = \frac{15}{2}$; $x = \frac{15}{4}$

10. (a) $x = 6$ **(b)** $x = -5.5$ **(c)** $x = -3.5$
   (d) $x = 7.75$ **(e)** $x = -0.75$ **(f)** $x = -3$
   (g) $x = \frac{17}{8}$ **(h)** $x = \frac{s + t}{2}$

11. (a) zeros at $x = 0$, $x = 5$; football hits ground after 5 s

   (b) $(2.5, 31.25)$

   (c)

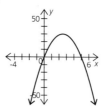

   (d) The maximum height of 31.25 m occurs after 2.5 s.

12. (a)

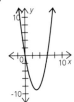

(b) $y = (x - 3)^2 - 9$

13. shift and stretch the graph of $y = x^2$.

14. (a)

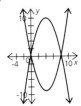

(b) $y = \frac{5}{8}(x - 4)^2 - 10$, $y = -\frac{5}{8}(x - 4)^2 + 10$

(c) positive coefficient = opens up, negative coefficient = opens down

15. 100 m

16. 30 m: $2x + y = 30$, $xy = $ maximum, maximum area $= 112.5$ m^2; 50 m: $2x + y = 50$, $xy = $ maximum, maximum area $= 312.5$ m^2; 70 m: $2x + y = 70$, $xy = $ maximum, maximum area $= 612.5$ m^2

17. (a) The x-coordinate of the vertex is half way between the zeros; substitute this for x.

(b) positive second differences = minimum, negative second differences = maximum

(c) Set each factor to 0 and solve the resulting equations.

(d) optimal value = y-coordinate of the vertex

18. 2.45

Practise 3.3, page 272

(a) $-4, -1$ **(b)** $9, -7$ **(c)** $3, -3$

(d) $\frac{2}{3}, -6$ **(e)** $\frac{1}{4}, \frac{3}{5}$ **(f)** $\frac{1}{2}, -5$

Practise, Apply, Solve 3.4, page 280

1. (a) 5, 30 **(b)** $-50, 50$

(c) $-4, 1$ **(d)** $-5, -1$

(e) none **(f)** none

2. (a) $x = 17.5$ **(b)** $x = 0$

(c) $x = -1.5$ **(d)** $x = -3$

(e) $x = 0$ **(f)** $x = 2.5$

3. (a) ii **(b)** iii

(c) i **(d)** iv

(e) vi **(f)** v

4. (a) maximum

(b) minimum

(c) maximum

(d) minimum

5. (a) $-4, -2; x = -3, (-3, -1)$

(b) $-5, 2; x = -\frac{3}{2}; \left(\frac{-3}{2}, \frac{49}{4}\right)$

(c) $-4, -1; x = -2.5; (-2.5, -2.25)$

(d) $1, -3; x = -1; (-1, 4)$

(e) $3, 2; x = 2.5; (2.5, 0.25)$

(f) $-1, 4; x = 1.5; (1.5, -6.25)$

(g) $-1, 3; x = 1; (1, -12)$

(h) $-3, 3; x = 0; (0, 18)$

6. (a) zeros 10, -10; optimal value 600

(b) zeros 7.5, -8; optimal value 480.5

(c) zeros 16, -12.5; optimal value 101.5

(d) zeros 8, -3; optimal value 2268.75

(e) zeros 8, -4; optimal value 800.25

7. (a)   **(b)**

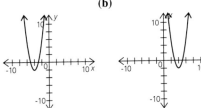

(c)   **(d)**

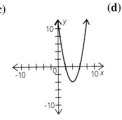
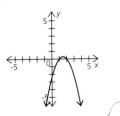

(e)   **(f)**

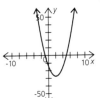
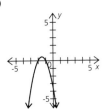

(g)   **(h)**

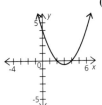
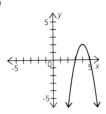

(i)

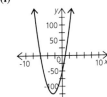

8. (a) $a = \frac{5}{9}$ **(b)** $a = -\frac{1}{8}$

(c) $a = \frac{1}{8}$ **(d)** $a = \frac{8}{5}$ **(e)** $a = -\frac{3}{8}$

9. (a) $y = -\frac{5}{8}(x + 2)(x - 4)$, down

(b) $y = \frac{5}{8}(x + 2)(x - 4)$, up

(c) $y = \frac{2}{5}(x + 2)(x + 5)$, up

(d) $y = -\frac{2}{5}(x + 2)(x + 5)$, down

(e) $y = \frac{1}{4}(x - 3)(x - 8)$, up

(f) $y = -\frac{1}{4}(x - 3)(x - 8)$, down

10. (a) (b)

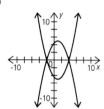

(c) (d)

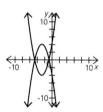

(e) (f)

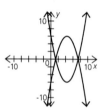

11. (a) $y = -\frac{3}{2}(x - 3)(x - 7)$

(b) $y = \frac{8}{25}(x + 1)(x + 6)$

(c) $y = -\frac{5}{16}(x + 1)(x - 7)$

(d) $y = -\frac{2}{9}x(x + 9)$

12. (a) $x = 1$

(b) $y = 2(x + 3)(x - 5)$

(c) $(1, -32)$

(d)

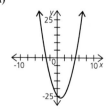

13. (c) $x = -1$

(d) $x = -1, x = 5$

(e) $(2, 45)$

(f) $y = -5(x + 1)(x - 5)$

(g) $x = 5$ is the time when the ball hits the ground. $x = -1$ is point where the ball would have started from is thrown from the ground.

14. At 15 m from the hole, the ball is 5.1 m above ground. ($y = -\frac{1}{250}(x + 50)(x - 50)$), letting origin be the base of the tree.

15. $y = -\frac{3}{10}x^2 + 100$

16. $y = -0.004(x + 140.5)(x - 140.5)$

17. (a)

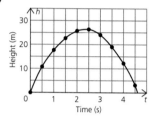

(b) $x = 0$ or $x = 4.6$ **(c)** $y = -5x(x - 4.6)$

(d) 26.45 m

18. (a)

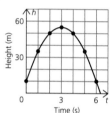

$x = -0.1$ or $x = 6.1$
$y = -5.8(x - 6.1)(x + 0.1)$
10 m

(b) 54.3 m after 2.5 s, 54.3 m after 3.5 s

(c) after 3 s   **(d)** after 6.1 s

19. (a) $2997.56   **(b)** 547   **(c)** $5.48

20. (a) $y = -0.0012(x + 250)(x - 50)$

(b) cost of making the vehicles

21. (a) Create an equation in factored form from each zero valued, then substitute the values from the point into the equation and solve for the resulting unknown quantity a.

(b) the zeros

(c) anything multiplied by 0 gives 0; so at least one of the factors must be 0

22. (a) (4)   **(b)** (1)

(c) (2)   **(d)** (5)

23. (a)

2.5	3	3.5	4	4.5	5	5.06
32.125	30.9	27.225	21.1	12.525	1.5	0

(b) $y = -4.9t^2 + 24.5t + 1.5$

(c) 23.844 m

(d) 32.125

Practise 3.5, page 288

1. (a) $(x + 2)(x + 1) = x^2 + 3x + 2$
   (b) $(x - 2)(x + 1) = x^2 - x - 2$
   (c) $(x + 2)(x - 2) = x^2 - 4$
   (d) $(2x + 2)(x + 2) = 2x^2 + 6x + 4$

2. (a) $x^2 + 5x + 6$ (b) $2x^2 + 7x + 6$
   (c) $x^2 - x - 6$ (d) $2x^2 - 8x + 6$

3. Because you "distributed" each term of one binomial by multiplying it by each of the terms in the second term. Then distributing the second term

5. (a) $x^2 + 7x + 12$ (b) $2x^2 + 5x + 2$
   (c) $6x^2 + 5x + 1$ (d) $x^2 + x - 2$
   (e) $2x^2 - 5x + 3$ (f) $6x^2 + x - 1$

Practise 3.6, page 291

(a) $y = x^2$ (b) $y = 3x^2 - 4$
(c) $y = -x^2 + 5x - 6$
(d) $y = -0.4621x^2 + 1839.1652x - 1829699.7454$

Practise, Apply, Solve 3.7, page 297

1. (a) $m^2, 6$ (b) k^2, k
   (c) $4r, -12$ (d) $-5x, -2x$
   (e) $6n^2, -4n$ (f) $-15m, 6$

2. (a) $d^2 + 3d + 2$ (b) $h^2 + h - 6$
   (c) $p^2 + p - 12$ (d) $a^2 - 5a + 6$
   (e) $w^2 - 6w + 9$ (f) $t^2 + 8t + 16$

3. (a) $2n^2 + 7n + 3$ (b) $3q^2 - 5q - 2$
   (c) $6x^2 - x - 1$ (d) $10m^2 + 13m - 3$
   (e) $4r^2 + 12r + 9$ (f) $16m^2 - 4$
   (g) $2a^2 + 4a - 30$ (h) $-2m^2 + 14m - 24$
   (i) $140h^2 + 15h - 90$ (j) $-42 + 148f - 96f^2$
   (k) $45h^2 + 3hk - 6k^2$ (l) $120x^2 + 42x - 36$

4. (a) $x^2 + 6x + 9$ (b) $x^2 - 14x + 49$
   (c) $x^2 + 16x + 64$ (d) $4x^2 + 4x + 1$
   (e) $16x^2 - 24x + 9$ (f) $25x^2 + 70x + 49$

5. (a) 2   (b) 2
   (c) $(x - 4)$ (d) $(x - 6)$ (e) $(x - 3)$
   (f) $x, 5x$ (g) $6x, x$ (h) $6x, x$
   (i) $(2y + 3)$ (j) $(2y + 3)$ (k) $(3x - 5)$
   (l) $(5x + 1)$

6. (a) $5 + 3 = 8$ but $(5)(3) \neq 10$
   (b) $-2 + 8 = 6$ but $(-2)(8) \neq -8$
   (c) $(2c)(3c) = 6c^2$ but $5(3c) + 3(2c) \neq 19c$
   (d) $(-5)(-3) = 15$
   but $(-5)(5d) + (2d)(-3) \neq -19d$

7. (a) $8m^2 + 4m - 12$
   (b) $9m^2 + 12m + 4$

8. (a) $y = -\frac{1}{3}x^2 + 2x$ (b) $y = -\frac{3}{4}x^2 + 6x - 9$
   (c) $y = \frac{5}{4}x^2 - 5$ (d) $y = \frac{4}{5}x^2 + \frac{28}{5}x + \frac{24}{5}$

9. (a) $m + 2$ (b) $x + 4$

10. (a) $y = -\frac{5}{16}(x - 3)^2 + 5$, down
    (b) $y = (x + 3)^2 - 4$, up
    (c) $y = \frac{1}{7}(x - 5)^2 - \frac{4}{7}$, up
    (d) $y = \frac{1}{7}(x - 2)^2 - \frac{16}{7}$, up

(e) $y = -\frac{7}{25}(x - 3)^2 + 7$, up

11. (b) $y = -5(x - 1)^2 + 5$
    (c) $y = -5x^2 + 10x$
    (d) The quadratic model is better for the data because the data represents a quadratic relationship.

12. (a)

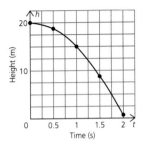

(b) after 2.1 s
(c) $x = -2.02$ and $x = 2.02$
(d) $y = -4.9x^2 + 20$
(e) $y = -4.89x^2 - 0.009x + 19.99$

13. $y = 0.000\ 36x^2 + 4$

14. (a) $y = -x^2 + 10.5x + 2970$
    (b) \$5.25   (c) \$5.25

15. $y = -\frac{1}{48}x^2 + 192$

16. (a) expand and complete the square
    (b) factored form, because it gives the zeros and then you can find the vertex
    (c) discriminant is negative - there are no real roots

17. (a) $8x^2 + 11x - 3$ (b) $2x^2 - 18$
    (c) $7x^2 - 15x + 10$ (d) $-22x^2 - 64x - 54$
    (e) $7x^2 + 52x - 77$ (f) $-8x^2 + 52x - 11$

18. (a) $x^2 + 6x + 9$ (b) $4x^2 - 8x + 4$
    (c) $64x^3 + 96x^2y + 48xy^2 + 8y^3$
    (d) $x^4 - 8x^2 + 16$
    (e) $x^4 - 45x^2 + 324$
    (f) $9x^4 + 36x^3 + 30x^2 - 12x + 1$
    (g) $x^4 - 4x^3 + 6x^2 - 4x + 1$

Practise, Apply, Solve 3.8, page 307

1. (a) 7, 8   (b) $-8, 2$
   (c) $-4, 3$ (d) $-5, 7$

2. (a) $(x + 1)(x + 2)$ (b) $(x + 4)(x + 1)$
   (c) $(f - 3)^2$ (d) $(c - 3)(c + 5)$
   (e) $(g - 3)(g + 6)$ (f) $(r - 2)(r + 4)$
   (g) $(m - 7)(m + 2)$ (h) $(n - 4)(n - 5)$
   (i) $(x - 2)(x - 8)$ (j) $(a - 3)^2$
   (k) $(x - 4)(x - 5)$ (l) $(y + 4)^2$
   (m) $(x - 4)(x + 9)$ (n) $(b - 8)(b + 4)$
   (o) $(x - 7)(x - 8)$ (p) $(v - 3)(v + 9)$
   (q) $(t - 6)(t + 8)$ (r) $(p - 8)(p - 9)$

3. (a) $3(x + 3)(x + 5)$ (b) $2(y - 6)(y + 5)$
   (c) $3(a + 1)(a + 2)$ (d) $5(x - 1)^2$
   (e) $6(x + 5)(x - 1)$ (f) $x(x + 4)(x + 1)$
   (g) $8(m - 6)(m - 7)$ (h) $21(x + 2)(x - 1)$
   (i) $7(x + 7)(x - 3)$

4. **(a)** $(x + 5)(x - 5)$ **(b)** $(c + 7)(c - 7)$
(c) $(a + 6)(a - 6)$ **(d)** $(x + 9)(x - 9)$
(e) $(d + 11)(d - 11)$ **(f)** $(b + 8)(b - 8)$
(g) $(3x + 2)(3x - 2)$ **(h)** $(8a + 1)(8a - 1)$
(i) $(5p + 7)(5p - 7)$ **(j)** $(4c + 9)(4c - 9)$
(k) $2(5r + 6)(5r - 6)$ **(l)** $7(y + 2)(y - 2)$

5. **(a)** $(3x - 1)^2$ **(b)** $(5x + 2)^2$ **(c)** $(2a - 5)^2$
(d) $(7c + 3)^2$ **(e)** $(10x - 9)^2$ **(f)** $(6g + 5)^2$
(g) $(3v - 2)^2$ **(h)** $(8c + 1)^2$ **(i)** $(4d - 3)^2$

6. **(a)** $(2t - 3)(t + 2)$ **(b)** $(3m + 1)(m - 4)$
(c) $(5x - 1)(2x + 1)$ **(d)** $(3x + 2)^2$
(e) $(3x - 2)^2$ **(f)** $(2x - 5)(2x - 3)$
(g) $(2y + 1)(y + 1)$ **(h)** $(3b + 1)(b - 2)$
(i) $(2c - 3)(c + 4)$ **(j)** $(3x + 1)(2x + 1)$
(k) $(5a - 1)(a - 2)$ **(l)** $(3m + 2)(2m - 5)$
(m) $(2d + 1)(d + 2)$ **(n)** $(3w - 2)(2w - 3)$
(o) $(5b + 3)(2b - 1)$

7. **(a)** $3a(a + 2)$ **(b)** $2x(1 - 4y)$
(c) $(5a + 3)(5a - 3)$ **(d)** $(x + 3)(x + 4)$
(e) $(y - 4)(y - 7)$ **(f)** $(4a - 1)^2$
(g) $(x + 2)(x + 4)$ **(h)** $(5b - 4)(b - 2)$
(i) $2(5x - 4)(x - 2)$ **(j)** $3(d + 12)(d - 12)$
(k) $(3d + 1)(2d + 1)$ **(l)** $(8c - 1)(7c + 2)$
(m) $2(g - 4)(g + 3)$ **(n)** $(3x - 4)(3x + 4)$
(o) $xy^2(xyz - 2)$

8. **(a)** $y = (x + 2)(x - 2)$; $-2, 2$; $(0, -4)$
(b) $y = (x + 2)(x + 4)$; $-2, -4$; $(-3, -1)$
(c) $y = (x - 5)(x - 1)$; $5, 1$; $(3, -4)$
(d) $y = -(x - 6)(x + 4)$; $6, -4$; $(1, 25)$
(e) $y = (x + 1)^2$; -1; $(-1, 0)$
(f) $y = -(x - 6)(x + 3)$; $6, -3$; $(1.5, 20.25)$

9. 162 m^2

10. No, only those which cross the x-axis can be.

11. **(a)** after 6 s **(b)** 45 m

12. **(a)** 30 m **(b)** after 3 s
(c) after 0.5 s **(d)** 31.25 m

13. **(a)** \$81 000 **(b)** 1000
(c) 0 snowboards or 2000 snowboards sold

14. **(a)** \$8 000 000 **(b)** 700 000
(c) 500 000 or 900 000 games produced

15. **(a)** factor it or graph to obtain the roots, and can then find the vertex quickly
(b) you know the x-intercepts (zeros)

16. **(a)** $h = -0.0502(d - 21.9)(d + 1.2)$
(b) s and t are the points where the shot is on the ground.

17. **(a)** cannot factor
(b) cannot factor
(c) $2(2x + 5)(2x - 5)$
(d) $\left(\dfrac{a}{8} + \dfrac{b}{7}\right)\left(\dfrac{a}{8} - \dfrac{b}{7}\right)$
(e) $\left(\dfrac{c^2}{4} + \dfrac{d^2}{4}\right)\left(\dfrac{c}{2} + \dfrac{d}{3}\right)\left(\dfrac{c}{2} - \dfrac{d}{3}\right)$
(f) $(25m^4n^2 + 4p^4)(5m^2n + 2p^2)(5m^2n - 2p^2)$
(g) $(6 + w)(14 - w)$
(h) *cannot factor in R*
(i) $(x - y + 3z)(x - y - 3z)$
(j) $(a + 3 + b)(a + 3 - b)$

(k) $(2ab + 3c)^2$
(l) $(3x - 1 + 2y)(3x - 1 - 2y)$

18. Yes, it was effective, because with the new equation, Soundz starts making a profit with fewer CD players made, and makes more profit that would be made earlier.

Practise, Apply, Solve 3.9, page 315

1. **(a)** $x = 2$ or $x = -5$ **(b)** $y = 0$ or $y = 5$
(c) $m = -\dfrac{1}{2}$ or $m = 3$ **(d)** $t = \dfrac{2}{3}$ or $t = -3$
(e) $x = \dfrac{1}{2}$ or $x = \dfrac{2}{3}$ **(f)** $r = 3$ or $r = -2$
(g) $a = 0$ or $a = 5$ **(h)** $x = -\dfrac{3}{4}$ or $x = \dfrac{2}{5}$
(i) $p = \dfrac{3}{4}$ or $p = \dfrac{2}{7}$

2. **(a)** $n = -10$ or $n = 3$ **(b)** $y = -4$ or $y = -\dfrac{1}{2}$
(c) $m = -5$ or $m = -3$
(d) $y = 3$ or $y = -2$ **(e)** $x = 5$ or $x = -3$
(f) $m = 1$ or $m = -1$ **(g)** $n = \dfrac{1}{2}$ or $n = -\dfrac{1}{2}$
(h) $x = \dfrac{5}{4}$ or $x = -\dfrac{5}{4}$ **(i)** $n = \dfrac{1}{3}$
(j) $x = -5$ or $x = 2$ **(k)** $x = -3$ or $x = -2$
(l) $x = -\dfrac{1}{2}$ or $x = 4$

3. **(a)** $x = 7$ or $x = -6$ **(b)** $x = 7$ or $x = -3$
(c) $a = 8$ or $a = -6$ **(d)** $m = -10$ or $m = 3$
(e) $x = \dfrac{3}{2}$ or $x = -\dfrac{1}{3}$ **(f)** $x = 3$ or $x = -\dfrac{5}{2}$
(g) $y = -\dfrac{1}{2}$ or $y = -4$ **(h)** $x = -\dfrac{2}{5}$ or $x = -3$
(i) $m = \dfrac{1}{2}$ or $m = -3$

4. 14 m by 4 m

5. **(a)** $x = 1$ or $x = -1$ **(b)** $x = 3$ or $x = 2$
(c) $x = 3$ or $x = -\dfrac{7}{2}$

6. **(a)** $3, -2$ **(b)** $6, -3$
(c) $5, 2$ **(d)** none
(e) $3, -\dfrac{17}{6}$ **(f)** $6, 2$

8. **(a)** 5000 m **(b)** 30 s **(c)** 3 s

9. **(a)** 1.5 s **(b)** 2.1 s
(c) The velocity is increasing.

10. 5 m

11. It will be reduced to 4.27 m.

12. **(a)** 188 000 **(b)** 68 000 **(c)** 1963 or 1992
(d) no (the parabola does not intersect the x-axis)

13. **(a)** 15 m **(b)** 4.8 s
(c) 5.2 s **(d)** 41.45 m

14. 92.5 m

15. **(a)** 6.816 m **(b)** 45 km/h

16. 17.09 m

17. 12 m by 9 m

18. 20.48 m by 20.48 m

19. **(a)** substitute for y in the equation; solve by factoring if possible, after rearranging in $ax^2 + bx + c = 0$ form. Graph the new relation and solve graphically.

(b) 2; in a distance-time graph, a zero corresponding to a negative time value would not be reasonable.

20. Earth: $h = 2.3 + 50t - 4.9t^2$, 129.85 m, 10.2 s, 1.5 s; Mercury: $h = 2.3 + 50t - 1.862t^2$, 337.96 m, 26.9 s, 3.9 s; Venus: $h = 2.3 + 50t - 3.969t^2$, 159.77 m, 12.6 s, 1.8 s; Mars: $h = 2.3 + 50t - 1.96t^2$, 321.18 m, 25.6 s, 3.7 s; Jupiter: $h = 2.3 + 50t - 12.446t^2$, 52.52 m, 4.1 s, 0.6 s; Saturn: $h = 2.3 + 50t - 5.292t^2$, 120.40 m, 9.5 s, 1.4 s; Uranus: $h = 2.3 + 50t - 4.459t^2$, 142.47 m, 11.3 s, 1.6 s; Neptune: $h = 2.3 + 50t - 9.31t^2$, 69.43 m, 5.4 s, 0.8 s; Pluto: $h = 2.3 + 50t - 0.392t^2$, 1596.69 m, 127.6 s, 18.6 s; different masses and different densities

21. 10.67 m apart

Chapter 3 Review, page 323

1. (a) linear **(b)** cubic **(c)** exponential
(d) linear **(e)** linear

2. (a) $N_6 = 156$, $N_7 = 210$, $N_8 = 272$
(b) $N_n = 4n^2 + 2n$

3. (a) (d)

(b) quadratic
(c) $y = -5x^2 + 1200$
(e) about 15.5 s

4. (a) $x = -7$ **(b)** $x = 3.1$ **(c)** $x = -1$
(d) $x = -\frac{1}{8}$ **(e)** $x = \frac{79}{16}$ **(f)** $x = \frac{3}{4}$

5. (a) maximum **(b)** $x = \frac{3}{2}$
(c) positive (it is a maximum)

6. (a) $w = 0$ or $w = 18$, $w = 9$, maximum, $(9, 81)$
(b) $L = 0$ or $L = 10$, $L = 5$, maximum, $(5, 25)$
(c) $x = 0$ or $x = \frac{1}{4}$, $x = \frac{1}{8}$, maximum, $\left(\frac{1}{8}, \frac{1}{4}\right)$
(d) $t = 0$ or $t = 5$, $t = \frac{5}{2}$, maximum, $\left(\frac{5}{2}, \frac{125}{4}\right)$
(e) $x = 0$ or $x = -\frac{5}{2}$, $x = -\frac{5}{4}$, minimum, $\left(\frac{-5}{4}, \frac{-75}{8}\right)$
(f) $w = 0$ or $w = 7$, $w = \frac{7}{2}$, maximum, $\left(\frac{7}{2}, \frac{147}{2}\right)$

7. (a) $y = \frac{1}{2}(x + 1)^2 - 2$
(b) $y = -\frac{1}{4}(x - 40)^2 + 100$
(c) $y = \frac{1}{270}(x - 90)^2 - 30$
(d) $y = -\frac{2}{21}x^2 + 42$

8. (a) $x = -3$ or $x = 1$, $x = 20$ or $x = 60$, $x = 0$ or $x = 180$, $x = -21$ or $x = 21$
(b) -1, 40, 90, 0

9. (a) $y = \frac{1}{2}(x - 5)(x - 9)$
(b) $y = -\frac{4}{25}(x + 3)(x - 7)$
(c) $y = \frac{3}{4}(x + 6)(x - 2)$
(d) $y = \frac{8}{45}(x + 9)(x + 5)$

10. (a) \$2
(b) Answers may vary. (eg cost of owning/operating a car)
(c) Answers may vary.

11. (a) $x^2 + 9x + 20$ **(b)** $x^2 - 7x + 10$
(c) $x^2 - x - 42$ **(d)** $4x^2 - 9$
(e) $12x^2 + 7x - 10$ **(f)** $30x^2 + 32x - 14$
(g) $30 - 8x - 6x^2$ **(h)** $20a^2 + 2ab - 6b^2$
(i) $4m^2 + 12mn + 9n^2$ **(j)** $-6x^2 - 21x + 12$
(k) $30u^2 - 55uv - 50v^2$ **(l)** $12x^2 - 14x - 40$

12. (a) $y = -x^2 + 2x + 3$
(b) $y = 2.5x^2 + 37.5x + 135$
(c) $y = 0.01x^2 + 1.6x - 15.36$
(d) $y = -\frac{11}{24}(x^2 - 49)$

13. (a) $y = -\frac{4}{3}x^2 + \frac{8}{3}x + \frac{32}{3}$
(b) $y = -\frac{1}{2}x^2 + 2x + 16$

14. (a) $(x + 5)(x - 3)$ **(b)** $(m + 4)(m - 1)$
(c) $(r - 2)^2$ **(d)** $(q - 5)(q + 2)$
(e) $(x + 1)(6x - 1)$ **(f)** $(2d + 1)(3d - 2)$
(g) $(x + 3)(x - 3)$ **(h)** $(2x + 5)(2x - 5)$
(i) $(3x + 2)^2$ **(j)** $3(m + 3)(m - 2)$
(k) $2(2p - 1)(2p + 3)$ **(l)** $3(3x + 4)(3x - 4)$

15. (a) $b = 5$ or $b = 2$ **(b)** 3500

16. (a) $x = 6$ or $x = -5$ **(b)** $x = 8$ or $x = -4$
(c) $x = -7$ or $x = -5$ **(d)** $x = -7$ or $x = 3$
(e) $x = -9$ or $x = 4$ **(f)** $x = 5$
(g) $x = \frac{2}{3}$ or $x = \frac{1}{2}$ **(h)** $x = \frac{1}{3}$ or $x = -\frac{4}{3}$
(i) $x = 7$ or $x = 6$

17. (a) $x = 5$ or $x = -6$ **(b)** $x = -4$ or $x = -3$
(c) $x = -1$ or $x = \frac{3}{2}$ **(d)** $x = \frac{3}{2}$ or $x = \frac{2}{3}$

18. (a)

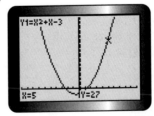

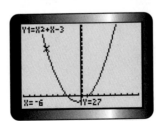

(b)

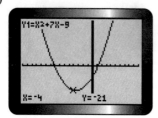

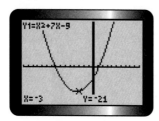

(c)

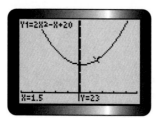

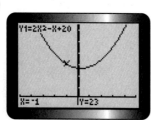

(d)

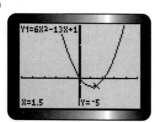

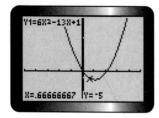

19. (a) 65 m   **(b)** 3 s   **(c)** 4.74 s
20. (a) 1 m   **(b)** 2.8 m

Chapter 3 Review Test, page 337

1. (a) quadratic   **(b)** neither
   (c) linear   **(d)** neither
2. (a) minimum   **(b)** $x = 3$
   (c) negative
3. (a) $x = 5$ **(b)** $x = -9$ or $x = 19$
   (c) $\frac{1}{7}x^2 - \frac{10}{7}x - \frac{171}{7}$
4. (a)

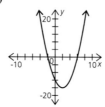

(b)

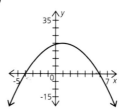

5. (a) $10x^2 - 11x - 6$ **(b)** $15a^2 - 14ab - 8b^2$
   (c) $-10x^2 + 25x + 210$
6. (a) $(x - 7)(x - 2)$ **(b)** $(4x + 5)(4x - 5)$
   (c) $(3x + 4)(2x - 1)$ **(d)** $2(x + 3)(x + 2)$
7. (a) $x = 3$ or $x = -7$ **(b)** $x = -2$ or $x = -6$
   (c) $x = \frac{1}{3}$ or $x = -\frac{5}{2}$
8. (a) The second difference from 3 to 8 is constant.
   (b) $y = -4.87x^2 + 37.46x + 13.55$
   (c) 16 m, after 3.8 s, 85.58, 8 s
   (d) $y = -4.87x^2 + 37.46x + 13.55$
9. (a) 3000   **(b)** 7600
   (c) 2556   **(d)** 2061
   (e) The function is always increasing.
10. $8

Chapter 4

Getting Ready, page 340

1. (a) yes   **(b)** no   **(c)** yes
2. It allows you to find the x-intercepts or zeros.
3. (a) 3   **(b)** 3
   (c) 5.5   **(d)** 3.05
   (e) $-1.91\overline{6}$ **(f)** -7
4. (a) $y = x^2 + 9x + 20$ **(b)** $y = 2x^2 + x - 6$
   (c) $y = -3x^2 - 9x + 84$ **(d)** $y = x^2 + 10x + 25$
   (e) $y = -5x^2 + 5x$ **(f)** $y = 2x^2 + 12x + 12$
5. (a) linear   **(b)** quadratic
   (c) quadratic   **(d)** linear
   (e) neither   **(f)** quadratic

(g) quadratic   (h) neither
(i) neither (circle)

6. (a) $2x(x - 4)$ (b) $(x + 3)(x + 2)$
(c) $(x - 10)(x + 6)$ (d) $(x - 4)^2$
(e) $3(x - 5)(x + 2)$ (f) $(w + 6)(w - 6)$
(g) $(3x + 2)(x + 4)$ (h) $(2x - 5)^2$
(i) $2(5x - 3)(5x + 3)$

7. (a) $-5, 3$ (b) $4, -1$
(c) $0, -3$ (d) $0, 10$
(e) $7, -5$ (f) $4, -4$
(g) 4 (h) $3, -6$
(i) $\sqrt{10}, -\sqrt{10}$

8. (a) $y = -\frac{1}{2}(x + 3)(x - 7)$
(b) $y = -3(x + 2)^2$

9. (a) $2, -4; (-1, -9);$

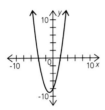

(b) $1, 4; (2.5, 2.5);$

(c) $-1, 3; (1, 8);$

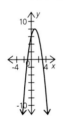

(d) $-3, 0; (-1.5, -2.25);$

(e) $2; (2, 0);$

(f) $-2, -6; (-4, -2);$

10. (a) $y = x^2$ (b) $y = (x - 3)(x - 5)$
11. (a) quadratic
(b)

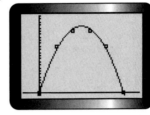

(c) 21.6 m   (d) 5 s
(e) $y = -3.4x^2 + 17x + 0.36$ (f) 21.6 m

12. $R = (5 + 0.5x)(400 - 25x)$
13. (a) $A'(-4, 6), B'(-10, 4), C'(-4, -2)$
(b) $A'(2, -4), B'(-4, -2), C'(2, 4)$
(c) $A'(6, 1), B'(0, -1), C'(6, -7)$
(d) $A'(-2, 4), B'(4, 2), C'(-2, -4)$

Practise, Apply, Solve 4.2, page 351

1. (a) $(-5, -4)$ (b) $x = -5$
(c) down
(d)

2. (a) $(2, 5), x = 2$, up   (b) $(-3, -2), x = -3$, down
(c) $(4, 0), x = 4$, up   (d) $(0, 0), x = 0$, up
(e) $(0, 2), x = 0$, down   (f) $(-7, 4), x = -7$, down

3. (a) $y = x^2 - 4x + 4$ (b) $y = 3x^2 + 24x + 48$
(c) $y = x^2 - 6x + 12$ (d) $y = -2x^2 - 4x - 2$
(e) $y = 4x^2 - 8x - 2$ (f) $y = -\frac{2}{3}x^2 - 4x - 11$

4. If they are both positive, the parabola opens upward; if they are both negative, it opens downward.

5. (a) $y = 2x^2 + 3$ (b) $y = -3(x - 2)^2$
(c) $y = -(x - 3)^2 - 2$
(d) $y = 0.5(x + 3.5)^2 + 18.3$

6. (a) yes   (b) no
(c) no   (d) yes
(e) yes

7. (a) $y = -2x^2 + 3$ (b) $y = (x - 2)^2$
(c) $y = 3(x + 3)^2 + 2$ (d) $y = -\frac{5}{16}(x - 5)^2 - 3$

8. examples:
(a) $(-2, -5)$ (b) $(-1, 9)$
(c) $(-5, 14)$ (d) $(9, -8)$

9. (a) $(0, -5)$, $(1, -4)$, $(-1, -4)$;

(b) $(-3, 0)$, $(0, 9)$, $(-6, 9)$;

(c) $(2, -5)$, $(0, -1)$, $(4, -1)$;

(d) $(0, 12)$, $(1, 9)$, $(-1, 9)$;

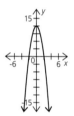

(e) $(-1, -5)$, $(0, -3)$, $(-2, -3)$;

(f) $(3, 8)$, $(1, 6)$, $(-1, 0)$;

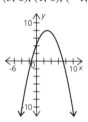

10. (a) $y = (x + 1)^2 - 4$ **(b)** $y = 2(x - 4)^2 - 2$
(c) $y = -(x - 4)^2 + 4$ **(d)** $y = -\frac{1}{2}x^2 + 4$

11. (a) $y = -\frac{9}{4}(x + 3)(x - 7)$
(b) $y = -\frac{9}{4}x^2 + 9x + \frac{189}{4}$
(c) $(2, \frac{225}{4})$
(d) $y = -\frac{9}{4}(x - 2)^2 + \frac{225}{4}$

12. $y = -\frac{1}{2}(x - 3)^2 + \frac{25}{2}$

13. $y = -\frac{8}{25}(x - 5)^2 + 8$

14. (a) $(0, 0)$, $(2, 0)$ **(b)** $(1, -2)$
(c) $\frac{0 + 2}{2} = 1$ **(d)** $(-2, 16)$
(e) $y = 2(x - 1)^2 - 2$

15. (a) quadratic
(b)

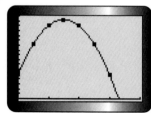

(c) $(1.5, 16.25)$
(d) $y = -5(x - 1.5)^2 + 16.25$
(e) 8.4 m, 15.9 m
(f) not effective—yields negative height

16. (a) quadratic
(b)

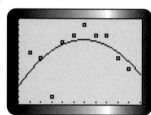

(c) $(1993, 241)$
(d) $y = -\frac{3}{16}(x - 1993)^2 + 241$
(e) 171 **(f)** 114

17. (a)

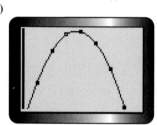

(b) $y = -1200(x - 1.85)^2 + 4107$
(c) 3915 **(d)** \$1.85

18. (a)

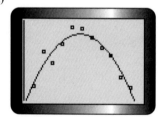

(b) $y = -\frac{106}{25}(x - 1984)^2 + 496$
(c) 224 640
(d) $-589\ 440$; no, cannot go below 0

19. (a) 2, 6

(b) $y = -2(x - 2)(x - 6)$

(c) (4, 8)

(d) $y = -2(x - 4)^2 + 8$

20. (a) zeros, direction of opening

(b) vertex, direction of opening

(c) direction of opening

21. (a) 0.776 m

(b) 29 m

(c) 28.2 m, up—before the maximum height

(d) no—negative height at this time, according to model

(e) 4.83 s

(f) 40.089 m

22. $5, 300 customers; keep charge the same

23. (a) (h, k)

(b) $x = h$

(c) $a > 0, a < 0$

24. (a) $y = -\frac{1}{160}(x - 30)(x + 80)$

(b) $(-25, 18.9)$

25. $y = 2(x - 2)^2 - 8$

Practise, Apply, Solve 4.3, page 363

1. (a) iv
(b) ii
(c) i
(d) iii

2. (a) vi
(b) i
(c) iv
(d) ii

3. (a) translate up 5 units

(b) translate right 3 units

(c) reflected about y-axis, vertically stretched by 3

(d) translated left 7 units

(e) compressed vertically by factor of 2

4. (a)

(b)

(c)

(d)

(e)

(f)

5. (a) constant: a, k; changed: h

(b) constant: k, h; changed: a

(c) constant: a, h; changed: k

6. examples:

(a) $y = -x^2, y = -2x^2$

(b) $y = 2x^2, y = 3x^2$

(c) $y = -\frac{1}{2}x^2, y = -\frac{1}{3}x^2$

(d) $y = 2(x + 5)^2, y = (x + 5)^2 - 2$

7. (a) reflected in x-axis, translate 9 up

(b) translate 3 right

(c) translate 2 left, 1 down

(d) reflect in x-axis, translate 6 down

(e) reflect in x-axis, vertical stretch by factor of 2, translate 4 right and 16 up

(f) horizontal compression by factor of 2, translate 6 left and up 12

(g) reflect in x-axis, horizontal compression by factor of 2, translate 4 left and 7 down

(h) vertical stretch by factor of 5, translate 4 right and 12 down

(i) vertical stretch by factor of 3, horizontal compression by factor of 4, translate 1 right and 5 up

8. (a)

(b)

(c)

(d)

(e)

(f)

9. (a) translate 2 down, horizontal compression by factor of 2, $y = \frac{1}{2}x^2 - 2$

(b) reflect in x-axis, translate 4 right, $y = -(x - 4)^2$

(c) reflect in x-axis, translate 3 down, vertical stretch factor of 2, $y = -2x^2 - 3$

(d) reflect in x-axis, translate 2 down and 4 left, $y = -(x + 4)^2 - 2$

10. examples: $y = (x + 3)^2 + 5$, $y = -(x + 3)^2 + 5$ (reflect in x-axis), $y = 2(x + 3)^2 + 5$ (vertical stretch by factor of 2)

11. (a) 2   **(b)** 0

(c) 1   **(d)** 2

12. (a) $y = 5(x - 2)^2 - 20$ **(b)** $y = \frac{1}{2}(x - 2)^2 - 2$

(c) $y = 5x^2 - 4$ **(d)** $y = (x - 2)^2 - 1$

(e) $y = -(x - 4)^2 - 8$

13. (a) $y = x^2 + 4$ **(b)** $y = -(x - 5)^2$

(c) example: $y = 2(x - 2)^2 - 3$

(d) example: $y = -\frac{1}{2}(x + 3)^2 + 5$

(e) example: $y = 2(x - 4)^2 - 8$

(f) example: $y = -\frac{1}{2}(x - 3)^2 - 4$

14. (a) $(0, -8)$, $y = 2x^2 - 8$

(b) $(0, -4)$, $y = 2x^2 - 4$

(c) In (a), the "2 ×" applies to the whole equation, while in (b) it applies only to the $y = x^2$ part.

(d) vertical stretch by factor of 2, translate 4 down

15. The coordinates are the maximum height of the balloon, $y = -0.04(x - 27.2)^2 + 29.6$

16. (a) $y = x^2 - 7$

(b) $y = \frac{3}{2}(x + 4)^2$

(c) $y = \frac{1}{3}x^2 + 10$

(d) $y = -2(x - 5)^2 - 8$

17. examples: vertical stretch factor of 2: $y = 10x^2$, $y = -10x^2$; horizontal compression by factor of 2: $y = \frac{5}{2}x^2$, $y = -\frac{5}{2}x^2$; translate 2 up and 7 down: $y = 5x^2 + 2$, $y = -5x^2 - 7$; translate 2 right: $y = 5(x - 2)^2$, $y = -5(x - 2)^2$; translate 2 left: $y = 5(x + 2)^2$, $y = -5(x + 2)^2$

18. The slower the acceleration due to gravity, the longer the object takes to hit the ground. Fastest Neptune; slowest Mars.

19. 5.3 s

20. (a) $y = x^2 + 2$, $y = -x^2 + 2$, $y = 2x^2 + 2$, $y = -2x^2 + 2$, $y = \frac{1}{2}x^2 + 2$, $y = -\frac{1}{2}x^2 + 2$

(b) $y = x^2 + 6$, $y = x^2 + 4$, $y = x^2 + 2$, $y = x^2 - 2$, $y = x^2 - 4$, $y = x^2 - 6$

21. (a) The centre moves.

(b) a divides the radius in the x-direction and h divides it in the y-direction

(c) a compresses or divides the radius in the x-direction; b compresses or divides the radius in the y-direction; h moves the x-coordinate of the centre of the circle; k moves the y-coordinate of the centre of the circle.

Practise, Apply, Solve 4.4, page 376

1. (a) $x = 0$, $x = -3$ **(b)** $w = 2$, $w = -7$

(c) $x = \frac{8}{3}$, $x = -\frac{5}{2}$ **(d)** $t = 0$, $t = \frac{45}{2}$

(e) $z = 6$, $z = -6$ **(f)** $x = 3$

2. (a) $0, -5$; -2.5 **(b)** $5, -2$; 1.5

(c) 4; 4 **(d)** $1, -1$; 0

(e) $20, -1$; 9.5 **(f)** $0, 7$; 3.5

(g) $-2.5, 15.5$; 6 **(h)** $-6, 4$; -1

(i) $\frac{7}{2}, -\frac{5}{2}$; $\frac{1}{2}$ **(j)** $-\frac{2}{3}, \frac{8}{3}$; 1

3. (a) $(2, 0)$, $(-6, 0)$, $(-2, -16)$

(b) $(0, -8)$, $(2, -8)$, $(1, -9)$

(c) $(2, 0)$, $(-3, 0)$, $(-0.5, -6.25)$

(d) $(0, 2)$, $(-4, 2)$, $(-2, -2)$

(e) $(0, 5)$, $(4, 5)$, $(2, 17)$

(f) $(0, -3)$, $(5, -3)$, $(2.5, -15.5)$

4. (a) $y = (x - 5)(x - 1)$, $(3, -4)$, $y = (x - 3)^2 - 4$

(b) $y = -2(x - 4)(x - 2)$, $(3, 2)$, $y = -2(x - 3)^2 + 2$

(c) $y = \frac{1}{2}(x + 4)(x - 2)$, $(-1, -\frac{9}{2})$, $y = \frac{1}{2}(x + 1)^2 - \frac{9}{2}$

(d) $y = (2x - 5)(2x - 1)$, $(\frac{3}{2}, -4)$, $y = (x - \frac{3}{2})^2 - 4$

(e) $y = -3x(x + 4)$, $(-2, 12)$, $y = -3(x + 2)^2 + 12$

(f) $y = 2(x - 5)(x + 3)$, $(1, -32)$, $y = 2(x - 1)^2 - 32$

5. (a) $(0, 5)$, $(6, 5)$, $(3, -4)$, $y = (x - 3)^2 - 4$

(b) $(0, -11)$, $(4, -11)$, $(2, -15)$, $y = (x - 2)^2 - 15$

(c) $(0, -11)$, $(6, -11)$, $(3, 7)$, $y = -2(x - 3)^2 + 7$

(d) $(0, -13), (-6, -13), (-3, -4),$
$y = -(x + 3)^2 - 4$

(e) $(0, 3), (4, 3), (2, 5), y = -\frac{1}{2}(x - 2)^2 + 5$

(f) $(0, 11), (5, 11), (2.5, -1.5),$
$y = 2(x - 2.5)^2 - 1.5$

6. Use partial factoring to find two equidistant points. Then find axis of symmetry, and substitute value into get y-coordinate, which gives the vertex.

7. (a) 11.25 m   **(b)** 3 s
(c)

8. (a) 1977   **(b)** 1214.8 t   **(c)** 1522 t
9. (a) 1968   **(b)** 4237.3
(c) Yes, it has started to decrease.
10. (a) 1997   **(b)** $5.09   **(c)** $14.81
11. Here are five possible answers:
$y = \left(-\frac{11}{72}\right)x^2 + 22, \; y = \left(-\frac{23}{144}\right)x^2 + 23,$
$y = \left(-\frac{1}{6}\right)x^2 + 24, \; y = \left(-\frac{25}{144}\right)x^2 + 25,$
$y = \left(-\frac{13}{72}\right)x^2 + 26$

12. (a) number of tickets sold, expenses
(b) $7.50, $897.50, 225 tickets
(c) $12.97, 61 tickets or $2.03, 359 tickets
13. (a) $5.75, $1776.88
(b) $13.45, 47 tickets
14. 11 250 m²
15. No, the height at 8 m from axis of symmetry is 26.9 m.
16. (a) $R = (10 + x)(2000 - 100x)$
(b) factored form, $5, $22 500
(c) $5, $22 500
(d) method **(b)**, partial factoring, each method is easier in different forms
17. (a) 190.8 m   **(b)** 4.59 s   **(c)** 87.5 m
18. (a) $y = \frac{x^2}{100} + 4$ **(b)** 6.25 m
19. 13.7 m
20. $y = a\left(x + \frac{b}{2a}\right)^2 + c - \frac{b^2}{4a}$
21. (a) complete factoring: x-intercepts, find axis of symmetry, x-coordinate of vertex, substitute into equation to get y-coordinate of vertex; partial factoring: gives two points with the same y-coordinate, find axis of symmetry, x-coordinate of vertex, substitute into equation to get y-coordinate of vertex
(b) If the equation is in standard form, it cannot be factored completely.

22. (a) $y = -\frac{1}{5}(x)(x - 8)$ and $y = -\frac{1}{5}(x - 2)(x - 10)$
or $y = -\frac{1}{5}x^2 + \frac{8}{5}x$ and $y = -\frac{1}{5}x^2 + \frac{12}{5}x - 4$
or $y = -\frac{1}{5}(x - 4)^2 + 3.2$ and
$y = -\frac{1}{5}(x - 6)^2 + 3.2$
(b) 3.2 m

Practise 4.5, page 383

(a) $(2, -1)$ **(b)** $(3, -5)$
(c) $(0, -25)$ **(d)** $(-0.75, 17.125)$
(e) $(155, 48\ 050)$ **(f)** $(-2.25, -15.125)$

Practise, Apply, Solve 4.6, page 390

1. (a) 4   **(b)** 4   **(c)** 9
(d) 16   **(e)** 25   **(f)** 36
(g) 100   **(h)** 81   **(i)** 49
2. (a) 14   **(b)** 6   **(c)** 12
(d) 18   **(e)** 10   **(f)** 20
(g) 2   **(h)** 16   **(i)** 24
3. (a) $-2, -4$ **(b)** $3, -9$ **(c)** $5, -25$
4. (a) $y = (x + 2)^2 - 4$ **(b)** $y = (x - 4)^2 - 16$
(c) $y = (x + 3)^2 - 7$ **(d)** $y = (x + 5)^2 - 37$
(e) $y = (x + 6)^2 - 51$ **(f)** $y = (x - 7)^2 - 29$
(g) $y = (x - 3)^2 - 17$ **(h)** $y = (x - 5)^2 - 30$
(i) $y = (x + 10)^2 - 120$
5. (a) minimum $(3, 5)$ **(b)** maximum $(2, -25)$
(c) minimum $(-4, -7)$
6. (a) $\frac{1}{4}$ **(b)** $\frac{9}{4}$ **(c)** $\frac{81}{4}$
(d) $\frac{25}{4}$ **(e)** $\frac{225}{4}$ **(f)** 0.0625
(g) 0.01   **(h)** 0.0064   **(i)** $\frac{b^2}{4}$
7. (a) $2, -2, -4$
(b) $-3, -2, 17$
(c) $\frac{1}{2}, 3, \frac{1}{2}$
8. (a) $y = 2(x + 2)^2 - 2$ **(b)** $y = 3\left(x - \frac{3}{2}\right)^2 - \frac{27}{4}$
(c) $y = -(x - 3)^2 + 9$ **(d)** $y = -4(x - 1)^2 + 13$
(e) $y = 2(x - 1)^2 + 3$ **(f)** $y = -3(x - 1)^2 - 4$
(g) $y = -3(x + 2)^2 + 17$
(h) $y = 5(x + 1)^2 - 16$
(i) $y = -\frac{1}{2}(x - 6)^2 + 23$
(j) $y = \frac{1}{5}(x + 5)^2 + 4$
(k) $y = \frac{1}{2}(x - 4)^2 - 2$
(l) $y = -\frac{1}{10}(x + 3)^2 + 0.5$
9. (a) $y = (x - 2)^2 + 3$
(b) $y = (x + 4)^2 - 10$
(c) $y = \frac{1}{2}(x - 2)^2 + 3$
(d) $y = -(x - 3)^2 - 2$
(e) $y = -3(x + 3)^2 + 40$
(f) $y = 2(x + 5)^2 - 7$

10. $y = 2(x - 3)^2 - 11$, vertical stretch by factor of 2, right 3, down 11 units

11. 2000 m

12. 15 min, $160

13. 10 cm by 10 cm, 100 cm^2

14. 75 m by 75 m, 5625 m^2

15. 30 m by 60 m

16. 150 m by 225 m, 33 750 m^2

17. (a) 13, 13   (b) 20.21, 5.79

18. $1.70

19. (a) completing the square easier: has fewer steps and gives the vertex

    (b) 6 m   (c) 2.095 s

20. 10 368 m^2

21. In step 2, "$\frac{9}{4} - \frac{9}{4}$" should be "$\frac{9}{16} - \frac{9}{16}$"

    step 3: $y = 2(x + \frac{3}{4})^2 - \frac{9}{8} + 4$

    step 4: $y = 2(x + \frac{3}{4})^2 + \frac{23}{8}$

22. (a) $126.48

    (b) (c)

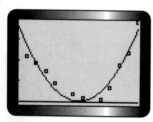

    (d) $y = \frac{1}{1114}(x - 66)^2 + 6$

    (f) $y = 0.0008x - 65.96)^2 + 6.04$

    (g) 66 km/h, 6 L/100 km

    (h) Use highways but do not speed; avoid stop-and-go traffic.

23.   i. Answers will vary. Completing the square would work for all.

    ii. complete factoring; partial and complete factoring give two other points on graph

    iii. $(3, -49)$, $(2, -12)$, $(\frac{4}{5}, -\frac{68}{25})$, $(1, -12)$, $(3.5, 68.425)$, $(20.5, 8283.75)$, $(1, 10)$, $(-\frac{1}{2}, -\frac{115}{2})$, $(-1, 8)$, $(4.25, -27.5)$

24. $y = (x - 1)^2 - 36$; partial factoring and completing the square; factoring; completing the square is entirely algebraic, so no need for graph

25. 7.5 cm by 7.5 cm

26. 1

27. (a) $y = (x + \frac{b}{2})^2 - \frac{b^2}{4} + C$

    (b) $y = (x + \frac{10}{2})^2 - \frac{100}{4} + 7$

    (c) $y = (x + 5)^2 - 18$

28. (a) $y = a(x + \frac{b}{2a})^2 - \frac{b^2}{4a}$, yes, $-\frac{b^2}{4a}$

    (b) $y = y = a(x + \frac{b}{2a})^2 - \frac{b^2}{2a} + C$

Practise, Apply, Solve 4.7, page 403

1. (a) $x = 4, -4$ (b) $x = 15, -15$
    (c) $t = \sqrt{50}, -\sqrt{50}$ (d) $b = 7, -7$
    (e) $c = 12, -12$ (f) $x = \sqrt{3}, -\sqrt{3}$
    (g) no real solution   (h) $f = \sqrt{8}, -\sqrt{8}$

2. (a) $x = 3, -3$ (b) $x = -3, 2$
    (c) $x = 0, 3$ (d) $x = -4, -3$
    (e) $x = 5$ (f) $x = 1, 12$
    (g) $x = 0, 4$ (h) $x = \frac{5}{2}, -3$
    (i) $x = 5, -5$

3. (a) 1, 5
    (b) Answers will vary. Factoring is easier for equations with no a-value.
    (c) x-intercepts at $(1, 0)$, $(5, 0)$

4. (a) $x = \frac{5}{3}, -\frac{3}{2}$ (b) $x = 4, -4$
    (c) $x = -5, -4$ (d) no real solution
    (e) $x = 0, \frac{11}{5}$ (f) $\frac{8}{3}, -\frac{5}{4}$
    (g) $x = 2, 3$ (h) $x = 4, -3$
    (i) $x = 4 \pm \sqrt{40}$

5. (a) none   (b) 2   (c) 2
    (d) none   (e) 1   (f) 2
    (g) 1   (h) 2   (i) 2

6. (a) $x = 4.24, -0.24$ (b) $x = 1.5, -1$
    (c) $x = 1.47, -0.27$ (d) $m = 4.30, 0.70$
    (e) $w = -0.28, -2.39$ (f) $x = 0.71, 3.29$
    (g) $x = 0.42, 3.58$ (h) $y = -0.25$
    (i) $m = 0.59, -3.93$

8. (a) 764.48 cm^2 (b) 6.443 cm

9. 1738 km

10. (a) 5.35, 0.65   (b) 5.35, 0.65
    (c) (a)

11. (a) 4   (b) 2.5, -4
    (c) 9, 1   (d) no real roots
    (e) 1.24, -3.24 (f) 6.95, -12.95
    (g) 1.72, 1.28   (h) 0.28, -9.31
    (i) 7.19, 0.81

12. (a) 71.65 m   (b) 4.56 s
    (c) 75.42 m   (d) 7.8 s

13. (a) $7.2606 billion   (b) 1990, 1998
    (c) 1994

14. 2.02 s

15. (a) 107.67 km/h   (b) 97.44 m
    (c) example: 20 car lengths

16. 12 cm by 9 cm

17. $b = 8, h = 10$

18. $2.75 or $14.25

19. $4.50, $5.50

20. (a) $x = 2.50, -4.0$
    (c) 2.5, -4

21. (a) $3692, $4512, $4864, $4550, $3444, $1946
    (d) $R = t(1230 - 78t)$
    (e) $6.75 to $9
    (f) $7.88, $4840.47, $7.75

22. (a) $E = 5020 - 312t$
    (b) $P = -78t^2 + 1542t - 5020$; $15.65, $4.12
    (c) $9.88, $2601, $10, no

23. (a) $E = 5020 - 273t$
(b) $P = -78t^2 + 1503t - 445$, \$15.60, \$3.66
(c) \$9.63, \$2785, \$9.75, no
24. 2.1 m
25. 10 cm
26. 100 cm by 100 cm
27. 12 units, 9 units
28. 80 m
29. (a) You could factor

$$4x^2 - 10x - 24 = 0$$
$$2(2x^2 - 5x - 12) = 0$$
$$2(2x + 3)(x - 4) = 0$$
$$\therefore x = -\frac{3}{2} \text{ or } x = 4$$

You could use the quadratic formula

$$x = \frac{-b \pm \sqrt{b^2 - 4ac}}{2a}$$
$$= \frac{-(-10) \pm \sqrt{100 - 4(4)(-24)}}{2(4)}$$
$$= \frac{10 \pm \sqrt{100 + 384}}{8}$$
$$= \frac{10 \pm \sqrt{484}}{8}$$
$$= \frac{10 \pm 22}{8}$$
$$\therefore x = -\frac{12}{8} = -\frac{3}{2} \text{ or } x = \frac{32}{8} = 4$$

You could graph.

30. $x = h \pm \sqrt{\dfrac{-k}{a}}$
31. $(-1.7, 5.6), (-5.3, -1.6)$
32. $3.1, -1.5$

Chapter 4 Review, page 418

1. (a) (4, 0), up   **(b)** (−2, −5), up
   (c) (0, 6) down
2. (a) $y = \frac{5}{2}x^2 + 7$ **(b)** $y = -2(x - 3)^2$
   (c) $y = \frac{1}{2}(x + 1)^2 - 4$
3. (a) yes, no, no
   (b) examples: (0, 7), (2, −2), (1, −2)
4. (a) $y = -2(x + 1)(x - 5)$
   (b) $y = -2(x - 2)^2 + 18$
5. (a) 9.4 m   **(b)** 29 m   **(c)** no
6. (a) (2, 1), x = 2, up   **(b)** (−4, 0), x = −4, down
   (c) (−1, −8), x = −1, up
7. (a) vertical stretch by a factor of 5, down 4,
      2 intercepts
   (b) reflect in x-axis, vertical compression by a factor
      of $\frac{1}{4}$, right 5, 1 intercept
   (c) reflect in x-axis, vertical stretch by a factor of 3,
      left 2, down 7, no intercepts
8. 12.02 s
9. (a) (1, 0), (−7, 0); x = −3; (−3, −16);
      $y = (x + 3)^2 - 16$
   (b) (0, −8), (6, −8); x = 3; (3, −17);
      $y = (x - 3)^2 - 17$

(c) (−3, 0), (7, 0); x = 2; (2, 50);
   $y = -2(x - 2)^2 + 50$
(d) (0, 2), (−4, 2); x = −2; (−2, −10);
   $y = 3(x + 2)^2 - 10$
(e) (0, 0), (−5, 0); x = −2.5; (−2.5, −6.25);
   $y = (x + 2.5)^2 - 6.25$
(f) (0, 21), (1, 11); x = 5.5; (5.5, 9.25);
   $y = (x - 5.5)^2 - 9.25$
(g) (0, −35), (1, −35); x = 0.5; (0.5, −36);
   $y = 4(x - 0.5)^2 - 36$
(h) (0, −6), (1, 5); x = −5; (−5, −31);
   $y = (x + 5)^2 - 31$
(i) (0, −11), (1, −1); x = 3; (3, 7);
   $y = -2(x - 3)^2 + 7$
10. (a) 1.1 m   **(b)** 2.3 s
11. (a) $R = -3000f^2 + 147\ 00f$
   (b) \$2.45
   (c) riders 7350, revenue \$18 007.50
12. (a) $y = (x + 3)^2 - 12$ **(b)** $y = -2(x + 2)^2 - 3$
   (c) $y = \frac{1}{2}(x + 5)^2 - \frac{39}{2}$ **(d)** $y = 3(x + 1)^2 - 8$
13. (a) 20.8 m   **(b)** partial factoring
14. (a) \$15   **(b)** \$3957
   (c) revenue from toques and scarves is independent
      of the ticket price
15. (a) 5, −5   **(b)** 0, 4   **(c)** 7, −5
   (d) 7, −1   **(e)** $\frac{5}{3}, -\frac{3}{2}$ **(f)** −2, −8
16. (a) none   **(b)** 2   **(c)** none
   (d) 1   **(e)** 2   **(f)** 2
17. (a) 3   **(b)** 11, −1   **(c)** 3, 1
   (d) (−2.19, 1.52) **(e)** no real roots **(f)** −0.30, −6.70
   (g) $\frac{5}{2}$ **(h)** 7.16, 0.84   **(i)** 0.43, −4.82
18. (a) 24.5 m   **(b)** 2.8 s
   (c) 39.59 m   **(d)** 5.6 s
19. (b) \$3.3, 501; \$19.7, 9   **(c)** \$11.5

Chapter 4 Review Test, page 429

1. (a) (0, 7), x = 0, up
   (b) (3, 0), x = 3, up
   (c) (−1, 10), x = −1, down
   (d) (0, −12), x = 0, up
   (e) (−2, −3), x = −2, down
   (f) (5, 6), x = 5, down
2. (a) down 7   **(b)** right 3
   (c) reflect in x-axis, left 1, up 10
   (d) vertical stretch by factor of 3, down 12
   (e) reflect in x-axis, compression by factor of 2,
      left 2, down 3
   (f) reflect in x-axis, vertical stretch by factor of 2,
      right 5, up 6
3. (a) $y = 3(x + 6)^2$ **(b)** $y = -\frac{3}{2}(x - 3)^2 + 7$
   (c) $y = -\frac{3}{8}(x + 4)^2 - 2$**(d)** $y = -\frac{1}{2}(x - 1)^2 + 8$
4. (a) $3x^2 + 36x + 108$ **(b)** $-\frac{3}{2}x^2 + 9x - \frac{13}{2}$

(c) $-\frac{3}{8}x^2 - 3x - 8$ (d) $-\frac{1}{2}x^2 + x - \frac{33}{2}$

5. (a) 0   **(b)** 1   **(c)** 2

6. (a) $y = -\frac{17}{450}x^2 + 8.5$ **(b)** 1.84 m

(c) 26.2 m

7. (a) 0.584 m   **(b)** 39 m

(c) 38.56 m, up, time is before ball reaches maximum height

(d) No, y is negative.

(e) 5.61 s

8. (a) $(-2, -50)$, $y = 2(x + 2)^2 - 50$, $(0, 42)$, $(1, -32)$

(b) $(-\frac{3}{2}, -\frac{31}{2})$, $y = 2(x + \frac{3}{2})^2 - \frac{31}{2}$, $(0, -11)$, $(1, -3)$

(c) $(2, 27)$, $y = -3((x - 2)^2 + 27$, $(1, 24)$, $(0, 15)$

(d) $(3, -13)$, $y = (x - 3)^2 - 13$, $(0, -4)$, $(1, -9)$

(e) $(1.375, 62.5625)$, $y = 4(x - 1.375)^2 - 62.5625$, $(0, -55)$, $(1, -62)$

(f) $(-2, -31)$, $y = 5(x + 2)^2 - 31$, $(0, -11)$, $(1, 14)$

9. 6144 m²

10. (a) $y = (x - 3)^2 + 2$ **(b)** $y = -3(x - 3)^2 + 56$

11. (a) 1   **(b)** 2

(c) 0

12. (a) Find the vertex by completing the square of partial factoring—the vertex is the maximum height.

(b) 57 m   **(c)** 6.4 s

13. It gives two equidistant points that can be used to find the axis of symmetry, which is equidistant from each x-coordinate. Those points are not on the x-axis, so they are not roots.

Cumulative Review Test 2, page 431

1. (a) quadratic   **(b)** linear

2. (a) $(4, 6)$ **(b)** 6

(c) $x = 4$ **(d)** $x = 0$ or $x = 8$

(e) $y = -\frac{3}{8}(x - 4)^2 + 6$

3. (a)

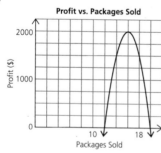
Profit vs. Packages Sold

(b) $y = -125(x - 16)^2 + 2000$

(c) $1500   **(d)** 13 or 19

4. (a) $8x^2 - 10x - 3$ **(b)** $15h^2 - 11hk + 2k^2$

(c) $9x^2 - 30x + 25$ **(d)** $g^2 - 8g + 16$

5. (a) $(x + 5)(x - 3)$ **(b)** $3(x + 2)(x + 3)$

(c) $(3x - 2)^2$ **(d)** $(4a + 5b)(4a - 5b)$

(e) $(4x + 1)(3x - 2)$

6. (a)

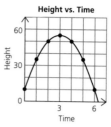
Height vs. Time

(b) 10 m   **(c)** 6.32 s

(d) 55 m   **(e)** 1.59 s, 4.41 s

7. (a) flip the graph, stretch by a factor of 2, shift left 5, shift down 3

(b)

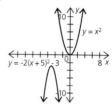

8.

9. (a) $x = -12$ or $x = 6$ **(b)** $x = -\frac{4}{3}$ or $x = \frac{5}{2}$

10. (a) $13.65   **(b)** 2000

(c) $5.64 - this will occur at $t = \frac{5}{3}$ (1994-95)

11. (a) Domestic: 1994, linear 545 576, quadratic 513 122; 2000: linear 642 981, quadratic 610 527; imported: 1994, linear 71 969, quadratic 141 825; 2000: linear 186 221, quadratic 256 077

(b) The domestic predictions are probably more accurate because the model is linear and gradually increasing.

12. (a)

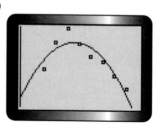

(b) $-673.86x^2 + 2\ 680\ 816x - 2\ 665\ 999\ 342$

(d) 160 715   **(e)** 1989

Review of Essential Skills—Part III

Rate, Ratio, and Proportions, page 440

1. **(a)** 4 : 5   **(b)** 5 : 3   **(c)** 6 : 1
   (d) 7 : 3   **(e)** 4 : 7
2. **(a)** 4 : 5   **(b)** 3 : 5   **(c)** 1 : 3
   (d) 2 : 15   **(e)** 1 : 2   **(f)** 10 : 13
3. **(a)** 4 m   **(b)** 18 m   **(c)** 24.5 m
   (d) 48.4 m   **(e)** 27 m
4. **(a)** 80 beats/min   **(b)** 80 km/h
   (c) $4.95/kg   **(d)** 45 words/min
5. **(a)** $x = 8$ **(b)** $x = 63$
   (c) $x = 32$ **(d)** $x = 10$
   (e) $x = 12$ **(f)** $x = 40$
   (g) $x = 52$ **(h)** $x = 2$
6. **(a)** 4   **(b)** 9   **(c)** 10
   (d) 4, 24   **(e)** 3, 15
7. **(a)** $x = 2.8$ **(b)** $x = 10.8$
   (c) $x = 67.86$ **(d)** $x = 177.69$
   (e) $x = 4.62$ **(f)** $x = 63$
   (g) $x = 66.67$ **(h)** $x = 3.8$
8. 1015 people
9. 1.4 L

Angle Relationships, page 442

(a) $x = 70°, y = 50°, z = 110°$
(b) $x = 115°, y = 65°, z = 65°$
(c) $x = 20°, y = 160°, z = 160°$
(d) $x = 50°, y = 60°, z = 70°$
(e) $x = 80°, y = 60°, z = 60°$
(f) $x = 54°, y = 54°, z = 126°$
(g) $x = 60°, y = 120°, z = 120°$
(h) $x = 30°, y = 40°, z = 50°$

Congruent Figures, page 444

1. The opposite sides are equal, the short side on both is the same length, the long side on each is the same length.
2. **(a)** $\angle J = \angle S, \angle K = \angle P, \angle L = \angle Q, \angle M = \angle R$
   (b) $JK = SP, KL = PQ, LM = QR, MJ = RS$
3. $x = 20,\ y = 25, z = 5$
4. **(a)** LM **(b)** $\angle N$
   (c) LO **(d)** $\angle B$
   (e) $\angle D$ **(f)** BC
   (g) $\angle L$ **(h)** NO

Chapter 5

Getting Ready, page 448

1. **(a)** $a = 80°, b = 60°, c = 40°, d = 120°$
   (b) $e = 5\sqrt{5}$ cm, $f = 5$ cm
   (c) $g = 35°, h = 55°$
   (d) $i = 160°, j = 20°$
   (e) $k = 110°, l = 70°, m = 70°$
   (f) $x = 5$ cm, $n = 3$ cm, $m = 4$ cm

2. **(a)** $AC = \sqrt{7}, \angle B = 41.4°, \angle C = 48.6°$
   (b) $DF = 1.3$ cm, $EF = 2.6$ cm, $\angle D = 100°$
   (c) $HI = 12$ cm, $\angle G = 67.4°, \angle I = 22.6°$
   (d) angle not contained
3. **(a)** 10 (rational)   **(b)** 6.4807... (irrational)
   (c) 36 (rational)   **(d)** 6 (rational)
   (e) 4.89897... (irrational)
   (f) $\frac{2}{3}$ (rational)
4. **(a)** $A = 93.53$ cm^2, $P = 36$ cm
   (b) $A = 100\pi$ cm^2, $P = 20\pi$ cm
   (c) $A = 96$ cm^2, $P = 40$ cm
   (d) $A = 22$ cm^2, $P = 20$ cm
5. **(a)** $m = 2, y = 2x - 4$ **(b)** $m = -2, y = -2x + 2$
   (c) $m = -\frac{3}{2}, y = -\frac{3}{2}x + 4$
   (d) $m = \frac{3}{10}, y = \frac{3}{10}x - 3$
   (e) $m = 0, y = 4$
6. **(a)** 5 : 6   **(b)** 1 : 2
   (c) $\frac{1}{2}$ **(d)** $-\frac{1}{3}$
7. **(a)** $x = 3$ **(b)** $y = \frac{17}{4}$
   (c) $w = 52$ **(d)** $a = -15$
   (e) $b = -\frac{28}{3}$ **(f)** $x = -1$
8. **(a)** Yes, corresponding sides and angles are equal
   (b) $AB = WX, BC = XY, CD = YZ, DA = ZW$
   (c) $\angle A = \angle W, \angle B = \angle X, \angle C = \angle Y, \angle D = \angle Z$
9. **(a)** $\angle A \cong \angle L, \angle B \cong \angle M, \angle C \cong \angle N$
   (b) $AB \cong LC, BC \cong MN, CA \cong NL$
10. $x = 2, y = 15, z = 6$
11. size, shape

Practise 5.1, page 454

1. **(a)** $\angle A = 51°, \angle B = 111°, \angle C = 18°$
   (b) $AC = 3.56$ cm, $\angle BAC = 105°, \angle ACB = 40°$
   (c) $AC = 3.26$ cm, $BC = 1.46$ cm, $\angle BCA = 110°$

Practise, Apply, Solve 5.2, page 462

1. **(a)** SSS~; 2, all lengths given
   (b) SAS~; 2, $KJ = 4.58$ cm, $KB = 3.66$ cm, $JC = 3.30$ cm
2. **(a)** ASA≅; $\triangle ABC \cong \triangle YZX$
   (b) SSS≅; $\triangle ABC \cong \triangle ZYX$
   (c) SAS≅; $\triangle ABC \cong \triangle ZXY$
3. **(a)** $\triangle MNO$ **(b)** $\triangle FDE, \triangle JLK, \triangle HGI$
4. **(a)** similar; SAS~; $\angle A = \angle D, \angle B = \angle E,$
   $\angle C = \angle F, AB = 2DE, BC = 2EF, AC = 2DF$
   (b) congruent; SSS≅; $\angle G = \angle J, \angle H = \angle L,$
   $\angle I = \angle K, GH = JL, GI = JK, HI = LK$
   (c) similar; ASA~; $\angle M = \angle Q, \angle N = \angle P,$
   $\angle MON = \angle QOP, MN = 2QP, MO = 2OQ,$
   $NO = 2PO$
   (d) similar; ASA~; $\angle V$ common, $\angle UTV = \angle RSV,$
   $\angle VRS = \angle VUT, RS = \frac{14}{9}UT, RV = \frac{14}{9}UV,$
   $SV = \frac{14}{9}TV$

(e) similar; $AA\sim$, $\angle W = \angle A$, $\angle X = \angle Z$,
   $\angle WYZ = \angle AYZ$, $\frac{WX}{AZ} = \frac{WY}{AY} = \frac{XY}{ZY}$

5. (a) $SAS\cong$; $\angle A = \angle E$, $\angle B = \angle D$, $\angle ACB = \angle ECD$,
   $BC = DC$, $AC = EC$, $AB = ED$
   (b) $SAS\cong$; $\angle B = \angle D$, $\angle A = \angle E$, $\angle ACB = \angle ECD$,
   $AB = ED$, $AC = EC$, $BC = DC$
   (c) $ASA\cong$; $\angle A = \angle E$, $\angle B = \angle D$, $\angle ACB = \angle ECD$,
   $AB = ED$, $BC = DC$, $AC = EC$
   (d) $SAS\cong$; $\angle A = \angle E$, $\angle ABC = \angle EDC$,
   $\angle ACB = \angle ECD$, $AC = EC$, $BC = DC$,
   $AB = ED$

6. (a) $x = 60°$, $y = 30°$ (b) $a = 8$ m, $z = 40°$
   (c) $b = 5.5$ cm, $c = \sqrt{23}$ cm
   (d) $c = 7$ cm, $d = 10.6$ cm, $e = 5.3$ cm
   (e) $f = 5$ cm, $g = 5$ cm

7. (a) $\angle A = 60°$, $CD = 5$ cm
   (b) $\angle ADE = 60°$, $\angle ECD = 50°$, $\angle EDC = 40°$
   (c) $\angle C = \angle A = 55°$, $BD = 4$ cm
   (d) $DE = 2.4$ cm   (e) $AB = 28$ cm
   (f) $AB = 8.4$ cm, $BD = 9$ cm

8. $\frac{a}{c} = \frac{x}{z}$, $az = cx$, $\frac{a}{x} = \frac{c}{z}$

9. $ASA\cong$

10. (a) $L = 90°$, $\sim\Delta$
    (b) $PR = 36$ cm, $QR = 39$ cm

11. same angles, proportional sides

Practise 5.3, page 466

1. (a) $XY = 2.5$ cm, $YZ = 3.5$ cm, $XZ = 2.475$ cm
   (b) $XY = 10$ cm, $YZ = 14$ cm, $XZ = 9.9$ cm
   (c) $XY = 6$cm, $YZ = 8.4$ cm, $XZ = 5.94$ cm
   (d) $XY = 3.75$cm, $YZ = 5.25$ cm, $XZ = 3.7125$ cm

Practise, Apply, Solve 5.4, page 474

1. $18.5°$
2. 2 m
3. (a) 6 m   (b) 200 m²
4. 16.2 m
5. (a) 1 cm in small = 3 cm in large, 1 : 3
   (b) 4.05 L
6. (a) hypotenuse = distance from top of head
      (real → shadow); the assumption is good; people
      usually stand reasonably straight.
   (b) distance from top of tower (real → shadow)
   (c) same angles (Shirin and tower)
   (d) 125 : 8   (e) 25 m
7. (a) 3.0 m   (b) 2 m up, $\frac{4}{3}$ m out
   (c) ladders are parallel   (d) 9 m
8. (a) (AA~)   (b) 20 : 1   (c) 520 m
9. 12.0 m
10. 11.2 m
11. 25 m
12. 161.7 m
13. 16 m

14. (b) building-ground = 90°, person-ground = 90°,
       sun's rays *
   (c) height of person and his or her shadow
       (or angles)
15. span 13 m, length of post 4.6 m
16. (a) He knew distance between cities and found
       angle between them from centre of earth.
    (b) accuracy

Practise, Apply, Solve 5.6, page 485

1. (a) -3 (b) $-\frac{1}{2}$
   (c) 1 (d) -2.75
2. (a) $71.6°$ (b) $14.0°$ (c) $26.6°$
   (d) $14.0°$ (e) $-26.6°$ (f) $-26.6°$
3. (a) 1.43 (b) $y = 1.43x + 5$
   (c) -3.50
4. (a) $y = \sqrt{3}x - 2$, x-intercept $\frac{2\sqrt{3}}{3}$
   (b) $y = x - 9$, x-intercept 9, y-intercept -9
5. $y = -0.36x + 4.09$
6. $y = -\sqrt{3}x - 5\sqrt{3}$
7. (a) $\frac{6}{5}$ (b) $-\frac{5}{6}$
   (c) $\frac{61}{5}$ (d) $50.2°$
   (e) $39.8°$
8. (a) $y = \frac{1}{\sqrt{3}}x - 4$ (b) $y = 0.84x + 0.32$
9. (a) $y = 2x \to 63.4°$, $y = -3x \to 71.6°$
   (b) $135°$ (or $45°$)
10. (a) $\left(\frac{8}{7}, \frac{46}{7}\right)$
    (b) $y = 4x + 2 \to 76.0°$, $y = -3x + 10 \to -71.6°$
    (c) $147.6°$ (or $32.4°$)
11. (a) $DE \to m = \frac{1}{2}$, $EC \to m = -2$
    (b) $26.6°$ (c) $63.4°$
    (d) $90°$ (e) negative reciprocals
    (f) yes
12. (a) $53.13°$ (b) $106.26°$
    (c) centre angle = 2 × circumference angle
13. (a) $31.0°$ (b) $59.0°$ (c) 3 m
14. (a) 107.4 m   (b) 74.3 m
15. no, $\tan 4° = 0.07$ or 7%
16. $10\sqrt{3}$ m
17. (a) For a given slope, there is a definite angle
       between the line and the x-axis.
    (b) Look up the slope in the table on p. 484 and
       read across to find the angle.
18. (a) 8.4 m   (b) $55°$
19. (a) 18.40 m   (b) 85.75 m, 135.75 m
    (c) same

Practise, Apply, Solve 5.7, page 496

1. (b) $\sin Y = \frac{XZ}{YZ}$, $\cos Y = \frac{YX}{YZ}$, $\tan Y = \frac{XZ}{YX}$

2. (a) 0.5736 **(b)** 0.5000 **(c)** 1.000
(d) 0.2588 **(e)** 0.3090 **(f)** 0.7813
(g) 0.0349 **(h)** 0.1219
3. (a) 32° **(b)** 65° **(c)** 77°
(d) 60° **(e)** 14° **(f)** 5°
(g) 45° **(h)** 62° **(i)** 58°
4. (a) 4.6 **(b)** 5.1 **(c)** 6.9
(d) 5.6 **(e)** 69.1 **(f)** 5.2
5. (a) 68° **(b)** 61° **(c)** 59°
(d) 39° **(e)** 64° **(f)** 30°
6. (a) $\sin B = \frac{3}{5}$, $\cos B = \frac{4}{5}$, $\tan B = \frac{3}{4}$

(b) $\sin B = \frac{4}{5}$, $\cos B = \frac{3}{5}$, $\tan B = \frac{4}{3}$

(c) $\sin B = \frac{12}{13}$, $\cos B = \frac{5}{13}$, $\tan B = \frac{12}{5}$

(d) $\sin B = \frac{1}{\sqrt{2}}$, $\cos B = \frac{1}{\sqrt{2}}$, $\tan B = 1$

7. (a) 36.9° **(b)** 53.1°
(c) 67.4 **(d)** 45°

8. (a) $\frac{1}{2}$ **(b)** $\frac{\sqrt{3}}{2}$

(c) $\frac{3}{5}$ **(d)** $\frac{4}{5}$

(e) 53° **(f)** 78°

9. (a) $\sin 50° = \frac{x}{90}$, $\cos 40 = \frac{x}{90}$, $x = 68.9°$

(b) $\tan 51° = \frac{x}{30}$, $\tan 39° = \frac{30}{x}$, $x = 37.0°$

10. (a) 5.2 m **(b)** 6.4 m
11. (a) 12.2 m **(b)** 8.0 km
12. Answers will vary.
13. $\tan 50° = \frac{y}{120}$, $y = 143.0$ cm

14. 25.5 m
15. 3.09 m
16. (a) 45° **(b)** 60°
(c) 36.9°
17. (a) 117.5 mm **(b)** 9.6 km
(c) 14.4 km **(d)** 14.4 km
18. (a) $x = 45°$, $y = 45°$
(b) $x = 60°$, $y = 30°$
(c) $x = 36.9°$, $y = 53.1°$
19. $\sin A = \frac{250}{1600}$, $\angle A = 8.9°$

20. (a) change 12 to 22.5
(b) correct
(c) change 4.706 to 0.4706
(d) correct
(e) change 65° to 62°
(f) correct
21. (a) 20° **(b)** 79°
(c) 48° **(d)** 68°
22. (a) $\angle A = 51°$, $\angle B = 39°$
(b) $\angle A = 26°$, $\angle B = 64°$
23. no, 79°
24. (a) 8.2 cm **(b)** 8.7 cm
(c) 44.4° **(d)** 60.0°
25. (a) 71.6° **(b)** 14.0° **(c)** 26.6°
(d) 14.0° **(e)** −26.6° **(f)** −26.6°
26. (a) $x = 61.9°$, $y = 28.1°$, $z = 17$ cm

(b) $a = 45°$, $b = 45°$, $e = 7\sqrt{2}$ cm
(c) $j = 4\sqrt{3}$ cm, $i = 8$ cm
(d) $x = 18°$, $j = 9.5$ cm, $l = 3.1$ cm
(e) $x = 18°$, $q = 3.2$ cm, $n = 10.5$ cm
(f) $x = 64.2°$, $y = 25.8°$, $q = \sqrt{19}$ cm
(g) $x = 66.0°$, $y = w = 132.0°$
(h) $a = \frac{20}{3}$ cm, $b = \frac{10}{3}$ cm, $x = 65.8°$
27. 1635.4 m
28. no, $\tan^{-1}\left(\frac{1}{9}\right) = 6.3°$; no, $\tan^{-1}\left(\frac{1}{7.5}\right) = 7.6°$
29. 28.9°
30. 14.8 km
31. (a) $y = 0.75x - 4$
(b) $y = 1.11x - 0.22$
32. (a) $\tan^{-1}(-3) = -71.6°$, $\tan^{-1}(2) = 63.4°$
(b) 135° or 45°
33. (a) $\left(\frac{8}{7}, \frac{46}{7}\right)$
(b) $\tan^{-1}(-3) = -71.6°$, $\tan^{-1}(4) = 76.0°$
(c) 147.6° or 32.4°
34. $\angle A = \sin^{-1}(\sin A)$
35. Changing the lengths of the sides will create similar triangles. The values of the trigonometric ratios of corresponding sides in similar triangles will be equal.

Practise, Apply, Solve 5.8, page 509

1. 54.8°
2. 567.1 m
3. 24.4°
4. 35.8°
5. 42.0°
6. 52.0 m
7. 38.7°
8. 7.1 m
9. 9.4 m
10. 23.8 km
11. 5.85 m
12. 311.1 m
13. (a) 58.8° **(b)** 193 sections
14. (a) 26.6° **(b)** 11.3° **(c)** 5.7° **(d)** 4.8°
15. 7.9° west
16. Possible answers: sketch showing all information; statement regarding which trigonometric ratio to use, full solution.
17. 20.6 m
18. (a) 143.4 cm²
(b) $V = 4779.1$ cm³, $SA = 2647.5$ cm²
19. (a) 12 shafts **(b)** 176 sections
20. (a) $\tan \angle PAB = \frac{y}{x}$, $\sin \angle PAB = y$, $\cos \angle PAB = x$
(b) (0.98, 0.17), $(\cos θ, \sin θ)$, $(\cos(θ + 10), \sin(θ + 10))$

(c)

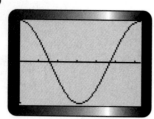

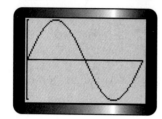

(d) (0.891, 0.454)

(e) compressed by a factor of 5, stretched by a factor of 4

(f) same, different scale

Chapter 5 Review, page 515

1. **(a)** $\triangle ABC \cong \triangle DEC$, $AC = 4$ cm, $\angle CDE = 50°$
   (b) $\triangle DEF \cong \triangle BCD$, $BD = 6$ cm, $\angle BDA = 110°$
2. **(a)** $\triangle ABC \sim \triangle EDC$, $CD = \frac{10}{3}$ cm
   (b) $\triangle XYZ \sim \triangle VWZ$, $q = 5$ cm, $r = 6.25$ cm, $p = 6.75$ cm
   (c) $\triangle PQR \sim \triangle TSR$, $a = 45°$, $b = 90°$, $x = 5.6$ cm
   (d) $\triangle ABC \sim \triangle EFD$, $x = 48.2°$, $y = 2$ cm
3. **(a)** AA, 10 cm, 18 cm   **(b)** AA, 36 cm, 27 cm
   (c) AA, 4.6 cm, 24.0 cm
4. 462 m
5. 6 m
6. 2.09 m
7. **(a)** 71.6° **(b)** 18.4°   **(c)** −31.0° **(d)** 56.3°
8. $y = 1.19x − 0.62$
9. **(a)** 1.55 km   **(b)** 2.02 km
10. 135°, 45°, 135°, 45°
11. **(a) i.** $\sin A = \frac{1}{\sqrt{5}}$, $\cos A = \frac{2}{\sqrt{5}}$, $\tan A = \frac{1}{2}$
    ii. $\angle A = 26.6°$
    (b) i. $\sin A = \frac{10}{13}$, $\cos A = \frac{\sqrt{69}}{13}$, $\tan A = \frac{10}{\sqrt{69}}$
    ii. $\angle A = 50.3°$
12. **(a)** $a = 10.4$ cm, $b = 2.7$ cm
    (b) $c = 19.2$ cm, $d = 16.1$ cm
13. **(a)** $ST = 17.5$ cm, $\angle TSR = 59°$, $\angle STR = 31°$
    (b) $NM = 14.3$ cm, $\angle NML = 55°$, $LN = 20.5$ cm
14. 12.8°
15. 7.5 km
16. 85.7°
17. 2764.6 m
18. 49.3 m

Chapter 5 Review Test, page 526

1. **(a)** $x = 18.2$ cm, $y = 53.1$ cm

(b) $a = 17.1$ cm, $b = 47.0$ cm
(c) $c = 33.7°$
(d) $\theta = −56.3°$
(e) $E = 63.4°$, $F = 53.2°$
(f) $w = 12.5$ cm, $z = 19.5$ cm
2. **(a)** $\sqrt{3}$
   (b) $\sin 60 = \frac{\sqrt{3}}{2}$, $\cos 60 = \frac{1}{2}$, $\tan 60 = \sqrt{3}$
3. 5645.6 m
4. 1.17 km
5. **(a)** $\angle Z = 75°$, $XY = 71.1$ cm, $XZ = 19.0$ cm
   (b) $AB = 28.0$ cm, $\angle A = 46.0°$, $\angle C = 44.0°$
6. 11.0 cm²
7. **(a)** 1.6°   **(b)** The 14 m tower is closer

Chapter 6

Getting Ready, page 530

1. **(a)** 5 cm   **(b)** 17 cm
2. 9.4 m
3. **(a)** 65°   **(b)** 45°
4. **(a)** 10   **(b)** 4.2   **(c)** 4, 6   **(d)** 0.9
5. **(a)** $x^2 + 4x + 4$ **(b)** $9x^2 + 12x + 4$
   (c) $a^2 − 2ay + y^2$ **(d)** $x^2 − 4xy + 4y^2$
6. **(a)** 0.469   **(b)** 0.225   **(c)** 0.616
   (d) 0.990   **(e)** 1.111   **(f)** 0.727
7. **(a)** 41.366   **(b)** 77.523
   (c) 19.440   **(d)** 1356.593
8. **(a)** $−\frac{2}{3}$ **(b)** ±6.44
9. **(a)** 56°   **(b)** 25°   **(c)** 0°
   (d) 83°   **(e)** 36°   **(f)** 86°
10. **(a)** 53°   **(b)** 30°   **(c)** 66°
11. No, 2 sides have a side ratio of 1 : 3, while the other is $1 : 2\frac{2}{3}$
12. **(a)** $\angle C = \angle D$, $\angle A = \angle O$, $\angle T = \angle G$
    (b) $CA \sim DO$, $AT \sim OG$, $CT \sim DG$
13. **(a)** $\triangle ABG \sim \triangle DCG$, $\angle G = \angle G$: opposite, $\angle A = \angle D$ & $\angle B = \angle C$: z-pattern
    (b) $\frac{AB}{DC} = \frac{BG}{CG} = \frac{GA}{GD}$
14. **(a)** $x = 21$ cm   **(b)** $j = 6$
15. **(a)** $\triangle ABC \sim \triangle AED$ **(b)** $AE = 6.9$
16. **(a)** $b = 7.6$ m, $\angle A = 58.8°$, $\angle C = 31.2°$
    (b) $y = 8.7$ cm, $z = 10.3$ m, $\angle X = 50°$
    (c) $AB = 8.9$ cm, $BD = 7.1$ cm, $CE = 6.4$ cm, $\angle ABC = 53°$, $\angle ACB = 106°$, $\angle DBC = 127°$, $\angle BCE = 74°$, $\angle CED = 106°$

Practise, Apply, Solve 6.2, page 538

1. **(a)** 96 cm   **(b)** 100 cm
2. $TR = 0.57$ cm
3. **(a)** $a = 5$ cm
   (b) $n = 3.33$ cm, $m = 4.5$ cm
   (c) $c = 35$ cm, $d = 5$ cm
   (d) $x = 4.7$ cm, $y = 6$ cm
   (e) $p = 40$ cm, $q = 50$ cm

4. 16.7 m

5. 48 m

6. rise 57.5 cm, run 191.6 cm

7. $AB = 54$ m

8. farther away

9. (a) $AC = 11.5$ **(b)** $BD = 3.1$

10. $AC = 8$

11. 10 cm, 16 cm

12. (a) ratio of heights of 2 similar triangles

     (b) 1 : 16 666.7   **(c)** 75 000.15 cm

13. (a) 67 m   **(b)** 98 m

14. No, the ratio is different, 1.7 : 1.4

15. 3.92 m

16. (a) 1) See if two angles of one match two angles of another.

     2) See if two pairs of corresponding sides are equal.

     (b) (c)

     1) Sketch the triangles so they are both created the same way.

     2) Determine whether or not the triangles are similar.

     3) In what order do the sides and angles match up?
     What information has been provided? Is it marked on the diagram?

     4) Set up equations for the equal ratios and solve for the required unknown quantity.

     (c) ratios of proper sides

17. Kiddie $1.46 per regular height, as opposed to regular: $1.75; Kiddie is better buy.

18. $\frac{x}{y} = \frac{y}{z}$ by similarity, therefore $y^2 = xz$.

19. 4.8 m, 3.96 m

20. 135 cm

Practise, Apply, Solve 6.3, page 549

1. (a) 37.9 cm   **(b)** 21 cm

2. (a) 101.6°   **(b)** 60.9°

3. $a = b = 26.1$ cm

4. $y = 6.5$ cm

5. (a) $\angle P = 53.1°$

     (b) using simple trigonometry

6. $u = 89.6$ cm

7. $q = 12.7$ cm

8. 24°

9. $t = 268.9$ m, $h = 385.7$ m, $\angle R = 59°$

10. $a = 41.9$ m, $t = 44.9$ m, $\angle A = 67°$

11. Two sides and unknown angle across from one of the sides or two angles and any side, unknown angle across from one side or either one of the two unknown sides.

12. 181.2 cm

13. 27.6 m

14. 10.76 m

15. 16.7 m, 12.2 m

16. 11.9 m

17. (a) $\frac{\sin L}{l} = \frac{\sin M}{m} = \frac{\sin N}{n}$

     (b) $180° - \angle P - \angle Q = \angle R, \frac{\sin R}{r} = \frac{\sin P}{p}$

     (c) two sides and one angle (find other angle) or two angles and one side (find other side)

18. 49.0 m

19. (a) $a = 6.9$ **(b)** area $= 19.7$ units^2

20. 8.2 cm

21. (a) $\frac{b}{\sin B}$ **(b)** $\frac{a}{b}$

     (c) $\frac{\sin A}{\sin C}$ **(d)** $\frac{a \sin B}{b \sin A}$

Practise, Apply, Solve 6.4, page 554

1. 14.9 m

2. 3.02 km

3. 22.5 m

4. 6.24 m, 13.54 m

5. 2nd plane, 0.8 km as opposed to 0.96 km

6. 101.2 m

7. 24.6 cm

8. 17.6 cm

9. 17.06 cm

10. 32.62 m

11. (a) use data to create a triangle, use data to solve for value wanted

     (b) is it a triangle? determine if there is enough data to use the sine law

     (c) 2 sides, 1 angle opposite unknown side

12. 48.55 m

Practise, Apply, Solve 6.6, page 566

1. (a) no   **(b)** no

     (c) yes   **(d)** no

     (e) no   **(f)** yes

2. $x = 13.2$ cm

3. (a) $t = 5.81$ cm, $\angle A = 66.9°$, $\angle C = 50.1°$

     (b) $z = 5.38$ cm, $\angle X = 36.4°$, $\angle Y = 56.6°$

     (c) $i = 23.05$ cm, $\angle E = 48°$, $\angle P = 60°$

4. $\angle A = 44.4°$

5. 20.95 cm

6. 3.9 cm

7. 59.73 cm

8. 38.1 km

9. 6.3°

10. 30°

11. 7.13 km, yes, if you assume that NW $= 45°$ or else no

12. (a) sides 4.17 cm   **(b)** 38.9°

13. (a) 26.7 cm   **(b)** 36.6 cm

     (c) 44.4 cm   **(d)** 51 cm

14. 40.4 m

15. 157 km

16. 14.2 km

17. 171 m

18. (a) 1518.8 km   **(b)** 179.8 km
19. 6.94 km
20. 22°
21. $\angle AOB = 57.5°$
22. (a) $p^2 = q^2 + r^2 - 2qr \cos \angle P$
$q^2 = p^2 + r^2 - 2pr \cos \angle Q$
$r^2 = p^2 + q^2 - 2pq \cos \angle R$
  (b) find one unknown side between two given
    angles with one other side given
  (c) find unknown angle corresponding to unknown
    side, given two sides and one angle
    corresponding to one of the known sides
23. (a) 104.5°   **(b)** 109.5°
  (c) sides bigger, base bigger, height bigger;
    therefore volume bigger
24. SR2 63.9 km
25. (a) 13.04 cm   **(b)** 16.87 cm
26. $P = 10.9$ cm, $A = 8.2$ cm^2
27. (a) N 67° W   **(b)** 695.17 km/h

Practise, Apply, Solve 6.7, page 574

1. (a) 24.2 km   **(b)** 85.2 km
2. (a) 64°   **(b)** 15.78 cm
3. 274.15 m
4. 43.5°
5. 78.47 m
6. 672.6 m
7. (a) 95.17 km   **(b)** 12 000 km^2
8. 26.03 km
9. (a) 43.2 m   **(b)** 13.3 m
10. 2.5 km
11. 59.59 m
12. (a) 10.4 cm   **(b)** 374.4 cm^2
13. Albacore 137.21 km, Bonito 104 km
14. 85.5°, 85.5°, 95.5°, 94.5°
15. 5.2 m
16. (a) 135°   **(b)** 6.4
17. (a) cosine law   **(b)** sine law
18. 331.92 m
19. (a) $\dfrac{a}{\sin A} = \dfrac{e}{\sin E} = \dfrac{f}{\sin F}$
$a^2 = e^2 + f^2 - 2ef \cos A$
$e^2 = a^2 + f^2 - 2af \cos E$
$f^2 = a^2 + e^2 - 2ae \cos F$
  (b)

Number of Known Sides	Number of Known Angles	Method of Solution
1	2	sine law
2	1 (uncontained)	cosine law
2	1 (contained)	sine law
3	0	cosine law

20. 34.77 m
21. 66.7 m
22. (a) 34.39 m   **(b)** 14.43 m longer

Chapter 6 Review, page 580

1. 8 cm
2. $x = 2$ cm, $y = 8$ cm
3. (a) $DE = 7.5$ cm   **(b)** $BC = 7$ cm
  (c) 2 : 3   **(d)** 4 : 9
4. $b = 5.07$ cm
5. $\angle R = 72.15°$
6. 295.44 m
7. $t = 5.94$ m
8. 70.53°
9. 58.17°
10. $a = 6.5$ cm, $\angle M = 75.9°$, $\angle T = 36.1°$
11. 9.4 m
12. 21.2 m

Chapter 6 Review Test, page 586

1. $CE = 0.9$ m, $BC = 16.8$ m
2. 5.33 m from the wall
3. $\angle C = 14°$
4. $m = 26.06$ m
5. $d = 5.82$ cm, $\angle E = 81°$, $\angle F = 31°$
6. $p = 22.67$ cm, $q = 16.15$ cm, $\angle R = 52°$
7. (a)
8. 98.2°
9. 126.96 m
10. (a) 24.93 m   **(b)** 8.45 m

Cumulative Review Test 3, page 587

1. (a) congruent, 70°   **(b)** similar, 4 cm
  (c) similar, similar; $BD = 4.8$ cm, $AD = 6.4$ cm,
    $DC = 3.6$ cm
2. $(0, 0): 71.6°, (2, 0): 63.4°, \left(\dfrac{4}{5}, \dfrac{12}{5}\right): 45°$
3. (a) $\sin x = \dfrac{12}{15}$, $\cos x = \dfrac{9}{15}$, $\tan x = \dfrac{12}{9}$; 53.13°
  (b) $\sin x = \dfrac{7.5}{9}$, $\cos x = \dfrac{4.975}{9}$, $\tan x = \dfrac{7.5}{4.975}$, 56.44°
4. (a) $a = 10.0$ cm, $c = 11.1$ cm, $\angle C = 48°$
  (b) $a = 36.5$ cm, $b = 32.8$ cm, $\angle C = 26°$
  (c) $b = 8.8$ cm, $c = 6.5$ cm, $\angle A = 80°$
  (d) $\angle A = 67.4°$, $\angle B = 50.7°$, $\angle C = 61.9°$
  (e) $b = 5.1$ cm, $\angle A = 90.9°$, $\angle C = 49.1°$
5. 61.0 m
6. 9.5 m
7. Constable Abel, at 102 m from the pirate radio
  station, is closer.
8. 25 s
9. 36.22 m

Glossary

acute angle: an angle that is less than 90°.

acute triangle: a triangle in which all interior angles are acute angles.

algebraic expression: an acceptable combination of at least one variable and possibly numbers and operation symbols. For example, x, $2x$, and $12r^2 + 7s$ are all algebraic expressions.

algebraic modelling: representing a number pattern with an algebraic expression, or representing a relation with an equation or a formula.

algorithm: a specific set of instructions for finding the solution to a problem.

altitude: the line segment representing the height of a polygon, drawn from a vertex of the polygon perpendicular to the opposite side.

analytic geometry: the branch of mathematics that uses the x-y plane to determine equations that represent lines and curves.

angle: a geometric figure formed by two rays with a common end point.

angle bisector: a line separating an angle into two equal parts.

angle of declination: see *inclination*.

angle of depression: see *elevation*.

angle of elevation: see *elevation*.

angle of inclination: see *inclination*.

apothem: the perpendicular distance from the centre of a regular polygon to one of the sides.

application: a practical situation outside of mathematics in which mathematical concepts and skills can be used to solve problems.

area: the measure of the surface of a figure, in terms of the number of unit squares needed to cover the figure.

average: see *measure of central tendency*. In common use, *average* is the same as *mean*.

axis: a line drawn for reference when locating points in a coordinate system.

axis of symmetry: a line dividing a plane figure into two parts, each of which is a mirror image of the other.

binomial: an algebraic expression that contains two terms, for example, $4x - 7y$ or $5x^2 + 3$.

Cartesian coordinates: a system for locating points in the x-y plane using ordered pairs that represent a point's distance along the perpendicular x- and y-axes.

centre of dilation: see *dilation*.

centre of mass: see *centroid*.

centroid of a triangle: the point where the three medians of a triangle intersect. Also called the centre of mass or balance point (for a thin, triangular solid).

chord: a line segment joining two points on a curve.

circle: the set of all points in a plane that are the same distance (called the radius) from a fixed point in the plane (called the centre).

circumcentre of a triangle: the centre of the circle that passes through all three vertices of a triangle.

coefficient: the factor by which a variable is multiplied. For example, in the term $3z$, the coefficient of s is 3; in the term by, the coefficient of y is b.

completing the square: the process of adding a constant to a given quadratic expression to form a perfect square trinomial.

complex number: in advanced mathematics, the sum of a real number and an imaginary number.

concurrent lines: lines that intersect at a common point.

congruence: the property shared by geometric figures that are identical in shape and size. The symbol for congruence is $\cong$, as in $\triangle ABC \cong \triangle DEF$.

coordinate plane: see *x-y plane*.

coordinates: a set of numbers used to define a position. In the x-y plane, coordinates are in the form of ordered pairs (x, y).

correlation coefficient: a measure of how well the points in a scatter plot fit an algebraic model. A value close to 1 or -1 indicates a good fit; a value close to 0 indicates a poor fit.

cosine: one of the primary trigonometric ratios (abbreviation cos). In a right triangle, the ratio of the length of the side adjacent to an angle to the length of the hypotenuse.

curve of best fit: the curve that best represents the relation between the variables for a set of points on a scatter plot.

degree of a polynomial: the highest exponent that appears in any term.

dependent variable: in an algebraic relation, the variable whose value depends on the value of another variable. Often represented by y.

diagonal: a line segment joining two vertices of a polygon that are not next to each other.

difference of squares: a technique of factoring applied to an expression of the form $a^2 - b^2$, which can be factored as $(a + b)(a - b)$.

difference table: an extended table of values that adds the finite differences for the dependent variable.

dilatation: see *dilation*.

dilation: a transformation that enlarges or reduces a figure. Lines joining corresponding points on the original and transformed figures meet at the centre of dilation.

direct variation: the relation exhibited by two variables where one variable is a constant multiple of the other.

directrix: the line which, together with a focus point, defines the shape of a parabola.

discriminant: the expression $b^2 - 4ac$, derived from the quadratic equation $ax^2 + bx + c$. If the discriminant is greater than 0, equal to 0, or less than 0, then the equation has two, one, or no real roots, respectively. See *quadratic formula*.

distributive property: $a(b + c) = ab + ac$

dynamic geometry software: computer programs with a wide array of features that allow the user to construct, manipulate, and measure geometric figures.

elevation: the angle between a line and the horizontal. Called elevation if the line is above the horizontal, or depression if it is below.

elimination: a method used to solve linear systems by matching coefficients of one variable by multiplication, then adding or subtracting the equations to eliminate that variable.

equation: a statement that two mathematical expressions have the same value, that is, they stand for the same number.

equilateral triangle: a triangle with three sides of equal length.

evaluate: to determine a particular value for an expression.

expanded form of a quadratic relation: see *standard form*.

exponent: the use of a superscript in mathematics to denote repeated multiplication. For example, 4^3 means $4 \times 4 \times 4$ and the exponent is 3.

exponential notation: scientific notation used by calculators to display numbers that are too small or too large to fit in the calculator screen. For example, the number 243 980 000 000 may appear as "2.4398 11" on the calculator screen. This indicates that the number is equivalent to 2.4398×10^{11}.

extrapolate: to estimate a value that is beyond the range of the given data by following a pattern.

factor: to express a number or algebraic expression as the product of two or more numbers or algebraic expressions. The numbers or algebraic expressions in such a product are also called factors. For example, $a^2 - b^2$ can be factored as $(a + b)(a - b)$. Or $24 = 2 \times 2 \times 2 \times 3$.

factored form of a quadratic relation: a quadratic relation in the form $y = a(x - s)(x - t)$. This form reveals that the zeros of the relation are s and t.

figurate numbers: a sequence of numbers that can be represented by an arrangement of equally spaced points in the shape of regular polygons: triangles, squares, etc.

finite differences: in a table of values where the x-coordinates are evenly spaced, the first differences are the differences between consecutive y-coordinates. The second differences are the differences between consecutive first differences, and so on. For a linear relation, the first differences are constant. For a quadratic relation, the first differences are not constant, but the second differences are constant.

first-degree equation: an equation in which the exponent of the variable is 1. For example, $2(6x - 3) = -8 + 3x + 1$.

first-degree inequation: an inequality in which the exponent of the variable is 1. For example, $3 - 2x \le 7x - 15$.

first-degree polynomial: a polynomial in which the exponent of the variable is 1. For example, $8x - 17$.

first differences: see *finite differences*.

focus: see *directrix*.

function: the relation between two variables such that for any value of the independent variable (usually x), there is only one corresponding value of the dependent variable (usually y).

g (acceleration due to gravity): the rate at which a free-falling object accelerates. At the surface of the earth, $g = 9.8$ m/s^2.

generalize: to create a general rule to represent a pattern or relation between variables.

geostationary: a satellite in an orbit such that it always remains above the same point on the earth's surface.

graphing calculator: a hand-held calculator that allows the user to create a graph from an equation, construct a scatter plot from a table of values, determine the equation of a curve of best fit for a scatter plot, and perform statistical calculations, among other tasks. Many graphing calculators can also be used in conjunction with scientific probes to collect and display data from physical measurements (for example, position, temperature, and force).

graphing software: a computer program that performs many of the same functions as a graphing calculator.

guess-and-check: a problem-solving strategy using a sequence of refined estimates. Each estimate is checked against the original problem and used to formulate a better estimate.

hypotenuse: in a right triangle, the side opposite the right angle.

imaginary number: in advanced mathematics, a number of the form ai, where a is a real number and $i^2 = -1$.

incentre: the centre of the incircle of a polygon. The incircle is the circle inside a polygon that touches every side.

incircle: see *incentre*.

inclination: the angle between a line and another line or plane of reference. Called *inclination* if the first line is above the line of reference, or *declination* if it is below.

independent variable: in an algebraic relation, a variable whose values may be freely chosen and upon which the values of other variables depend. Often represented by x.

infer from data: a method of reasoning that leads to a conclusion, based on a relation between variables in a set of data.

integer: a positive or negative whole number from the set …, -2, -1, 0, 1, 2, …

intercept: the distance from the origin of the x-y plane to the point where a graph meets either the x- or y-axis (x-intercept or y-intercept respectively).

interpolate: to estimate a value that is between elements of given data.

intersection: in geometry, the point or points that are common to two or more figures. For example, two lines that intersect have one point in common.

irrational: a real number that cannot be expressed exactly as the ratio of two integers, for example, π or . In decimal notation, equivalent to an infinite, non-repeating decimal.

isosceles triangle: a triangle with two sides of equal length.

kite: a quadrilateral with two pairs of equal adjacent sides.

line of best fit: the straight line that best describes the relation between the two variables in a scatter plot.

line segment: part of a line, consisting of two end points and all points between them.

linear equation: an equation that represents a linear relation between two variables, typically in the form $y = ax + b$.

linear regression: a method (performed with a calculator) to find the best-fit linear equation for the data in a scatter plot. Although you can always use linear regression, this does not necessarily mean that there is a linear relation between the variables.

linear relation: a relation between two variables that appears as a straight line when graphed. Also called a linear function. Represented by a first-degree equation involving two variables.

linear system: a set of equations (at least two) that represent linear relations between the same two variables.

locus: the path traced by a point moving according to some definite mathematical rule. For example, a circle is the locus of a point moving in a plane and always at the same distance from a fixed point in the same plane.

manipulate: to apply arithmetic operations or factoring to algebraic expressions.

mathematical model: a mathematical description (such as a diagram, graph, table of values, formula, equation, physical or computer model) of a real situation.

maximum: the greatest value taken by a dependent variable.

mean: the sum of several numbers divided by the count of how many numbers there are.

measure: the indication, in standard units, of the size of something. For geometric figures, there are measures of length, area, volume, and angle.

measure of central tendency: a value that can represent a set of data. For example, see *mean, median,* and *mode.*

median: *(Geometry)* a line that joins a vertex of a triangle to the midpoint of the opposite side. *(Statistics)* The middle number of a set of numbers arranged in order. If there are an even number of numbers in the set, the median is the mean of the two middle numbers.

method of elimination: see *elimination.*

method of substitution: see *substitution.*

midpoint: the point in a line segment that divides the line segment into two equal points.

midsegment: the line segment formed by joining the midpoints of two adjacent sides of a polygon.

minimum: the least value taken by a dependent variable.

mode: the number that occurs most often in a set of numbers.

monomial: an algebraic expression with one term, for example, $6x^2$ or $-13y$.

multiple trials: the repetition of an experiment several times to increase the accuracy of the results. The results of each individual trial are combined by a method such as averaging, so that any random occurrences that affect an individual trial have less impact on the accuracy of the results.

natural number: one of the counting numbers from the set 1, 2, 3, …

nonlinear relation: a relation between two variables that does not fit a straight line when graphed.

non-real number: a number that is not in the set of real numbers, for example, $3i$.

obtuse triangle: a triangle in which one of the angles is an obtuse angle, that is, an angle greater than 90° and less than 180°.

optimal (or optimum) value: the maximum or minimum value of a variable.

ordered pair: a pair of numbers where the order is important. The coordinates of a point in the x-y plane form an ordered pair. The ordered pairs (3, 5) and (5, 3) represent different points.

origin: the intersection of two or more axes in a coordinate system. The reference point from which a length is measured.

orthocentre: the point where the three altitudes of a triangle intersect.

parabola: an open curve shaped like the graph of $y = x^2$. It is also the locus of a point that is equidistant from a fixed point and a fixed line.

parallel lines: lines in the same plane that never meet.

parallelogram: a quadrilateral with opposite sides that are parallel.

partial factor: method for finding two points on opposite sides of the axis of symmetry of a parabola, when the standard form relation cannot be completely factored. For the quadratic relation $y = ax^2 + bx + c$, partial factoring gives $y = x(ax + b) + c$.

perfect square: *(quadratic expression)* a trinomial of the form $a^2x^2 + 2abx + b^2$, which can be factored as $(ax + b)^2$.

perimeter: the length of the boundary of a plane figure.

period: the block of repeating digits in a repeating decimal number.

perpendicular: two lines that intersect at a right angle.

perpendicular bisector: a line that is perpendicular to a line segment and passes through the midpoint of the line segment.

pixel: basic element of a computer display. Images are formed by specifying the colour and brightness of each pixel in a large, rectangular array of pixels.

plane: a flat surface. The line joining any two points in a plane is also completely within the plane.

point of intersection: see *intersection*.

polygon: a closed figure formed by three or more line segments in a plane. Examples include triangles, quadrilaterals, hexagons, and decagons.

polynomial: an algebraic expression consisting of one or more terms, usually of the form $a + bx + cx^2 + \ldots$, where a, b, c, ... are numbers.

population: the total number of individuals or subjects involved in a survey or sample.

primary trigonometric ratios: the basic ratios of trigonometry—sine, cosine, and tangent.

proof: a logical procedure to show that a statement is always true.

proportional: one variable is proportional to another if the ratio of corresponding values is always the same. For example, the perimeter of a square is proportional to the length of one side.

Pythagorean theorem: in a right triangle, the square of the length of the hypotenuse is equal to the sum of the squares of the lengths of the other two sides.

quadratic equation: an equation containing only terms with variables having whole number exponents, where at least one of the variables has an exponent of 2, and the exponents of the other variables are less than 2. For example, $-12x^2 - 31x + 27 = 0$ is a quadratic equation.

quadratic formula: the formula that determines the roots of a quadratic equation in the form $ax^2 + bx + c = 0$. The formula states that the values of the roots are

$$x = \frac{-b \pm \sqrt{b^2 - 4ac}}{2}$$

quadratic function: a function represented by a quadratic equation. For example, $y = x^2 - 3x + 9$.

quadratic regression: a method (performed with a calculator) to find the best-fit quadratic equation for the data in a scatter plot. Although you can always use quadratic regression, this not necessarily mean that there is a quadratic relation between the variables.

quadratic relation: a relation between two variables that can be represented by a quadratic function.

quadrilateral: a polygon with four sides.

quotient: the result of dividing one number by another. For example, if 5 is divided by 2, the quotient is 2.5.

radius: the distance from the centre of a circle to a point on the circle.

rate triangle: a right triangle drawn to show the rate of change in the y-variable compared to the x-variable for two points in the x-y plane.

ratio: a number or quantity compared with another, expressed in symbols as $a : b$. The ratio $a : b$ is equivalent to the quotient $\frac{a}{b}$.

rational number: a number of the form where a and b are integers and $b \neq 0$.

ray: part of a line that starts at an end point and extends indefinitely in one direction.

real number: any number that can be represented by a point on the number line. Every real number is either rational or irrational.

real root of an equation: a solution to an equation that is a real number.

realistic (or real-world) situation: a description of an event or events encountered in everyday life, or an experiment imitating such an event.

reciprocal: the multiplier of a number that give 1 as the result. For example, is the reciprocal of 2. The *negative* reciprocal is the multiplier of a number that gives −1 as the result. The negative reciprocal of $\frac{a}{b}$ is $-\frac{b}{a}$. (a, $b \neq 0$).

rectangle: a parallelogram in which the interior angles are right angles.

reflection: a transformation of a geometrical figure that produces a mirror image of the figure with respect to a line, which is called the axis of symmetry.

region on the *x-y* plane: an bounded by curves or lines on the *x-y* plane.

regression: a method used to determine the equation of the line or curve that best fits or represents the distribution of points on a scatter plot. See *linear regression* and *quadratic regression.*

relation: an identified property that connects two sets of numbers or two variables. Can be expressed as a table of values, a graph, or an equation.

rhombus: a parallelogram with all sides of equal length.

right triangle: a triangle with one right angle.

rise: the vertical distance between two points. See *run.*

root of an equation: a value of the variable that makes the equation true. For example, 2 is a root of the equation $x^2 - x - 2 = 0$. Also called a solution to the equation.

rotation: a transformation of a geometrical figure in which each point of the figure moves around a fixed point by the same angle.

run: the horizontal distance between two points. See *rise.*

scale: the ratio between the size of an object in a drawing and the size of the actual object.

scale drawing: a drawing that is the same shape as an actual object and whose size is determined by the scale.

scalene triangle: a triangle with no equal sides.

scatter plot: a graphical method of showing the relation between two variables in a table of values by plotting points on a coordinate grid. The coordinates of each point represent a pair of values of the two variables.

scientific probe: a device used with a graphing calculator or a computer to directly collect data from physical measurements (for example, position or temperature).

second-degree polynomial: a polynomial containing only terms with variables having whole number exponents, where at least one of the variables has an exponent of 2, and the exponents of the other variables are less than 2. For example, $-3x^2 - 2x + 5$ and $6y^2$ are second-degree polynomials.

second differences: see *finite differences.*

segment. see *line segment.*

similar triangles: triangles in which corresponding sides are proportional. The symbol for similarity is ~, as in $\triangle ABC \sim \triangle DEF.$

sine: one of the primary trigonometric ratios (abbreviation sin). In a right triangle, the ratio of the length of the side opposite an angle to the length of the hypotenuse.

sine law: in any triangle ABC, with sides a, b, and c opposite angles A, B, and C respectively,
$$\frac{a}{\sin A} = \frac{b}{\sin B} = \frac{c}{\sin C}$$

slope: a measure of the steepness of a line, expressed as the rise (vertical distance) divided by the run (horizontal distance) between any two points on the line.

solution: the set of values that result in a true statement when they replace the unknowns in an equation.

spreadsheet: computer software used to create tables and allow the user to enter formulas for repeated calculations.

square: *(Geometry)* a rectangle with equal sides. *(Algebra)* a quantity multiplied by itself (sometimes called perfect square).

square numbers: figurate numbers derived from a square shape, that is, 1, 4, 9, 16, …

square root: one of the two equal factors of a number. For example, the square root of 49 is 7. In symbols, $\sqrt{49} = 7$.

standard form (of a quadratic relation): a quadratic relation in the form $y = ax^2 + bx + c$. Also called expanded form.

substitution: the process of replacing part of an algebraic expression with another algebraic expression or value. Also, a method used to solve linear systems by rearranging one equation so that it can be substituted into the other equation.

symmetry: see *axis of symmetry.*

system of equations: a set of two or more equations in two or more variables.

table of values: a table used to record the values of two variables in a relation.

tangent: one of the primary trigonometric ratios (abbreviation tan). In a right triangle, the ratio of the length of the side opposite an angle to the length of the adjacent side.

term: part of an algebraic expression, separated from the rest by plus or minus signs. For example, in $2x^2 + x - 10$, the terms are $2x^2$, x, and -10.

transformation: changing a graph or a geometrical figure by translation, rotation, dilation, or reflection.

translation: a transformation of a geometrical figure in which each point moves the same distance and in the same direction.

trapezoid: a quadrilateral in which one pair of opposite sides is parallel and unequal in length.

trend: a pattern of general direction or movement, often for a variable that is measured against time. Represented by the line or curve of best fit in a scatter plot.

triangle: a polygon with three sides.

trigonometry: the branch of mathematics concerned with the properties of triangles and calculations based on these properties.

UTM: Universal Transverse Mercator system. An international standard for assigning coordinate pairs to points on the earth's surface.

variable: a symbol representing some quantity that can take on any of a set of values. For example, x and y are variables in the algebraic expression $5x^2 - 12y + 67$.

vertex of a parabola: the point where a parabola intersects its axis of symmetry; the maximum or minimum point.

vertex of a polygon: a point of intersection of two sides of a polygon.

vertex form of a quadratic relation: a quadratic relation in the form $y = a(x - h)^2 + k$. This form reveals that the vertex of the corresponding parabola is at (h, k).

vertical stretch factor: a coefficient in an equation that determines the degree to which the corresponding graph is vertically stretched.

whole number: a natural number or zero, from the set 0, 1, 2, 3, …

***x*-axis:** see *x-y plane.*

***x-y* plane:** a coordinate system based on the intersection of two perpendicular lines called axes. The *x*-axis is the horizontal axis, while the *y*-axis is the vertical axis. The origin is the point of intersection of the two axes.

***y*-axis:** see *x-y plane.*

zeros of a relation: the *x*-intercepts of the graph of the relation.

Index

Technology Index

Chapter 1 Opener, page 41: PhotoLink/PhotoDisc; Page 42 left: Kevin Frayer/CP Picture Archive, top right: Tom Hanson/CP Picture Archive; Page 43: Michael Newman/Photo Edit; Page 46: Murleen Fergason/Photo Edit; Page 47: © Bill Varie/CORBIS; Page 51: Dick Hemingway; Page 52: © John Boykin/Photo Edit; Page 53 top: © Richard Hamilton Smith/CORBIS, bottom: Kevin Frayer/ CP Picture Archive; Page 54: D. Berry/PhotoLink/ PhotoDisc; Page 55 upper: The Western Reserve Historical Society, Cleveland, Ohio, lower: © Minnesota Historical Society/CORBIS; Page 56: Keith Brofsky/PhotoDisc; Page 61: Steve Mason/PhotoDisc; Page 63 upper: PhotoDisc, lower: Kevin Frayer/CP Picture Archive; Page 66: Dick Hemingway Page 71: © Lawrence Manning/CORBIS; Page 72: © Michael S. Yamashita/CORBIS; Page 73: Courtesy of Dusa McDuff; Page 76: © R.W. Jones/CORBIS; Page 83: John A. Rizzo/PhotoDisc; Page 84: © Mark Gibson/PhotoDisc; Page 85 upper: Kevin Frayer/CP Picture Archive, lower: Courtesy of Etta Falconer; Page 86 © Spencer Grant/Photo Edit; Page 89: K.M Westermann/CORBIS; Page 93: Nick Koudis/PhotoDisc; Page 95: Kevin Frayer/CP Picture Archive; Page 96: Dick Hemingway; Page 100: © George Hall/CORBIS; Page 102: © Galen Rowell/CORBIS; Page 103: © CORBIS; Page 104 upper: © Sean Aidan; Eye Ubiquitous/CORBIS, Page 104 lower: Kevin Frayer/CP Picture Archive; Page 105: © Kevin Fleming/CORBIS; Page 108: Canadian Olympic Association; Page 110: Ryan McVay/PhotoDisc; Page 113: Patrick Clark/PhotoDisc; Page 114 upper: Geostock/PhotoDisc, lower: © Michael Pole/CORBIS; Page 115: © Wally McNamee/CORBIS; Page 116: David Buffington/PhotoDisc; Page 117: Kevin Frayer/CP Picture Archive; Page 117: Bill Becker/CP Picture Archive

Chapter 2 Opener, page 139: © Roger Ressmeyer/CORBIS; Page 140 left: A.R. Templeton, right: Edmond Von Hoorick/PhotoDisc; Page 141: Pat Bowers and Cheryl Schafter/PhotoDisc; Page 144: © Roger Ressmeyer/CORBIS; Page 146: Dick Hemingway; Page 148: © Paul Almasy/CORBIS; Page 150: Bob Semple; Page 151: Alan and Sandy Carey/PhotoDisc; Page 152: A.R. Templeton; Page 153: Internetwork Media/PhotoDisc; Page 156 top: © Wolfgang Kaehler/CORBIS, bottom: © Tecmap Corporation/ Eric Curry/CORBIS; Page 157: © Joseph Sohn; ChromoSohn/CORBIS; Page 159: Dick Hemingway; Page 165: A. R. Templeton; Page 167: © Archivo Iconograpfico, SA/CORBIS; Page 168: Edmond Von Hoorick/PhotoDisc; Page 174 top: © Michael S. Yamashita, middle: PhotoDisc; Page 175: A.R. Templeton; Page 176: Dick Hemingway; Page 179: Tomi/PhotoLink/PhotoDisc; Page 182: Fototeca Storica Nazionale/PhotoDisc; Page 184 both: A. R. Templeton; Page 186 top: Jim Sugar Photography/CORBIS, lower: Dick Hemingway;

Page 188: © Jim Sugar Photography/CORBIS; Page 196: © Wolfgang Kaehler/CORBIS; Page 197 upper: © Jonathan Blair/CORBIS, lower: A.R. Templeton; Page 198: Dick Hemingway; Page 199: Courtesy of Princeton University; Page 204: A.R. Templeton

Chapter 3 Opener, page 241: © Wolfgang Kaehler/CORBIS; Page 242 upper: Doug Menuez/PhotoDisc, lower: © Michael Freeman/CORBIS; Page 243: © Richard Cummins/CORBIS; Page 246 upper: StockTrek/PhotoDisc, lower: © Steve Chenn/CORBIS; Page 248: Mary Evans Picture Library; Page 251: Kim Steele/PhotoDisc; Page 253: Photo Courtesy of the University of Waterloo. Reproduced with permission of the family of James Wesley Graham; Page 255: © Charles O'Rear/CORBIS; Page 259: © Joseph Sohm; Chromosohm/CORBIS; Page 260: Doug Menuez/PhotoDisc; Page 261: © Jim Zuckerman/CORBIS; Page 265: © Dean Conger/CORBIS; Page 268: © Duomo/CORBIS; Page 269 middle: Siede Preis/PhotoDisc, lower: Doug Menuez/PhotoDisc; Page 272: Mary Evans Picture Library; Page 273: PhotoLink/PhotoDisc; Page Page 274: Dick Hemingway; Page 275: Courtesy of York University, Faculty of Pure and Applied Science; Page 282: © Gail Mooney/CORBIS; Page 284 upper: Nora Penhole/CP Picture Archive, lower: Steve Mason/PhotoDisc; Page 285: Tony Freeman/Photo Edit; Page 286: Doug Menuez/PhotoDisc; Page 287: Dick Hemingway; Page 289: Mary Evans Picture Library; Page 290: PhotoLink/PhotoDisc; Page 292: Dick Hemingway; Page 299: Dick Hemingway; Page 300: © Alison Wright/CORBIS; Page 301 upper: © Buddy Mays/CORBIS, lower: Doug Menuez/PhotoDisc; Page 302: Dick Hemingway; Page 309 upper: © Gilbert Lundt; TenoSoirt/CORBIS, lower: Doug Menuez/PhotoDisc; Page 310: © Sandy Felsenthal/CORBIS; Page 316: © Chris Simpson; Cordaiy Photo Library Ltd./CORBIS; Page 317 upper: Nigel Shuttleworth/Life File/PhotoDisc, lower: Dick Hemingway

Chapter 4 Opener, Page 339: © R.W. Jones/CORBIS; Page 340: Nelson Photo; Page Page 344: E. Going Jacobs/Image Bank; Page 352: © Richard Cummins/CORBIS; Page 356: Nelson Photo; Page 378: © Dave G. Houser/CORBIS; Page 380: © Gunter Marx/CORBIS; Page 381: Courtesy of Doug Johnstone; Page 386: A.R. Templeton; Page 394: Nelson Photo; Page 402: A.R. Templeton; Page 404: © Danny Lehman/CORBIS; Page 407: Nelson Photo; Page 408: Dick Heminway; Page 409: Dick Hemingway; Page 410: Dick Hemingway; Page 411 both: Dick Hemingway; Page 412: Dick Hemingway; Page 413: Dick Hemingway; Page 415: Dick Hemingway

Chapter 5 Opener, page 445: David Buffington/ PhotoDisc; page 446 top: © Roger Ressmeyer/CORBIS, lower: Dick Hemingway; Page 447 top: Dick Hemingway, lower: © NASA/Roger Ressmeyer/CORBIS; Page 454: Steve Cole/PhotoDisc; Page 455: Dick Hemingway; Page 464 top: © Dave G. Houser/CORBIS, bottom: © Roger Ressmeyer/CORBIS; Page 467: Jeff Maloney/PhotoDisc; Page 468: © Michael S. Yamashita/CORBIS; Page 474: Dick Hemingway; Page 478 upper: © Roger Ressmeyer/CORBIS, bottom: Dick Hemingway; Page 480 top: Mike Hawkins/CP Picture Archive, middle: C. Borland/PhotoLink/ PhotoDisc, bottom: © Mark Richards/Photo Edit; Page 482: Donovan Reese/PhotoDisc; Page 488: © Dean Conger/CORBIS; Page 489: © Roger Ressmeyer/ CORBIS; Page 491: Mary Evans Picture Library; Page 492 upper: Dick Hemingway, lower: Texas Instruments; Page 498: Victor Last/Geographical Visual Aids; Page 501: © Gunter Marx/CORBIS; Page 502: © Tim Wright/CORBIS; Page 509 upper: Janis Christie/ PhotoDisc, lower: Bob Templeton; Page 511: © Roger Ressmeyer/CORBIS

Chapter 6 Opener, page 527: © Charles E. Rotkin/CORBIS; Page 528 both: StockTrek/PhotoDisc; Page 529: G. Vidakovic/Visuals Unlimited; Page 532: left: © C. Boys/CORBIS, right: © 1985 Art Matrix/First Light; Page 533: © Kevin Fleming/CORBIS; Page 534: © Scott T. Smith/CORBIS; Page 540: Doug Menuez/PhotoDisc; Page 542: Bill Aron/PhotoEdit; Page 544, StockTrek/PhotoDisc; Page 545: Ryan McVay/PhotoDisc; Page 551 top: © Christian Sarramon/CORBIS, lower both: Ryan McVay/PhotoDisc; Page 552: Dick Hemingway; Page 553 top: © Todd Gipstein/CORBIS; Page 556: © Sally A. Morgan; Ecoscene/CORBIS; Page 557 top: © Kevin R. Morris/CORBIS, lower: StockTrek/PhotoDisc; Page 558 top: © The Purcell Team/CORBIS, bottom: Joaquin Palting/PhotoDisc; Page 559: Mary Evans Picture Library; Page 560: Dick Hemingway; Page 561: Mary Evans Picture Library; page 563: © Robert Estall/CORBIS; Page 566: Donovan Reese/PhotoDisc; Page 567 © Wally McNamee/CORBIS; Page 568 top: © Natalie Fobes/CORBIS, bottom: Steve Mason/PhotoDisc; Page 570: StockTrek/PhotoDisc; Page 571: © Roger Ressmeyer/CORBIS; Page 575: Bob Rowan; Progressive Image/CORBIS; Page 576: © Stephen Frink/CORBIS; Page 577: Geostock/PhotoDisc.